eMedg

online and in-print Internet directories in medicine

MW00994722

Psychiatry

September 2001 — August 2002

AN INTERNET
RESOURCE GUIDE

Consulting Editor

Phillip R. Slavney, M.D.

Eugene Meyer III Professor of Psychiatry and Medicine
Johns Hopkins University School of Medicine

Visit **Psychiatry**
at www.eMedguides.com

Access code: **0364**

eMedguides.com, Inc., Princeton, New Jersey

For electronic browsing of this book, see
http://www.eMedguides.com/psychiatry

The publisher offers discounts on the eMedguides
series of books. For more information, contact:

Sales Department
eMedguides.com, Inc.
15 Roszel Road
Princeton, NJ 08540
tel   800-230-1481 x16
fax   609-520-2023
e-mail   sales@eMedguides.com
web   http://www.eMedguides.com/books

This book is set in Avenir, BaseNine, Gill Sans, and
Sabon typefaces and was printed and bound in the
United States of America.

10 9 8 7 6 5 4 3 2 1

ISBN 0-9700525-5-3

Psychiatry
AN INTERNET RESOURCE GUIDE

Daniel R. Goldenson, *Publisher*

Alysa M. Wilson, *Editor-in-Chief*

Karen B. Schwartz, *Executive Editor*

Phillip R. Slavney, M.D., *Consulting Editor*
Eugene Meyer III Professor of Psychiatry and Medicine
Johns Hopkins University School of Medicine

Karen M. Albert, MLS,
Consulting Medical Librarian
Director of Library Services, Fox Chase Cancer Center

Ravpreet S. Syalee, *Production Editor*

Barbara Morrison, *Manuscript Editor*

Joyce Milione, Kim Seok, *Production Assistants*

Sue Bannon, *Designer*

eMedguides.com, Inc.
15 Roszel Road, Princeton, NJ 08540

Raymond C. Egan, *Chairman of the Board*

Daniel R. Goldenson, *President*

Adam T. Bromwich, *Chief Operating Officer*

Raymond Egan, Jr., *Marketing Director*

Book Orders & Feedback
Book orders • http://www.eMedguides.com/books
Phone orders • 800.230.1481 ×16
Facsimile • 609.520.2023
E-mail • psychiatry@eMedguides.com
Web • http://www.eMedguides.com/psychiatry

2001–2002
Annual Editions

Disclaimer

eMedguides.com Online

Instant access to every Web site in this book at www.eMedguides.com!

This volume, *in its entirety*, can be browsed online at eMedguides.com. Simply point and click to surf to the latest Web sites in your specialty! eMedguides.com is continually updated with URL and content changes, as well as new sites in each specialty. Start your search for medical information, in any specialty, with the trusted assistance of eMedguides.com.

THREE WAYS TO SURF WITH AN EMEDGUIDE:

FAST Drill down at eMedguides.com to the Web information you seek.

FASTER Find a site in the print edition and type the URL into your browser.

FASTEST Find a site in the print edition and type in the e-Link code instead of the URL (for example, go to site G-1234 by typing: www.eMedguides.com/G-1234).

GENERAL MEDICINE REFERENCE
Part Two of every book (General Medical Web Resources) is always available in the sidebar.

E-LINK WITH THE URL
Type in the e-Link code (found next to each entry in this book) after www.eMedguides.com/. You will go directly to the site you seek, even if the URL has changed.

TELL US ABOUT A SITE
When you find a terrific site, tell us about it. Fill out a simple form and we may add your site immediately to eMedguides.com, and we may include it in our next print edition too.

BUY MORE BOOKS
Quickly order books in any of our available specialties, including patient guides, from our online store.

FREE JOURNALS & ASSOCIATIONS
Hundreds of links to journals and associations in each of over 20 specialties are provided.

BROWSE THE TABLE OF CONTENTS
You can quickly find every topic using the full table of contents.

FULL PRINT EDITION, ONLINE
Click to view the sites in a topic. An access code is required; you can find it on the title page of this book.

E-LINK OR SEARCH
Enter an e-Link code (found next to each site in this book) or enter a text string to search the entire specialty.

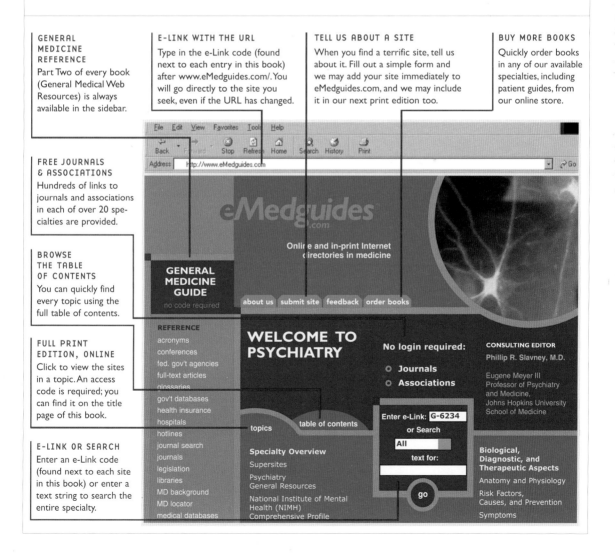

Summary Table of Contents

TABLE OF CONTENTS

PART TWO **General Medical Web Resources**

10. REFERENCE INFORMATION AND NEWS SOURCES. 347

11. PROFESSIONAL TOPICS AND CLINICAL PRACTICE. . . . 403

PREFACE

The medical world continues to have a growing presence on the Internet in 2001, despite the demise of many individual information portals. Specialty Web sites and sites for associations, institutes, research centers, academic institutions, and government programs proliferate, and Webmasters are becoming more conscientious in maintaining up-to-date information.

For the medical community and the public at large, use of the Internet to access medical information continues to increase. Clinicians research disorders and medical developments on the World Wide Web, and gain access to more publications than they could ever access in the past. Patients find information about their disorders that helps them communicate effectively with their physicians. And researchers have an extraordinary universe of information available, as well as the ability to communicate to colleagues in any part of the world.

This second edition of *Psychiatry: An Internet Resource Guide* has been extensively updated and revamped, with hundreds of new Web sites and sources as well as dozens of additional journals, organizations, and institutions. In the year since the publication of the first edition of this book, many psychiatrists have communicated with us about additional Web sites to add, and we have incorporated all useful suggestions. In addition, we have expanded the topical coverage of the volume in all areas with a much-enlarged Table of Contents.
The full content of the Guide is continually updated at the Publisher's Web site, www.eMedguides.com. To make access to individual Web sites easier, every Web site has been given an identification number, so that direct access can be achieved by entering a much shorter domain name in the address bar. Any site, therefore, can be reached by entering "www.eMedguides.com/" followed by the code next to each descriptive site paragraph. When Web site addresses change, as they often do, they will be updated in the database so that the identification number points to the new location.

Learning from the experience of the past year, I recommend the use of this guide for allied health professionals and medical students, in addition to clinicians. For all audiences, the volume serves as a structured textbook survey of the field of psychiatry on the Internet, and as a handy reference tool covering all aspects of this field. For the research-oriented user, the volume provides access to a very large number of medical journal Web sites, most of which offer abstracts of articles in the current issue. And some journals are beginning to provide full-text access as well.

It is my hope that this medical reference book will be used actively by the many psychiatrists and healthcare professionals with a desire to draw on the power of the Internet.

Daniel R. Goldenson
Publisher

1

INTRODUCTION

1.1 WELCOME TO eMEDGUIDES

Welcome to eMedguides and to the second edition of *Psychiatry: An Internet Resource Guide*. As a user of this book, you have a gateway to an extraordinary amount of information, now much expanded, to help you find every useful resource in your field, from electronic journals to selected Web sites on dozens of common and uncommon diseases and disorders.

Over the past year, eMedguides have reached hundreds of thousands of physicians, healthcare professionals, researchers, and medical students. We have published guides to cardiology, dermatology, endocrinology and metabolism, infectious diseases and immunology, neurology and neuroscience, psychiatry, oncology and hematology, respiratory and pulmonary medicine, and urology and nephrology. Several more important specialties are on the way.

This second edition volume is built upon a comprehensive table of contents in order to provide a broad overview of topics and issues in the field. We have added hundreds of additional Web sites, revising every category to meet the demanding information requirements of our sophisticated audience.

We would like to thank our Consulting Medical Editor, Phillip R. Slavney, M.D., Eugene Meyer III Professor of Psychiatry and Medicine, Johns Hopkins University School of Medicine, for his continued contributions to the preparation of this volume. In addition, we appreciate the assistance and guidance from our Consulting Medical Librarian, Karen M. Albert, Director of Library Services for the Fox Chase Cancer Center.

How to Benefit Most from this Book

The most efficient method for finding information in this volume is to scan the table of contents. Our aim has been to organize the material logically, topic by topic, giving descriptions of Web sites that we feel our readers will want to visit. Part One focuses exclusively on the field of psychiatry, including neurological, diagnostic, and therapeutic aspects, as well as recent books, CME sites, disorder resources, journal access, organization sites, and other topical information. Part Two concentrates on the broad fields of medicine reference, clinical practice, and patient education. This includes online databases, sources of current news and legislation, library access sites, government agencies, pharmaceutical data, student resources, and patient planning information.

A very extensive index is also included, covering all included topics and Web site titles, to make the fact-finding mission as efficient as possible.

Physicians and researchers will find that a wide array of material exists in the field. In addition to "supersites," many individual diseases, diagnoses, and therapies have dedicated Web sites intended for professional audiences. We have provided a comprehensive list of journal Web sites that provide access to thousands of articles and abstracts every month. A further exploration can lead to content-rich government sites, hospital and school departments, clinical research centers, recent drug trial results, and sites that provide quick updates on news, CME, and upcoming conferences.

Although much of the material in this book is intended for a professional medical audience, key patient Web resources are also provided. Physicians may wish to refer patients to these sites. Many patient sites include up-to-date news and research and clear descriptions of diseases and their treatments.

Finding a Site on the Internet

We provide the full URL for each site in this volume, which can be typed into the address bar of your Internet browser. With our second edition, we also provide an identification number called an "e-Link" number, which will quickly take you to a specific Web site. Simply type in the eMedguides address, followed by a forward slash (/), followed by the e-Link number (found in the box next to each Web site in this book). For example, to reach the National Institutes of Health, enter www.eMedguides.com/g-0050. The e-Link number is associated with a Web site address in our database. Since we update Web addresses continually, you will always be directed to the appropriate address. This is especially important for medical Web site addresses, which change quite often as new information is added to bring sites up to date.

All of the content in this volume can also be accessed at our Web site, www.eMedguides.com, using the entry code found on the title page of this book. At our site you can explore the field by simply clicking on Web sites, as with a traditional Web directory. General medical sites are located in the sidebar, while specialty-specific information can be reached from the Psychiatry section (use www.eMedguides.com/psychiatry as a shortcut).

The Benefits of Both Print and Online Editions

We feel that both the print and online editions of eMedguides play an important role in the information gathering process. The print edition is a "hands-on" tool, enabling the reader to thumb through a comprehensive directory, finding Web information and topical sources that are totally new and unexpected. Each page can provide discoveries of resources previously unknown to the reader that may never have been the subject of an online search. Without knowing what to expect, the reader can be introduced to useful Web site information just by glancing at the book, looking through the detailed table of contents, or examining the extensive index. This type of browsing is difficult to achieve online.

The online edition serves a different purpose. It provides direct links to each Web site so the user can visit the destination instantaneously, without having to type the Web address or our new e-Link identification code into a browser. In addition, there are search features in this edition that can be used to find specific information quickly, and then the user can print out only what he or she wishes to use.

The online edition also represents the most up-to-date information about our selected Web sites. We update our database throughout the year adding new resources as they become available, and editing those that change. The eMedguides Web site also provides a platform for communication—our Submit a Site feature lets you share your online discoveries with us, and hence other readers in a future update.

We hope you will find the print and online versions of this volume to be useful Internet companions, always on hand to consult.

1.2 RATINGS AND SITE SELECTION

Site Selection Criteria

Our medical research staff has carefully chosen the sites for this guide. We perform extensive searches for all of the topics listed in our table of contents and then select only the sites that meet established criteria. The pertinence and depth of content, presentation, and usefulness for physician and advisory purposes are taken into account.

The sites in this physician guide contain detailed reference material, news, clinical data, and current research articles. We also include and appropriately identify numerous sites that may be useful for patient reference. The large majority of our Web sites are provided by government, university, medical association, and research organizations. Sites operated by private individuals or corporations are only included if they are content-rich and useful to the physician. In these cases, we clearly identify the operator in the title or description of the site.

In addition, if a site requires a fee, some fees, or a free registration/disclosure of personal information, we indicate this information at the end of the site description.

Ratings Guide

Those sites that are selected based on these criteria are subsequently rated on a scale of one apple (🍎) to three apples (🍎🍎🍎). This rating only applies to the pool of sites that are in this guide; many sites are not included in this volume. A one-apple site, therefore, is considered worthy of inclusion but may not be outstanding.

A three-apple site tends to have greater depth and more extensive information, or particularly hard-to-find resources.

Abbreviations

See "Medical Abbreviations and Acronyms" under "Reference Information and News Sources" in Part 2 for Web sites that provide acronym translation. Below are a few acronyms you will find throughout this volume:

APA   American Psychiatric Association
CDC   Centers for Disease Control and Prevention
CME   Continuing Medical Education
FAQ   Frequently Asked Questions
NIMH   National Institute of Mental Health

NIH   National Institutes of Health
PDQ   Physician Data Query
URL   Uniform Resource Locator (the address of a Web site on the Internet)

1.3 GETTING ONLINE

The Internet is growing at a rapid pace, but many individuals are not yet online. What is preventing people from jumping on the "information highway"? There are many factors, but the most common issue is a general confusion about what the Internet is, how it works, and how to access it.

The following few pages are designed to clear up any confusion for readers who have not yet accessed the Internet. We will look at the process of getting onto and using the Internet, step by step.

It is also helpful to consult other resources, such as the technical support department of the manufacturer or store where you bought your computer. Although assistance varies widely, most organizations provide startup assistance for new users and are experienced with guiding individuals onto the Internet. Books can also be of great assistance, as they provide a simple and clear view of how computers and the Internet work, and can be studied at your own pace.

What is the Internet?

The Internet is a large network of computers that are all connected to one another. A good analogy is to envision a neighborhood, with houses and storefronts, all connected to one another by streets and highways. Often the Internet is referred to as the "information super-highway" because of the vastness of this neighborhood.

The Internet was initially developed to allow people to share computers, that is, share part of their "house" with others. The ability to connect to so many other computers quickly and easily made this feasible. As computers proliferated and increased in computational power, people started using the Internet for sending information quickly from one computer to another.

For example, the most popular feature of the Internet is electronic mail (e-mail). Each computer has a mailbox, and an electronic letter can be sent instantly. People also use the Internet to post bulletins, or other information, for others to see. The process of sending e-mail or viewing this information is simple. A computer and a connection to the Internet are all you need to begin.

How is an Internet connection provided?

The Internet is accessed either through a "direct" connection, which is found in businesses and educational institutions, or through a phone line. Phone line connections are the most common access method for users at home, although direct connections are becoming available for home use. There are many complex options in this area; for the new user it is simplest to use an existing phone line to experience the Internet for the first time. A dual telephone jack can be purchased at many retail stores. Connect the computer to the phone jack, and then use the provided software to connect to the Internet. Your computer will dial the number of an

Internet provider and ask you for a user name and password. Keep in mind that while you are using the Internet, your phone line is tied up, and callers will hear a busy signal. Also, call waiting can sometimes interrupt an Internet connection and disconnect you from the Internet.

Who provides an Internet connection?

There are many providers at both the local and national levels. One of the easiest ways to get online is with America Online (AOL). They provide software and a user-friendly environment through which to access the Internet. Because AOL manages both this environment and the actual connection, they can be of great assistance when you are starting out. America Online takes you to a menu of choices when you log in, and while using their software you can read and send e-mail, view Web pages, and chat with others.

Many other similar services exist, and most of them also provide an environment using Microsoft or Netscape products. These companies, such as the Microsoft Network (MSN) and Earthlink, also provide simple, easy-to-use access to the Internet. Their environment is more standard and not limited to the choices America Online provides.

Internet connections generally run from $10-$20 per month (depending on the length of commitment) in addition to telephone costs. Most national providers have local phone numbers all over the country that should eliminate any telephone charges. The monthly provider fee is the only direct charge for accessing the Internet.

How do I get on the Internet?

Once you've signed up with an Internet provider and installed their software (often only a matter of answering basic questions), your computer will be set up to access the Internet. By simply double-clicking on an icon, your computer will dial the phone number, log you in, and present you with a Web page (a "home" page).

What are some of the Internet's features?

From the initial Web page there are almost limitless possibilities of where you can go. The address at the top of the screen (identified by an "http://" in front) tells you where you are. You can also type the address of where you would like to go next. When typing a new address, you do not need to add the "http://". The computer adds this prefix automatically after you type in an address and press return. Once you press return, the Web site will appear in the browser window.

You can also navigate the Web by "surfing" from one site to another using links on a page. A Web page might say, "Click here for weather." If you move the mouse pointer to this under-lined phrase and click the mouse button, you will be taken to a different address, where weather information is provided.

The Internet has several other useful features. E-mail is an extremely popular and important service. It is free and messages are delivered instantly. Although you can access e-mail through a Web browser (AOL has this feature), many Internet services provide a separate e-mail program for reading, writing, and organizing your correspondence. These programs send and retrieve messages from the Internet.

Another area of the Internet offers chat rooms where users can hold roundtable discussions. In a chat room you can type messages and see the replies of other users around the world. There are chat rooms on virtually every topic, although the dialog certainly varies in this free-for-all forum. There are also newsgroups on the Internet, some of which we list in this book. A newsgroup is similar to a chat room but each message is a separate item and can be viewed in sequence at any time. For example, a user might post a question about Lyme disease. In the newsgroup you can read the question and then read the answers that others have provided. You can also post your own comments. This forum is usually not managed or edited, particularly in the medical field. Do not take the advice of a chat room or newsgroup source without first consulting your physician.

How can I find things on the Internet?

Surfing the Internet, from site to site, is a popular activity. But if you have a focused mission, you will want to use a search engine. A search engine can scan lists of Web sites to look for a particular site. We provide a long list of medical search engines in this book.

Because the Internet is so large and unregulated, sites are often hard to find. In the physical world it is difficult to find good services, but you can turn to the yellow pages or other resources to get a comprehensive list. Physical proximity is also a major factor. On the Internet, the whole world is at your doorstep. Finding a reliable site takes time and patience, and can require sifting through hundreds of similar, yet irrelevant, sites.

The most common way to find information on the Internet is to use a search engine. When you go to the Web page of a search engine, you will be presented with two distinct methods of searching: using links to topics, or using a keyword search. The links often represent the Web site staff's best effort to find quality sites. This method of searching is the core of the Yahoo! search engine (http://www.yahoo.com). By clicking on Healthcare, then Disorders, then Lung Cancer, you are provided with a list of sites the staff has found on the topic.

The keyword approach is definitely more daring. By typing in search terms, the engine looks through its list of Web sites for a match and returns the results. These engines typically only cover 15% of the Internet, so it is not a comprehensive process. They also usually return far too many choices. Typing lung cancer into a search engine box will return thousands of sites, including one entry for every site where someone used the words lung cancer on a personal Web page.

Where do eMedguides come in?

eMedguides are organized listings of Web sites in each major medical specialty. Our team of editors continually scours the Net, searching for quality Web sites that relate to specific specialties, disorders, and research topics. More importantly, of the sites we find, we only include those that provide professional and useful content. eMedguides fill a critical gap in the Internet research process. Each guide provides more than 1,000 Web sites that focus on every aspect of a single medical discipline.

Other Internet search engines rely on teams of "surfers" who can only cover a subject on its surface because they survey the entire Internet. Search engines, even medical search engines, return far too many choices, requiring hours of time and patience to sift through. eMedguides, on the other hand, focus on medical and physician sites in a specialty. With an eMedguide in hand, you can quickly identify the sites worth visiting on the Internet and jump right to them. At our site, http://www.eMedguides.com, you can access the same listings as in this book and can simply click on a site to go straight to it. In addition, we provide continual updates to the book through the site and annually in print. Our editors do the surfing for you and do it professionally, making your Internet experience efficient and fulfilling.

Our new e-Link identification code is the fastest way to surf the Internet. Simply append the code number to the eMedguides address (www.eMedguides.com/c-0101) to be taken directly to the site you are reading about in the book.

Taking medical action must involve a physician

As interesting as the Internet is, the information that you will find is both objective and subjective. Our goal is to expose our readers to Web sites on hundreds of topics for informational purposes only. If you are not a physician and become interested in the ideas, guidelines, recommendations, or experiences discussed online, bring these findings to a physician for personal evaluation. Medical needs vary considerably, and a medical approach or therapy for one individual could be entirely misguided for another. Final medical advice and a plan of action must come only from a physician.

PSYCHIATRY
WEB RESOURCES

2

QUICK REFERENCE

2.1 PSYCHIATRY DISORDER SUMMARIES

Internet Mental Health Internet Mental Health offers fact sheets on 50 of the most common mental disorders. Information includes descriptions, diagnoses, treatments, current research, and links to online brochures offering additional information on the disorders. Disorders are listed both alphabetically and categorically for easy reference.
http://www.mentalhealth.com/fr20.html

Medical College of Wisconsin: Neurological Disorders An A-to-Z listing of neurological disorder descriptions is presented at the Medical College of Wisconsin Physicians & Clinics Web site. Disease description information is provided by the National Institute of Neurological Disorders and Stroke of the National Institutes of Health. Links to relevant articles can be found.
http://www.healthlink.mcw.edu/neurological-disorders

Mentalwellness.com: Basic Information on Mental Disorders A brief description of a variety of mental illnesses is available from this site, including anxiety disorders, bipolar disorder, clinical depression, dementia, schizoaffective disorder, and schizophrenia. Links are also available to fact sheets from the National Institute of Mental Health.
http://www.mentalwellness.com

Merck Manual of Diagnosis and Therapy: Psychiatric Disorders This chapter of the online Merck Manual presents 12 psychiatric disorder chapters, from anxiety disorders to schizophrenia and related diseases. Each section offers general information about the disorder classification, as well as relevant etiological, diagnostic, and therapeutic considerations.
http://www.merck.com/pubs/mmanual/section15/sec15.htm

National Institute of Mental Health (NIMH): Public Resources This National Institute of Mental Health site for the public offers links to pages devoted to information on major mental disorders, including anxiety disorders, learning disorders, bipolar disorder, obsessive-compulsive disorder, depression, panic disorder, attention deficit hyperactivity disorder, phobias, autism, posttraumatic stress disorder, generalized anxiety disorder, and schizophrenia. Information on medications, other mental disorders, and clinical trials is also available. http://www.nimh.nih.gov/publicat/index.cfm

Psych Central: Mental Disorders: Symptoms   An index of mental disorder symptoms is provided on this Web page. There are more than 60 adult disorders including anorexia, bipolar disorder, depression, and schizophrenia. More than 20 childhood disorders are also listed, as well as a short list of personality disorders. Symptoms and diagnostic criteria are drawn from the American Psychiatric Association's *Diagnostic and Statistical Manual of Mental Disorders, Fourth Edition*.
http://psychcentral.com/disorders/

2.2 PSYCHIATRY GLOSSARIES

American Academy of Child and Adolescent Psychiatry (AACAP): Teenage Mental Illness Glossary   The AACAP assists parents and families in understanding developmental, behavioral, emotional, and mental disorders affecting children and adolescents. A glossary of teenage mental illnesses lists approximately 20 disorders with full descriptions.
http://www.aacap.org/Web/aacap/about/glossary/index.htm

Glossary of Children's Mental Health Terms   As a service of the Center for Mental Health Services (CMHS), this glossary contains terms frequently encountered when dealing with the mental health needs of children. Italicized items have separate entries in the glossary, for additional reader reference.
http://www.mentalhealth.org/publications//allpubs/CA-0005/Glossary.htm

Glossary of Mental Health Terms   This online dictionary provides concise definitions of common mental health disorders, from agoraphobia to Tourette's disorder, as well as other related terms, such as behavior modification and separation anxiety.
http://www.therapistfinder.net/glossary/

Glossary On-Line: Psychiatry   Psychiatry On-Line offers definitions of symptoms, syndromes, and other terminology of the psychiatric field at this easy-to-navigate page. Visitors are free to make suggestions regarding additions to the site. http://www.priory.com/gloss.htm

How to Speak Psychiatry: A Psychiatric Glossary   This resource page offers professionals and consumers a convenient reference to common terminology in the psychiatric field, with an abundance of clear and concise entries.
http://wwwsvh.stvincents.com.au/MHS/this%20is%20the%20glossary.html

Online Dictionary of Mental Health   An award-winning site, this online dictionary of information offers coverage of numerous mental health disciplines. Rather than simply presenting conventional definitions, this untraditional resource contains links to a multitude of sites, offering a variety of information and differing viewpoints related to this A-to-Z collection of terms, as a service of the University of Sheffield.
http://www.shef.ac.uk/~psysc/psychotherapy/

Vocabulary of Loss: A Suicide, Grief, and Ethics Glossary Over 500 definitions of selected terms are presented at this collection of technical and clinical definitions in behavioral health. Disorder-related and pharmacologic terms are included, as well as terminology related to research, patient care, and grieving. http://members.tripod.com/~LifeGard/index-2.html

2.3 PSYCHIATRY NEWS AND HEADLINES

American Psychiatric Association (APA): Psychiatric News This publication is a primary means of communication between the organization and its members regarding legislative and judicial affairs, news, and clinical and research developments in the field. The most current printing is available online and contains reports, commentaries, and editorials, as well as classified advertising and conference details. Visitors will find subscription information and access to back issues at the site.
http://pn.psychiatryonline.org

Doctor's Guide: Psychiatry News Dozens of daily articles on new developments in psychiatry are provided at this useful Web site. For a review of medical news developments in different fields, the user can navigate to any topic or specialty of interest, such as depression, by clicking on "All News" and then selecting the appropriate specialty or field.
http://www.docguide.com

Individual.com: Psychiatry and Psychology News Current news stories for a variety of medical specialties, including psychology and psychiatry, can be accessed through this Web page.
http://www.individual.com/browse/category.shtml?level1=46610&level2=46618

Medscape: Psychiatry and Mental Health Medscape offers psychiatry news from Reuters and other sources at this site, with articles mainly related to therapy, treatment guidelines, research, and pharmaceutical advances. General medical news is provided under clinical, regulatory, professional, epidemiology, legal, science, public health, and managed care headings. General health news for nonprofessionals is also available under the heading, "What Your Patients are Reading.
(free registration) http://aids.medscape.com/
Home/Topics/psychiatry/directories/dir-PSY.News.html

Mental Health News on the Net Operated by the Center for Mental Health Services, a federal agency, this site provides important daily articles from numerous newspapers, news organizations, journals, and other sources of interest to the mental health community. It is one of the most comprehensive sources of current mental health news on the Internet.
http://www.mentalhealth.org/newsroom/index.htm

Mental Help Net: Daily News   Collected from Johns Hopkins, Yahoo! Health, *Science Daily,* National Alliance for the Mentally Ill, the National Institute of Mental Health, *Psychotherapy Finances,* and the American Psychiatric Association, this site offers mental health news and research findings that are updated daily. The subject areas include behavioral healthcare policy issues and technical findings and developments in the medical field.
http://www.mentalhelp.net/news/daily.htm

 NewsRounds: Psychiatry   The most recent news stories related to psychiatry are provided on this site. The stories are drawn from sources such as Reuters, *Psychology Times,* and the National Institutes of Health. A free registration is required to access the articles.
(free registration) http://www.newsrounds.com/specialty/psychiatry/

 Psychiatric Times   This site provides visitors with monthly articles related to psychiatric therapy, pharmaceuticals, and other psychiatry topics. Articles can be accessed by author, continuing medical education (CME) credit, title, and topic. Articles are available each month for CME credit. Visitors can also access subscription information and writers' guidelines.
http://www.mhsource.com/psychiatrictimes.html

 PsychLinx: Current Articles and News in Psychiatry   Drawn from a variety of journals and news sources, this site offers the most recent psychiatry news stories. An abstract and citation is offered for each story. Sources include the *International Journal of Psychoanalysis,* Reuters, and *Archives of Gerontology and Geriatrics.*
http://www.psychlinx.com/

2.4 Conferences in Psychiatry

A number of key Web sites that offer event calendars along with details of conference programs and locations are provided here. Although a comprehensive conference calendar is provided by the PSL Group's *Doctor's Guide* (our first listing), the other listed sites have valuable additional listings. Taken together, this group provides an overall source of conference scheduling information for the year.

 Forward Conference Calendar   This partial listing of conferences and meetings for the years 2001-2006 is compiled by the Doctor's Guide to Medical Conferences and Meetings. Dates and locations are provided at the Web site. Upon visiting this site, the reader can click on any conference listing for additional information. The conference list is continually updated and should be consulted frequently.
http://www.docguide.com/crc.nsf/web-bySpecDisp?OpenForm&spec=Psychiatry

 AllConferences.net   A directory of conferences, conventions, workshops, and events is featured on this Web page for a variety of disciplines including health and social science. http://www.allconferences.net

Behavioral Healthcare Meetings Developed by Dr. Myron Pulier, this Web site offers an A-to-Z directory of behavioral healthcare meetings and conventions, listed by the first letter of the organization. Hundreds of organizations are listed. The site also offers links to general resources in behavioral healthcare covering topics such as evidence-based medicine, psychology schools, and psychotherapy.
http://www.umdnj.edu/psyevnts/psyjumps.html#Meetings

Health On the Net (HON) Foundation: Conferences and Events A searchable database of medical meetings, both in the United States and abroad, is presented on this Web page. Psychiatry and psychology are among the medical specialties represented. There is a brief description of each, along with a link for further conference information. Some offer CME credit.
http://www.hon.ch/cgi-bin/confevent

Healthcare Conferences.com A database of healthcare conferences is featured on this Web page, with four years of conferences available. Visitors can browse the conferences by specialty, including psychiatry and psychology. Search results return the conference title, date, location, contact, information, and Web site link. There is also a free monthly e-mail notification service for new conferences added in one's specialty. The site also offers comprehensive links to shopping, travel, accommodation, insurance, maps, and weather information.
http://www.healthcareconferences.com

MedicalConferences.com: Psychiatry Sponsored by a privately owned company based in the United Kingdom this site provides a search engine that enables the visitor to type in "psychiatry" or other topics into the keyword space in order to receive a comprehensive listing of conferences to be held over the next 12 months or longer. Each conference is an active link in itself, further permitting the visitor to obtain more detailed information about the event. There are over 100 meetings in the database for psychiatry, and more are added on a regular basis.
http://www.medicalconferences.com/search.html

MediConf Online: Psychiatry Forthcoming Meetings MediConf Online provides a searchable database of forthcoming meetings and conferences in every major medical specialty. For each meeting there is a listing that includes the dates, contact details, and a link to the city where the visitor can learn about accommodations, weather, and other topics of interest. Information is provided for psychiatry and psychology meetings, and for over 400 events up to the year 2008. http://www.mediconf.com/online.html

Medscape: Psychiatry Conference Summaries Conference proceedings are provided on this site for psychiatry conferences dating back to 1998, some for CME credit. Proceedings cover topics such as death and dying, Alzheimer's disease, menopause, child and adolescent psychiatry, and depression.
(free registration) http://psychiatry.medscape.com/Home/Topics/psychiatry/directories/dir-PSY.ConfSummaries.html

Mental Health Net: Conference Calendar Visitors to this site can search for a conference or workshop by a number of different fields including date, location, title, sponsor, or availability of continuing education credits. The results offer the title of the conference, location, Web site, sponsor, contact information, number of CE credits, and targeted profession. http://mentalhelp.net/mhn/calendar/db.cgi/

 Professional Events Calendar by Month for Mental Health A service of the Center for Mental Health Services, the site offers visitors an opportunity to search for meetings, conferences, and conventions nationwide. Users may search by month of event or event topic. The search engine returns a list of upcoming events with brief descriptions, location, and contact information for each. http://www.mentalhealth.org/calendar/searchcal.asp

2.5 MENTAL HEALTH STATISTICS

 FedStats: One Stop Shopping for Federal Statistics FedStats, maintained by the Federal Interagency Council on Statistical Policy, serves as a comprehensive directory of statistical resources of interest to the public. The site offers an alphabetical index of materials, a site search engine, and a "Fast Facts" section for the latest economic and social indicators. Also available are data access tools for locating key statistics from federal agency databases, such as the Substance Abuse and Mental Health Services Administration, the National Institutes of Health, and the Agency for Healthcare Research and Quality. http://www.fedstats.gov

 National Center for Health Statistics (NCHS) FASTATS is a service of the National Center for Health Statistics, providing state and national statistics on health-related topics. Statistical coverage of diseases, alcohol use, births, deaths, disability/impairments, divorce, drug use (illegal and therapeutic), exercise/physical activity, health insurance coverage, immunization, life expectancy, minority health, occupational safety and health, and numerous additional topics is provided. Links from the main site include the FASTSTATS center, which offers quick reference to mental health statistics in the United States and a comprehensive, downloadable document on mental health expenditures. http://www.cdc.gov/nchs/

 National Mental Health Association: Mental Health Statistics Statistics on the prevalence and economic costs of mental illness in the U.S. are featured on this Web page. The statistics cover adults, children and adolescents, AIDS patients, the homeless, and jail inmates. http://www.nmha.org/infoctr/factsheets/15.cfm

 Numbers Count: Mental Illness in America The National Institute of Mental Health offers statistics on depression, bipolar illness, suicide, schizophrenia, anxiety disorders, panic disorder, obsessive-compulsive disorder, post-

traumatic stress disorder, social phobia, attention-deficit/hyperactivity disorder, and autism in this informative fact sheet.
http://www.nimh.nih.gov/publicat/numbers.cfm

SAMHSA: Substance Abuse and Mental Health Statistics   This site of the Substance Abuse and Mental Health Services Administration (SAMHSA) offers visitors national statistics on alcohol, tobacco, substance abuse treatment, and additional mental health topics. Surveys on drug abuse, answers to FAQs, and newly released analytic and methodological papers on special topics and treatment needs are found. Individual series links include the Drug Abuse Warning Network (DAWN) series, and data systems from the Office of Applied Studies include public use data files and online data analysis and archives in mental illness and substance abuse. http://www.samhsa.gov/oas/oasftp.htm

Statistics: A Service of the Center for Mental Health Services   This site contains links to the National Institute of Mental Health where recent study results can be accessed. Study results are provided by the World Health Organization, the World Bank, and Harvard University on the most common mental health disorders and estimated economic cost to society. Additional articles cover the complex behavior of suicide with its age, gender, and racial differences; information on older persons from the Administration on Aging; and statistics on the national indicators of child well-being, including detailed tables and limitations of data.
http://www.mentalhealth.org/cmhs/mentalhealthstatistics/statistics.htm

2.6 TOPICAL SEARCHES

American Psychiatric Association (APA): Search Tool   The search tool at the American Psychiatric Association Web page provides visitors with a comprehensive database of information. These resources are also available through the site map and include information on public policy, clinical resources, research resources, patient information, and medical education.
http://www.psych.org

AtHealth: Mental Health Topics   Basic information about specific mental health topics is provided in nearly 50 topic categories, including such subjects as written expression disorder and amnesia. Additional links offer access to a mental health professional database of specialists in the specified area as well as to a bookstore, medication information, and a mental health newsletter.
http://www.athealth.com/Consumer/Disorders/Disorders.html

Health Sciences Library System (HSLS): Mental Health Resources   This continuously updated page contains a listing of some of the best mental health resources on the World Wide Web, pertaining to 15 particular conditions and providing general mental health information. State and local resources,

Internet guides and sites, related organizations, and related consumer guides are provided on topics ranging from addiction to violence.
http://www.hsls.pitt.edu/intres/index.html?type=mental

MEDLINEplus: Health Information Mental Health and Behavior Topics Selected by the National Library of Medicine, this topical index leads the visitor to comprehensive resource listings for each mental health disorder. Related categories, National Library of Medicine/National Institutes of Health resources, governmental resources, basic research, clinical trials, diagnosis, and information in Spanish are included for each disorder. Related organizations, treatment information, and material regarding the disorder in special populations can also be found.
http://www.nlm.nih.gov/medlineplus/mentalhealthandbehavior.html

Mental Health InfoSource At the Mental Health InfoSource home page, users can find a symptom/disorder list leading to complete information on nearly 40 mental health topics including bipolar disorder, dissociation, fear, eating disorders, obsessive-compulsive disorder, and seasonal affective disorder. General details are accessible for each topic listed. Separate ask-the-expert sections are available for both consumer and professional questions. Access to additional links and authoritative articles is also provided.
http://www.mhsource.com

Mental Health Links These links, provided by the Center for Mental Health Services (CMHS), cover a broad range of over 60 mental health divisions of the CMHS and lead the visitor to a home page specific to each disorder or topic. The connections offered at these CMHS sites provide access to articles, organizations, support services, and a comprehensive assortment of related resources.
http://www.mentalhealth.org/links/KENLINKS.htm

Mental Health Net: Topical Search This site provides an A-to-Z listing of the most common mental health problems and disorders as well as links to treatment details and information on a wide variety of other health and medical issues. A resource section includes connections to information on alcohol and substance abuse, attention-deficit/hyperactivity disorder, sleep disorders, personality disorders, eating disorders, depression, anxiety, and schizophrenia.
http://mentalhelp.net/dxtx.htm

National Alliance for the Mentally Ill (NAMI): Link Manager The NAMI Link Manager provides its users with links to a multitude of informative Web pages on mental illness. Visitors can select among a list of nearly 40 mental health categories ranging from advocacy to youth. Most mental illnesses are included with additional information provided on governmental, research, and international issues. http://www.apollonian.com/namilocals/linkmgr/linkmgr.asp

National Institute of Mental Health (NIMH): Search Engine The National Institute of Mental Health offers its own search engine to gain access to information by disorder or topic. This page explains the use of the search

tool which draws upon a vast database of mental health articles, summaries, definitions, research laboratories, and other vital resources.
http://www.nimh.nih.gov/search/search_form.cfm

 National Institute of Mental Health (NIMH): Search Tool Information on the National Institute of Mental Health Web page can be searched through this site. Resources available include clinical trials, funding opportunities, and information specific to consumers, professionals, and researchers.
http://www.nimh.nih.gov/search/Search_Form.cfm

 Online Dictionary of Mental Health The Online Dictionary of Mental Health is presented by Human-Nature.com as a global information resource and research tool, compiled by and for Internet mental health resource users. A large assortment of disciplines contributing to the understanding of mental health are covered, and links to many sites offer varying viewpoints on mental health issues. A mental health search engine provides the ability to search over 100 major information resources, including many organizations that do not have their own internal search engines. Interesting discussion Web groups, such as a debate on the validity of modern psychoanalysis, are accessible.
http://www.human-nature.com/odmh/index.html

2.7 CLINICAL STUDIES AND TRIALS

ALL TRIALS

 Centerwatch: Clinical Trials Listing Service (by disorder) Designed for both patients and healthcare professionals, this site provides an extensive listing of therapeutic clinical trials organized by disorder. Over 50 psychiatry disorders are arranged alphabetically by type. It is international in scope and provides data on more than 5,200 clinical trials, sponsored by both industry and government, that are actively recruiting patients. Keyword search accessible, it also covers information on new FDA-approved drug therapies. Trials are listed by geographical region within each disorder.
http://www.centerwatch.com/studies/listing.htm

 ClinicalTrials.gov Clinical trial information is provided on this site for the public. The database can be searched by keyword or browsed by condition or sponsor. Search results yield the purpose of the study, a detailed description of the study, eligibility requirements, and contact information. In addition, the site contains related resources that include a fact sheet on understanding clinical trials. http://clinicaltrials.gov/

 Pharmaceutical Research Plus: ClinicalTrials.com Patients will find a clinical trial database, searchable by topic or location, for a wide variety of illnesses on this site. Search results consist of a brief description of the study and eligibility criteria. There is also an e-mail alert service on future clinical trials, FAQs, information on FDA-approved drugs, and a database of organizations that work with different illnesses. Professionals will find information on adding their clinical trials, or organizations, to the site. Additional services offered include patient recruitment strategies.

http://www.clinicaltrials.com/

NIH CLINICAL TRIALS

Centerwatch: NIH Trials Listing (by disease) Centerwatch provides a convenient resource for accessing information on clinical trials at the NIH. These are clinical trials publicized by the NIH, located at the Warren Grant Magnuson Clinical Center in Bethesda, Maryland. Trials are organized by disorder and have short descriptions.

http://www.centerwatch.com/patient/nih/nih_index.html

2.8 DRUG PIPELINE: APPROVED AND DEVELOPMENTAL DRUGS

Internet Mental Health: Medication Research Visitors to this site can conduct searches of PubMed for citations related to specific drug research. Over 150 drug names are listed at the site. Users can also limit searches to specific subtopics, including administration and dosage, adverse effects, chemistry, comparative studies, metabolism, pharmacokinetics, and many other subjects.

http://www.mentalhealth.com/drugrs/index.html

Mental Health InfoSource: Approved Drugs More than 100 pharmaceutical drugs currently approved by the Food and Drug Administration for the treatment of psychiatric disorders are listed at this site. Information includes generic and brand names, a general description of the drug's action, and a list of approved indications.

http://www.mhsource.com/resource/approved.html

Neurology and Neuroscience Drugs Under Development More than 350 new drugs are under development in all major neurology and neuroscience areas. This Web site is a detailed source providing the product names, pharmaceutical company developers, indications, and status.

http://www.phrma.org/searchcures/newmeds/

New Medicines in Development for Mental Illness The full text of a report on new medicines for mental illnesses, from the year 2000, is presented on this Web page by the Pharmaceutical Research and Manufacturers of America. There are also articles on the drug development and approval process, as well as medicines currently in clinical testing.

http://www.phrma.org/searchcures/newmeds/mentalillsurv2000/

2.9 LISTSERVS AND NEWSGROUPS

Behavior OnLine   This Web page offers more than 20 discussion forums, whose participants are primarily non-physician mental health professionals. Shame and affect theory, classical Adlerian psychotherapy, cognitive therapy, and anxiety disorders are, and online clinical work are topics of discussion. In addition, the site offers full-text articles from the *Journal of Online Behavior,* along with links to organizations and related resources.
http://www.behavior.net/

InterPsych   This site provides a large list of links to psychiatry-related online forums for professionals and other interested parties. Included are forums for major psychiatric disorders, psychotherapy, research design, telehealth, and computers in mental health. The scope of each forum is summarized, and information on the leader, membership, and other statistics are provided. The by-laws of the association and information regarding affiliation with InterPsych are present. http://www.shef.ac.uk/~psysc/InterPsych/inter.html

PsychNet-UK: Psychology Newsgroups   More than 50 psychology LISTSERVs are provided at this site for e-mail discussion of topics such as depression, recovery, anxiety, psychology research, and schizophrenia. There are also related newsgroups in the areas of neuroscience, cognitive science, and artificial intelligence.
http://www.psychnet-uk.com/psychology_newsgroups/mental_health_newsgroups.htm

2.10 ONLINE TEXTS AND TUTORIALS

eMedicine: Psychiatry   Intended for professionals, this site offers detailed clinical tutorials on more than 50 psychiatric disorders. Topics include alcohol-related psychosis, anorexia nervosa, bipolar disorder, panic disorder, and Tourette syndrome. Each tutorial offers an overview, along with symptoms, differentials, diagnostic workup, treatment options, follow-up, and a bibliography.
http://www.emedicine.com/med/PSYCHIATRY.htm

Merck Manual of Diagnosis and Therapy: Psychiatric Disorders
Section 15, Psychiatric Disorders, of the *Merck Manual of Diagnosis and Therapy,* is featured on this Web site. The online chapters cover psychiatry in medicine, somatoform disorders, anxiety disorders, dissociative disorders, mood disorders, and suicidal behavior. Additional chapters are dedicated to personality disorders, psychosexual disorders, schizophrenia, psychiatric emergencies, drug use and dependence, and eating disorders. The chapters are written in clinical terms. http://www.merck.com/pubs/mmanual/section15/sec15.htm

3

Journals, Articles, and Latest Books

3.1 Journals and Articles on the Internet: Psychiatry

Directories of Electronic Journals

Mental Health Net: Links to Journals This site allows users to search over 1,600 journals for relevant publications. Journals can be accessed by specifying type of journal, language (English, Dutch, French, German, or Spanish), and subject matter. Users can also search by keyword. Links to journal sites include a description of resources at the site and publishing information.
http://mentalhelp.net/journals

Selected Psychiatry Articles

Behavioral and Mental Disorder Reviews for Primary Care Providers As a service of MCP Hahnemann University Libraries, this comprehensive listing provides references and complete citations to more than 30 indexed review articles in the field of psychiatry, with topics divided into such categories as behavioral disorders, mood disorders, psychotic disorders, dementia, substance abuse and addictive disorders, and anxiety and stress-related disorders. Links to primary care journals available on the Internet, as well as the psychiatry chapter of the University of Iowa's Family Practice Handbook, may be accessed.
http://library.mcphu.edu/resources/reviews/psych.htm

Menninger Articles on Mental Health This Web site lists links to online articles on various psychiatric disorders, such as addiction, eating disorders, personality disorders, sleep, anxiety, and schizophrenia. In addition, links to the Menninger Institute's different programs; reference materials; a telephone directory; a bulletin; services for adults, children, and corporations, and a referral service are present. General information about the institute is also listed.
http://www.menninger.edu/tmc_info_articles.html

Psychiatric News Maintained by the American Psychiatric Association, this site offers the most recent issue of *Psychiatric News*. Topics covered in the

newspaper include professional news, government news, legal news, residents' forum, annual meeting news, and clinical and research news.
http://pn.psychiatryonline.org/

 PsychLinx.com Directed to mental health professionals, this site offers recent news stories for a variety of psychiatric specialties including addiction, anxiety, eating disorders, mood disorders, personality disorders, and psychopharmacology. http://www.psychlinx.com/index.cfm?subspec_id=86

 SciCentral.com This site offers research news related to psychiatry and mental health. Full-text articles are provided. The site also offers links to special reports, directories of Web sites, journals, discussion groups, and educational materials.
http://www.sciquest.com/cgi-bin/ncommerce3/ExecMacro/sci_level3.d2w/report?
nav_banner=health&resource=articles&gateway=H-psychi&Tmstmp=48793

INDIVIDUAL JOURNAL WEB SITES

The following journals may be accessed on the Internet. Our table of information for each journal identifies content that is accessible free-of-charge or with a free registration and also identifies content that requires a password and fee for access. We have indicated if back issues are accessible. Journals are listed in alphabetical order by title.

 Academic Psychiatry
Publisher: American Association of Directors of Psychiatric Residency Training and the Association for Academic Psychiatry **Free:** Table of Contents, Abstracts, Articles
Pay: None http://ap.psychiatryonline.org

 Addiction
Publisher: Carfax Publishing **Free:** Table of Contents **Pay:** Abstracts, Articles
http://www.tandf.co.uk/journals/carfax/09652140.html

 Addiction Abstracts
Publisher: Carfax Publishing **Free:** Table of Contents, Abstracts **Pay:** Articles
http://www.tandf.co.uk/journals/carfax/09687610.html

 Administration and Policy in Mental Health
Publisher: Kluwer Academic Publishers **Free:** Table of Contents, Articles **Pay:** Abstracts
http://www.wkap.nl/journalhome.htm/0894-587X

 Advances in Biological Psychiatry
Publisher: S. Karger AG **Free:** Table of Contents, Abstracts **Pay:** Articles
http://www.karger.com/bookseries/adbip/adbip.htm

 Advances in Mind Body Medicine
Publisher: Harcourt Publishers Ltd. **Free:** Table of Contents, Abstracts **Pay:** Articles
http://www.harcourt-international.com/journals/ambm/

Advances in Psychiatric Treatment
Publisher: Royal College of Psychiatrists **Free:** Table of Contents **Pay:** Abstracts, Articles
http://apt.rcpsych.org/

Age and Aging
Publisher: Oxford University Press **Free:** Table of Contents, Abstracts **Pay:** Articles
http://ageing.oupjournals.org/

Aging & Mental Health
Publisher: Carfax Publishing **Free:** Table of Contents, Abstracts **Pay:** Articles
http://www.tandf.co.uk/journals/carfax/13607863.html

Aging, Neuropsychology, and Cognition
Publisher: Swets & Zeitlinger Publishers **Free:** Table of Contents, Abstracts **Pay:** Articles
http://www.swets.nl/sps/journals/anc.html

AIDS and Behavior
Publisher: Kluwer Academic Publishers **Free:** Table of Contents, Abstracts **Pay:** Articles
http://www.wkap.nl/journalhome.htm/1090-7165

Alcohol
Publisher: Elsevier Science **Free:** Table of Contents, Abstracts **Pay:** Articles
http://www.elsevier.nl/locate/alcohol

Alcohol and Alcoholism
Publisher: Oxford University Press **Free:** Table of Contents, Abstracts **Pay:** Articles
http://alcalc.oupjournals.org/

Alcoholism: Clinical and Experimental Research
Publisher: Lippincott Williams & Wilkins **Free:** Table of Contents, Abstracts **Pay:** Articles
http://www.alcoholism-cer.com/

Alzheimer's Disease Review
Publisher: Sanders-Brown Center on Aging **Free:** Table of Contents, Abstracts, Articles
Pay: None http://www.coa.uky.edu/ADReview

American Journal of Community Psychology
Publisher: Kluwer Academic Publishers **Free:** Table of Contents, Abstracts **Pay:** Articles
http://www.wkap.nl/journalhome.htm/0091-0562

American Journal of Family Therapy
Publisher: Brunner-Routledge **Free:** Table of Contents **Pay:** Articles
http://www.tandf.co.uk/journals/pp/01926187.html

American Journal of Geriatric Psychiatry
Publisher: American Association for Geriatric Psychiatry, HighWire Press **Free:** Table of
Contents, Abstracts, Articles **Pay:** None http://ajgp.psychiatryonline.org

American Journal of Medical Genetics: Neuropsychiatric Genetics
Publisher: John Wiley & Sons, Inc.   **Free:** Table of Contents, Abstracts   **Pay:** Enhanced Abstracts, Articles   http://www.interscience.wiley.com/jpages/0148-7299/

American Journal of Occupational Therapy
Publisher: American Occupational Therapy Association   **Free:** None   **Pay:** Articles
http://www.aota.org/nonmembers/area7/links/LINK03.asp

American Journal of Orthopsychiatry
Publisher: American Orthopsychiatric Association   **Free:** Table of Contents, Abstracts   **Pay:** Articles   http://www.amerortho.org/ajo.htm

American Journal of Psychiatry
Publisher: American Psychiatric Association   **Free:** Table of Contents, Abstracts, Articles   **Pay:** None   http://ajp.psychiatryonline.org

American Journal of Psychoanalysis
Publisher: Kluwer Academic Publishers   **Free:** Table of Contents   **Pay:** Articles
http://www.wkap.nl/journalhome.htm/0002-9548

American Journal of Psychology
Publisher: University of Illinois Press   **Free:** Table of Contents, Abstracts   **Pay:** Articles
http://www.press.uillinois.edu/journals/ajp.html

American Journal on Addictions
Publisher: Brunner-Routledge   **Free:** Table of Contents, Abstracts   **Pay:** Articles
http://www.tandf.co.uk/journals/tf/10550496.html

American Journal on Mental Retardation
Publisher: American Association on Mental Retardation   **Free:** Table of Contents, Abstracts   **Pay:** Articles   http://aamr.allenpress.com/aamronline/?request=index-html

American Psychologist
Publisher: American Psychological Association   **Free:** Table of Contents, Abstracts   **Pay:** Articles   http://www.apa.org/journals/amp.html

Annals of Clinical Psychiatry
Publisher: Kluwer Academic/Plenum Publishing Corporation   **Free:** Table of Contents   **Pay:** Abstracts, Articles   http://www.aacp.com/annals.html

Annual Review of Psychology
Publisher: Annual Reviews   **Free:** Table of Contents, Abstracts   **Pay:** Articles
http://psych.annualreviews.org/current.shtml

Anxiety, Stress and Coping
Publisher: Gordon and Breach Publishing Group   **Free:** Table of Contents, Abstracts   **Pay:** Articles   http://www.gbhap-us.com/journals/356/356-top.htm

Aphasiology
Publisher: Psychology Press **Free:** Table of Contents, Abstracts **Pay:** Articles
http://www.tandf.co.uk/journals/pp/02687038.html

 Applied & Preventive Psychology
Publisher: Cambridge University Press **Free:** Table of Contents **Pay:** Abstracts, Articles
http://us.cambridge.org/ObjectBuilder/ObjectBuilder.iwx?ProcessName=ProductPage&Merchant_Id=1&Section_ID=54X&pcount=&product_id=2000962184&page=journals

 Applied Cognitive Psychology
Publisher: John Wiley & Sons, Inc. **Free:** Table of Contents, Abstracts **Pay:** Articles
http://www.interscience.wiley.com/jpages/0888-4080/

 Applied Neuropsychology
Publisher: Lawrence Erlbaum Associates, Inc. **Free:** Table of Contents, Abstracts
Pay: Articles http://www.erlbaum.com/Journals/journals/AN/an.htm

 Applied Psychological Measurement
Publisher: SAGE Inc. **Free:** Table of Contents, Abstracts **Pay:** Articles
http://www.sagepub.com/Shopping/Journal.asp?id=4676

 Archives of Clinical Neuropsychology
Publisher: Elsevier Science **Free:** Table of Contents **Pay:** Articles
http://www.elsevier.nl/inca/publications/store/8/0/2

 Archives of General Psychiatry
Publisher: American Medical Association **Free:** Table of Contents, Abstracts **Pay:** Articles
http://archpsyc.ama-assn.org

 Archives of Psychiatric Nursing
Publisher: W. B. Saunders Company **Free:** None **Pay:** Table of Contents, Articles
http://167.208.232.26/catalog/wbs-prod.pl?0883-9417

 Archives of Sexual Behavior
Publisher: Kluwer Academic Publishers **Free:** Table of Contents, Abstracts **Pay:** Articles
http://www.wkap.nl/journalhome.htm/0004-0002

 Archives of Suicide Research
Publisher: Kluwer Academic/Plenum Publishing Corporation **Free:** Table of Contents
Pay: Abstracts, Articles
http://kapis.www.wkap.nl/kapis/CGI-BIN/WORLD/journalhome.htm?1381-1118

 Archives of Women's Mental Health
Publisher: Springer Wien New York **Free:** Table of Contents, Abstracts **Pay:** Articles
http://link.springer.de/link/service/journals/00737/index.htm

Attachment and Human Development
Publisher: Routledge Publishers **Free:** Table of Contents **Pay:** Abstracts, Articles
http://www.tandf.co.uk/journals/routledge/14616734.html

Autism
Publisher: SAGE Inc. **Free:** Table of Contents, Abstracts **Pay:** Articles
http://www.sagepub.com/Shopping/Journal.asp?id=4586

Basic and Applied Social Psychology
Publisher: Lawrence Erlbaum Associates, Inc. **Free:** Table of Contents, Abstracts
Pay: Articles   http://www.erlbaum.com/Journals/journals/BASP/basp.htm

Behavior Genetics
Publisher: Kluwer Academic Publishers **Free:** Table of Contents, Abstracts **Pay:** Articles
http://www.wkap.nl/journalhome.htm/0001-8244

Behavior Modification
Publisher: SAGE Inc. **Free:** Table of Contents, Abstracts **Pay:** Articles
http://www.sagepub.com/index1.asp?id=journal.asp?id=4674

Behavioral and Brain Sciences
Publisher: Cambridge University Press **Free:** Table of Contents **Pay:** Abstracts, Articles
http://www.bbsonline.org/

Behavioral and Cognitive Psychotherapy
Publisher: Cambridge University Press **Free:** Registration required to access Table of Contents and Abstracts **Pay:** Articles
http://uk.cambridge.org/journals/bcp/intro.htm

Behavioral Interventions
Publisher: John Wiley & Sons, Inc. **Free:** Table of Contents, Abstracts **Pay:** Articles
http://www.interscience.wiley.com/jpages/1072-0847/

Behavioral Medicine
Publisher: Heldref Publications **Free:** None **Pay:** Table of Contents, Abstracts, Articles
http://www.heldref.org/

Behavioral Neuroscience
Publisher: American Psychological Association **Free:** Table of Contents, Abstracts
Pay: Articles   http://www.apa.org/journals/bne.html

Behavioral Sciences & the Law
Publisher: John Wiley & Sons, Inc. **Free:** Table of Contents, Abstracts **Pay:** Articles
http://www.interscience.wiley.com/jpages/0735-3936/

Behaviour Research and Therapy
Publisher: Elsevier Science **Free:** Table of Contents, Abstracts **Pay:** Articles
http://www.elsevier.com/locate/brat

P-0125 JOURNAL

Behavioural Pharmacology
Publisher: Lippincott, Williams & Wilkins **Free:** Table of Contents **Pay:** Abstracts, Articles
http://www.behaviouralpharm.com

P-0126 JOURNAL

Biological Psychiatry
Publisher: Elsevier Science **Free:** Table of Contents **Pay:** Abstracts, Articles
http://www-east.elsevier.com/bps/bpsline.htm

P-0127 JOURNAL

Bipolar Disorders
Publisher: Munksgaard International Publishers **Free:** Table of Contents **Pay:** Abstracts, Articles   http://journals.munksgaard.dk/bipolardisorders

P-0128 JOURNAL

Brain
Publisher: Oxford University Press **Free:** Table of Contents, Abstracts **Pay:** Articles
http://brain.oupjournals.org

P-0129 JOURNAL

Brain and Cognition
Publisher: Academic Press **Free:** Table of Contents, Abstracts **Pay:** Articles
http://www.academicpress.com/www/journal/br.htm

P-0130 JOURNAL

British Journal of Clinical and Social Psychiatry
Publisher: Society of Clinical Psychiatrists **Free:** Table of Contents, Abstracts, Articles
Pay: None http://www.scpnet.com/BJCSP.htm

P-0131 NEW JOURNAL

British Journal of Clinical Psychology
Publisher: British Psychological Society **Free:** Table of Contents, Abstracts **Pay:** Articles
http://www.bps.org.uk/publications/jCP_1.cfm

P-0132 NEW JOURNAL

British Journal of Developmental Disabilities
Publisher: British Society for Developmental Disabilities **Free:** Table of Contents, Abstracts, Articles **Pay:** None http://www.bjdd.org/

P-0133 NEW JOURNAL

British Journal of Developmental Psychology
Publisher: British Psychological Society **Free:** Table of Contents, Abstracts **Pay:** Articles
http://www.bps.org.uk/publications/jDP_1.cfm

P-0134 NEW JOURNAL

British Journal of Educational Psychology
Publisher: British Psychological Society **Free:** Table of Contents, Abstracts **Pay:** Articles
http://www.bps.org.uk/publications/jEP_1.cfm

P-0135 NEW JOURNAL

British Journal of Guidance & Counseling
Publisher: Carfax Publishing **Free:** Table of Contents, Abstracts **Pay:** Articles
http://www.tandf.co.uk/journals/carfax/03069885.html

P-0136 NEW JOURNAL

British Journal of Health Psychology
Publisher: British Psychological Society **Free:** Table of Contents, Abstracts **Pay:** Articles
http://www.bps.org.uk/publications/jHH_1.cfm

British Journal of Medical Psychology

Publisher: British Psychological Society **Free:** Table of Contents, Abstracts **Pay:** Articles
http://www.bps.org.uk/publications/jHP_1.cfm

British Journal of Psychiatry

Publisher: Royal College of Psychiatrists **Free:** Table of Contents, Abstracts **Pay:** Articles
http://bjp.rcpsych.org/

British Journal of Social Psychology

Publisher: British Psychological Society **Free:** Table of Contents, Abstracts **Pay:** Articles
http://www.bps.org.uk/publications/jSP_1.cfm

Bulletin of the Menninger Clinic

Publisher: Guilford Press **Free:** Table of Contents, Abstracts **Pay:** Articles
http://www.guilford.com/periodicals/jnme.htm

Child Abuse and Neglect

Publisher: Elsevier Science **Free:** Table of Contents, Abstracts **Pay:** Articles
http://www.elsevier.com/locate/chiabuneg

Child Abuse Review

Publisher: John Wiley & Sons, Inc. **Free:** Table of Contents, Abstracts **Pay:** Articles
http://www.interscience.wiley.com/jpages/0952-9136/

Child and Adolescent Psychiatric Clinics

Publisher: W. B. Saunders Company **Free:** None **Pay:** Table of Contents, Articles
http://www.harcourthealth.com/
scripts/om.dll/serve?action=searchDB&searchDBfor=home&id=ccap

Child and Adolescent Psychiatry Online

Publisher: Priory Lodge Education, Ltd. **Free:** Table of Contents, Articles, Abstracts
Pay: None http://www.priory.com/psychild.htm

Child and Adolescent Psychopharmacology News

Publisher: Guilford Press **Free:** None **Pay:** Table of Contents, Articles
http://www.guilford.com/periodicals/jncp.htm

Child Neuropsychology

Publisher: Swets & Zeitlinger Publishers **Free:** Table of Contents, Abstracts **Pay:** Articles
http://www.swets.nl/sps/journals/child.html

Child Psychiatry and Human Development

Publisher: Kluwer Academic/Plenum Publishing Corporation **Free:** Table of Contents
Pay: Abstracts, Articles   http://www.wkap.nl/journalhome.htm/0009-398X

Child Psychology and Psychiatry Review

Publisher: Cambridge University Press **Free:** Registration required to access Table of
Contents and Abstracts **Pay:** Articles   http://uk.cambridge.org/journals/cpr/cprifc.htm

Clinical Child and Family Psychology Review

Publisher: Kluwer Academic Publishers **Free:** Table of Contents, Abstracts **Pay:** Articles
http://www.wkap.nl/journalhome.htm/1096-4037

Clinical Child Psychology and Psychiatry

Publisher: SAGE Publications **Free:** Table of Contents, Abstracts **Pay:** Articles
http://www.sagepub.co.uk/journals/details/j0063.html

Clinical Neuropsychologist

Publisher: Swets & Zeitlinger Publishers **Free:** Table of Contents, Abstracts **Pay:** Articles
http://www.swets.nl/sps/journals/tcn.html

Clinical Psychiatry News

Publisher: International Medical News Group **Free:** Table of Contents, Abstracts, Articles
Pay: None
http://www.medscape.com/IMNG/ClinPsychNews/public/journal.ClinPsychNews.html

Clinical Psychology and Psychotherapy

Publisher: John Wiley & Sons, Inc. **Free:** Registration required to access Table of Contents
and Abstracts **Pay:** Articles http://www.interscience.wiley.com/jpages/1063-3995

Clinical Psychology Review

Publisher: Elsevier Science **Free:** Table of Contents, Abstracts **Pay:** Articles
http://www.elsevier.nl/locate/clinpsychrev

Clinical Psychology: Science & Practice

Publisher: American Psychological Association **Free:** Table of Contents, Abstracts
Pay: Articles http://clipsy.oupjournals.org/

Clinician's Research Digest

Publisher: American Psychological Association **Free:** None **Pay:** Table of Contents,
Abstracts, Articles http://www.apa.org/journals/crd.html

Cognition

Publisher: Elsevier Science **Free:** Table of Contents, Abstracts **Pay:** Articles
http://www.elsevier.nl/locate/cognit

Cognitive Brain Research

Publisher: Elsevier Science **Free:** Table of Contents, Abstracts **Pay:** Articles
http://www.elsevier.nl/locate/cogbrainres

Cognitive Neuropsychiatry

Publisher: Psychology Press **Free:** Table of Contents, Abstracts **Pay:** Articles
http://www.tandf.co.uk/journals/pp/13546805.html

Cognitive Neuropsychology

Publisher: Psychology Press **Free:** Table of Contents, Abstracts **Pay:** Articles
http://www.tandf.co.uk/journals/pp/02643294.html

Cognitive Psychology
Publisher: Academic Press **Free:** Table of Contents, Abstracts **Pay:** Articles
http://www.apnet.com/www/journal/cg.htm

Cognitive Science
Publisher: Cognitive Science Society, Inc. **Free:** Table of Contents, Abstracts **Pay:** Articles
http://www.umich.edu/~cogsci/about.html

Cognitive Therapy and Research
Publisher: Plenum Press **Free:** Table of Contents **Pay:** Abstracts, Articles
http://www.sci.sdsu.edu/CAL/CTR/CTR.html

Community Mental Health Journal
Publisher: Kluwer Academic Publishers **Free:** Table of Contents **Pay:** Articles
http://www.wkap.nl/journalhome.htm/0010-3853

Comprehensive Psychiatry
Publisher: W.B. Saunders Company **Free:** None **Pay:** Articles
http://167.208.232.26/catalog/wbs-prod.pl?0010-440X

Consciousness and Cognition
Publisher: Academic Press **Free:** Table of Contents, Abstracts **Pay:** Articles
http://www.apnet.com/www/journal/cc.htm

Consulting Psychology Journal: Practice and Research
Publisher: American Psychology Association **Free:** Table of Contents, Abstracts
Pay: Articles   http://www.apa.org/journals/cpb.html

Contemporary Hypnosis
Publisher: Allen Press, Inc. **Free:** None **Pay:** Table of Contents, Articles
http://www.allenpress.com/cgi-bin/test-cat.cgi?journal=contemp_hyp

Contemporary Psychology
Publisher: American Psychological Association **Free:** Table of Contents, Abstracts
Pay: Articles
http://www.apa.org/journals/cnt.html

Counselling Psychology Quarterly
Publisher: Carfax Publishing **Free:** Table of Contents, Abstracts **Pay:** Articles
http://www.tandf.co.uk/journals/carfax/09515070.html

Criminal Behavior and Mental Health
Publisher: Allen Press, Inc. **Free:** None **Pay:** Table of Contents, Abstracts, Articles
http://www.allenpress.com/cgi-bin/test-cat.cgi?journal=cbmh

Crisis Intervention and Time-Limited Treatment
Publisher: Gordon and Breach Publishing Group **Free:** Table of Contents, Abstracts
Pay: Articles   http://www.gbhap-us.com/journals/398/398-top.htm

P-0173	
JOURNAL	

Crisis: The Journal of Crisis Intervention and Suicide Prevention

Publisher: Hogrefe & Huber Publishers   **Free:** Table of Contents, Abstracts, Editorials
Pay: Articles   http://www.hhpub.com/journals/crisis/index.html

Culture, Medicine, and Psychiatry

Publisher: Kluwer Academic Publishers **Free:** Table of Contents **Pay:** Abstracts, Articles
http://kapis.www.wkap.nl/kapis/CGI-BIN/WORLD/journalhome.htm?0165-005X

Current Opinion in Psychiatry

Publisher: Lippincott Williams & Wilkins **Free:** Table of Contents **Pay:** Abstracts, Articles
http://www.co-psychiatry.com/

Current Research in Social Psychology

Publisher: University of Iowa **Free:** Table of Contents, Abstracts **Pay:** Articles
http://www.uiowa.edu/~grpproc/crisp/crisp.html

Current Therapeutics Online

Publisher: Adis International   **Free:** Table of Contents, Selected Abstracts and Articles
Pay: Articles http://www.ctonline.com.au

CyberPsychology and Behavior

Publisher: Mary Ann Liebert, Inc. **Free:** Table of Contents, Abstracts, Articles **Pay:** None
http://www.liebertpub.com/cpb/default1.asp

Dementia and Geriatric Cognitive Disorders

Publisher: S. Karger AG **Free:** Table of Contents, Abstracts **Pay:** Articles
http://www.karger.com/journals/dem

Depression and Anxiety

Publisher: John Wiley & Sons, Inc. **Free:** Registration required to access Table of Contents
and Abstracts **Pay:** Articles
http://www.interscience.wiley.com/jpages/1091-4269

Development and Psychopathology

Publisher: Cambridge University Press **Free:** Table of Contents **Pay:** Articles
http://uk.cambridge.org/journals/dpp/dppifc.htm

Developmental Neuropsychology

Publisher: Lawrence Erlbaum Associates, Inc.   **Free:** Table of Contents, Abstracts
Pay: Articles http://www.erlbaum.com/Journals/journals/DN/dn.htm

Developmental Psychology

Publisher: American Psychological Association   **Free:** Table of Contents, Abstracts
Pay: Articles http://www.apa.org/journals/dev.html

Developmental Review

Publisher: Academic Press **Free:** Table of Contents, Abstracts, Articles **Pay:** None
http://www.apnet.com/www/journal/dr.htm

Deviant Behavior
Publisher: Taylor & Francis Group **Free:** Table of Contents, Abstracts **Pay:** Articles
http://www.tandf.co.uk/journals/tf/01639625.html

Drug and Alcohol Dependence
Publisher: Elsevier Science **Free:** Table of Contents, Abstracts **Pay:** Articles
http://www.elsevier.nl/locate/drugalcdep

Drug and Alcohol Review
Publisher: Carfax Publishing **Free:** Table of Contents **Pay:** Articles
http://www.tandf.co.uk/journals/carfax/09595236.html

Drug Dependence, Alcohol Abuse and Alcoholism
Publisher: Elsevier Science **Free:** None **Pay:** Table of Contents, Articles
http://www.elsevier.nl/locate/drug

Dyslexia
Publisher: John Wiley & Sons, Inc. **Free:** Table of Contents, Abstracts **Pay:** Articles
http://www.interscience.wiley.com/jpages/1076-9242/

Eating Disorders
Publisher: Brunner-Routledge Publishing **Free:** None **Pay:** Table of Contents, Abstracts, Articles http://www.brunner-routledge.com/journals/EDI.htm

ECT Online
Publisher: Priory Lodge Education, Ltd. **Free:** Articles, Table of Contents **Pay:** None
http://www.priory.co.uk/psych/ectol.htm

Electronic Journal of Cognitive and Brain Sciences
Publisher: Zoltan Nadasdy **Free:** Table of Contents, Abstracts, Articles **Pay:** None
http://speedy2.md.huji.ac.il/ejcbs/ejcbs.html

Environment and Behavior
Publisher: SAGE Inc. **Free:** None **Pay:** Table of Contents, Abstracts, Articles
http://www.sagepub.com/index1.asp?id=journal.asp?id=4727

Epilepsy & Behavior
Publisher: Academic Press **Free:** Table of Contents, Abstracts **Pay:** Articles
http://www.apnet.com/eb

Evidence-Based Mental Health
Publisher: Centre for Evidence-Based Mental Health, Oxford **Free:** Table of Contents, Abstracts, Articles **Pay:** None
http://www.psychiatry.ox.ac.uk/cebmh/ebmh/index.html

Exceptionality
Publisher: Lawrence Erlbaum Associates, Inc. **Free:** Table of Contents, Abstracts **Pay:** Articles http://www.erlbaum.com/Journals/journals/EX/ex.htm

Experimental and Clinical Psychopharmacology
Publisher: American Psychological Association   **Free:** Table of Contents, Abstracts **Pay:** Articles   http://www.apa.org/journals/pha.html

Experimental Gerontology
Publisher: Elsevier Science **Free:** Table of Contents, Abstracts **Pay:** Articles
http://www.elsevier.nl/locate/expgero

Family Therapy News
Publisher: American Association for Marriage and Family Therapy **Free:** None **Pay:** Table of Contents, Articles   http://www.aamft.org/resources/ftn_menu.htm

Forensic Psychiatry Online
Publisher: Priory Lodge Education, Ltd.   **Free:** Table of Contents, Abstracts, Articles **Pay:** None   http://www.priory.com/forpsy.htm

Gender and Psychoanalysis
Publisher: International Universities Press **Free:** None **Pay:** Table of Contents, Articles http://www.iup.com/order.cfm?bookno=GAP&action=info&J=J

General Hospital Psychiatry
Publisher: Elsevier Science **Free:** Table of Contents **Pay:** Abstracts, Articles
http://www.elsevier.nl/inca/publications/store/5/0/5/7/6/1

Geriatrics
Publisher: Advanstar Communications, Inc.   **Free:** Table of Contents, Abstracts **Pay:** Articles   http://www.geri.com/journal/corporate.html

German Journal Of Psychiatry
Publisher: German Journal of Psychiatry   **Free:** Table of Contents, Abstracts, Articles **Pay:** None   http://www.gwdg.de/~bbandel/gjp-homepage.htm

Gerontologist
Publisher: Gerontological Society of America **Free:** Table of Contents **Pay:** Abstracts, Articles   http://www.geron.org/journals/gerontologist.html

Gerontology
Publisher: S. Karger AG **Free:** Table of Contents, Abstracts **Pay:** Articles
http://www.karger.com/journals/ger/ger_jh.htm

Gestalt Review
Publisher: Analytic Press, Inc. **Free:** Table of Contents, Abstracts **Pay:** Articles
http://www.analyticpress.com/gestalt_review.html

Group
Publisher: Kluwer Academic Publishers **Free:** Table of Contents, Abstracts **Pay:** Articles
http://www.wkap.nl/journalhome.htm/0362-4021

Group Analysis
Publisher: SAGE Inc. **Free:** Table of Contents, Abstracts **Pay:** Articles
http://www.sagepub.com/Shopping/Journal.asp?id=4577

Harvard Mental Health Letter
Publisher: HMS Harvard Health Publications **Free:** Topic Highlights **Pay:** Articles
http://www.health.harvard.edu/aboutmental.shtml

Harvard Review of Psychiatry
Publisher: Oxford University Press **Free:** Table of Contents, Abstracts **Pay:** Articles
http://hrp.oupjournals.org/contents-by-date.0.shtml

Health Psychology
Publisher: American Psychological Association **Free:** Table of Contents, Abstracts
Pay: Articles   http://www.apa.org/journals/hea.html

History of Psychology
Publisher: American Psychological Association **Free:** Table of Contents, Abstracts
Pay: Articles   http://www.apa.org/journals/hop.html

Human Psychopharmacology
Publisher: John Wiley & Sons, Inc. **Free:** Registration required to access Table of Contents
and Abstracts **Pay:** Articles
http://www.interscience.wiley.com/jpages/0885-6222

In Session: Psychotherapy in Practice
Publisher: John Wiley & Sons, Inc. **Free:** Table of Contents, Abstracts **Pay:** Articles
http://www.interscience.wiley.com/jpages/1077-2413/info.html

Infant Mental Health Journal
Publisher: John Wiley & Sons, Inc. **Free:** Registration required to access Table of Contents
and Abstracts **Pay:** Articles
http://www.interscience.wiley.com/jpages/0163-9641

International Clinical Psychopharmacology
Publisher: Lippincott Williams & Wilkins **Free:** Table of Contents **Pay:** Abstracts, Articles
http://www.intclinpsychopharm.com

International Forum of Psychoanalysis
Publisher: Taylor & Francis Group **Free:** Table of Contents **Pay:** Abstracts, Articles
http://www.tandf.co.uk/journals/tfs/0803706x.html

International Journal of Behavioral Development
Publisher: Psychology Press **Free:** Table of Contents, Abstracts **Pay:** Articles
http://www.tandf.co.uk/journals/pp/01650254.html

P-0220 NEW JOURNAL

International Journal of Behavioral Medicine
Publisher: Lawrence Erlbaum Associates, Inc. **Free:** Table of Contents, Abstracts
Pay: Articles http://www.erlbaum.com/Journals/journals/IJBM/ijbm.htm

P-0221 JOURNAL

International Journal of Clinical and Experimental Hypnosis
Publisher: Sage Publications **Free:** Table of Contents, Abstracts **Pay:** Articles
http://sunsite.utk.edu/IJCEH/ijcehframes.htm

P-0222 JOURNAL

International Journal of Eating Disorders
Publisher: John Wiley & Sons, Inc. **Free:** Registration required to access Table of Contents
and Abstracts **Pay:** Articles
http://www.interscience.wiley.com/jpages/0276-3478

P-0223 JOURNAL

International Journal of Geriatric Psychiatry
Publisher: John Wiley & Sons, Inc. **Free:** Registration required to access Table of Contents
and Abstracts **Pay:** Articles
http://www.interscience.wiley.com/jpages/0885-6230

P-0224 JOURNAL

International Journal of Group Psychotherapy
Publisher: Guilford Publications **Free:** Table of Contents **Pay:** Abstracts, Articles
http://www.guilford.com/periodicals/jngr.htm

P-0225 JOURNAL

International Journal of Intensive Short-Term Dynamic Psychotherapy
Publisher: John Wiley & Sons, Inc. **Free:** Registration required to access Table of Contents
and Abstracts **Pay:** Articles http://www.interscience.wiley.com/jpages/1096-7028

P-0226 JOURNAL

International Journal of Law and Psychiatry
Publisher: Elsevier Science **Free:** Table of Contents **Pay:** Abstracts, Articles
http://www.elsevier.com/locate/ijlawpsy

P-0227 NEW JOURNAL

International Journal of Mental Health
Publisher: M. E. Sharpe **Free:** Table of Contents, Abstracts **Pay:** Articles
http://www.mesharpe.com/imh_main.htm

P-0228 NEW JOURNAL

International Journal of Methods in Psychiatric Research
Publisher: Allen Press, Inc. **Free:** None **Pay:** Table of Contents, Abstracts, Articles
http://www.allenpress.com/cgi-bin/test-
cat.cgi?journal=int_j_of_methods_in_psych_research

P-0229 NEW JOURNAL

International Journal of Neuropsychopharmacology
Publisher: Cambridge University Press **Free:** None **Pay:** Table of Contents, Articles
http://uk.cambridge.org/journals/pnp/

P-0230 JOURNAL

International Journal of Obesity and Related Metabolic Disorders
Publisher: Nature Publishing Group **Free:** Table of Contents **Pay:** Articles
http://www.nature.com/ijo

International Journal of Psychiatry in Medicine
Publisher: Baywood Publishing Company **Free:** Table of Contents, Abstracts **Pay:** Articles
http://psychiatry.mc.duke.edu/ijpm/index.html

International Journal of Psychoanalysis
Publisher: Institute of Psychoanalysis, London **Free:** Users must register with CatchWord Journal Service to view Table of Contents, Abstracts, and Articles. **Pay:** None
http://www.ijpa.org

International Journal of Psychophysiology
Publisher: Elsevier Science **Free:** Table of Contents, Abstracts **Pay:** Articles
http://www.elsevier.nl/locate/ijpsycho

International Journal of Psychosocial Rehabilitation
Publisher: Southern Development Group **Free:** Table of Contents, Articles **Pay:** None
http://www.psychosocial.com

International Journal of Psychotherapy
Publisher: Carfax Publishing **Free:** Table of Contents, Abstracts **Pay:** Articles
http://www.tandf.co.uk/journals/carfax/13569082.html

International Journal of Stress Management
Publisher: Kluwer Academic Publishers **Free:** Table of Contents, Abstracts **Pay:** Articles
http://www.wkap.nl/journalhome.htm/1072-5245

International Psychogeriatrics
Publisher: International Psychogeriatric Association **Free:** Table of Contents, Abstracts **Pay:** Articles
http://www.ipa-online.org/ipaonline/html/
publications/InternationalPsychogeriatrics/default.htm

International Review of Psychiatry
Publisher: Carfax Publishing **Free:** Table of Contents **Pay:** Articles
http://www.tandf.co.uk/journals/carfax/09540261.html

Issues in Mental Health Nursing
Publisher: Taylor & Francis Group **Free:** Table of Contents, Abstracts **Pay:** Articles
http://www.tandf.co.uk/journals/tf/01612840.html

Journal for Specialists in Group Work
Publisher: SAGE Inc. **Free:** Table of Contents, Abstracts **Pay:** Articles
http://www.sagepub.com/index1.asp?id=journal.asp?id=4747

Journal of Abnormal Child Psychology
Publisher: Kluwer Academic Publishers **Free:** Table of Contents, Abstracts **Pay:** Articles
http://www.wkap.nl/journalhome.htm/0091-0627

| P-0242 |
| JOURNAL |

Journal of Abnormal Psychology
Publisher: American Psychological Association **Free:** Table of Contents, Abstracts
Pay: Articles   http://www.apa.org/journals/abn.html

| P-0243 |
| JOURNAL |

Journal of Adolescence
Publisher: Academic Press **Free:** Table of Contents, Abstracts **Pay:** Articles
http://www.academicpress.com/www/journal/adnojs.htm

Journal of Adolescent Research
Publisher: SAGE Inc. **Free:** Table of Contents, Abstracts **Pay:** Articles
http://www.sagepub.com/Shopping/Journal.asp?id=4721

Journal of Adult Development
Publisher: Kluwer Academic Publishers **Free:** Table of Contents, Abstracts **Pay:** Articles
http://www.wkap.nl/journalhome.htm/1068-0667

| P-0246 |
| JOURNAL |

Journal of Affective Disorders
Publisher: Elsevier Science **Free:** Table of Contents **Pay:** Abstracts, Articles
http://www.elsevier.nl/inca/publications/store/5/0/6/0/7/7/

| P-0247 |
| JOURNAL |

Journal of Anxiety Disorders
Publisher: Elsevier Science **Free:** Table of Contents **Pay:** Abstracts, Articles
http://www.elsevier.com/locate/inca/801

| P-0248 |
| JOURNAL |

Journal of Applied Behavior Analysis
Publisher: Society for the Experimental Analysis of Behavior, Inc. **Free:** Table of Contents,
Abstracts **Pay:** Articles
http://www.envmed.rochester.edu/wwwrap/behavior/jaba/jabahome.htm

Journal of Applied Psychology
Publisher: American Psychological Association **Free:** Table of Contents, Abstracts
Pay: Articles http://www.apa.org/journals/apl.html

| P-0250 |
| JOURNAL |

Journal of Attention Disorders
Publisher: Multi Health Systems, Inc. **Free:** Table of Contents, Abstracts **Pay:** Articles
http://www.mhs.com/jad

| P-0251 |
| JOURNAL |

Journal of Autism and Developmental Disorders
Publisher: Kluwer Academic Publishers **Free:** Table of Contents, Abstracts **Pay:** Articles
http://www.wkap.nl/journalhome.htm/0162-3257

| P-0252 |
| JOURNAL |

Journal of Behavior Therapy and Experimental Psychiatry
Publisher: Elsevier Science **Free:** Table of Contents **Pay:** Abstracts, Articles
http://www.elsevier.nl/inca/publications/store/3/3/9/

| P-0254 |
| JOURNAL |

Journal of Behavioral Medicine
Publisher: Kluwer Academic Publishers **Free:** Table of Contents **Pay:** Articles
http://www.wkap.nl/journalhome.htm/0160-7715

Journal of Black Psychology
Publisher: SAGE Inc. **Free:** Table of Contents, Abstracts **Pay:** Articles
http://www.sagepub.com/index1.asp?id=journal.asp?id=4643

Journal of Child & Adolescent Psychopharmacology
Publisher: Mary Ann Liebert, Inc. **Free:** Table of Contents, Abstracts, Articles **Pay:** None
http://www.liebertpub.com/cap/default1.asp

Journal of Child and Adolescent Group Therapy
Publisher: Kluwer Academic Publishers **Free:** Table of Contents, Abstracts **Pay:** Articles
http://www.wkap.nl/journalhome.htm/1053-0800

Journal of Child Psychology and Psychiatry and Allied Disciplines
Publisher: Cambridge University Press **Free:** Table of Contents **Pay:** Articles
http://uk.cambridge.org/journals/cpp/cppifc.htm

Journal of Child Psychotherapy
Publisher: Routledge Publishers **Free:** Table of Contents, Abstracts **Pay:** Articles
http://www.tandf.co.uk/journals/routledge/0075417X.html

Journal of Clinical and Experimental Neuropsychology
Publisher: Swets & Zeitlinger Publishers **Free:** Table of Contents, Abstracts **Pay:** Articles
http://sun.swets.nl/sps/journals/jcen.html

Journal of Clinical Child Psychology
Publisher: Lawrence Erlbaum Associates, Inc. **Free:** Table of Contents, Abstracts
Pay: Articles   http://www.erlbaum.com/Journals/journals/JCCP/jccp.htm

Journal of Clinical Geropsychology
Publisher: Kluwer Academic Publishers **Free:** Table of Contents, Abstracts **Pay:** Articles
http://www.wkap.nl/journalhome.htm/1079-9362

Journal of Clinical Psychiatry
Publisher: Physicians Postgraduate Press **Free:** Table of Contents **Pay:** Abstracts, Articles
http://www.psychiatrist.com

Journal of Clinical Psychoanalysis
Publisher: International Universities Press, Inc. **Free:** Table of Contents, Abstracts, Articles
Pay: None   http://plaza.interport.net/nypsan/jcp.html

Journal of Clinical Psychology
Publisher: John Wiley & Sons, Inc. **Free:** Table of Contents, Abstracts **Pay:** Enhanced
Abstracts, Articles   http://www.interscience.wiley.com/jpages/0021-9762/

Journal of Clinical Psychology in Medical Settings
Publisher: Kluwer Academic Publishers **Free:** Table of Contents, Abstracts **Pay:** Articles
http://www.wkap.nl/journalhome.htm/1068-9583

P-0267
JOURNAL
Journal of Clinical Psychopharmacology
Publisher: Lippincott Williams & Wilkins **Free:** Table of Contents **Pay:** Articles
http://www.psychopharmacology.com

P-0268
JOURNAL
Journal of Cognition and Development
Publisher: Lawrence Erlbaum Associates, Inc. **Free:** Table of Contents, Abstracts
Pay: Articles http://www.erlbaum.com/Journals/journals/JCD/jcd.htm

P-0269
JOURNAL
Journal of Cognitive Neuroscience
Publisher: MIT Press **Free:** Table of Contents, Abstracts **Pay:** Articles
http://jocn.mitpress.org/

P-0270
JOURNAL
Journal of Cognitive Psychotherapy
Publisher: International Association for Cognitive Psychotherapy **Free:** Table of Contents,
Abstracts **Pay:** Articles
http://psy.ed.asu.edu/~jcp/index.html

P-0271
JOURNAL
Journal of Cognitive Rehabilitation
Publisher: NeuroScience Publishers **Free:** None **Pay:** Articles
http://www.neuroscience.cnter.com/jcr/NSP/Default.htm

P-0272
JOURNAL
Journal of Communication Disorders
Publisher: Elsevier Science **Free:** Table of Contents, Abstracts **Pay:** Articles
http://www.elsevier.com/locate/inca/505768?menu=cont

P-0273
JOURNAL
Journal of Community & Applied Social Psychology
Publisher: John Wiley & Sons, Ltd. **Free:** Table of Contents, Abstracts **Pay:** Articles
http://www.interscience.wiley.com/jpages/1052-9284/

P-0274
JOURNAL
Journal of Community Psychology
Publisher: John Wiley & Sons, Inc. **Free:** Table of Contents, Abstracts **Pay:** Articles
http://www.interscience.wiley.com/jpages/0090-4392/

P-0275
JOURNAL
Journal of Comparative Psychology
Publisher: American Psychological Association **Free:** Table of Contents, Abstracts
Pay: Articles http://www.apa.org/journals/com.html

P-0276
JOURNAL
Journal of Constructivist Psychology
Publisher: Taylor & Francis Group **Free:** Table of Contents, Abstracts **Pay:** Articles
http://www.tandf.co.uk/journals/tf/10720537.html

P-0277
JOURNAL
Journal of Consulting and Clinical Psychology
Publisher: American Psychological Association **Free:** Table of Contents, Selected Articles
Pay: Articles http://www.apa.org/journals/ccp.html

P-0278
JOURNAL
Journal of Contemporary Psychotherapy
Publisher: Kluwer Academic Publishers **Free:** Table of Contents, Abstracts **Pay:** Articles
http://www.wkap.nl/journalhome.htm/0022-0116

Journal of Counseling Psychology

Publisher: American Psychological Association   **Free:** Table of Contents, Abstracts   **Pay:** Articles   http://www.apa.org/journals/cou.html

Journal of Cross-Cultural Psychology

Publisher: SAGE Inc.   **Free:** Table of Contents, Abstracts   **Pay:** Articles
http://www.sagepub.com/index1.asp?id=journal.asp?id=4663

Journal of Development and Physical Disabilities

Publisher: Kluwer Academic Publishers   **Free:** Table of Contents, Abstracts   **Pay:** Articles
http://www.wkap.nl/journalhome.htm/1056-263X

Journal of Developmental and Behavioral Pediatrics

Publisher: Lippincott Williams & Wilkins   **Free:** Table of Contents, Abstracts   **Pay:** Articles
http://www.jrnldbp.com

Journal of ECT

Publisher: Lippincott Williams & Wilkins   **Free:** Table of Contents   **Pay:** Articles
http://www.ectjournal.com

Journal of Educational Psychology

Publisher: American Psychological Association   **Free:** Table of Contents, Abstracts   **Pay:** Articles   http://www.apa.org/journals/edu.html

Journal of Family Psychology

Publisher: American Psychological Association   **Free:** Table of Contents, Abstracts   **Pay:** Articles   http://www.apa.org/journals/fam.html

Journal of Family Therapy

Publisher: Blackwell Publishers   **Free:** Table of Contents, Abstracts   **Pay:** Articles
http://www.blackwellpublishers.co.uk/asp/journal.asp?ref=0163-4445

Journal of Forensic Psychiatry

Publisher: Routledge Publishers   **Free:** Table of Contents, Abstracts   **Pay:** Articles
http://www.tandf.co.uk/journals/routledge/09585184.html

Journal of Marital and Family Therapy

Publisher: American Association for Marriage and Family Therapy   **Free:** None
Pay: Articles http://www.aamft.org/resources/jmft_menu.htm

Journal of Mind and Behavior

Publisher: Institute of Mind and Behavior, Inc.   **Free:** Table of Contents, Abstracts
Pay: Articles   http://kramer.ume.maine.edu/~jmb/

Journal of Nervous and Mental Disease

Publisher: Lippincott Williams & Wilkins   **Free:** None   **Pay:** Articles
http://www.wwilkins.com/NMD

Journal of Neurology, Neurosurgery, and Psychiatry
Publisher: BMJ Publishing **Free:** Table of Contents, Abstracts **Pay:** Articles
http://jnnp.bmjjournals.com

Journal of Neuropsychiatry and Clinical Neurosciences
Publisher: American Neuropsychiatric Association, HighWire Press **Free:** Table of Contents, Abstracts, Articles **Pay:** None   http://neuro.psychiatryonline.org

Journal of Occupational and Organizational Psychology
Publisher: British Psychological Society **Free:** Table of Contents, Abstracts **Pay:** Articles
http://www.bps.org.uk/publications/jOP_1.cfm

Journal of Occupational Health Psychology
Publisher: American Psychological Association   **Free:** Table of Contents, Abstracts **Pay:** Articles http://www.apa.org/journals/ocp.html

Journal of Pain and Symptom Management: Including Supportive and Palliative Care
Publisher: Elsevier Science **Free:** Table of Contents, Abstracts **Pay:** Articles
http://www.elsevier.com/locate/jpainsymman

Journal of Pediatric Psychology
Publisher: Oxford University Press **Free:** Table of Contents, Abstracts **Pay:** Articles
http://jpepsy.oupjournals.org/

Journal of Personality and Social Psychology
Publisher: American Psychological Association **Free:** Table of Contents, Selected Articles **Pay:** Articles   http://www.apa.org/journals/psp.html

Journal of Personality Disorders
Publisher: Guilford Publications **Free:** Table of Contents, Abstracts **Pay:** Articles
http://www.guilford.com/periodicals/jnpd.htm

Journal of Psychiatric and Mental Health Nursing
Publisher: Blackwell Science Ltd. **Free:** Table of Contents **Pay:** Articles
http://www.blacksci.co.uk/~cgilib/jnlpage.bin?Journal=JPMHN&File=JPMHN&Page=aims

Journal of Psychiatric Practice
Publisher: Lippincott Williams & Wilkins **Free:** Table of Contents, Abstracts **Pay:** Articles
http://www.practicalpsychiatry.com

Journal of Psychiatric Research
Publisher: Elsevier Science **Free:** Table of Contents **Pay:** Abstracts, Articles
http://www.elsevier.com/inca/publications/store/2/4/1

Journal of Psychiatry
Publisher: CSS Publishing **Free:** Table of Contents **Pay:** Abstracts, Articles
http://www.medical-library.org/j_psych.htm

Don't type in long URLs – add the site number to the eMedguides URL: www.eMedguides.com/**c-1234**.

Journal of Psychiatry and Neuroscience
Publisher: Canadian Medical Association   **Free:** Table of Contents, Abstracts   **Pay:** Articles
http://www.cma.ca/jpn/index.htm

Journal of Psychopharmacology
Publisher: Sage Publications   **Free:** Table of Contents, Abstracts   **Pay:** Articles
http://www.sagepub.co.uk/journals/details/j0102.html

Journal of Psychosomatic Research
Publisher: Elsevier Science   **Free:** Table of Contents   **Pay:** Abstracts, Articles
http://www.elsevier.com/locate/inca/525474?menu=cont

Journal of Psychotherapy Practice and Research
Publisher: American Psychiatric Association   **Free:** Table of Contents, Abstracts, Articles
Pay: None   http://jppr.psychiatryonline.org

Journal of Rational-Emotive & Cognitive-Behavior Therapy
Publisher: Kluwer Academic Publishers   **Free:** Table of Contents, Abstracts   **Pay:** Articles
http://www.wkap.nl/journalhome.htm/0894-9085

Journal of Reproductive and Infant Psychology
Publisher: Carfax Publishing   **Free:** Table of Contents, Abstracts   **Pay:** Articles
http://www.tandf.co.uk/journals/carfax/02646838.html

Journal of Sex & Marital Therapy
Publisher: Brunner-Routledge   **Free:** Table of Contents, Abstracts   **Pay:** Articles
http://www.tandf.co.uk/journals/pp/0092623X.html

Journal of Sex Research
Publisher: Society for the Scientific Study of Sexuality   **Free:** Table of Contents
Pay: Abstracts, Articles   http://www.ssc.wisc.edu/ssss/jsr.htm

Journal of Substance Abuse Treatment
Publisher: Elsevier Science   **Free:** Table of Contents, Abstracts   **Pay:** Articles
http://www.elsevier.com/locate/jsat

Journal of the Academy of Psychiatry and the Law
Publisher: American Academy of Psychiatry and the Law   **Free:** Table of Contents,
Abstracts   **Pay:** Articles   http://www.cc.emory.edu/AAPL/journal.htm

Journal of the American
Academy of Child and Adolescent Psychiatry
Publisher: Lippincott Williams & Wilkins   **Free:** Table of Contents, Abstracts   **Pay:** Articles
http://www.aacap.org/journal/journal.htm

Journal of the American Academy of Psychoanalysis
Publisher: American Academy of Psychoanalysis   **Free:** Table of Contents   **Pay:** None
http://aapsa.org/jaap.html

Journal of the American Geriatrics Society
Publisher: Blackwell Science **Free:** Table of Contents, Abstracts **Pay:** Articles
http://www.blackwellscience.com/journals/geriatrics/index.html

Journal of the American Medical Association
Publisher: American Medical Association **Free:** Table of Contents, Articles, Abstracts
Pay: None http://jama.ama-assn.org

Journal of the American Psychoanalytic Association
Publisher: American Psychoanalytic Association **Free:** Table of Contents, Abstracts
Pay: Articles http://apsa.org/japa/index.htm

Journal of the Experimental Analysis of Behavior
Publisher: Society for the Experimental Analysis of Behavior, Inc. **Free:** Table of Contents,
Abstracts **Pay:** Articles
http://www.envmed.rochester.edu/wwwrap/behavior/jeab/jeabhome.htm

Journal of the International Neuropsychological Society
Publisher: Cambridge University Press **Free:** Registration required to access Table of
Contents and Abstracts **Pay:** Articles http://uk.cambridge.org/journals/ins/insifc.htm

Journal of Traumatic Stress
Publisher: Kluwer Academic Publishers **Free:** None **Pay:** Articles
http://www.wkap.nl/journalhome.htm/0894-9867

Legal and Criminological Psychology
Publisher: British Psychological Society **Free:** Table of Contents, Abstracts **Pay:** Articles
http://www.bps.org.uk/publications/jLC_1.cfm

Medscape: Mental Health
Publisher: Medscape **Free:** Table of Contents, Abstracts, Articles **Pay:** None
http://psychiatry.medscape.com/Medscape/psychiatry/journal/public/mh.journal.html

Memory & Cognition
Publisher: Psychonomic Society **Free:** Table of Contents, Abstracts **Pay:** Articles
http://www.psychonomic.org/mrc.htm

Mental Retardation
Publisher: American Association on Mental Retardation **Free:** Table of Contents, Abstracts
Pay: Articles http://aamr.allenpress.com/aamronline/?request=index-html

Molecular Psychiatry
Publisher: Stockton Press **Free:** Table of Contents, Abstracts **Pay:** Articles
http://www.naturesj.com/mp/

Motivation and Emotion
Publisher: Kluwer Academic Publishers **Free:** Table of Contents, Abstracts **Pay:** Articles
http://www.wkap.nl/journalhome.htm/0146-7239

Don't type in long URLs – add the site number to the eMedguides URL: www.eMedguides.com/**C-1234**.

P-0328
JOURNAL

Narcolepsy & Sleep Disorders Newsletter
Publisher: WebSciences, Brain Information Service **Free:** Articles **Pay:** None
http://www.narcolepsy.com

P-0329
JOURNAL

Neurocase
Publisher: Oxford University Press **Free:** Table of Contents, Abstracts **Pay:** Articles
http://neucas.oupjournals.org/contents-by-date.0.shtml

P-0330
JOURNAL

Neurogenetics
Publisher: Springer-Verlag **Free:** Table of Contents, Abstracts **Pay:** Articles
http://link.springer.de/link/service/journals/10048/index.htm

P-0331
JOURNAL

Neurology and Clinical Neurophysiology
Publisher: MIT Press **Free:** Table of Contents, Articles **Pay:** Articles
http://www-mitpress.mit.edu/e-journals/CONE/

P-0332
NEW JOURNAL

Neuropsychiatry, Neuropsychology, and Behavioral Neurology
Publisher: Lippincott Williams & Wilkins **Free:** Table of Contents, Abstracts **Pay:** Articles
http://www.neuneubeneu.com/

P-0333
NEW JOURNAL

Neuropsychobiology
Publisher: S. Karger AG **Free:** Table of Contents, Abstracts **Pay:** Articles
http://www.karger.ch/journals/nps/nps_jh.htm

P-0334
JOURNAL

Neuropsychologia
Publisher: Elsevier Science **Free:** Table of Contents **Pay:** Articles
http://www.elsevier.nl/inca/publications/store/2/4/7

P-0335
NEW JOURNAL

Neuropsychological Rehabilitation
Publisher: Psychology Press **Free:** Table of Contents, Abstracts **Pay:** Articles
http://www.tandf.co.uk/journals/pp/09602011.html

P-0336
JOURNAL

Neuropsychology
Publisher: American Psychological Association   **Free:** Table of Contents, Abstracts
Pay: Articles   http://www.apa.org/journals/neu.html

P-0337
NEW JOURNAL

Neuropsychology Review
Publisher: Kluwer Academic Publishers **Free:** Table of Contents, Abstracts **Pay:** Articles
http://www.wkap.nl/journalhome.htm/1040-7308

P-0338
JOURNAL

Neuropsychopharmacology
Publisher: Elsevier Science **Free:** Table of Contents **Pay:** Abstracts, Articles
http://www.elsevier.com/inca/publications/store/5/0/5/7/7/8/

P-0340
JOURNAL

New England Journal of Medicine
Publisher: New England Journal of Medicine **Free:** Table of Contents **Pay:** Articles, Abstracts http://content.nejm.org

P-0341 JOURNAL	**Nordic Journal of Psychiatry** **Publisher:** Taylor & Francis Group **Free:** Table of Contents **Pay:** Abstracts, Articles http://www.tandf.co.uk/journals/tfs/08039488.html
P-0342 NEW JOURNAL	**Patient Education and Counseling** **Publisher:** Elsevier Science **Free:** Table of Contents, Abstracts **Pay:** Articles http://www.elsevier.com/locate/pateducou
P-0343 NEW JOURNAL	**Personality and Social Psychology Bulletin** **Publisher:** SAGE Inc. **Free:** Table of Contents, Abstracts **Pay:** Articles http://www.sagepub.com/index1.asp?id=journal.asp?id=4723
P-0344 JOURNAL	**Perspectives in Psychiatric Care** **Publisher:** Nursecom Inc. **Free:** Table of Contents **Pay:** Articles http://www.nursecominc.com/html/ppc.html
P-0345 JOURNAL	**Perspectives: A Mental Health Magazine** **Publisher:** Mental Health Net **Free:** Table of Contents, Articles **Pay:** None http://mentalhelp.net/perspectives
P-0346 JOURNAL	**Pharmabulletin** **Publisher:** Mental Health Research Institute **Free:** None **Pay:** Articles http://www.mhri.edu.au/pda/Bulletin3.html
P-0347 JOURNAL	**Pharmacopsychiatry** **Publisher:** Thieme **Free:** Selected forthcoming topics **Pay:** Articles http://www.thieme.com/SID1990610712328/journals/pubid-735607186.html
P-0348 JOURNAL	**Philosophy, Psychiatry, and Psychology** **Publisher:** Johns Hopkins University Press **Free:** Table of Contents, Abstracts **Pay:** Articles http://muse.jhu.edu/journals/philosophy_psychiatry_and_psychology/
P-0349 JOURNAL	**Prevention and Treatment** **Publisher:** American Psychological Association **Free:** Table of Contents, Abstracts **Pay:** Articles http://journals.apa.org/prevention
P-0350 NEW JOURNAL	**Professional Psychology: Research and Practice** **Publisher:** American Psychological Association **Free:** Table of Contents, Abstracts **Pay:** Articles http://www.apa.org/journals/pro.html
P-0351 JOURNAL	**Progress in Neuropsychopharmacology and Biological Psychiatry** **Publisher:** Elsevier Science **Free:** Table of Contents, Abstracts **Pay:** Articles http://www.elsevier.com/locate/pnpbp

PSYCHE

Publisher: Association for the Scientific Study of Consciousness   **Free:** Table of Contents, Articles   **Pay:** None   http://psyche.cs.monash.edu.au

Psychiatric Annals

Publisher: Slack Inc.   **Free:** Free to all U.S. AMA members   **Pay:** Table of Contents, Articles   http://www.slackinc.com/general/psyann/psyahome.htm

Psychiatric Bulletin

Publisher: Royal College of Psychiatrists   **Free:** Table of Contents, Abstracts   **Pay:** Articles   http://pb.rcpsych.org/

Psychiatric Care

Publisher: Stockton Press   **Free:** Table of Contents, Abstracts   **Pay:** Articles   http://www.stockton-press.co.uk/pc/index.html

Psychiatric Genetics

Publisher: Lippincott Williams & Wilkins   **Free:** Table of Contents   **Pay:** Abstracts, Articles   http://www.psychgenetics.com/

Psychiatric News

Publisher: American Psychiatric Association   **Free:** Table of Contents, Articles   **Pay:** None   http://pn.psychiatryonline.org

Psychiatric Quarterly

Publisher: Kluwer Academic Publishers   **Free:** None   **Pay:** Articles   http://www.wkap.nl/journalhome.htm/0033-2720

Psychiatric Services

Publisher: American Psychiatric Association   **Free:** Table of Contents, Abstracts   **Pay:** Articles   http://psychservices.psychiatryonline.org

Psychiatric Times

Publisher: CME Incorporated   **Free:** Table of Contents, Articles   **Pay:** None   http://www.mhsource.com/psychiatrictimes.html

Psychiatry

Publisher: Elsevier Science   **Free:** None   **Pay:** Table of Contents, Abstracts, Articles   http://www.elsevier.com/locate/psychiatry

Psychiatry and Clinical Neurosciences

Publisher: Blackwell Science   **Free:** Table of Contents   **Pay:** Abstracts, Articles   http://www.blacksci.co.uk/products/journals/xpcn.htm

Psychiatry Online

Publisher: Priory Lodge Education, Ltd.   **Free:** Table of Contents, Abstracts, Articles   **Pay:** None   http://www.priory.co.uk/psych.htm

Psychiatry Research
Publisher: Elsevier Science **Free:** Table of Contents, Abstracts **Pay:** Articles
http://www.elsevier.com/locate/psychres

Psychiatry Research: Neuroimaging
Publisher: Elsevier Science **Free:** Table of Contents, Abstracts **Pay:** Articles
http://www.elsevier.nl/locate/psychresns

Psychiatry, Psychology, and Law
Publisher: Australian Academic Press **Free:** Table of Contents, Abstracts **Pay:** Articles
http://www.australianacademicpress.com.au/Publications/ppl/ppl1.html

Psychiatry: Interpersonal and Biological Processes
Publisher: Guilford Press **Free:** Table of Contents, Abstracts **Pay:** Articles
http://www.guilford.com/periodicals/jnps.htm

Psycho-Oncology
Publisher: John Wiley & Sons, Inc. **Free:** Registration required to access Table of Contents and Abstracts **Pay:** Articles
http://www3.interscience.wiley.com/cgi-bin/jtoc?ID=5807

Psychoanalytic Dialogues
Publisher: Analytic Press, Inc. **Free:** Table of Contents, Abstracts **Pay:** Articles
http://www.analyticpress.com/psychoanalytic_dialogues.html

Psychoanalytic Inquiry
Publisher: Analytic Press, Inc. **Free:** Table of Contents, Abstracts **Pay:** Articles
http://www.analyticpress.com/psychoanalytic_inquiry.html

Psychoanalytic Psychology
Publisher: American Psychological Association **Free:** Table of Contents, Abstracts
Pay: Articles   http://www.apa.org/journals/pap.html

Psychodynamic Counselling
Publisher: Routledge Publishers **Free:** Table of Contents, Abstracts **Pay:** Articles
http://www.tandf.co.uk/journals/routledge/13533339.html

Psychological Abstracts
Publisher: American Psychological Association **Free:** Table of Contents, Abstracts
Pay: Articles   http://www.apa.org/psycinfo/products/psycabs.html

Psychological Assessment
Publisher: American Psychological Association **Free:** Table of Contents, Abstracts
Pay: Articles   http://www.apa.org/journals/pas.html

Psychological Bulletin
Publisher: American Psychological Association **Free:** Table of Contents, Abstracts
Pay: Articles   http://www.apa.org/journals/bul.html

Psychological Medicine

Publisher: Cambridge University Press **Free:** Table of Contents **Pay:** Articles
http://uk.cambridge.org/journals/psm/psmifc.htm

Psychological Methods

Publisher: American Psychological Association **Free:** Table of Contents, Abstracts
Pay: Articles   http://www.apa.org/journals/met.html

Psychological Review

Publisher: American Psychological Association **Free:** Table of Contents, Abstracts
Pay: Articles   http://www.apa.org/journals/rev.html

Psychology and Aging

Publisher: American Psychological Association **Free:** Table of Contents, Abstracts
Pay: Articles   http://www.apa.org/journals/pag.html

Psychology and Health

Publisher: Gordon and Breach Publishing Group **Free:** Table of Contents, Abstracts
Pay: Articles   http://www.gbhap-us.com/journals/340/340-top.htm

Psychology Health & Medicine

Publisher: Carfax Publishing **Free:** Table of Contents, Abstracts **Pay:** Articles
http://www.tandf.co.uk/journals/carfax/13548506.html

Psychology of Addictive Behaviors

Publisher: American Psychological Association **Free:** Table of Contents, Abstracts
Pay: Articles   http://www.apa.org/journals/adb.html

Psychology Online Journal

Publisher: Joseph R. Dunn, Ph.D. **Free:** Table of Contents, Articles **Pay:** None
http://www.psychjournal.com/

Psychoneuroendocrinology

Publisher: Elsevier Science **Free:** Table of Contents **Pay:** Abstracts, Articles
http://www.elsevier.com/locate/psyneuen

Psychopathology

Publisher: S. Karger AG **Free:** Table of Contents, Abstracts **Pay:** Articles
http://www.karger.com/journals/psp/psp_jh.htm

Psychopharmacology

Publisher: Springer-Verlag **Free:** Table of Contents, Abstracts **Pay:** Articles
http://link.springer.de/link/service/journals/00213/index.htm

Psychophysiology

Publisher: Cambridge University Press **Free:** Table of Contents, Abstracts **Pay:** Articles
http://uk.cambridge.org/journals/pgy/

Psychosomatic Medicine
Publisher: Lippincott Williams & Wilkins **Free:** Table of Contents, Abstracts **Pay:** Articles
http://www.psychosomatic.org/pm.html

Psychosomatics
Publisher: Academy of Psychosomatic Medicine **Free:** Table of Contents, Abstracts
Pay: Articles http://psy.psychiatryonline.org

Psychotherapy and Psychosomatics
Publisher: S. Karger AG **Free:** Table of Contents, Abstracts **Pay:** Articles
http://www.karger.ch/journals/pps/pps_jh.htm

Psychotherapy Patient
Publisher: Haworth Press **Free:** Table of Contents, Abstracts **Pay:** Articles
http://bubl.ac.uk/journals/soc/psypat

Psychotherapy Research
Publisher: Society for Psychotherapy Research **Free:** Table of Contents **Pay:** Abstracts, Articles http://www.psychotherapyresearch.org/journal.html

Recent Advances in Neuropsychopharmacology
Publisher: Elsevier Science **Free:** Table of Contents, Abstracts **Pay:** Articles
http://www.elsevier.nl/locate/isbn/0080263828

Rehabilitation Psychology
Publisher: American Psychological Association **Free:** Table of Contents, Abstracts
Pay: Articles http://www.apa.org/journals/rep.html

Review of General Psychology
Publisher: American Psychological Association **Free:** Table of Contents, Abstracts
Pay: Articles http://www.apa.org/journals/gpr.html

Scandinavian Journal of Behavior Therapy
Publisher: Scandinavian University Press **Free:** Table of Contents **Pay:** Abstracts, Articles
http://www.tandf.co.uk/journals/tfs/02845717.html

Schizophrenia Bulletin
Publisher: Medscape **Free:** Table of Contents, Abstracts, Articles **Pay:** None
http://www.medscape.com/govmt/NIMH/SchizophreniaBulletin/public/journal.SB.html

Schizophrenia Research
Publisher: Elsevier Science **Free:** Table of Contents, Abstracts **Pay:** Articles
http://www.elsevier.com/locate/schres

Seminars in Clinical Neuropsychiatry
Publisher: W. B. Saunders Company **Free:** Table of Contents, Abstracts **Pay:** Articles
http://www.harcourthealth.com/
scripts/om.dll/serve?action=searchDB&searchDBfor=home&id=scnp

Sexual Abuse: A Journal of Research and Treatment
Publisher: Kluwer Academic Publishers **Free:** Table of Contents, Abstracts **Pay:** Articles
http://www.wkap.nl/journalhome.htm/1079-0632

Sexual Dysfunction
Publisher: Blackwell Science **Free:** Table of Contents **Pay:** Abstracts, Articles
http://www.blackwell-science.com/products/journals/sdy.htm

Sexualities
Publisher: SAGE Inc. **Free:** Table of Contents, Abstracts **Pay:** Articles
http://www.sagepub.com/Shopping/Journal.asp?id=4608

Sleep
Publisher: Academy of Sleep Medicine **Free:** Table of Contents, Abstracts **Pay:** Articles
http://www.journalsleep.org/

Social Psychiatry and Psychiatric Epidemiology
Publisher: Springer-Verlag **Free:** Table of Contents, Abstracts **Pay:** Articles
http://link.springer.de/link/service/journals/00127/index.htm

Stress Medicine
Publisher: John Wiley & Sons, Inc. **Free:** Registration required to access Table of Contents
and Abstracts **Pay:** Articles
http://www3.interscience.wiley.com/cgi-bin/jtoc?ID=3723

Stress: The International Journal on the Biology of Stress
Publisher: Gordon and Breach Publishing Group **Free:** Table of Contents, Abstracts
Pay: Articles   http://www.gbhap-us.com/journals/405/405-top.htm

Substance Abuse
Publisher: Kluwer Academic Publishers **Free:** Table of Contents, Abstracts **Pay:** Articles
http://www.wkap.nl/journalhome.htm/0889-7077

The American Journal of Drug and Alcohol Abuse
Publisher: Dekker **Free:** Table of Contents, Abstracts **Pay:** Articles
http://www.dekker.com/servlet/product/productid/ADA

The American Psychoanalyst
Publisher: American Psychoanalytic Association **Free:** Table of Contents, Abstracts, Articles
Pay: None   http://apsa.org/tap/index.htm

The Counseling Psychologist
Publisher: Sage Publications **Free:** Table of Contents, Abstracts **Pay:** Articles
http://www.sagepub.com/index1.asp?id=journal.asp?id=4733

The Family Journal
Publisher: SAGE Publications **Free:** Table of Contents, Abstracts **Pay:** Articles
http://www.sagepub.com/index1.asp?id=journal.asp?id=4751

The Therapist

Publisher: European Therapy Studies Institute **Free:** Table of Contents, Abstracts
Pay: Articles   http://www.the-therapist.ltd.uk

Theory & Psychology

Publisher: SAGE Inc. **Free:** Table of Contents, Abstracts **Pay:** Articles
http://www.sagepub.com/Shopping/Journal.asp?id=4619

Transactional Analysis Journal

Publisher: International Transactional Analysis Association **Free:** Table of Contents, Articles
Pay: None   http://www.tajnet.org

Transcultural Psychiatry

Publisher: SAGE Publications **Free:** Table of Contents, Abstracts **Pay:** Articles
http://www.sagepub.co.uk/journals/details/j0183.html

Trauma, Violence & Abuse

Publisher: SAGE Inc. **Free:** Table of Contents, Abstracts **Pay:** Articles
http://www.sagepub.com/Shopping/Journal.asp?id=13010

Traumatology

Publisher: Green Cross Foundation **Free:** Table of Contents, Articles, Abstracts **Pay:** None
http://www.fsu.edu/~trauma

Trends in Cognitive Sciences

Publisher: Elsevier Science **Free:** Table of Contents, Abstracts **Pay:** Articles
http://www.elsevier.com/locate/issn/13646613

Violence & Abuse Abstracts

Publisher: SAGE Inc. **Free:** Table of Contents, Abstracts **Pay:** Articles
http://www.sagepub.com/Shopping/Journal.asp?id=4718

Violence Against Women

Publisher: SAGE Inc. **Free:** Table of Contents, Abstracts **Pay:** Articles
http://www.sagepub.com/Shopping/Journal.asp?id=4673

Violence and Victims

Publisher: Springer Publishing Co. **Free:** Table of Contents **Pay:** Abstracts, Articles
http://www.springerjournals.com/vv/home.htm

Work & Stress

Publisher: Taylor & Francis Group **Free:** Table of Contents, Abstracts **Pay:** Articles
http://www.tandf.co.uk/journals/tf/02678373.html

World Federation for Mental Health

Publisher: World Federation for Mental Health **Free:** Table of Contents, Articles, Abstracts
Pay: None   http://www.wfmh.com/newsletter.htm

3.2 Books on Psychiatry Published in 2000/2001

The following listing contains books published during the past 12 months in the field of Psychiatry. We have categorized the books under major topics, although many of the books contain material that extends beyond the highlighted subject. All of these books may be purchased through Amazon at http://www.amazon.com.

The following topics appear below, in order:

General
Abnormal Psychology
Addiction/Substance Abuse
Alzheimer's Disease
Anti-Psychiatry
Anxiety Disorders
Attention Deficit/
    Hyperactivity Disorders
Autism
Behavior Therapy
Behavioral Science
Biological Psychiatry
Child Abuse
Child and Adolescent
    Psychiatry
Clinical Practice
Comorbidity
Complementary and
    Alternative Medicine
Computers in Psychiatry
Counseling
Cultural Psychiatry
Death and Bereavement
Dementia

Developmental Disabilities
Diagnostics
Drug Induced Disorders
Education
Emergency Psychiatry
Epilepsy
Ethics
Evolutionary Psychiatry
Forensic Psychiatry
Healthcare and
    Managed Care
Historical
Homelessness
Homosexuality
Infertility
Informatics
Interdisciplinary
Law
Long-Term Care
Measurement and Assessment
Mood Disorders
Munchausen Syndrome
Neuroimaging
Neuromuscular Diseases

Neuropsychiatry
Occupational Medicine
Pain
Palliative Medicine
Panic Disorder
Personality Disorders
Pharmacology
Philosophical Issues
Posttraumatic Stress Disorder
Psychiatric Nursing
Psychiatry and Religion
Psychoendocrinology
Psychopathology
Research
Schizophrenia
Self-Injurious Behaviors
Sexuality
Sleep Disorders
Statistics
Testing and Evaluation
Therapeutics
Women's Health

GENERAL

A Century of Psychiatry, Psychotherapy and Group Analysis: A Search for Integration (International Library of Group Analysis), Ronald Sandison. Jessica Kingsley Pub, 2000, ISBN: 185302869X.

A Primer on Mental Disorders, Thomas E. Allen (Editor), Mayer C., M.D. Liebman, Crandall Lee, md Park. Scarecrow Press, 2000, ISBN: 0810839199.

A War of Nerves: Soldiers and Psychiatrists in the Twentieth Century, Ben Shephard, Benjamin Heim Shepard. Harvard Univ Pr, 2000, ISBN: 0674005929.

Annual Progress in Child Psychiatry and Child Development, 1999, Margaret E. Hertzig, M.D., Ellen A. Farber, Ph.D. Brunner/Mazel, 2000, ISBN: 1583910468.

Appleton & Lange's Review of Psychiatry, Ivan Oransky. McGraw-Hill Professional Publishing, 2000, ISBN: 0838503705.

Blueprints in Psychiatry, Michael J. M.D.Murphy, Ronald L., M.D.Cowan, Lloyd I., M.D. Sederer. Blackwell Science Inc, 2000, ISBN: 0632044888.

Blueprints Q & A Step 2: Psychiatry, Michael S., M.D. Clement. Blackwell Science Inc, 2000, ISBN: 0632045922.

Check Up from the Neck Up: Ensuring Your Mental Health in the New Millennium, Joan Andrews, Denise E. Davis. Hope Pr, 2000, ISBN: 1878267094.

Clinical Handbook of Psychiatry and the Law, Thomas G. Gutheil, Paul S. Appelbaum. Lippincott Williams & Wilkins, 2000, ISBN: 0781720311.

Clinician's Thesaurus, 5th Edition, Edward L., Ph.D. Zuckerman. Guilford Press, 2000, ISBN: 157230569X.

Contemporary Psychiatry, F. Henn (Editor), N. Sartorius (Editor), H. Helmchen (Editor), H. Lauter. Springer Verlag, 2000, ISBN: 354065805X.

Core Psychiatry, Padraig Wright, Julian Stern, Michael Phelan. W B Saunders Co, 2000, ISBN: 0702024902.

Critical Perspectives on Mental Health, Vicki Coppock, John Hopton. Routledge, 2000, ISBN: 1857288807.

Current Diagnosis & Treatment in Psychiatry, Michael H. Ebert (Editor), Peter T., M.D.Loosen, Barry, M.D. Nurcombe. McGraw-Hill Professional Publishing, 2000, ISBN: 0838514626.

Disorders of Brain and Mind, Maria A. Ron (Editor), Anthony S. David (Editor). Cambridge Univ Pr (Short), 2000, ISBN: 0521778514.

Encyclopedia of Mental Health, Ada P. Kahn, Jan Fawcett. Facts on File, Inc., 2000, ISBN: 0816040621.

Geriatric Mental Health Care, Gary J. Kennedy. Guilford Press, 2000, ISBN: 1572305924.

Human Development, Diane E. Papalia, Sally Wendkos Olds, Ruth Duskin Feldman. McGraw Hill College Div, 2000, ISBN: 0072321393.

Kaplan and Sadock's Pocket Handbook of Clinical Psychiatry, Benjamin J., M.D.Sadock, Virginia A., M.D. Sadock. Lippincott Williams & Wilkins Publishers, 2000, ISBN: 0781725321.

Kaplan & Sadock's Comprehensive Textbook of Psychiatry (2 Volume Set), Benjamin J. Sadock (Editor), Virginia A. Sadock (Editor). Lippincott Williams & Wilkins Publishers, 2000, ISBN: 0683301284.

Narrative Gerontology- Theory, Research, And Practice, Gary M. Kenyon (Editor), Phillip G. Clark (Editor), B. De Vries. Springer Pub Co, 2000, ISBN: 0826113893.

New Oxford Textbook of Psychiatry, Michael G. Gelder (Editor), Juan J. Lopez-Ibor (Editor), Nancy Andreasen. Oxford Univ Press, 2000, ISBN: 0192629700.

Nms Psychiatry, James H. Scully. Lippincott Williams & Wilkins Publishers, 2000, ISBN: 0683307916.

Pocket Reference for Psychiatrists, Md. Susan C. Jenkins, Joyce A. Tinsley, Susan C. Jenkins, Jon A. Van Leon. Amer Psychiatric Pr, 2000, ISBN: 1585620084.

Postgraduate Psychiatry: Clinical and Scientific Foundations, Tim Amos, Helen Barker, Helen Forshaw, Louis Appleby. Butterworth-Heinemann Medical, 2000, ISBN: 0750635037.

Psychiatric Secrets, James L. Jacobson, Alan M. Jacobson. Lippincott Williams & Wilkins Publishers, 2000, ISBN: 1560534184.

Psychiatry, 2002 Edition, Rhoda K Hahn, Lawrence J. Albers, Christopher Reist. Current Clinical Strategies, 2000, ISBN: 1929622023.

Psychiatry: A Colour Text, Stevens, L. Stevens. Churchill Livingstone, 2000, ISBN: 0443057036.

Psychiatry at a Glance (At a Glance), Cornelius Katona, M Robertson. Blackwell Science Inc, 2000, ISBN: 0632055545.

Psychiatry: Current Trends and Practices, Chittaranjan Andrade. Oxford Univ Press, 2000, ISBN: 0195649850.

Psychological Concepts and Biological Psychiatry: A Philosophical Analysis (Advances in Consciousness Research, V.28), Peter Zachar. John Benjamins Pub Co, 2000, ISBN: 1556199910.

Psychology, Passer-Smith. McGraw Hill College Div, 2000, ISBN: 0073657956.

Psychology for Psychiatrists, Deepa S. Gupta (Editor), Rajinder M. Gupta (Editor). Whurr Pub Ltd, 2000, ISBN: 1861561407.

Saunders' Pocket Essentials of Psychiatry (Saunders' Pocket Essentials), Basant K. Puri. W B Saunders Co, 2000, ISBN: 0702025755.

The American Psychiatric Press Textbook of Geriatric Neuropsychiatry, C. Edward Coffey (Editor), Jeffrey L. Cummings (Editor), Jeffery L. Cummings. Amer Psychiatric Pr, 2000, ISBN: 0880488417.

The Hatherleigh Guide to Psychiatric Disorders, Part II, Frederic F. Flach (Introduction), Hatherleigh. Hatherleigh Pr, 2000, ISBN: 157826023X.

The Insider's Guide to Mental Health Resources Online, 2000/2001 Edition, John M. Grohol, Edward L., Ph.D. Zuckerman. Guilford Press, 2000, ISBN: 1572305495.

The Little Black Book of Psychiatry (Little Black Book (Malden, Mass.).), David P. Moore. Blackwell Science Inc, 2000, ISBN: 0865425620.

The Primary Care Physician's Guide to Common Psychiatric and Neurologic Problems: Advice on Evaluation and Treatment from Johns Hopkins, Phillip R. Slavney (Editor), Eugene Meyer (Editor), Orest Hurko (Editor). Johns Hopkins Univ Pr, 2000, ISBN: 0801865530.

The Therapist's Internet Handbook: More Than 1300 Web Sites and Resources for Mental Health Professionals, Robert F. Stamps, Peter M. Barach. W.W. Norton & Company, 2000, ISBN: 0393703428.

The Year Book of Psychiatry and Applied Mental Health 2000 (Year Book of Psychiatry and Applied Mental Health, 2000), John A . Talbott (Editor), James C., M.D. Ballenger (Editor), richa Frances. Mosby-Year Book, 2000, ISBN: 0815127391.

Unmet Need in Psychiatry: Problems, Resources, Responses, Gavin Andrews (Editor), Scott Henderson (Editor). Cambridge Univ Pr (Short), 2000, ISBN: 052166229X.

Users and Abusers of Psychiatry: A Critical Look at Psychiatric Practice, Lucy Johnstone. Brunner/Mazel, 2000, ISBN: 0415211557.

Abnormal Psychology

Abnormal Psychology: A Discovery Approach, Steven Schwartz. Mayfield Publishing Company, 2000, ISBN: 1559342668.

Casebook in Abnormal Psychology: Revised Edition, Timothy A. Brown, Barlow H. Brown, David H. Barlow. Wadsworth Pub Co, 2000, ISBN: 0534363164.

Addiction/
Substance Abuse

A Community Reinforcement Approach to Addiction Treatment (International Research Monographs in the Addictions), Robert J. Meyers. Cambridge Univ Pr (Short), 2000, ISBN: 0521771072.

Beating Heroin, Dr Neil Beck. Dr. Neil Beck, 2000, ISBN: 0957798105.

Behavioral Therapy for Rural Substance Abusers: A Treatment Intervention for Substance Abusers, Carl G. Leukefeld (Editor), Cynthia Brown, Lon Hays. Univ Pr of Kentucky, 2000, ISBN: 0813109841.

Combining Medication and Psychosocial Treatments for Addictions, Helen M. Pettinati, Joseph Volpicelli (Editor), A. Thomas McLellan, Thomas A. McLellan, Charles O'Brien. Guilford Press, 2000, ISBN: 1572306181.

Alzheimer's Disease

Alzheimer's Disease: Advances in Etiology, Pathogenesis, and Therapeutics, Khalid Iqbal, Sangram S. Sisodia (Editor), Bengt Winblad (Editor). John Wiley & Sons, 2000, ISBN: 0471521760.

The Experience of Alzheimer's Disease: Life Through a Tangled Veil, Steven R. Sabat. Blackwell Pub, 2000, ISBN: 0631216650.

Anti-Psychiatry

Commonsense Rebellion: Debunking Psychiatry, Confronting Society: An A to Z Guide to Rehumanizing Our Lives, Bruce E. Levine. Continuum Pub Group, 2000, ISBN: 0826413153.

Manufacturing Victims: What the Psychology Industry is doing to people 3rd ed revised, Tana, Dr. Dineen, Dr Tana Dineen. Robert Davies Multimedia, 2000, ISBN: 1552070328.

Out of Its Mind: Psychiatry in Crisis, J. Allan Hobson, Jonathan Leonard. Perseus Books, 2000, ISBN: 0738202517.

Psychiatry on Trial: Fact and Fantasy in the Courtroom, Ben, M.D. Bursten. McFarland & Company, 2000, ISBN: 0786410787.

Punishing The Patient: How Psychiatrists Misunderstand and Mistreat Schizophrenia, Richard, Ph.D. Gosden. Scribe Publications Pty Ltd, 2000, ISBN: 0908011520.

Anxiety Disorders

Anxiety Disorders in Adults: An Evidence-Based Approach to Psychological Treatment (Guidebooks in Clinical Psychology), Peter D. McLean, Sheila R. Woody. Oxford Univ Press, 2000, ISBN: 0195116259.

Anxiety Disorders in Children and Adolescents: Research, Assessment and Intervention, Wendy K. Silverman (Editor), Ph. D. A. Treffers (Editor). Cambridge Univ Pr (Short), 2000, ISBN: 0521789664.

The Varieties of Psychedelic Experience: The Classic Guide to the Effects of Lsd on the

Human Psyche, Robert, Ph.D. Masters, Jean, Ph.D. Houston. Park Street Pr, 2000, ISBN: 0892818972.

ATTENTION DEFICIT/ HYPERACTIVITY DISORDERS

ADHD: Attention-Deficit Hyperactivity Disorder in Children and Adults, Paul H. Wender. Oxford Univ Pr (Trade), 2000, ISBN: 0195113489.

Attention, Genes and Attention Deficit Hyperactivity Disorder, Florence Levy (Editor), David A. Hay (Editor). Psychology Pr, 2000, ISBN: 1841691933.

The Hidden Disorder: A Clinician's Guide to Attention Deficit Hyperactivity Disorder in Adults, Robert J., Phd Resnick. American Psychological Association (APA), 2000, ISBN: 1557987246.

AUTISM

Autism and Play, Jannik Beyer, Lone Gammeltoft. Jessica Kingsley Pub, 2000, ISBN: 1853028452.

Breaking Autism's Barrier: A Father's Story, Bill Davis, Wendy Goldband Schunick (Contributor). Jessica Kingsley Pub, 2000, ISBN: 1853029793.

Exploring the Spectrum of Autism and Pervasive Developmental Disorders: Intervention Strategies, Carolyn Murray-Slutsky, Betty A. Paris. Therapy Skill Builders, 2000, ISBN: 076165500X.

BEHAVIOR THERAPY

Essentials of Behavioral Assessment (Essentials of Psychological Assessment), Cecil B. Reynolds, Randy W. Kamphaus.

John Wiley & Sons,. 2000, ISBN: 0471353671.

From Social Anxiety to Social Phobia: Multiple Perspectives, Stefan G. Hofmann (Editor), Patricia Marten Dibartolo (Editor). Allyn & Bacon, 2000, ISBN: 0205281893.

BEHAVIORAL SCIENCE

Behavioral Science, Sahler. W B Saunders Co, 2000, ISBN: 0721670938.

Behavioral Science for the Boards and Wards, Carlos, M.D. Ayala, Brad, M.D. Spellberg. Blackwell Science Inc, 2000, ISBN: 0632045787.

Change Your Brain, Beverly Potter, Timothy LearyFrancis. Ronin Publishing, 2000, ISBN: 1579510175.

BIOLOGICAL PSYCHIATRY

Biological Psychiatry (Principles of Medical Biology a Multi-Volume Compendium , Vol 14), E. Edward Bittar (Editor), Neville Bittar (Editor). Elsevier Science, 2000, ISBN: 1559388196.

Love Sick: Lessons on Relationships from Biological Psychiatry, Andrew Abarbanel. Bull Pub Co, 2000, ISBN: 0923521542.

Models of the Mind: A Framework for Biopsychosocial Psychiatry, Stephen L., Jr. Dilts, Stephen L. Dilts Jr. Brunner/Mazel, 2000, ISBN: 1583910719.

CHILD ABUSE

Treatment of Child Abuse: Common Ground for Mental Health, Medical, and Legal Practitioners, Robert M., M.D. Reece (Editor). Johns Hopkins Univ Pr, 2000, ISBN: 0801863201.

Child and Adolescent Psychiatry

Adolescent Psychiatry: Developmental and Clinical Studies: Annals of the American Society for Adolescent Psychiatry (Serial), Aaron H. Esman (Editor). Analytic Pr, 2000, ISBN: 0881631981.

Basic Handbook of Hcild Psychiatry. , ASIN: 0465005918.

Building Solutions in Child Protective Services, Insoo Kim Berg, Susan Kelly. W.W. Norton & Company, 2000, ISBN: 039370310X.

But I Didn't Say Goodbye: For parents and professionals helping child suicide survivors, Barbara Rubel. Griefwork Center, Inc., 2000, ISBN: 1892906007.

Childhood Disorders, Philip C. Kendall. Psychology Pr, 2000, ISBN: 0863776094.

Childhood Psychotherapy: A Bioenergetic Approach, C.D. Ventling (Editor). S. Karger Publishing, 2000, ISBN: 3805571496.

Children of Social Trauma: Hungarian Psychoanalytic Case Studies, Terez Virag, Sari Gerloczy (Illustrator), Emma Rober-Evans (Translator). Jessica Kingsley Pub, 2000, ISBN: 1853028487.

Children Who Murder: A Psychological Perspective, Robert V. Heckel, David M. Shumaker. Praeger Pub Text, 2000, ISBN: 0275966186.

Clinical Assessment of Child and Adolescent Behavior, H. Booney Vance (Editor), Andres J. Pumariega, Booney Vance. John Wiley & Sons, 2000, ISBN: 0471380466.

Depressed Child and Adolescent: Developmental and Clinical Perspectives, Ian M.

Goodyer (Editor). Cambridge Univ Pr (Short), 2000, ISBN: 0521794269.

Do-Watch-Listen-Say: Social and Communication Intervention for Children With Autism, Kathleen Ann Quill. Paul H Brookes Pub Co, 2000, ISBN: 1557664536.

Drawn to the Flame: Assessment and Treatment of Juvenile Firesetting Behavior (Practitioner's Resource Series), Robert F. Stadolnik. Professional Resource Exchange, 2000, ISBN: 1568870639.

Early Childhood Development and Its Variations (Lea's Early Childhood Education Series), Suzanne L. Krogh. Lawrence Erlbaum Assoc, 2000, ISBN: 0805828842.

Essays on Issues in Applied Developmental Psychology and Child Psychiatry (Mellen Studies in Psychology, V. 1), Amer Hosin (Editor). n Mellen Press, 2000, ISBN: 0773475192.

Expressive Therapy With Troubled Children, P. Gussie Klorer. Jason Aronson, 2000, ISBN: 0765702231.

Helping Children to Overcome Fear: The Healing Power of Play, Russell Evans. Anthroposophic Press, 2000, ISBN: 1903458021.

Language Impairment and Psychopathology in Infants, Children, and Adolescents (Developmental Clinical Psychology and Psychiatry, V. 45), Nancy Cohen. , ISBN: 0761920250.

Of Mice and Metaphors: Therapeutic Storytelling with Children, Jerrold R. Brandell. Basic Books, 2000, ISBN: 0465007120.

Pediatric Disorders of Regulation in Affect and Behavior: A Therapist's Guide to Assessment and Treatment (Practical Resources for the Mental Health Profes-

sional), Georgia A. DeGangi. Academic Pr, 2000, ISBN: 0122087704.

Post Traumatic Stress Disorder in Children and Adolescents, Kedar Nath Dwivedi. Whurr Pub Ltd;, 2000, ISBN: 1861561636.

Problematic Behavior During Adolescence (McGraw-Hill Series in Developmental Psychology), Jeffrey J. Haugaard. McGraw Hill College Div, 2000, ISBN: 0072316853.

Psychotherapy for Children and Adolescents: Directions for Research and Practice, Alan E. Kazdin. Oxford Univ Press, 2000, ISBN: 0195126181.

Psychotherapy With Children and Adolescents (Cambridge Child and Adolescent Psychiatry Series), Helmut Remschmidt (Editor). Cambridge Univ Pr (Short), 2000, ISBN: 0521772745.

Psychotic Disorders in Children and Adolescents (Developmental Clinical Psychology and Psychiatry (Cloth), 44), Robert L. Findling, S. Charles Schulz, Javad H. Kashani, el Harlan. Sage Publications, 2000, ISBN: 0761920196.

Structured Psychotherapy Groups for Sexually Abused Children and Adolescents, Billie Farmer Corder. Professional Resource Exchange, 2000, ISBN: 1568870582.

The Adolescent Psychotherapy Progress Notes Planner, L. Mark Peterson, William P. McInnis, Arthur E., Jr. Jongsma. John Wiley & Sons, 2000, ISBN: 0471381047.

The Borderline Psychotic Child: A Selective Integration, Trevor Lubbe (Editor). Routledge, 2000, ISBN: 0415222192.

The Child Psychotherapy Progress Notes Planner (Practice Planners), William P. McInnis, L. Mark Peterson, Arthur E., Jr. Jongsma. John Wiley & Sons, 2000, ISBN: 0471381020.

The Psychoanalytic Study of the Child (Psychoanalytic Study of the Child, 55), Albert J., M.D. Solnit (Editor), Peter B., M.D. Neubauer, samue Abrams. Yale Univ Pr, 2000, ISBN: 0300083718.

Transition to Adulthood: A Resource for Assisting Young People With Emotional or Behavioral Difficulties (Systems of Care for Children's Mental health, Hewitt B. Clark (Editor), Maryann, Ph.D. Davis (Editor). Paul H Brookes Pub Co, 2000, ISBN: 1557664544.

Treatments That Work With Children: Empirically Supported Strategies for Managing Childhood Problems, Edward R. Christophersen, Susan L. Mortweet. American Psychological Association (APA), 2000, ISBN: 1557987599.

Understanding Children With Language Problems (Cambridge Approaches to Linguistics), Shula Chiat. Cambridge Univ Pr (Short), 2000, ISBN: 0521573866.

Using Literature to Help Troubled Teenagers Cope With Health Issues (Greenwood Press 'Using Literature to Help Troubled Teenagers' Series), Cynthia Ann Bowman (Editor), Jan Cheripko. Greenwood Publishing Group, 2000, ISBN: 0313305315.

CLINICAL PRACTICE

Bridges for Healing: Intregrating Family Therapy and Psychopharmacology, Roy, M.D. Resnikoff. Brunner/Mazel, 2000, ISBN: 1583910506.

Building Your Ideal Private Practice: A Guide for Therapists and Other Healing Professionals, Lynn Grodzki. W.W. Norton & Company, 2000, ISBN: 0393703312.

Clinical Decision-Making in Psychiatry, Siegfried Kasper, Joseph Zohar. Dunitz Martin Ltd, 2000, ISBN: 1853175943.

Clinical Practice in Adolescent Psychiatry, Gowers, Fulbrook, Ellis, Morrison, Blackburn, Curran, Wattis, Lynch, Roger Coakes, Sellors. Butterworth-Heinemann, 2000, ISBN: 0750641185.

Concise Guide to Consultation- Liaison Psychiatry, James R. Rundell, Michael G., M.D Wise, M.D. James R. Rundell, Rundell James R.. Amer Psychiatric Pr, 2000, ISBN: 0880483946.

Concise Guide to the Psychiatric Interview of Children and Adolescents (Concise Guides (American Psychiatric Press).), Caludio Cepeda (Editor), Claudio M.D. Cepeda, Dr. Cepeda is currently on the faculty of the University of Texas Health Science Center at San Antonio.. Amer Psychiatric Pr, 2000, ISBN: 088048330X.

Consultation: School Mental Health Professional As Consultants, Jon Carlson, Don, Jr. Dinkmeyer, John Carlson. Accelerated Development, 2000, ISBN: 1560328495.

Consultation/Liaison Psychiatry, Michael Blumenfield. Lippincott Williams & Wilkins Publishers, 2000, ISBN: 0781724724.

Craft of Psychotherapy: Twenty-Seven Studies, I. H. Paul. Jason Aronson, 2000, ISBN: 1568218400.

How Therapists Change: Personal and Professional Reflections, Marvin R. Goldfried (Editor). American Psychological Association (APA), 2000, ISBN: 1557987270.

In Session: The Bond Between Women and Their Therapists, Deborah A. Lott, Marie Cohen Ph.D., Marie Cohen. W H Freeman & Co, 2000, ISBN: 0716740257.

Letters from the Clinic: Letter Writing in Clinical Practice for Mental Health Professionals, Derek Steinberg. Routledge, 2000, ISBN: 0415205042.

Listening to Patients: Relearning the Art of Healing in Psychotherapy, Richard G. Druss. Oxford Univ Press, 2000, ISBN: 0195135938.

Memory Disorders in Psychiatric Practice, G. E. Berrios (Editor), John R. Hodges (Editor). Cambridge Univ Pr (Short), 2000, ISBN: 0521576717.

Mental Health Professionals in Medical Settings: A Primer (Norton Professional Books), Joellen Patterson (Editor), Jo Ellen Patterson, Joe Scherger, Richard Bischoff, C.J. Peek, Richard Heinrich. W.W. Norton & Company, 2000, ISBN: 039370338X.

On Being a Clinical Supervisor: Psychodynamic Psychotherapy Teaching and Learning, Rosemary Marshall Balsam. International Universities Press, 2000, ISBN: 082365642X.

Professional Orientation to Counseling, Nicholas A. Vacc, Larry C. Loesch, Nicolas Vacc. Accelerated Development, 2000, ISBN: 1560328517.

Psychiatric Care of the Medical Patient, Alan, M.D. Stoudemire (Editor), Barry S., M.D. Fogel (Editor), donn Greenberg. Oxford Univ Press, 2000, ISBN: 0195124529.

Psychology and Psychiatry: Integrating Medical Practice, Jeannette Milgrom, Jeanette Milgrom, Graham Burrows. John Wiley & Sons, 2000, ISBN: 0471981087.

Resilient Practitioner, The: Burnout Prevention and Self-Care Strategies for Counselors, Therapists, Teachers, and Health Professionals, Thomas M. Skovholt. Allyn & Bacon, 2000, ISBN: 020530611X.

Self-Relations in the Psychotherapy Process, J. Christopher Muran (Editor). American Psychological Association (APA), 2000, ISBN: 1557987335.

Self-Supervision: A Primer for Counselors and Human Service Professionals, Patrick J. Morrissette. Unknown, 2000, ISBN: 1583910751.

Supervision in the Mental Health Professions: A Practitioner's Guide, Joyce Scaife, Francesca Inskipp. Brunner/Mazel, 2000, ISBN: 0415207134.

The Doctor-Patient Relationship in Pharmacotherapy, Allan Tasman, Michelle B. Riba, Kenneth R. Silk, al Tasman. Guilford Press, 2000, ISBN: 1572305967.

The Psychiatric Interview: A Guide to History Taking and the Mental State Examination, Saxby Pridmore. Harwood Academic Pub, 2000, ISBN: 9058231062.

Therapeutic Mastery: Becoming a More Creative and Effective Psychotherapist, Charles H. Kramer. Zeig Tucker & Co Inc, 2000, ISBN: 1891944428.

Three Spheres: A Psychiatric Interviewing Primer, David J. Robinson, Brian Chapman (Illustrator). Rapid Psychler Press, 2000, ISBN: 0968032494.

Values and Ethics in the Practice of Psychotherapy and Counselling, Fiona Barnes Palmer (Editor), Lesley Murdin (Editor). Taylor & Francis, 2000, ISBN: 0335204767.

COMORBIDITY

The Trauma Model: A Solution to the Problem of Comorbidity in Psychiatry, Colin A. Ross. Manitou Communications, 2000, ISBN: 0970452500.

COMPLEMENTARY AND ALTERNATIVE MEDICINE

Complementary and Alternative Medicine & Psychiatry _vol 19#1, Philip R., M.D. Muskin (Editor). Amer Psychiatric Pr, 2000, ISBN: 0880481749.

Understanding the Placebo Effect in Complementary Medicine, Peters. Churchill Livingstone, 2000, ISBN: 0443060312.

COMPUTERS IN PSYCHIATRY

Distance Writing and Computer-Assisted Interventions in Psychiatry and Mental Health (Developments in Clinical Psychology), Luciano L'Abate (Editor), Douglas K. Snyder. Ablex Pub Corp, 2000, ISBN: 1567505252.

COUNSELING

Counseling and Psychotherapy With Religious Persons: A Rational Emotive Behavior Therapy Approach, Stevan Lars Nielsen, W. Brad Johnson, Albert Ellis. Lawrence Erlbaum Assoc, 2000, ISBN: 0805828788.

Counselling for Eating Disorders (Counselling in Practice), Sara Gilbert. Sage Publications, 2000, ISBN: 0803977247.

Counselor Supervision: Principles, Process and Practice, Loretta, Ph.D. Bradley (Editor), Nicholas, Ph.D. Ladany (Editor). Accelerated Development, 2000, ISBN: 1560328738.

CULTURAL PSYCHIATRY

Cultural Cognition and Psychopathology, John F. Schumaker (Editor), Tony Ward

(Editor). Praeger Pub Trade, 2000, ISBN: 0275966046.

Exotic Deviance: Medicalizing Cultural Idioms-From Strangeness to Illness, Robert E. Bartholomew. Univ Pr of Colorado, 2000, ISBN: 0870815970.

Handbook of Cultural Psychiatry, Wen-Shing Tseng. Academic Pr, 2000, ISBN: 0127016325.

Intercultural Therapy, Jafar Kareem (Editor), Roland Littlewood (Editor). Blackwell Science Inc, 2000, ISBN: 0632052244.

Observing Organizations: Anxiety, Defense, and Culture in Health, R. D. Hinshelwood, Wilhelm Skogstad. Flamingo Pr, 2000, ISBN: 0415196299.

People: Psychology from a Cultural Perspective, David Matsumoto. Waveland Press, 2000, ISBN: 1577661133.

Psychiatric Aspects of Justification, Excuse and Mitigation in Anglo-American Criminal Law (Forensic Focus, 17), Alec Buchanan. Jessica Kingsley Pub, 2000, ISBN: 1853027979.

Race, Culture and Ethnicity in Secure Psychiatric Practice: Working with Difference, Charles Kaye (Editor), Tony Lingiah (Editor). Jessica Kingsley Pub, 2000, ISBN: 1853026964.

The First Session With African Americans: A Step by Step Guide, Janis Sanchez-Hucles. Jossey-Bass, 2000, ISBN: 0787947687.

Transcultural Psychiatry: Challenges for Diagnosis & Treatment Transcultural Psychiatry, Basel, March 1998 (Bibliotheca Psychiatrica, No 169), A. T. Yilmaz (Editor), M. G. Weiss (Editor), A. Riecher-Rossler (Editor). S. Karger Publishing, 2000, ISBN: 3805570481.

DEATH AND BEREAVEMENT

Dying: A Guide for Helping and Coping, Martin Shepard. The Permanent Press, 2000, ISBN: 0933256922.

Handbook of Bereavement Research: Consequences, Coping and Care, Margaret S. Stroebe (Editor), Wolfgang Stroebe (Editor), Robert O. Hansson (Editor), Henk Schut (Editor). American Psychological Association (APA), 2000, ISBN: 155798736X.

Traumatic and Nontraumatic Loss and Bereavement: Clinical Theory and Practice, Ruth Malkinson, Simon Shimshon Rubin, Eliezer Witztum. Psychosocial Pr, 2000, ISBN: 188784130X.

DEMENTIA

Cerebrovascular Disease and Dementia: Pathology, Neuropsychiatry and Management, Edmond Chiu, Lars, M.D.Gustafson, David, M.D.Ames, Marshal, Folstein. Dunitz Martin Ltd, 2000, ISBN: 1853177598.

Dementia (Fast Facts), Whalley, Breitner. Health Press, 2000, ISBN: 1899541780.

DEVELOPMENTAL DISABILITIES

Developmental Disability and Behaviour, Christopher Gillberg (Editor), Gregory O'Brien (Editor). Cambridge Univ Pr (Trd), 2000, ISBN: 1898683182.

Developmental Disabilties: A Neuropsychological Approach, David Freides (Editor). Blackwell Pub, 2000, ISBN: 1557865795.

Disabilities Sourcebook: Basic Consumer Health Information About Physical and Psychiatric Disabilities, Including Descrip-

tions of Major Causes of dis, Dawn D. Matthews (Editor). Omnigraphics, Inc., 2000, ISBN: 0780803892.

Psychiatric and Behavioural Disorders in Developmental Disabilities and Mental Retardation, Nick Bouras (Editor). Cambridge Univ Pr (Short), 2000, ISBN: 0521580765.

Your Values, My Values: Multicultural Services in Developmental Disabilities, Lilah Morton Pengra. Paul H Brookes Pub Co, 2000, ISBN: 155766448X.

DIAGNOSTICS

Console and Classify, Goldstein, Jan E. Goldstein. University of Chicago Press, 2000, ISBN: 0226301605.

Diagnosis in a Multicultural Context: A Casebook for Mental Health Professional (Multicultural Aspects of Counseling Series, 15), Freddy A. Paniagua. ge Publications, 2000, ISBN: 0761917888.

Diagnostic and Statistical Manual of Mental Disorders DSM-IV-TR (Text Revision). Amer Psychiatric Pr, 2000, ISBN: 0890420254.

Distinguishing Psychological From Organic Disorders: Screening for Psychological Masquerade, Robert L., M.D. Taylor. Springer Pub Co, 2000, ISBN: 082611329X.

Handbook of Polysomnogram Interpretation, Mark Pressman. Butterworth-Heinemann Medical, 2000, ISBN: 0750697822.

Handbook of Psychiatric Measures (Book with CD-ROM for Windows), American Psychiatric Association Task Force for the Handbook of psychi. Amer Psychiatric Pr, 2000, ISBN: 0890424152.

What's Behind the Symptom?: On Psychiatric Observation and Anthropological Understanding (Theory and Practice in Medical Anthropology and internation, Angel Martinez Hernaez, Susan M. Digiacomo (Translator), John Bates (Translator). Harwood Academic Pub, 2000, ISBN: 9057026120.

DRUG INDUCED DISORDERS

Drug Induced Neurological Disorders, K K Jain, Walter G Bradley. Hogrefe & Huber Pub, 2000, ISBN: 0889372195.

EDUCATION

Massachusetts General Hospital Psychiatry Update and Board Preparation, Theodore A. Stern (Editor), John B. Herman (Editor). McGraw-Hill Professional Publishing, 2000, ISBN: 0071354352.

Multiple Choice Questions for the MRCPsych: Part II Basic Sciences Examination, Gin S., Mb, Chb, Bsc Malhi, David, profess Goldbert. Butterworth-Heinemann, 2000, ISBN: 0750640898.

Pocket Psych: Psychiatry Study Cards, Annette M. Matthews. Lippincott Williams & Wilkins Publishers, 2000, ISBN: 0781729998.

Psychology: A Student's Handbook, Michael W. Eysenck. Psychology Pr, 2000, ISBN: 086377475X.

Review of General Psychiatry, Howard H. Goldman. McGraw-Hill Professional Publishing, 2000, ISBN: 0838584349.

Review of Suicidology, 2000, Silvia Sara Canetto, Ronald W. Maris (Editor), Morton M. Silverman. Guilford Press, 2000, ISBN: 1572305037.

Study Guide to the American Psychiatric Press Textbook of Geriatric Psychiatry, F. M., M.D. Baker. Amer Psychiatric Pr, 2000, ISBN: 088048697X.

EMERGENCY PSYCHIATRY

Crisis Intervention Handbook: Assessment, Treatment, and Research, Albert R. Roberts (Editor). Oxford Univ Press, 2000, ISBN: 019513365X.

Emergencies in Mental Health Practice, Phillip M. Kleespies (Editor). Guilford Press, 2000, ISBN: 1572305517.

Psychiatric Intensive Care, M. D. Beer (Editor), C. Patton (Editor), S. Pereira (Editor), Stephen Pereira. Greenwich Medical Media, 2000, ISBN: 1900151871.

EPILEPSY

Epilepsy and Sleep: Physiological and Clinical Relationships, Dudley S. Dinner, Hans O. Luders. Academic Pr, 2000, ISBN: 0122167708.

ETHICS

In Two Minds: A Casebook of Psychiatric Ethics (Oxford Medical Publications), Donna Lee Dickenson, K. W. M. Fulford. Oxford Univ Press, 2000, ISBN: 0192628585.

The Portable Ethicist for Mental Health Professionals: An A-Z Guide to Responsible Practice, Barton E. Bernstein, Thomas L., Jr Hartsell. John Wiley & Sons, 2000, ISBN: 0471382655.

The Transplant Patient: Biological, Psychiatric, and Ethical Issues in Organ Transplantation, Paula T. Trzepacz (Editor), Andrea F. Dimartini (Editor). Cambridge Univ Pr (Short), 2000, ISBN: 0521553547.

EVOLUTIONARY PSYCHIATRY

Evolutionary Psychiatry: A New Beginning, Anthony Stevens, John Price. Routledge, 2000, ISBN: 0415219795.

FORENSIC PSYCHIATRY

Adolescent Forensic Psychiatry, Susan Bailey, Mairead Dolan. Butterworth-Heinemann, 2000, ISBN: 0750640901.

Forensic Nursing and Multidisciplinary Care of the Mentally Disordered Offender, David Robinson (Editor), Alyson Kettles (Editor), Malcolm Rae (Preface). Jessica Kingsley Pub, 2000, ISBN: 1853027545.

Forensic Psychiatric Evidence, Julio Arboleda-Florez. Butterworth-Heinemann Ltd, 2000, ISBN: 0433408561.

Forensic Psychiatry, Gunn, Taylor, Misson, Foss, Corsan, Mackay, Freeman, Hull, Jennifer Hall, Fulbrook, Ellis, Morrison, Blackburn, Guy, Curran, Wattis, Lynch, Efron, Morgan, Roger Coakes, Sellors. , ISBN: 0750641835.

Mental Dissability Issues in the Criminal Justice System: What They Are, Who Evaluates Them, How and When, Harlow M. Huckabee. Charles C Thomas Pub Ltd, 2000, ISBN: 039807089X.

MMPI, MMPI-2, & MMPI-A in Court: A Practical Guide for Expert Witnesses and Attorneys, Kenneth S. Pope, James N. Butcher, Joyce Seelen. American Psychological Association (APA), 2000, ISBN: 1557985901.

Violence, Victims and Crime: Readings in Forensic Psychotherapy, Christopher Cordess (Editor). Jessica Kingsley Pub, 2000, ISBN: 1853027294.

HEALTHCARE AND
MANAGED CARE

Accountable Systems of Behavioral Health: A Provider's Guide, Howard A. Savin, Susan Soldivera Kiesling, Ronald P. Burd. John Wiley & Sons, 2000, ISBN: 078795005X.

Casebook for Managing Managed Care: A Self-Study Guide for Treatment Planning, Documentation, and Communication, Jeffrey P. Bjorck, Janet Brown, Michael Goodman. Amer Psychiatric Pr, 2000, ISBN: 0880487836.

Casebook for Managing Managed Care: A Self-Study Guide for Treatment Planning, Documentation, and Communication, Jeffrey P. Bjorck, Janet Brown, Michael Goodman. Amer Psychiatric Pr, 2000, ISBN: 0880487836.

Integrated Behavioral Healthcare, Nicholas A. Cummings (Editor), Victoria Follette (Editor), Steven C. Hayes (Editor), William O'Donohue (Editor), Steven C. Hayes. Academic Pr, 2000, ISBN: 0121987612.

Manage or Perish? - The Challenges of Managed Mental Health Care in Europe, Jose Guimon (Editor), Norman Sartorius (Editor). Kluwer Academic Pub, 2000, ISBN: 0306462109.

Managed Care & Developmental Disabilities: Reconciling the Realities of Managed Care with the Individual Needs of Persons with Disabilities, Dale Mitchell, Ph.D. Dale Mitchell. High Tide Pr, 2000, ISBN: 189269607X.

Shared Care in Mental Health, Mynors Wallace. Isis Medical Media, 2000, ISBN: 1901865738.

What the Oregon Health Plan Can Teach Us About Managed Mental Health Care (New *Directions for Mental Health Services, 85),* Rupert R. Goetz (Editor), Kathryn V. Ross (Editor). Jossey-Bass, 2000, ISBN: 0787914347.

HISTORICAL

American Psychiatry After World War II (1944-1994), Roy W. Menninger (Editor), John C. Nemiah (Editor). Amer Psychiatric Pr, 2000, ISBN: 0880488662.

Anna Freud: A View of Development, Disturbance and Therapeutic Techniques, Rose Edgcumbe. Routledge, 2000, ISBN: 0415101999.

Bion, Rickman, Foulkes, and the Northfield Experiments: Advancing on a Different Front, Tom Harrison. Jessica Kingsley Pub, 2000, ISBN: 1853028371.

Committed to the State Asylum: Insanity and Society in Nineteenth-Century Quebec and Ontario, James E. Moran. McGill Queens Univ Pr, 2000, ISBN: 0773521224.

Freud in the Pampas: The Emergence and Development of a Psychoanalytic Culture in Argentina, Mariano Ben Plotkin. Stanford Univ Pr, 2000, ISBN: 0804740607.

Freud, Jung, and Spiritual Psychology, Rudolf Steiner, Robert Sardello (Introduction), May Laird-Brown. Anthroposophic Pr, 2000, ISBN: 0880104929.

Madness in the Streets: How Psychiatry and the Law Abandoned the Mentally Ill, Rael Jean Isaac, Virginia C. Armat. Treatment Advocacy Center, 2000, ISBN: 0967993903.

HOMELESSNESS

Street Crazy: America's Mental Health Tragedy, Stephen B. Seager M.D.. Westcom Press, 2000, ISBN: 0966582772.

HOMOSEXUALITY

Homosexuality and the Mental Health Professions: The Impact of Bias (Gap Report (Group for the Advancement of Psychiatry), No 144), Group for the Advancement of Psychiatry. Analytic Pr, 2000, ISBN: 0881633186.

INFERTILITY

Complex Adoption and Assisted Reproductive Technology, Janet R. Shapiro, Isabel H. Paret, Vivian B., Shapiro, Robert Wood Johnson. Guilford Press, 2000, ISBN: 1572306289.

Experiencing Infertility: An Essential Resource, Debby Peoples, Harriette Rovner Ferguson. W.W. Norton & Company, 2000, ISBN: 0393320006.

INFORMATICS

Easy Coder: Psychiatry/Psychology, 2001, Paul K. Tanaka. Unicor Medical, Inc., 2000, ISBN: 1567811841.

INTERDISCIPLINARY

Anthropological Approaches to Psychological Medicine: Crossing Bridges, Vieda Skultans (Editor), John Cox (Editor). Jessica Kingsley Pub, 2000, ISBN: 1853027081.

Coping With Dyslexia (Coping) -- Children's, Karen Donnelly, Andrea Votava. Rosen Publishing Group, 2000, ISBN: 0823928500.

Learning Disabilities: Implications for Psychiatric Treatment Volume 19 (#5), M.D. Laurence L. Greenhill (Editor), Laurence L. Greenhill (Editor). Amer Psychiatric Pr, 2000, ISBN: 0880483830.

LAW

Essentials of New York Mental Health Law, Stephen H. Behnke, Marvin D. Bernstein, Michael Perlin. W W Norton & Company, 2000, ISBN: 0393703088.

Law and Mental Health Professionals, George W. O'Neill, Michael R. Lochow. American Psychological Association (APA), 2000, ISBN: 1557987645.

Law and Mental Health Professionals (Law & Mental Health Professionals Series), Dennis E. Cichon. American Psychological Association (APA), 2000, ISBN: 155798784X.

Law and Psychiatry in the Criminal Justice System, Samuel J. Brakel, Alexander D. Brooks. , ISBN: 0837730252.

LONG-TERM CARE

Practical Psychiatry in the Nursing Home: A Handbook for Staff, David K. Conn, Nathan Hermann (Editor), Alanna Kaye (Editor), dm Rewilak. Hogrefe & Huber Pub, 2000, ISBN: 0889372225.

Professional Psychology in Long Term Care: A Comprehensive Guide, Victor Molinari (Editor). Hatherleigh Pr, 2000, ISBN: 1578260353.

Psychiatry in the Nursing Home, D. Peter, M.D. Birkett (Editor). Haworth (T), 2000, ISBN: 0789012146.

MEASUREMENT AND ASSESSMENT

Barrow & McGee's Practical Measurement and Assessment, Kathleen A. Tritschler (Editor), harold Barrow. Lippincott Williams

& Wilkins Publishers, 20000, ISBN: 0683083937.

Evaluating Outcomes: Empirical Tools for Effective Practice, John D. Cone. American Psychological Association (APA), 2000, ISBN: 1557987238.

Multiple Intelligences and Personality Type: Tools and Strategies for Developing Human Potential, Dario Nardi. Telos Publications, 2000, ISBN: 0966462416.

MOOD DISORDERS

Behavior and Mood Disorders in Focal Brain Lesions, Julien Bogousslavsky (Editor), Jeffrey L. Cummings (Editor). Cambridge Univ Pr (Short), 2000, ISBN: 0521774829.

Bipolar Disorders: 100 Years After Manic-Depressive Insanity, A. Marneros (Editor), Jules Angst (Editor). Kluwer Academic Pub, 2000, ISBN: 0792365887.

Bipolar Medications: Mechanisms of Action, Husseini K. Manji (Editor), Charles L. Bowden (Editor), Robert H. Belmaker (Editor), Manji Husseini K.. Amer Psychiatric Pr, 2000, ISBN: 0880489278.

Depression, Baldwin, Hirschfeld. Health Press, 2000, ISBN: 1899541837.

Depression: A Cognitive Therapy Approach for Taming the Depression Beast, Mark Gilson, Arthur Freeman. Psychological Corp, 2000, ISBN: 0127844554.

Depression in Adults: The Latest Assessment and Treatment Strategies for Major Depressive Disorder, Anton O., Ph.D. Tolman. Compact Clinicals, 2000, ISBN: 1887537163.

Disorders of Affect Regulation: Alexithymia in Medical and Psychiatric Illness, Graeme J. Taylor, R. Michael Bagby, James D. A.

Parker. Cambridge Univ Pr (Short), 2000, ISBN: 0521778506.

MUNCHAUSEN SYNDROME

Munchausen Syndrome by Proxy Abuse: A Practical Approach, Mary Eminson (Editor), D. Mary Eminson (Editor), R. J. Postlethwaite. Butterworth-Heinemann Medical, 2000, ISBN: 0750640723.

NEUROIMAGING

Functional Neuroimaging in Child Psychiatry, Monique Ernst (Editor), Judith M. Rumsey (Editor), Joseph T. Coyle. Cambridge Univ Pr (Short), 2000, ISBN: 0521650445.

NEUROMUSCULAR DISEASES

Neuromuscular Diseases, Expert Clinicians' Views, Rahman Pourmand (Editor). Butterworth-Heinemann, 2000, ISBN: 0750670193.

Neuromuscular Disorders in Clinical Practice, Bashar, M.D. Katirji (Editor), Henry J, M.D. Kaminski (Editor), david Preston. Butterworth Architecture, 2000, ISBN: 0750671696.

NEUROPSYCHIATRY

Behavioral Neurology, Jonathan H. Pincus, Gary J. Tucker. Oxford Univ Press, 2000, ISBN: 0195137825.

Behavioral Neurology in the Elderly. CRC Press, 2000, ISBN: 0849320666.

Clinical Neurology for Psychiatrists, David M. Kaufman. W B Saunders Co, 2000, ISBN: 0721689957.

Integrative Neuroscience: Bringing Together Biological, Psychological and Clinical Models of the Human Brain. Harwood Academic Pub, 2000, ISBN: 9058230554.

Neurology for Psychiatrists, Gin Malhi. Blackwell Science Inc, 2000, ISBN: 1853179221.

Psychiatric Management in Neurological Disease, Edward C., M.D. Lauterbach (Editor). Amer Psychiatric Pr, 2000, ISBN: 0880487860.

Psychoneuroimmunology: Stress, Mental Disorders and Health, Karl Goodkin (Editor), Adriaan P. Visser (Editor). Amer Psychiatric Pr, 2000, ISBN: 0880481714.

Synopsis of Neuropsychiatry, Barry S. Fogel (Editor), Stephen M. Rao (Editor). Lippincott, Williams & Wilkins, 2000, ISBN: 0683306995.

The Effects of Early Adversity on Neurobehavioral Development: The Minnesota Symposia on Child Psychology, Charles A. Nelson (Editor). Lawrence Erlbaum Assoc, 2000, ISBN: 0805834060.

OCCUPATIONAL MEDICINE

Fitness for Duty: Principles, Methods, and Legal Issues, Anthony V., Ph.D. Stone. CRC Press, 2000, ISBN: 0849322863.

PAIN

Pain: What Psychiatrists Need to Know (Review of Psychiatry Series, V. 19, 2), Mary Jane Massie (Editor), M.D. Mary Jane Massey (Editor). Amer Psychiatric Pr, 2000, ISBN: 0880481730.

PALLIATIVE MEDICINE

Handbook of Psychiatry in Palliative Medicine, Harvey M. Chochinov (Editor), William Breitbart (Editor). Oxford Univ Press, 2000, ISBN: 0195092996.

PANIC DISORDER

Panic Disorder: Assessment and Treatment Through a Wide-Angle Lens, Frank M. Dattilio, Jesus A. Salas-Auvert. Zeig, Tucker & Theisen, Inc., 2000, ISBN: 1891944355.

PERSONALITY DISORDERS

Personality Disorder and Serious Offending: A Practitioner's Guide to Treatment and Care, Clive Meux, Chris Newrith, Pamela J. Taylor. Butterworth-Heinemann, 2000, ISBN: 0750638400.

Personality Disorders (Encyclopedia of Psychological Disorders), Linda N. Bayer, Linda Bayer-Berenbaum. Chelsea House Pub (Library), 2000, ISBN: 0791053172.

Personality Disorders in Children and Adolescents, Alan S. Weiner, Karen K. Bardenstein, Paulina F. Kernberg, Alan M. Weiner, Karen Bardenstein. Basic Books (Short Disc), 2000, ISBN: 0465095623.

The Personality Disorders: A New Look at the Developmental Self and Object Relations Approach: Theory - Diagnosis - Treatment, James F. Masterson. Zeig, Tucker & Theisen, Inc., 2000, ISBN: 1891944339.

PHARMACOLOGY

A Primer of Drug Action: A Concise, Nontechnical Guide to the Actions, Uses, and Side Effects of Psychoactive Drugs,

Robert M., M.D. Julien. W H Freeman & Co, 2000, ISBN: 0716751097.

Apothecarium & PsychiatryDrugs (CD-ROM for Windows, Package), Skyscape. Skyscape, Inc, 2000, ISBN: 0970450583.

Drug Information for Mental Health 2001, Matthew A. Fuller, Martha Sajatovic. Lexi Comp, 2000, ISBN: 1930598394.

Essential Psychopharmacology: Neuroscientific Basis and Practical Applications, Stephen M. Stahl. Cambridge Univ Pr (Short), 2000, ISBN: 0521787882.

Essential Psychopharmacology of Depression and Bipolar Disorder, Stephen M. Stahl, Nancy Munter (Illustrator). Cambridge Univ Pr (Short), 2000, ISBN: 0521786452.

Ethnicity and Psychopharmacology Volume 19#4, Pedro Ruiz (Editor), Ruiz Pedro. Amer Psychiatric Pr, 2000, ISBN: 0880482745.

Pharmacoeconomics in Psychiatry, David Taylor. Dunitz Martin Ltd, 2000, ISBN: 1853179256.

Pharmacotherapy for Mood, Anxiety, and Cognitive Disorders, Uriel, M.D. Halbreich (Editor), Stuart A., M.D. Montgomery (Editor), montgomer, Halbreich Uriel, Stuart A. Montgomery. Amer Psychiatric Pr, 2000, ISBN: 0880488859.

Prozac Backlash: Overcoming the Dangers of Prozac, Zoloft, Paxil, and Other Antidepressants with Safe, Effective Alternatives, Joseph Glenmullen. Simon & Schuster, 2000, ISBN: 0684860015.

Psychiatric Medications for Older Adults, Carl Salzman. Guilford Press, 2000, ISBN: 1572305789.

Stopping Anxiety Medication: Panic Control Therapy for Benzodiazepine Discontinuation Therapist Guide, Michael W. Otto, Jennifer C. Jones, Michelle G. Craske, dav Barlow,

David H. Barlow. Psychological Corp, 2000, ISBN: 0127844511.

The Psychopharmacology of Herbal Medications: Plant Drugs That Alter Mind, Brain, and Behavior, Marcello Spinella. MIT Press, 2000, ISBN: 0262692651.

PHILOSOPHICAL ISSUES

Between Conviction and Uncertainty: Philosophical Guidelines for the Practicing Psychotherapist (Suny Series, Alternatives in Psychology), Jerry N. Downing. State Univ of New York Pr, 2000, ISBN: 0791446271.

Concepts of the Self, Anthony Elliott. Polity Pr, 2000, ISBN: 0745623670.

Ethical Reasoning in the Mental Health Professions, Gary George Ford, Gary G Ford. CRC Press, 2000, ISBN: 0849320771.

Ethics, Culture, and Psychiatry: International Perspectives, Ahmad Ukashah (Editor), Julio Arboleda-Florez (Editor), N. Sartorius (Editor). Amer Psychiatric Pr, 2000, ISBN: 0880489995.

Of Two Minds: The Growing Disorder in American Psychiatry, T. M. Luhrmann. Knopf, 2000, ISBN: 0679421912.

On Looking Inward and Being Scientific: A Tribute to G.L. Engel, M.D., G.A. Fava (Editor). S. Karger Publishing, 2000, ISBN: 3805571070.

Pathology and the Postmodern: Mental Illness As Discourse and Experience, Dwight Fee (Editor). Sage Publications, 2000, ISBN: 0761952527.

Philosophy, Psychiatry and Psychopathy (Society for Applied Philosophy (In association with)), Christopher Heginbotham (Editor). Ashgate Publishing, 2000, ISBN: 1840148640.

Psychodynamic Perspectives on Abuse: The Cost of Fear, Una McCluskey (Editor), Carol-Ann Hooper (Editor). Jessica Kingsley Pub, 2000, ISBN: 1853026859.

Psychodynamic Perspectives on Sickness and Health, Paul Raphael Duberstein (Editor), Joseph M. Masling (Editor). American Psychological Association (APA), 2000, ISBN: 1557986681.

Role of Constructive Psychiatry: The Role of Constructs in Psychological and Educational Measurement, Henry I. Braun (Editor), Douglas N. Jackson (Editor), David E. Wiley. Lawrence Erlbaum Assoc, 2000, ISBN: 0805837981.

The Construction of Power and Authority in Psychiatry, Philip J. Barker (Editor), Phil Barker (Editor), Chris Stevenson (Editor). Butterworth-Heinemann, 2000, ISBN: 0750638397.

The Myth of Sanity: Divided Consciousness and the Promise of Awareness, Martha Stout. Viking Pr, 2000, ISBN: 0670894753.

Traumatic Pasts: History, Psychiatry, and Trauma in the Modern Age, 1870-1930 (Cambridge Studies in the History of Medicine), Mark S. Micale (Editor), Paul Frederick Lerner (Editor). Cambridge Univ Pr (Short), 2000, ISBN: 0521583659.

Understanding Human Consciousness. John Loper; , 2000, ISBN: 0967880203.

POSTTRAUMATIC STRESS DISORDER

Psychobiology of Posttraumatic Stress Disorder (Annals of the New York Academy of Sciences), Rachel Yehuda (Editor), Alexander C. McFarlane (Editor). New York Academy of Sciences, 2000, ISBN: 0801864356.

PSYCHIATRIC NURSING

Basic Concepts of Psychiatric Mental Health Nursing, Louise Rebraca Shives. Lippincott Williams & Wilkins Publishers, 2000, ISBN: 0781728134.

Lippincott's Manual of Psychiatric Nursing Care Plans, Judith Schultz. Lippincott Williams & Wilkins Publishers, 2000, ISBN: 078173004X.

Manual of Nursing Home Practice for Psychiatrists, American Psychiatric Council on Aging (Editor), James A. Greene. Amer Psychiatric Pr, 2000, ISBN: 0890422834.

PSYCHIATRY AND RELIGION

Psychiatry and Religion: The Convergence of Mind and Spirit, James K., M.D. Boehnlein (Editor). Amer Psychiatric Pr, 2000, ISBN: 0880489200.

PSYCHOENDOCRINOLOGY

Hormones, Gender and the Aging Brain: The Endocrine Basis of Geriatric Psychiatry, Mary F. Morrison (Editor). Cambridge Univ Pr (Short), 2000, ISBN: 0521653045.

PSYCHOPATHOLOGY

Developmental Psychopathology and Family Process, E. Mark Cummings, Susan B. Campbell, Patrick T. Davies. Guilford Press, 2000, ISBN: 1572305975.

Points of View: Stories of Psychopathology, James E., M.D. Mitchell. Brunner/Mazel, 2000, ISBN: 1583910050.

Psychopathology in Later Adulthood (Wiley Series in Adulthood and Aging), Susan

Krauss Whitbourne (Editor). John Wiley & Sons, 2000, ISBN: 0471193593.

RESEARCH

DMT: The Spirit Molecule: A Doctor's Revolutionary Research into the Biology of Near-Death and Mystical Experiences, Rick Strassman M.D.. Inner Traditions Intl Ltd, 2000, ISBN: 0892819278.

Elements of Clinical Research in Psychiatry, James E. Mitchell (Editor), Ross D, Crosby (Editor), Stephen a Wonderlich, David Adson. Amer Psychiatric Pr, 2000, ISBN: 0880488026.

Neuropeptides in Development and Aging (Annals of the New York Academy of Sciences), Bill E. Beckwith (Editor), Alois Saria (Editor), Bibie M. Chronwall (Editor). New York Academy of Sciences, 2000, ISBN: 0801864364.

SCHIZOPHRENIA

Schizophrenia and Mood Disorders: The New Drug Therapies in Clinical Practice, Peter E. Buckley (Editor), John L. Waddington (Editor), Peter F. Buckley. Butterworth-Heinemann, 2000, ISBN: 0750640960.

Schizophrenia in Children and Adolescents, Helmut Remschmidt (Editor). Cambridge Univ Pr (Pap Txt), 2000, ISBN: 0521794285.

Treatment of Schizophrenia: Status and Emerging Trends, H. D. Brenner (Editor), W Boker (Editor), R Genner (Editor). Hogrefe & Huber Pub, 2000, ISBN: 0889371954.

SELF-INJURIOUS BEHAVIORS

Self-Injurious Behaviors: Assessment and Treatment, Daphne Simeon (Editor), Eric Hollander (Editor). Amer Psychiatric Pr, 2000, ISBN: 0880488085.

SEXUALITY

Motherhood and Sexuality, Marie Langer. Other Press, LLC, 2000, ISBN: 1892746646.

SLEEP DISORDERS

100 Questions and Answers About Sleep and Sleep Disorders, Sudhansu, M.D. Chokroverty. Blackwell Science Inc, 2000, ISBN: 0865425833.

Clinical Companion to Sleep Disorders Medicine Second Edition, Sudhansu Chokroverty. Butterworth-Heinemann Medical, 2000, ISBN: 0750696877.

Overcoming Sleep Disorders: A Natural Approach, Brenda O'Hanlon, Chris Idzikowski. Crossing Pr, 2000, ISBN: 1580910149.

Treating and Managing Sleep Disorders: A Primer, Max Hirshkowitz, Robert L. Williams, Constance A. Moore. John Wiley & Sons, 2000, ISBN: 0471361755.

Treatment of Late-Life Insomnia, Kenneth L. Lichstein (Editor), Charles M. Morin (Editor). Sage Publications, 2000, ISBN: 0761915060.

STATISTICS

Statistics in Psychiatry, Graham Dunn. Edward Arnold, 2000, ISBN: 034067668X.

TESTING AND EVALUATION

Commissioned Reviews of 250 Psychological Tests (Mellen Studies in Psychology, V. 2), John Maltby (Editor), Christopher Alan

Lewis (Editor), Andrew Hill (Editor). Edwin Mellen Press, 2000, ISBN: 0773474544.

Conducting Insanity Evaluations, Second Edition, Richard Rogers, Daniel W. Shuman. Guilford Press, 2000, ISBN: 1572305215.

Neuropsychological Evaluation of the Older Adult: A Clinician's Guidebook, Joanne Green. Academic Pr, 2000, ISBN: 0122981901.

Psychometric Scaling: A Toolkit for Imaging Systems Development, Peter G. Engeldrum. Imcotek Press, 2000, ISBN: 0967870607.

The Mental Status Examination in Neurology, Richard L., M.D. Strub, F. William Black. F A Davis Co, 2000, ISBN: 0803604270.

THERAPEUTICS

Acute Care in the Community: Intensive Home Treatment (IHT) as Alternative to Psychiatric Admission, Neil Brimblecome. Whurr Pub Ltd, 2000, ISBN: 186156189X.

Advances in ABC Relaxation Research, Jonathan C. Smith (Editor). Springer Pub Co, 2000, ISBN: 0826113974.

Aggressive and Defiant Behavior: The Latest Assessment and Treatment Strategies for the Conduct Disorder, J. Mark, Ph.D. Eddy, Mark Eddy. Compact Clinicals, 2000, ISBN: 1887537155.

Art Therapy with Young Survivors of Sexual Abuse: Lost for Words, Jenny Murphy (Editor). Routledge, 2000, ISBN: 0415205700.

Behind the One-Way Mirror: Psychotherapy and Children, Katharine Davis Fishman. iUniverse.com, 2000, ISBN: 059509452X.

Cognitive Rehabilitation in Old Age, Robert D. Hill (Editor), Lars Backman (Editor), Anna Stigsdotter Neely. Oxford Univ Press, 2000, ISBN: 0195119851.

Cognitive-Behavioral Group Therapy for Specific Problems and Populations, John R. White (Editor), Arthur S. Freeman (Editor). American Psychological Association (APA), 2000, ISBN: 1557986908.

Collective Reflexology: The Complete Edition, Vladimir Mikhailovich Bekhterev, Lloyd H. Strickland (Editor), lockwood. Transaction Pub, 2000, ISBN: 0765800098.

Combinatorial Group Theory (Classics in Mathematics), Roger C. Lyndon, Paul E. Schupp. Springer Verlag, 2000, ISBN: 3540411585.

Dynamics of Personality Type, Understanding and Applying Jung's Cognitive Processes, Linda V. Berens. Telos Publications, 2000, ISBN: 0966462459.

Early Intervention in Psychotic Disorders (Nato Science Series: D Behavioural and Social Sciences, Volume 91), Tandy Miller (Editor), NATO Advanced Research Workshop on Early interven. Kluwer Academic Pub, 2000, ISBN: 0792367502.

Electroshock and Minors: A Fifty Year Review, Steve Baldwin, Melissa Oxlad. Greenwood Publishing Group, 2000, ISBN: 0313308616.

Healing the Hurt Behind Addictions and Compulsive Behaviors, Carol M. Howe. Carol Howe and Associates, 2000, ISBN: 1889642207.

Item Response Theory for Psychologists (Multivariate Applications Book Series.), Susan E. Embretson, Steve Reise, Steven Paul Reise. Lawrence Erlbaum Assoc, 2000, ISBN: 0805828192.

Management of Countertransference With Borderline Patients, Glen O. Gabbard, Sallye M. Wilkinson. Jason Aronson, 2000, ISBN: 0765702630.

Management of Stress and Anxiety in Medical Disorders, The, David H. Barlow (Editor), David I. Mostofsky. Allyn & Bacon, 2000, ISBN: 0205287042.

Mastery of Your Anxiety and Panic: Therapist Guide (3 Ed ed), Michelle G. Craske, David H. Barlow. Psychological Corp, 2000, ISBN: 0158132319.

Motivational Science: Social-Personality Perspective, Derek Steinberg. Routledge, 2000, ISBN: 0415205034.

Nicotine in Psychiatry: Psychopathology and Emerging Therapeutics, Melissa, M.D. Piasecki (Editor), Paul A., M.D. Newhouse (Editor), Piasecki Melissa, Newhouse Paul A.. Amer Psychiatric Pr, 2000, ISBN: 0880487976.

Practice of Electroconvulsive Therapy: Recommendations for Treatment, Training, and Privileging (A Task Force Report of the American Psychiatric Association). Amer Psychiatric Pr, 2000, ISBN: 0890422060.

Psychodynamic Group Psychotherapy, Third Edition, J. Scott Rutan, Walter N. Stone. Guilford Press, 2000, ISBN: 1572305185.

Psychodynamic Psychiatry in Clinical Practice, Third Edition, Glen O. Gabbard. Amer Psychiatric Pr, 2000, ISBN: 1585620025.

Psychosocial Occupational Therapy: A Holistic Approach, Franklin Stein, Susan K. Cutler, Susan K. Cutler Franklin Stein. Delmar Publishers, 2000, ISBN: 0769300324.

Transpersonal Psychotherapy: Theory & Practice, Elizabeth Wilde McCormick (Editor), Nigel Wellings (Editor). Continuum Pub Group, 2000, ISBN: 0304706787.

Understanding and Treating Violent Psychiatric Patients, Martha Crowner (Editor), Crowner Martha L.. Amer Psychiatric Pr, 2000, ISBN: 0880487526.

WOMEN'S HEALTH

Psychological Aspects of Women's Health Care: The Interface Between Psychiatry and Obstetrics and Gynecology, Nada L. Stotland (Editor), Donna E. Stewart (Editor). Amer Psychiatric Pr, 2000, ISBN: 088048831X.

4

CONTINUING MEDICAL
EDUCATION (CME)

4.1 CME RESOURCES: GENERAL

P-0424

Accreditation Council for Continuing Medical Education (ACCME)
The ACCME offers voluntary accreditation to providers of continuing medical education who are interested in being recognized further for their high standards and quality. At the ACCME Web site, visitors will discover necessary information regarding all aspects of the accreditation process, as well as the current activities of the organization regarding communications and quality control protocols.
http://www.accme.org

P-0425

American Medical Association (AMA): CME Locator The American Medical Association CME locator provides access to over 2,000 activities sponsored by CME providers that are either accredited by the Accreditation Council for Continuing Medical Education (ACCME) or approved by the American Medical Association. CME selections of United States, Canadian, and international conferences, seminars, workshops, and home study courses are contained in the database. By customizing a search through the selection of a specialty, location, and date, visitors are returned a locator result set, which provides access to course objectives and registration information.
http://www.ama-assn.org/iwcf/iwcfmgr206/cme

P-0426

CME Unlimited This nonprofit division of the Audio-Digest Foundation specializes in producing audio CME programs for delivery to physicians and allied healthcare professionals on a subscription basis. It provides a high-quality selection of over 6,000 continuing medical education products from medical associations, institutions, and societies via audio, video, and CD-ROM. The offerings at this Web site include more than a dozen specialty series and two jointly sponsored activities, with audio materials of medical symposia, review courses, and specialty meetings readily available. Each course listing includes its description, sponsor, target audience, accreditation, objectives, and faculty, in addition to a list of currently available formats.
http://www.landesslezak.com/cgi-bin/start.cgi/cmeu/index.htm

CMECourses.com   This free database yields several pages of CME courses in the field of mental health. Conference dates, prices, and activities, are provided, along with links to further program details and registration information.
http://www.cmesearch.com/search.asp?specialty=P

CMEWeb   CMEWeb is an online resource for participation in electronic CME courses. It is provided by American Health Consultants, a commercial group accredited by the Accreditation Council for Continuing Medical Education (AC-CME). CME resources are only available to registered members of the site, and registration requires a fee.
(fee-based) http://www.cmeweb.com/#pdr

Cyberounds   Cyberounds is an online, interactive forum moderated by distinguished professionals. It is available for use by physicians, medical students, and other selected healthcare professionals. All users must register to access resources at the site. Registration is free-of-charge but restricted to healthcare professionals. Continuing medical education opportunities, an online bookstore, links to sites relevant to a variety of specialties, and additional educational resources are available.
http://www.cyberounds.com

Harvard Medical School Department of Continuing Education
Resources provided by the home page of the Harvard Medical School Department of Continuing Education include a list of hospitals, medical groups, and health centers offering CME programs, as well as directories of specific CME programs. Visitors can search the directory of courses by topic, specialty, or date. Online registration forms are available. Information and online registration forms for home study programs, available on CD-ROM, audiocassette, or videocassette, are also found at the site.
http://www.med.harvard.edu/conted

Johns Hopkins University: Office of Continuing Medical Education
Visitors to this address will find comprehensive resources related to CME programs at Johns Hopkins University. The site offers a calendar of events, a site search engine for locating relevant CME programs, a listing of special programs available by appointment only, information on graduate certificate programs, and notices and a registration form for upcoming courses. Information on distance education, video programs on CD-ROM, and Webcast courses is also available. http://www.med.jhu.edu/cme

Medical Computing Today: CME Sites   Medical Computing Today provides a site that presents an alphabetical listing of currently available category I CME credit offerings listed by the Accreditation Council for Continuing Medical Education (ACCME). Principal areas of specialty covered at each of the nearly 90 sites are listed, and descriptions, credits, and associated costs are included in the CME entries. Registration for CME credit may be completed online. (some features fee-based) http://www.medicalcomputingtoday.com/0listcme.html

Medical Matrix: CME Courses Online   CME Courses Online provides access to nearly 40 sites offering CME programs. General learning modules are available via the Virtual Lecture Hall Health Professionals CME, HealthGate CME Courses, and Medscape's Online Articles for CME Reviews. The Cleveland Clinic Foundation, the National Institutes of Health, and Virtual Hospital Online also provide opportunities to access Internet-based CME courses, often with immediate feedback on performance. A multitude of top-rated CME modules and interesting feature sites include the "Interactive Patient," which provides users with the opportunity to view a simulated online patient, request history, perform exams, and review diagnostic data. Credit fees vary by organization site.

(some features fee-based) http://www.medmatrix.org

National Institutes of Health (NIH): Continuing Education   This continuing medical education site, sponsored by NIH and the Foundation for Advanced Education in the Sciences, invites users to participate in an online experiment in distance learning. Visitors can access consensus statements, details of the CME course, and a CME exam on a variety of health topics.

http://consensus.nih.gov/cme/cme.htm

Online CME Sites   Created by Bernard Sklar, M.D., this Web page offers an alphabetical listing of more than 100 sites offering ACCME-accredited online CME courses. Each site has information such as credit hours, awarding institution, cost, instruction type, and when the educational material was last updated. The topics covered are also described. In addition, each site description has hyperlinks directly to the site.

http://www.netcantina.com/bernardsklar/cmelist.html

4.2 CME Resources: Psychiatry

American Psychiatric Association (APA): CME Calendar   The APA provides a comprehensive calendar of CME courses organized by month at this location. A large number of course offerings are provided offering diversity and convenience.

http://www.psych.org/pract_of_psych/cmecalendar22201.cfm

American Psychiatric Association (APA): CME Online   Symposia from American Psychiatric Association annual meetings of 1999 and 1998 are featured at this site, intended to be used for CME credit. Downloading the information is free; however, there is a fee for processing the self-test and issuing a CME certificate. The two RealPlayer offerings focus on clinical challenges and strategies for depression, presented primarily in audio format.

(fee-based) http://www.apa.onlinecme.org/

Current CME Reviews: Psychiatry   At this Web page, Current CME Reviews offers user-friendly, educational opportunities for the practicing psychiatrist, neurologist, and primary care provider. The courses presented, offered in conjunction with the Mt. Sinai School of Medicine, offer numerous opportunities for professionals to test their knowledge of clinical educational materials prepared by noted experts in the field. Educational modules in alcoholism, depression, neuropsychiatry, and serotonin subsystems constitute a good portion of the opportunities available. CME certificates are mailed to physicians upon completion of online material and acceptance.

(some features fee-based) http://www.cme-reviews.com

Journal of Clinical Psychiatry: CME Page   Current CME articles from the *Journal of Clinical Psychiatry* are available to those who join the Net Society, free of charge. The full text of selected CME supplements, prerecorded presentations given by experts in the field of psychiatry, and selected Web audiographs derived from a teleconference of psychiatry experts are available at this collection of CME resources. The interactive Case and Comment series features case reports for practice in diagnosis and treatment, and Intercom allows visitors to read and hear about advances in the treatment of depression.

(free registration) http://www.psychiatrist.com/cmehome/index.htm

Medscape: Psychiatry: CME Center   Psychiatry and mental health CME programs are listed on this site categorized as clinical management, conference summaries, and treatment updates. All activities meet the requirements of the Accreditation Council for Continuing Medical Education.

(free registration)   http://psychiatry.medscape.com/Home/Topics/psychiatry/directories/dir-PSY.CMECenter.html

Mental Health InfoSource: Continuing Education   Dedicated to mental health continuing education, this Web page offers information on annual congresses, online courses, conferences, and a catalog of multimedia home study products. There are also links to articles in *Medicine & Behavior, Mental Health Economics,* and *Psychiatric Times,* some with CME credit. In addition, there are distance learning courses and a mental health book locator.

(some features fee-based) http://www.mhsource.com/edu/index.html

New York University: Department of Psychiatry: Interactive Testing in Psychiatry   The New York University Department of Psychiatry offers continuing education resources for psychiatrists and related professionals at this address. Professionals can complete up to seven modules, composed of 30 questions each, and receive continuing medical education credits from the university. Instant scoring and feedback are provided.

http://www.med.nyu.edu/Psych/itp.html

Psychiatric Times: CME   The current issue of this widely read publication can be perused at this page, and archived selections can be accessed. Visitors have the opportunity to earn instant Category I credit online after reading the clinical material and completing the online activity evaluation.

http://www.mhsource.com/psychiatrictimes.html

PSYCHIATRY OVERVIEW SITES

5.1 SUPERSITES

About.com: Mental Health Resources This site provides current news on mental health issues, online forums devoted to mental health, and links to bulletin boards and online newsletters. Links are also available to additional resources, including academic psychology, associations and institutes, colleges and universities, consumer sites, information on various mental health disorders, journals and publications, managed care, men's and women's resources, professional resources, self-help resources, trauma, and stress management.
http://mentalhealth.about.com/health/mentalhealth

American Psychiatric Association (APA) The American Psychiatric Association is a national and international association of psychiatric physicians. The site includes updates, public policy and advocacy information, clinical and research resources, membership information, medical education, related organizations, a library and publications, an events schedule, and psychiatric news.
http://www.psych.org

Internet Mental Health: Resources This site provides an extensive listing of links to academic, clinical, and commercial sites. Sites are divided into sections, including anxiety disorders, eating disorders, schizophrenia, general information, journals, lists of links, organizations, and universities.
http://www.mentalhealth.com/fr13.html

Karolinska Institutet: Mental Disorders A comprehensive directory of Web resources for mental disorders is provided on this site. The sites are separated into categories such as substance abuse, schizophrenia, and disorders of eating, childhood, sleep, mood, personality, and anxiety. The sites are drawn from sources around the world.
http://micf.mic.ki.se/Diseases/f3.html

MEDLINEplus: Mental Health Mental health resources for consumers and professionals are featured on this site. There are news releases, an overview of mental illness, information on alternative therapies, and clinical trials. In addition, there are several articles on coping with mental illness, symptoms, and research, as well as information on specific conditions such as substance abuse,

genetics and mental disorders, and personality disorders. Treatment information, medical glossaries, newsletters, policy information, and statistics are also found. Some publications are specifically targeted to children, seniors, women, teenagers, and Spanish-speaking populations.
http://www.nlm.nih.gov/medlineplus/mentalhealth.html

MedMark: Psychiatry MedMark, offering extensive listings of medical resources by specialty, serves as a valuable online directory for psychiatric resources worldwide. Direct connections are provided to associations, hospitals, laboratories, governmental sites, journals, publications, programs, and projects related to psychiatry. MedMark's psychiatry resource also presents connections to a variety of therapy and treatment information sources as well as hundreds of pages of consumer-oriented information.
http://www.medmark.org/psy

MedNets Professionals and the public will find links to numerous psychiatry databases and Web resources at this site provided by the MedNets community. The Web sites are divided into sections including clinical information, diseases, news and research, subspecialty and esoteric fields, centers of excellence, and miscellaneous links such as general psychiatry links and various sites provided by the British Medical Journal. There is also a section devoted to patient information that lists Web sites and databases relating to psychiatry and mental health. http://www.mednets.com/psychiac.htm

Medscape: Psychiatry Medscape's psychiatry division includes extensive links and information on treatment updates, conference summaries and schedules, news, practice guidelines, journals and books, patient resources, and other links relevant to the practice of psychiatry.
(free registration)
http://psychiatry.medscape.com/home/misc/redirHost.cfm?/psychiatry.medscape.com

Mental Health Links Organized alphabetically, this comprehensive Web resource provides a listing of more than 50 subject areas related to mental health, each of which is a link to a listing of further in-depth resources. It has been assembled by the Center for Mental Health Services, a division of the Mental Health Services Administration. Topics include abuse, advocacy, accessibility, aging, alternative treatment, Alzheimer's disease and anxiety.
http://www.mentalhealth.org/links/KENLINKS.htm

Mental Health Matters Mental Health Matters is designed to provide online resources for psychiatric professionals, students, and others interested in mental health issues. Links are included to mental health research sites, organized according to disorder, statistics, workshops and notices, mental health law, psychiatric libraries, professional societies, and databases, as well as to a list of speakers providing seminars on mental health. Also, a list of mental health meetings and conferences; numerous links to psychopharmacology, assessment and diagnostic tools, case management and clinical resources, grant and funding

sources, managed care, rehabilitation, and education resources; and a list of general psychiatry-related links are found at the site.
http://www.mental-health-matters.com/resources.html

Mental Health Net Mental Health Net provides professionals with informative links to resources on assessment issues, associations and organizations, therapy and diagnostic listings, grant information, medication, neuropsychology, psychiatry and law, academic departments, journals and newsgroups, employment opportunities, continuing education, government departments, and mental health - related products such as books and software, etc. Services for professionals listed at the site include conferences and workshop links, clinical yellow pages, and links to journal articles. Also, links to managed healthcare information, news, and online forums are provided. Public resources include free online books, chat rooms, therapist listings, disorders and treatment links, and a link for online psychiatric advice.
http://mentalhelp.net

MentalHealthSource.com Directory Organized alphabetically by topic area, the user-friendly MentalHealthSource.com Directory provides over 20 CNS disorder categories, a dozen mental health - related topic divisions, journals and news, treatment approaches and literature, and continuing medical education links. An academic department connects the user with top-ranked psychology and psychiatry university programs, and the assessment grouping provides a source of screening and diagnostic tools for the healthcare provider and patient alike. A comprehensive listing of links to most major mental health organizations is provided. Physicians and patients will find information and resources on virtually all aspects of the mental health field.
http://www.mhsource.com/hy/links.html

National Institute of Mental Health (NIMH) A wealth of information is provided on the National Institute of Mental Health site, of interest to patients and professionals. For professionals, there are conference and workshop proceedings, videos of conferences, research articles, and a newsletter. There is also information on clinical trials, research grants, and training. Some fact sheets are specifically targeted to professionals. Consumers will find detailed brochures and fact sheets on a variety of psychiatric disorders such as anxiety, depression, eating disorders, and medications.
http://www.nimh.nih.gov/

National Mental Health Association This nonprofit organization is dedicated to improving the mental health of Americans through education, advocacy, and research. The site has an active "Online Community" section with numerous discussion boards, as well as for news, announcements, and legislative alerts. In the same section are job listings, position papers, and research findings. The comprehensive "Resource Center" offers consumers a hotline, more than 60 brochures and fact sheets on mental health topics, and referrals to more

than 7,000 organizations nationwide. There is also a link for a site on depression screening.
http://www.nmha.org/

 Neurosciences on the Internet This site contains a large index of neuroscience resources. Links are included to clinical departments and centers, databases, diseases, exams and tutorials, neuroscience Internet guides, images, journals, mailing lists, online forums, associations, software, and general information about the World Wide Web for new users.
http://www.neuroguide.com

 New York Online Access to Health (NOAH): Mental Health A directory of Internet resources related to mental health is provided on this site by the New York Online Access to Health (NOAH). Hundreds of sites are listed in categories such as mental health problems, care and treatment, and information resources. The mental health problems section covers child and adolescent family problems, sexual assault, conditions and disorders, and suicide prevention. For care and treatment, there are sites on medications, recovery, tests and procedures, and hospital ratings. Information resources include advocacy, general resources, and Internet resources.
http://www.noah-health.org/english/illness/mentalhealth/mental.html

 Psychiatry and Behavioral Healthcare Resources Resources at this site include more than 4,000 mental health organizations, as well as anti-stigma information, and a clinical trials listing, compiled by Dr. Myron Pulier. Each organization has a hyperlink to its site, with a brief description. There is also information about sharing one's personal mental health story for a survey, as well as donating one's brain for science. Visitors can find events and conferences worldwide listed by date, city, or organization. In addition, a mental health/telehealth resource directory offers links on a variety of topics, including substance abuse, anxiety, attention deficit disorder, neuroanatomy, post-traumatic stress disorder, and psychopharmacology.
http://www.umdnj.edu/~pulierml/

 Psychiatry Online Based in Great Britain, this address provides brief and case reports, an archive of professional documents, cross-cultural mental health resources, news, a bulletin board, links to resources specific to child and adolescent psychiatry, forensic psychiatry resources, current research articles, continuing medical education materials, a forum for students, a side-effect registry, and links to worldwide psychiatry resources and other related sites. Links are also provided to similar resources produced from Italy and Brazil. Users can search the site for specific information and order books and other products at the site. Similar resources are available through links at this site in the areas of chest medicine, general practice, lifestyle issues, family practice, and pharmacy. This site is supported by an unrestricted educational grant from AstraZeneca.
http://www.priory.com/psych.htm

Psychwatch.com   This comprehensive resource contains a broad array of information for professionals in psychology and psychiatry. Visitors can sign up for the free weekly Psychwatch newsletter, which contains links to full-text articles from a variety of sources, or view the newsletter and archives online. The "Announcements" section offers a bulletin board, conference listings, grant information, and a job bank. Under "Other Resources," there are directories of Internet links related to topics such as grief, journals, licensure, organizations, tutorials, private practitioners, and research. Additional links organized under the "Disciplines" section, provide access to resources for clinical psychology, cognition, forensic psychiatry, neuropsychiatry, psychiatry, and statistics.
http://www.psychwatch.com/

PSYweb.com   PSYweb.com serves as a database of information on all aspects of psychiatry. Links are divided into sections on physiology, the brain, drugs, and mental health. Physiology links include a glossary of terms in physiological psychology, and the brain section provides anatomical information. Information under the drugs subheading is indexed according to trade, generic, and Canadian name, and provides links to in-depth fact sheets on the pharmaceutical profile and use of the drug. Information on drug indications in treating psychiatric diseases is also included. The mental health section is indexed according to clinical or cognitive disorders, common names, mental retardation, or personality disorder. Comprehensive disorder information includes a definition, diagnostic criteria, treatments, and other relevant information. Case studies, a glossary, reference lists, axis/disorder flow charts, mental disorder diagnosis sheets, specific disorder treatment plans, downloadable demonstrations, IQ testing, and other related links are present.
http://www.psyweb.com

5.2 GENERAL RESOURCES FOR PSYCHIATRY

About.com: Psychiatry   More than 3,300 Internet sites are listed on this Web page, related to psychiatry. In addition, there are links to specific psychiatry directories on forensic psychiatry, mental health, journals, child psychiatry, and biological psychiatry.
http://search.about.com/fullsearch.htm?terms=psychiatry&PM=59_0100_S

Ascend   This site has links to information, support, organizations, case studies, and other sites related to depression, grief, eating disorders, anxiety, personality disorders, stress disorders, psychoses, attention deficit/hyperactivity disorder, children's topics, treatment, and other relevant subjects. Books and other reference materials, as well as professional training information, can be found. http://members.tripod.com/~ascend2/index.html

AtHealth   The professional resources available at this Web site include newsletters regarding mental health information, a list of treatment centers, a directory of mental health professionals, continuing education and medication

information, a reference list, online articles, an extensive list of information about mental health disorders, and practice tools. This Web site also has directories of licensed mental health therapists and treatment centers, a list of books, and an online bookstore. The resources section has numerous links to information about disorders and treatments, as well as to support groups and organizations related to mental health. Topics links provide general information about common mental health disorders. Articles from mental health professionals and medication information are also readily available.
http://www.athealth.com

AtHealth: Resource Center   The "Resource Center" on the AtHealth Web page provides a wide variety of mental health resources. Organized by topic, these resources cover numerous mental health disorders, such as dementia, eating disorders, narcolepsy, and obsessive compulsive disorder. Additional topics cover therapies, organizations, and associations.
http://athealth.com/Consumer/rcenter/rcenter.html

CyberPsychLink   This resource inventory of sites related to psychology and psychiatry provides links to databases, newsletters and online journals, employment and funding information, LISTSERVs, organizations, psychology software, sites on teaching, and information on the history of psychology. In addition, there are links to self-help pages, general and specific psychology sites, and library catalogs.
http://cctr.umkc.edu/user/dmartin/psych2.html

Doctor's Guide: Psychiatry   This site offers news, Webcasts, and cases on psychiatry and related mental illness topics, including diagnosis and treatment of a variety of psychiatric disorders.
http://www.docguide.com/news/content.nsf/channel?OpenForm&dt=g&id=48DDE4A73E0
9A969852568880078C249&c=Psychiatry%20Other

Health Education Board for Scotland (HEBS) Web: Mental Health
This site contains links to comprehensive fact sheets on common mental health disorders such as anxiety, grief, depression, eating disorders, phobias, stress, and schizophrenia. The fact sheets contain information on causes, treatment, and other topics. Also, there is a list of mental health - related journal articles, information on leaflet ordering, mental health statistics, and support organizations.   http://www.hebs.scot.nhs.uk/menus/mental.htm

Leicester University Library: Major Information Sources for Psychiatry   Links to major online databases, including MEDLINE, PSYCHInfo, BIDS-EMBASE, and the Cochrane Library are available at this site, including a paragraph summarizing the resources. Links to more general databases, institutes, and societies are also listed at the site.
http://www.le.ac.uk/library/sources/subject8/lisupsic.html

MedExplorer: Mental Health   As a service of MedExplorer's megasite, this innovative, mental health section offers an extensive resource listing with over 80

links in the field of psychology and psychiatry. Included are such distinctive topics as dreams and nightmares, software to eradicate emotions, who's who in mental health, and ultra-sensitive people. Basic mental health links are included and over 250 health/medical newsgroups may be searched.
http://www.medexplorer.com/category.dbm?category=Mental%5FHealth

MedInfoSource   This comprehensive Web site allows access to online articles from *Medicine and Behavior,* and also has links to the latest medical psychiatric news, an interactive conference calendar, information on continuing education, and an ask-the-expert section for consumers. In addition, users can search a classified section for practice opportunities, products, residencies, and fellowships. The site also contains a number of other resources, including links to related mailing lists, association meetings, professional practices, drug manufacturers, managed- care companies, practice guidelines, medical and mental health association addresses, and treatment centers.
http://www.medinfosource.com

Medscout: Mental Health   This Web site hosts a great number of links to mental health organizations, associations, disorders information, position papers, national institutes and centers, and general mental health information on the Internet. In addition, the site contains links to clinical news, reference materials and products, alternative medicine, education, government issues, practice guidelines, hospitals and management, pharmaceutical information, research information, and telemedicine.
http://www.medscout.com/mental_health/

Mental Health InfoSource   Resources available for professionals at this site include mental health news, conference calendars, chat forums, question and answer forums, employment listings, pharmaceutical drug information, physician directories, association links, and managed-care contact details. Continuing medical education resources are available through an online store. Specific disorder sections presenting answers to consumer and professional questions, articles, current research updates, links to related sites, conference listings, and other resources are available for schizophrenia, bipolar disorders, AD/HD, depression, and many other topics.
http://www.mhsource.com

Mental Health Resources   A directory of Internet resources on mental health is provided on this site, courtesy of Katherine Daniels. Topics covered include common disorders such as anxiety and bipolar disorder, as well as therapy, organizations, reference, and law. For each disorder listed there are a number of links available.
http://www.cccnj.net/~daniels/guide/Mental.htm

Mental Help   Within this internationally based Web site, links to information on the major psychiatric illnesses, including diagnosis and treatment, are available. Professionals can organize clinical discussions online and access a doctor

referral database, a variety of psychiatry-related journals and other publications, and a large list of other mental health - related Web sites.
http://www.mentalhelp.com/Mental_Help_wellcome.htm

Planet Psych   Primarily for consumers, this site offers online counseling, a therapist directory, self-help exercises and information, a newsletter, a bulletin board, and a chat room. Links are available to mental disorders fact sheets and related sites, arranged according to diagnostic classifications defined by DSM-IV. Included are fact sheets on related mental health issues, such as anger management, substance abuse, parenting, behavioral health, relationship and sexuality issues, cyberpsychology, and child development, as well as basic information on psychiatric and psychological treatments.
http://www.planetpsych.com/index.htm

Psychiatric Disorder Info Center   As part of Neuroland's information resource for medical professionals, this Web page has links to Web sites on diagnosis, assessment, and treatment for various disorders, such as anxiety disorders, depression, bipolar disorders, delirium, and somatic syndromes. There are links to information on various treatments and drugs, such as neuroleptics and antidepressants. In addition, there are links to virtual hospitals that specialize in anxiety, mood disorders, and psychiatric emergencies and also provide clinical practice guidelines.
http://www.neuroland.com/psy/

Psychiatry.com   Psychiatry.com offers a broad array of resources for consumers and professionals. There are live news feeds on mental health, a discussion forum, and resources for students of psychiatry. A directory of Internet sites covers topics such as geriatric psychiatry, hospitals, mental health advocacy, mental retardation and psychiatry, psychiatric institutes, and forensic psychiatry.
http://www.psychiatry.com/

TherapistFinder.net   This site serves as a home of mental health resources on the Internet. Available at the site are a national directory of psychiatric therapists, hotlines to local and national mental health organizations, a list of mental health terms and fact sheets, links to medical publication search engines, and a professional network.
http://www.therapistfinder.net/index.html

Virtual Hospital: Patient Information by Organ System: Neurological/Psychiatric   This Web site has links to patient education reference materials on a variety of topics including common psychiatric disorders, such as depression and attention deficit/hyperactivity disorder, and neurological problems, such as facial nerve and brain injury. Additional resources are included on various assessment tests and techniques, hearing-related issues, pain clinics, Tourette's disorder, trichotillomania, and sleep disorders.
http://www.vh.org/Patients/IHB/OrgSys/NeuroPsych.html

Who's Who in Mental Health on the Web Professionals and consumers can search through informative profiles of mental health professionals by selecting a state, country, or keyword. Professionals can add their own profile to the directory. This site also contains links to related Web sites.
http://www.idealist.com/wwmhw

5.3 GENERAL RESOURCES FOR PSYCHOLOGY

 Academy of Psychological Clinical Science The Academy of Psychological Clinical Science is an alliance of leading and scientifically oriented doctoral training programs in clinical and health psychology in the United States and Canada. The site includes links to the various academic members, a list of officers, a mission statement, membership information, a history of the academy, and a link to related Web sites.
http://w3.arizona.edu/~psych/apcs/apcs.html

 American Psychological Association (APA) The American Psychological Association Web site provides numerous links including reference materials, publications, national and international research sites, education, conferences, government information, and help centers. Comprehensive information regarding the association is also available.
(fee-based) http://www.apa.org

 American Psychological Society (APS) The American Psychological Society aims to provide a forum for research and application to the science of psychology. The site offers information regarding membership, current news, conventions, and APS publications. Updates on funding opportunities and legislative events relevant to psychology are provided.
http://www.psychologicalscience.org

 Community Psychology Net This award-winning Web site serves both consumers and professionals with links to discussion lists, professional societies, education information, grant information, reference materials, and employment. There are links for students and others interested in graduate school, conferences, books, career choices, or the latest news. A bulletin board and library are also present.
http://www.cmmtypsych.net

 Health Psychology and Rehabilitation This site provides resources relating to the practice of psychology in medical and rehabilitation settings. There is online access to articles, viewpoints, and general information about health psychology; practice and research details; a reference list and bookstore; information about disorders and treatment; and information on the "Battery for Health Improvement" (BHI) psychological assessment test. Links to mailing lists of interest are also provided. In addition, there is a section of links regarding psychologists as primary healthcare providers.
http://www.healthpsych.com/index.html

NetPsychology This database of information and links provides professionals and consumers with the opportunity to access Internet information relating to psychology. Included are links to relevant articles, including mental health disorders and treatments, general information on psychological disorders, and other topics of interest to professionals. There are lists of newsgroups, discussion groups, and links to alternative or non-mainstream sites related to psychology. http://www.netpsych.com

Psych Net Mental Health Descriptions, symptoms, treatment, and support information for various mental health issues, such as abuse, eating disorders, personality disorders, and suicide, can be found at this site. In addition, there are links to hotline directories and related Web pages.
http://www.psychnet-uk.com/

Psych Web A comprehensive resource on psychology, this Web site offers connections to online information for students and teachers of psychology. There are online books, brochures, products, and tip sheets for psychology majors. There are also lists of Internet links related to scholarly resources, self-help resources, psychology departments, journals, other comprehensive sites, and the psychology of religion. In addition, visitors will find mind tools for effective thinking, as well as information on sport psychology. http://www.psychwww.com/

Psychology Information Online Created by a licensed psychologist, this site serves as a clearinghouse of resources, including links to sites and very informative and detailed fact sheets on various topics in psychology. Included is a national directory of psychologists, practice information, an extensive amount of resources on psychological disorders, information about psychologists and psychiatrists, answers to FAQs on psychological treatments, forensic psychology resources, a list of self-help books, and information on psychological treatments in general. The information presented within this site can by viewed by descriptive links, general links, or by using a topic index.
http://www.psychologyinfo.com

PsychREF: Resources in Psychology on the Internet This Web address offers connections to search engines, journals, and professional associations related to psychology, as well as providing a large amount of information on educational materials, research, conferences, online courses, and jobs. In addition, there are links to resources in such areas as clinical psychology, pharmacology, disorders, neuropsychology, and developmental psychology.
http://www.psychref.com

Psychweb This very informative site hosts an extensive number of psychology-related resources, divided into topics such as depression, behavior, biofeedback, cognition, disorders, government, learning, megasites, personality, organizations, academic departments, counseling, publications, and tests. Each topic site has links to relevant Web pages, support groups, personal pages, government institutes, associations, articles, and other resources.
http://www.psychweb.com

Warren Bush's Psychology Cyber-Synapse This site provides numerous links to Web sites and other online resources on psychology-related organizations; university departments; databases; bibliographies, and other reference sources; mailing lists and newsgroups; online journals; self-help information; fact sheets and other resources on mental disorders and other related issues. http://www.umm.maine.edu/BEX/Lehman/HomePage.Stuff/text/PSYCHOCYBER.html

5.4 Awards and Honors

Public recognition of important contributions to the field of psychiatry is achieved through awards and honors from major scientific, nonprofit, and corporate organizations. We have included sites in this section that list numerous available awards and honors. The reader should visit these Web sites directly to obtain the latest information on current awards and honors.

Awards of the American Psychiatric Association More than 20 different awards for achievement, authorship, education, fellowships, lectureships, and research and investigation are offered by the American Psychiatric Association. Each award is described in detail at this page, including information on the award's establishment, honorarium, funding, and deadline, if applicable. http://www.psych.org/opps_man/appg.cfm

American Academy of Child and Adolescent Psychiatry (AACAP): Awards Numerous awards are listed at this page of the AACAP site. Awards include honorariums for leadership in the field, awards for research on specific areas of adolescent psychiatry, and awards for prevention efforts. Journal awards for articles in the *Journal of the American Academy of Child and Adolescent Psychiatry* are also included. Contact and deadline information appears at the bottom of the list. http://www.aacap.org/Web/aacap/awards/awards.htm

5.5 Psychiatry Grant and Funding Sources

American Psychiatric Association (APA): Roster of Awards More than 85 awards conferred through the American Psychiatric Association are profiled at this site, each with detailed information on the name of the award, the purpose of the award, the type of recognition, and monetary aspects. Most of these awards are included separately in the "Awards and Honors" section of this volume. Those interested in awards should visit this APA site, since awards change, are added, and are eliminated from time to time. http://www.psych.org/libr_publ/award_current.cfm

GrantSelect More than 10,000 funding opportunities are contained in the GrantSelect database for a variety of disciplines including biomedical and healthcare. Although the database is available to subscribers only, a free 30-day

trial period is offered on the site. Subscribers can also subscribe to an e-mail alert service for new additions to the database.
(fee-based) http://www.grantselect.com

Links to Funding Sources   A compilation of more than a dozen links to sites offering information on research grants and funding is provided at this section of the Cambridge Center for Behavioral Studies Web site. Connections include the National Science Foundation, the Center for Biomedical Research Newsletter, the National Institute of Mental Health (NIMH) Guide for Grants and Contracts, and the National Institutes of Health (NIH).
http://www.behavior.org/links/links_fund.cfm

Mental Health Net: Grants Online   This address lists major Internet sites providing grants information, including foundations, associations, universities, and government institutes. Grants listed cover all areas of research and scholarship. Each site link is listed with a rating and detailed description of resources found at the site. Sources for articles, publications, and software related to grant writing are also found through this site.
http://mentalhelp.net/guide/pro28.htm

Program for Minority Research Training in Psychiatry (PMRTP)   This program, designed to increase the number of minority men and women in the field of psychiatric research, is fully described at the PMRTP Web site. Program goals, eligibility, training sites, and application information are summarized.
http://www.psych.org/res_res/pmrtp.cfm

Programs Offering Research Fellowship Opportunities   Organized by research field, over 30 links are provided to psychiatric fellowships at some of the finest research facilities in the nation. Some of the fellowship programs listed in this collection include neuroscience at Vanderbilt, geriatric psychiatry at Johns Hopkins, and addictions psychiatry at New York University.
http://www.psych.org/res_res/fellowship_opportunities.cfm

Van Ameringen Foundation/ APA Health Services Research Scholars
With support from the Van Ameringen Foundation, the American Psychiatric Association has generated several important data sets containing information on utilization, costs, and outcomes related to mental healthcare. The Web site describes the organization's mission to make these data sets more widely available to the mental health researcher through encouragement of research. Application information is provided.
http://www.psych.org/res_res/vanameringenfoundation112200.cfm

5.6 NATIONAL INSTITUTE OF MENTAL HEALTH (NIMH) PROFILE

NIMH DEPARTMENTS AND SERVICES

P-0541

National Institute of Mental Health (NIMH) The National Institute of Mental Health provides national leadership dedicated to understanding, treating, and preventing mental illnesses through basic research on the brain and behavior, as well as through clinical, epidemiological, and services research. Resources available at the site include staff directories, employment opportunities, NIMH history, and publications from activities of the National Advisory Mental Health Council and Peer Review Committees. News; a calendar of events; and information on clinical trials, funding opportunities, and intramural research are also provided. Pages tailored specifically for use by the public, health practitioners, or researchers contain mental disorder information, research fact sheets, statistics, science education materials, news, links to NIMH research sites, and patient education materials. Specific site features and resources of the National Institute of Mental Health are summarized in the following descriptions. http://www.nimh.nih.gov/

P-0542

Anxiety Disorders Education Program The Anxiety Disorders Education Program is a national education campaign developed by the NIMH to increase awareness among the public and healthcare professionals. The site provides a summary of the program, a description of anxiety disorders, including panic disorder, obsessive-compulsive disorder, posttraumatic stress disorder, phobias, and generalized anxiety disorder. News updates and public service announcements are also found at the site. Visitors can access library resources through the site, including full-text brochures and lists of books, pamphlets, videotapes, and other materials provided by other organizations. Professional resources include a list of meetings presenting NIMH exhibits and order information for patient education materials.
http://www.nimh.nih.gov/anxiety/anxiety/whatis/objectiv.htm

P-0543

Clinical Trials Clinical trials information includes general resources for taking part in clinical research studies at NIMH; *A Participant's Guide to Mental Health Clinical Research,* an online brochure; links to details of current NIMH intramural and extramural research projects; and recent articles related to clinical research. Other clinical trials databases accessible from this site include the Alzheimer's Disease Clinical Trials Database and the Rare Diseases Clinical Research Database.
http://www.nimh.nih.gov/studies/index.cfm

P-0544

Depression Education Program The Depression Education Program offers visitors depression facts for adolescents/students, employers, older adults, and women by topic, including bipolar disorder and co-occurrence of depres-

sion with medical disorders. General depression facts, research, and suicide facts are discussed, and access is provided to *Depression,* a brochure for depressed patients and their families.
http://www.nimh.nih.gov/publicat/depressionmenu.cfm

P-0545 **Does This Sound Like You?** This question is asked of visitors as they proceed through a series of pages describing anxiety disorders. Contact information is provided for additional information on each disorder, and the text stresses the prevalence of these disorders in the American population.
http://www.nimh.nih.gov/soundlikeyou.htm

P-0546 **National Institute of Mental Health (NIMH): Library** At this site, both professionals and consumers can obtain information on the most common types of anxiety disorders, including panic, obsessive-compulsive disorders, phobias, generalized anxiety, and posttraumatic stress disorders. Consumers can also access general information on the symptoms, treatment, and treatment center locations for these anxiety disorders.
http://www.nimh.nih.gov/anxiety/library/edu_res.htm

P-0547 **Research Resources** The Web site for Research Resources summarizes NIMH funding opportunities, research training activities, and employment opportunities. News for researchers, research reports, statistics, and links to NIMH Research Consortiums and other NIMH research Web sites are available. http://www.nimh.nih.gov/research/index.cfm

P-0548 **Resources for Practitioners** The Resources for Practitioners Web site includes links to clinical trials information, patient education materials available for download, anxiety disorders information, research reports and publications, research fact sheets, statistics, and Consensus Conference Reports, offering statements developed during NIH Consensus Development Conferences of relevance to the mental health field.
http://www.nimh.nih.gov/practitioners/index.cfm

P-0549 **Resources for the Public** The section devoted to Resources for the Public includes fact sheets on various mental illnesses, research fact sheets on current investigations, information on mental disorders and medications, statistics, questions and answers about psychotherapy research, and educational materials on mental disorders research. Materials are available in English and Spanish.
http://www.nimh.nih.gov/publicat/index.cfm

P-0550 **Science on Our Minds Series** The Science on Our Minds Series presents online articles on specific mental health topics, including general mental illness and government policy, youth and adolescent mental health topics, depression, suicide, bipolar disorder, anxiety disorders, schizophrenia, women's mental health, genetics, brain imaging and emotions research, and stress and brain development. http://www.nimh.nih.gov/publicat/soms.cfm

P-0551 **Suicide Research Consortium** The consortium works to coordinate suicide research efforts at the institute, and disseminate that information to the public. Their site offers a broad array of resources on suicide and suicide research, including a suicide fact sheet; FAQs; a graph of suicide rates by age, gender, and race; and recent suicide statistics from the Centers for Disease Control and Prevention. Other resources of interest include NIMH funding opportunities, information on the national strategy for suicide prevention, and a 200-page report (in adobe Acrobat PDF format) entitled, *Reviews of Measures of Suicidal Behavior: Assessment of Suicidal Behavior and Risk Among Children and Adolescents.* http://www.nimh.nih.gov/research/suicide.htm

NIMH RESEARCH

P-0552 **Extramural Funding Opportunities** An overview of the extramural programs of the NIMH is found at this site, in addition to links to division branches and program descriptions. By clicking on "Research Grants," visitors are taken to information on program announcements, request for applications, and research training and career development connections. Small business programs are included, and NIH forms and applications can be downloaded from the site. The Center for Scientific Review and review procedures for specific grant applications are accessible. Additional information on research funding contacts in the federal government and Community of Science funding opportunities from around the world, is found. Overviews and links to detailed information on research training grants, career development grants, and NIH training and career development sites are provided.
http://www.nimh.nih.gov/grants/grantinfo.cfm

P-0553 **Intramural Research** The NIMH Division of Intramural Research Programs (DIRP) encompasses a broad array of research activities that range from clinical investigation into the diagnosis, treatment, and prevention of mental illness to basic neuroscience studies conducted at the behavioral systems, cellular, and molecular levels. The division is composed of more than 500 scientists working in over 20 clinical branches and basic research laboratories, as well as a free-standing unit on molecular neurobiology, three specialized research sections and a programwide research services branch under the Office of the Scientific Director. The site offers details on the organization, training opportunities, technology transfer activities, future planning and evaluations reports, and links to the specific branches and laboratories within DIRP. http://intramural.nimh.nih.gov

P-0554 **Research Grants** NIMH supports research grants, research training, and career development programs dedicated to increasing knowledge and improving research methods on mental and behavioral disorders; to generate information regarding basic biological and behavioral processes underlying these disorders and the maintenance of mental health; and developing and improving mental health treatment and services. Research and research training supported by the institute may employ theoretical, laboratory, clinical, methodological, and field

studies, any of which may involve clinical, subclinical, and normal subjects and populations of all age ranges, as well as animal models appropriate to the system or disorder being investigated and to the state of the field.
http://www.nimh.nih.gov/grants/grantinfo.cfm

5.7 OTHER MENTAL HEALTH GOVERNMENT RESOURCES

Center for Mental Health Services (CMHS): Federal Resources
Throughout this division of the comprehensive Center for Mental Health Resources, many of the more prominent federal resource Web sites can be accessed. Divisions within the executive branch include the Center for Mental Health Services (CMHS), Substance Abuse and Mental Health Services Administration (SAMHSA), Center for Substance Abuse Prevention (CSAP), the Center for Substance Abuse Treatment (CSAT), the National Clearinghouse for Alcohol and Drug Information (NCADI), National Institute on Alcohol Abuse and Alcoholism (NIAAA), National Institute on Drug Abuse (NIDA), National Institute of Mental Health (NIMH), National Institute on Aging (NIA), and the Office of National Drug Control Policy (ONDCP).
http://www.mentalhealth.org/links/FEDLINKS.htm

Center for Mental Health Services (CMHS): Grantee Database
Searchable by city and state, this Web site of the Center for Mental Health Services provides an organization search engine for the discovery of over 150 CMHS grantees. Included are Projects for Assistance in Transition from Homelessness (PATH) and the Statewide Family Network Support Project. Contact information for each grantee is included.
http://www.cdmgroup.com/Ken-cf/CMHSGran.cfm

National Association of State Mental Health Program Directors (NASMHPD) Reflecting and advocating for the collective interests of state mental health authorities, the NASMHPD offers a specialized profiling system for descriptive organizational grant information. A listing of the NASMHPD's publications, its current projects, and performance measures can be viewed. To encourage communication and community participation in the delivery of mental health services, a performance indicator survey allows the user to research organizations by quality factors. The Research Institute receives research and training grants from the National Institute for Mental Health, which are outlined, and the National Technical Assistance Center brings news and information about the organization's technical assistance and training activities.
http://www.nasmhpd.org/nri

National Center for Posttraumatic Stress Disorder (NC-PTSD) The National Center for Posttraumatic Stress Disorder, a government agency under the U.S. Department of Veteran Affairs, carries out a broad range of multidisciplinary activities in research, education, and training in an effort to understand, diagnose, and treat PTSD in veterans who have developed psychiatric symptoms following exposure to traumatic stress. The site provides following exposure to traumatic stress. The site provides information about the organization and its activities, staff directories, employment and training opportunities, a database of traumatic stress literature, reference literature, tables of contents to *PTSD Research Quarterly* and *NC-PTSD Clinical Quarterly,* assessment instruments, and links to information about the disorder for the public. http://www.ncptsd.org

National Council on Sexual Addiction and Compulsivity (NCSAC)

This national nonprofit organization is devoted to the promotion of public and professional awareness of sexual addiction and compulsivity. In addition to detailed member information, there are media contact resources, a suggested reading list, NCSAC position papers on sexual addictions, support groups, and general information about sexual addiction and compulsivity.
http://www.ncsac.org/main.html

National Information Center for Children and Youth (NICHCY) with Disabilities

This national referral center serves professionals and nonprofessionals by providing information on children and adolescents with disabilities. At this site, one can access the center's publications, including fact sheets, summaries, news articles, parent and student guides, reference lists, and other information. There are links to state resource documents, FAQs, training information, a newsletter, related organizations and centers, conference information, and contact listings. http://www.nichcy.org

National Institute on Drug Abuse (NIDA)

A component of the National Institutes of Health, this organization supports international research, advocacy, and education on drug abuse and related issues. The site provides information on the mission and goals of the organization; current news; descriptive fact sheets on commonly abused drugs and their treatment; and links to publications, monographs, teaching materials and reports on various aspects of substance abuse and addiction. Other resources available at this site include conference details and summaries of previous meetings, relevant news articles, links to sites on the subdivisions of NIDA, funding and training opportunities and information, advocacy items, a clinical trial network, and links to the National Institutes of Health site and other professional organizations and centers related to substance abuse. http://www.nida.nih.gov/NIDAHome1.html

Substance Abuse and Mental Health Services Administration (SAMHSA)

The Substance Abuse and Mental Health Services Administration is the federal agency charged with improving the quality and availability of prevention, treatment, and rehabilitation services in order to reduce illness, death, disability, and cost to society resulting from substance abuse and mental illnesses. Resources include professional program, and budget information databases; information on substance abuse and mental health issues; statistics; updated news releases, and a search form for relevant documents. Links to other related centers are provided, as well as links to general information on substance abuse and mental health problems. http://www.samhsa.gov

6

NEUROLOGICAL, DIAGNOSTIC, AND THERAPEUTIC ASPECTS OF PSYCHIATRY

6.1 NEUROLOGICAL ASPECTS OF PSYCHIATRY

NEUROANATOMY

A Brief Introduction to the Brain This site from scientists in Mexico City offers an educational resource on neuroanatomy. Topics include anatomy of the nervous system; neurotransmitters; behavior, perception, and sensation; cerebral cortex, cognitive functions; second messengers; development of the nervous system; membrane potential; sleep; memory; synapse; and neural networks. Visual aids and links to more detailed discussions of important terms accompany educational text. http://ifcsun1.ifisiol.unam.mx/Brain/segunda.htm

Clinical Neurophysiology on the Internet Hundreds of sites are contained in this directory of clinical neurophysiology sites on the Internet. Categories include general information, basic neurophysiology, somatosensory evoked potentials, motor evoked potentials, brain stem auditory evoked responses, and electroencephalography. There are also categories for visual evoked potentials, motor nerve study by electromyography, and neurophysiological diagnostics. http://www.neurophys.com/contents.shtml

Harvard University: Whole Brain Atlas Every aspect of the human brain and associated brain disorders are explored through this extraordinary atlas developed by Dr. Keith A. Johnson, M.D., and J. Alex Becker of Harvard University. http://www.med.harvard.edu/AANLIB/home.html

HealthWeb: Neuroanatomy Sponsored by the John Crerar Library at the University of Chicago and HealthWeb, this site offers comprehensive information on neuroanatomy. There are detailed descriptions, along with illustrations, of the central nervous system, the brain, the peripheral nervous system, the spinal cord, and the senses. In addition, the site features a collection of digital images of the brain, the eye, and general neuroanatomy. There are also tutorials, neuroanatomy electronic journals, associations, and related resources. http://www.lib.uchicago.edu/hw/neuroanatomy/

Human Brain Atlas The Human Brain Atlas offers detailed, labeled images of the brain, courtesy of Katalin Hegedus, M.D., Ph.D., of the University of Debrecen, Hungary. The brain is shown from the perspective of cutting the brain coronally, along with sections stained for myelin. There are also tracts of the spinal cord. An A-to-Z index of labeled structures is provided in both English and Latin. A short list of related links, a tutorial on neuroanatomy, a directory of neuroanatomy and neuropathology links on the Internet, and an online neuropathology atlas are also available.
http://www.neuropat.dote.hu/anastru/anastru.htm

Limbic System: The Center of Emotions An article on the limbic system is featured on this Web page, hosted by the ePublication section of the State University of Campinas, Brazil. The article examines the three units of the brain: primitive, intermediate (limbic), and rational. Links at the bottom of the page lead to further sections of the article covering theories on the role of brain structures in the formation of emotions, a look at the main areas involved with emotions, and affective states.
http://www.epub.org.br/cm/n05/mente/limbic_i.htm

Moravian College: Neuroanatomy Review Information Useful glossaries explaining terms related to neuroanatomy, neurochemistry, and non-anatomical neurology concepts are available at this address. Unfamiliar terms are linked to a definition within the glossaries.
http://www.cs.moravian.edu/~kussmaul/cns/neuro.html

Neuroanatomy Lecture notes from a course on neuroanatomy at East Carolina University are featured on this site. Detailed information is provided on cells and cell structures; neurons, nerves, and tissue; bioelectricity; transmission of information between neurons; structure of the central nervous system; and evolution of the vertebrate nervous system. Vision, motor systems, and attention are covered in detail. In addition, there are descriptions of engrams, amnesia, types of memory, and language. Other topics include electrical activity of the brain and epilepsy, laterality, and development and handedness.
http://core.ecu.edu/psyc/grahamr/Lectures.html

North Carolina State University: Nervous System Gross Anatomy
This site offers a comprehensive educational resource for those requiring general information on neuroanatomy. The anatomy of the brain, spinal cord, cranial nerves, peripheral nerves, sympathetic nervous system, and parasympathetic nervous system are described with text and useful images.
http://courses.ncsu.edu/classes/psy502001/psy502/l4nsgros/ns_pg1.htm

Online Dictionary of Mental Health: Neuroanatomy and Neuropathology Links to more than 20 sites are found at this address, offering access to anatomy images, interactive brain maps, educational resources, labeled slides and diagrams, neural tissue images, muscle and nerve images, and resources specific to neuropathology. One site presents information in Italian.
http://www.human-nature.com/odmh/neuroanatomy.html

ScienceNet: Brain and Nervous System   ScienceNet, an information service based in the United Kingdom, specializes in explanations of complex topics in everyday language. Nearly 100 common questions about brain and nervous system morphology and function, diagnostic procedures, and other topics are answered through links at this site.
http://www.sciencenet.org.uk/database/Biology/Lists/braintable.html

University of Iowa Virtual Hospital: Fetal and Young Child Nervous System   The Virtual Hospital offers this comprehensive presentation of the fetal nervous system and the brain, including both normal and abnormal brain development, presented by Dr. Adel Afifi and Dr. Ronald Bergman.
http://www.vh.org/Providers/Textbooks/FetalYoungCNS/FetalYoungCNS.html

University of Utah: Neuroanatomy Tutorial   Labeled images of the brain and spinal cord are provided in detail on this site. Sixty photographs and MRI images are provided for external views of the brain and spinal cord, sagittal sections, coronal sections, transverse sections, as well as a collection of miscellaneous views.
http://www-medlib.med.utah.edu/WebPath/HISTHTML/NEURANAT/NEURANCA.html

Washington University: Neuroscience Tutorial   The basics of clinical neuroscience are explored through a detailed analysis of the human brain and its functions in this illustrated online tutorial at the Washington University School of Medicine.
http://thalamus.wustl.edu/Course

NEUROTRANSMITTERS

About.com: Neurotransmitters   Created to provide information about neurotransmitters, this site offers a listing of links to information on drugs and their effect on the brain, the purpose of neurotransmitters, cannabinoids, catecholamines, and histamine receptors. There is also a link to a similar site focused on pharmacology as well as to related Internet sites for neurotransmitters.
http://neuroscience.about.com/science/neuroscience/cs/generalnt/

Cerebral Institute of Discovery: Neurotransmitters   The Cerebral Institute of Discovery, started by parents of a son with cerebral palsy, disseminates information on neurology to the general public. This page devoted to neurotransmitters offers links to many relevant Internet resources, including educational sites for children and adults, multimedia resources, and images. Sites presenting current research from several investigators are also found through this address. http://cerebral.org/neurotrans.html

Indiana State University: Biochemistry of Neurotransmitters   The biochemistry of neurotransmitters is detailed on this Web page. A table of neurotransmitters displays the transmitter molecule, its source, and its site of synthesis. There are also descriptions of synaptic transmission, neuromuscular transmission, and neurotransmitter receptors. In addition, there is a discussion of acetylcholine, cholinergic agonists and antagonists, catecholamines, serotonin, and gamma-aminobutyric acid(GABA).

http://web.indstate.edu/thcme/mwking/nerves.html

Neurotransmitters Slide presentations on types and specific examples of neurotransmitters are found at this site presented by the Houston Community College System. Specific discussions of acetylcholine, dopamine, the dopamine hypothesis for schizophrenia, serotonin and norepinephrine, gamma-aminobutyric acid (GABA), endorphins, and psychoactive drugs are available at the address.

http://nwc.hccs.cc.tx.us/psyc/neuron2/index.htm

Neurotransmitters A brief tutorial on neurotransmitters is presented on this site, courtesy of the Iacono Neuroscience Clinic. The tutorial covers the four classes of neurotransmitters: acetylcholine, biogenic amines, excitatory amino acids, and neuropeptides. The purpose and complexity of neurotransmitters are explained.

http://www.pallidotomy.com/neurotransmitters.html

NEUROENDOCRINOLOGY

Neuroendocrinology of Mood Disorders An article on the neuroendocrinology of mood disorders is provided on this site by the American College of Neuropsychopharmacology. The article examines the relationship between stress and mood disorders, along with studies of the hypothalamic-pituitary-adrenocortical system. Studies discussed include the detamethasone suppression test, the corticotropin- releasing hormone test, and the combined dexamethasone and corticotropin-releasing hormone test. The role of corticosteroids is described, along with the potential role of neuroactive steroids in mood disorders. In addition, there is a discussion of the thyroid system, as well as the somatotropic system.

http://www.acnp.org/G4/GN401000096/CH094.html

Society of Behavioral Neuroendocrinology This society targets research professionals in the fields of behavior and neuroendocrinology. The site includes conference information, membership information, society officers, goals and bylaws of the society, and a link to related meetings. Publications resources include access to the official journal of the society, *Hormones and Behavior,* and to the *Journal of Neuroscience* and *Neuropeptides.*

http://www.sbne.org

NEUROIMAGING AND PATHOLOGY

American Society of Neuroimaging (ASN) Information on the American Society of Neuroimaging is featured on this Web page. Visitors will find the

ASN newsletter, as well as information on training, credentials, fellowships, courses, and workshops. In addition, there is a collection of neuroimaging case studies. http://www.asnweb.org/

Cognitive Neuroimaging Unit A division within both the Veterans Affairs Medical Center and the University of Minnesota School of Medicine, this unit in interested in brain mapping of cognitive functions in both healthy individuals and those with mental disorders. The history and mission of the unit, available facilities and resources, a staff directory, a bibliography of recent publications, a bulletin board highlighting recent activities, information on associated clinics, and links to related sites are all found at this address. Visitors can also access links to resources related to the tools the unit uses to process, analyze, and display positron emission tomography (PET) images.
http://james.psych.umn.edu

Harvard University: Whole Brain Atlas This comprehensive resource for images of normal and abnormal brain tissues offers an introduction to neuroimaging, an atlas of normal brain structure and blood flow, images of the "top 100 brain structures," vascular anatomy images, and images related to normal aging. Images related to specific cerebrovascular, neoplastic, degenerative, inflammatory, and infectious diseases are available at the site. Explanatory tours are available with some images.
http://www.med.harvard.edu/AANLIB/home.html

Johns Hopkins University: Division of Psychiatric Neuroimaging
The Division of Psychiatric Neuroimaging increases the understanding of the brain, behavior, genetics, and connections among these subjects through neuroimaging research. This site offers a mission statement; a faculty and staff directory; descriptions of current projects with methods, jobs, and internship information; and a bibliography of publications. Users can download some full-text articles from the site.
http://pni.med.jhu.edu

National Institute on Drug Abuse (NIDA) Notes: The Basics of Brain Imaging This site describes the main neuroimaging techniques used in drug abuse research, including positron emission tomography (PET), single photon emission computed tomography (SPECT), magnetic resonance imaging (MRI), and electroencephalography (EEG). Visitors will find explanations of information collected from these techniques and how each technique is performed.
http://www.nida.nih.gov/NIDA_Notes/NNVol11N5/Basics.html

Neuroanatomy and Neuropathology on the Internet A directory of neuroanatomy and neuropathology resources on the Internet is provided on this site, compiled and designed by Katalin Hegedus, M.D., Ph.D. More than 60 sites are listed in categories such as anatomy, histology, pathology, history, online tutorials, quizzes, books, journals, and related links. The site also offers links to atlases of neuroanatomy structures, and neuropathology. In addition, there are links to a neurological disorder Internet directory site, and a neuroradiology Internet directory site.

http://www.neuropat.dote.hu/

Proceedings of the National Academy of Sciences (PNAS): Papers from an NAS Colloquium on Neuroimaging of Human Brain Function

More than 20 full-text articles related to neuroimaging are available through this site. Visitors can read the article online or download a copy. Other resources include a list of papers citing the article, links to similar articles found at PNAS Online and PubMed, a link to the article's PubMed citation, and the ability to search MEDLINE for articles with the same authors.

http://www.pnas.org/content/vol95/issue3/index.shtml#COLLOQUIUM

University of Utah: CNS Pathology

An image library of central nervous system pathology is provided on this site. More than 120 images are featured, with captions, in categories such as CNS hemorrhage, infarction, edema and herniation, infections, congenital malformations, acquired and congenital degenerative diseases, dementias, and neoplasms. There is also a link for a tutorial on CNS degenerative diseases.

http://www-medlib.med.utah.edu/WebPath/CNSHTML/CNSIDX.html

NEUROPSYCHIATRY

American Academy of Clinical Neuropsychology (AACN)

This site presented by the American Academy of Clinical Neuropsychology allows users to search the AACN directory of members, view the articles and bylaws of the academy, view current AACN news, and access continuing education materials. Links to other neuropsychology sites are present.

http://www.med.umich.edu/abcn/aacn.html

American Board of Psychiatry and Neurology, Inc.

The mission of the American Board of Psychiatry and Neurology is to improve the quality of psychiatric and neurological care through a voluntary certification process for professionals. This site is designed to provide information on board certification, examinations, and policies of the board. It has an informative FAQ section and offers links to other related boards.

http://www.abpn.com

American Neuropsychiatric Association (ANPA)

Resources offered by the ANPA at this site include an e-mail news subscription service, a directory of members, an online newsletter, journal information, and links to related sites of interest to neuroscientists. A list of ANPA officers is also provided.

http://www.neuropsychiatry.com/ANPA/index.html

Association for Research in Nervous and Mental Disease (ARNMD)

The Web site of the Association for Research in Nervous and Mental Disease provides links to the history and mission of ARNMD, ARNMD publications

from 1920, an events calendar, 1998 meeting abstracts, and a list of program speakers and talks from the 1998 annual course.
http://www.arnmd.org/menu.html

Beth Israel Deaconess Medical Center and Harvard Medic School: Behavioral Neurology Unit   The Behavioral Neurology Unit presents an overview of psychiatry and neuropsychiatry services available, lists reasons for referral, and offers information on fellowships at this site. Clinical and laboratory research information is available by topic, and the site also offers a bibliography of recent publications and a faculty directory.
http://www.bih.harvard.edu/behavneuro/Npsychiat.html

Centre for Clinical Research in Neuropsychiatry   This center for psychiatric and neuroscience research, located in Western Australia, "focuses on the etiology, epidemiology, course, and outcome of major psychiatric disorders in adults and children," with special interest in genetics and family studies. Information about the centre, a staff directory, research details, a bibliography of recent publications, and seminar details are found at this site.
http://www.ccrn.uwa.edu.au

Fourth International Congress of Neuropsychiatry   Details for those interested in attending the International Congress in Neuropsychiatry in Israel for the year 2002 are provided on this Web page. The site offers general information on the conference, social and travel information, tours available, an intention form to be included in further announcements, and general information about Israel.   http://www.kenes.com/neuropsychiatry/wel.htm

Journal of Neuropsychiatry and Clinical Neurosciences: Search Tool
A search tool for the *Journal of Neuropsychiatry and Clinical Neurosciences* is provided on this Web page. Users can access full-text articles from February 1998 to the present; only abstracts are available for the period February 1989 to November 1997. Full-text articles are available to subscribers or by purchase through the Web site.
(some features fee-based) http://neuro.psychiatryonline.org/search.shtml

Literature, Cognition, and the Brain   In addition to a descriptive bibliography on the linkage of cognitive sciences and neurosciences with literature, this site provides links to conference information, abstracts, current research projects, reviews of relevant books, and a number of related Web sites, discussion groups, and other online resources.
http://www2.bc.edu/~richarad/lcb

Mental Health Net: Neurosciences and Neuropsychology   Various sites in neurosciences and neuropsychology are described and rated at this useful Internet resource. Sites such as Neuroworld provide information to neurologists, neurosurgeons, and interested consumers about many aspects of biofeedback, neurofeedback, neurophysiology, and other subspecialty topics. News-

groups, mailing lists in a variety of subspecialties, journals, and professional organizations are offered in this all-inclusive neurology resource.
http://mentalhelp.net/guide/pro10.htm

Neuropsychiatry.com   This site contains a catalog of Internet resources by disorder category, and users can search the site to quickly locate links to relevant sites. Resources are provided in neurology, neuropsychiatry, neuropsychology, psychiatry, and psychology. Some links are listed with short descriptions. Drug information, associations, support groups, continuing education resources, government sites, and funding sources are typical of the resources found under each disorder category.
http://www.neuropsychiatry.com/NPcom/pages/wwwlinks.html

Neuropsychology Central   This searchable site contains an online forum for interested professionals and consumers, informative resources for professionals, and links to sites on assessment, forensics, geriatrics, organizations, pediatric publications, training, and other topics of interest.
http://www.neuropsychologycentral.com

NIMH: Division of Intramural Research Neuropsychiatry Branch   The main focus of the Neuropsychiatry Branch of the National Institute of Mental Health is to study the effects of early intervention on the course of psychotic disorders, particularly schizophrenia. The site contains a bibliography of recent publications; employment opportunities; notice of meetings; references relevant to the study, treatment, and prevention of various neuropsychiatric disorders; a list of early intervention research and treatment facilities; and links to related sites. Descriptions of the NPB PREVENT program, a forum for the discussion and exchange of information between groups studying various forms of prevention for neuropsychiatric disorders, and the National Collaborative Study of Early Psychosis and Suicide (NCSEPS) are also available.
http://silk.nih.gov/silk/npb

University of Leicester: Neurosciences   This concise yet useful list of links provides general neuroscience resources as well as home pages to premier online neuroscience centers, such as the University of California Los Angeles Laboratory of Neuro Imaging. Incorporated into the list are such neuroscience topics as Parkinson's disease, Alzheimer's disease, neuroanesthesiology, neuroanatomy, and neuroimaging.
http://www.le.ac.uk/pcs/links/anlineur.html

What's New in Neuropsychiatry   This site offers links to news articles related to general issues in psychiatry and neuropsychiatry. Summaries are available in French, but links lead to English language articles.
(free registration) http://194.7.20.151/index.asp

6.2 SYMPTOMS AND RISK FACTORS

American Academy of Family Physicians (AAFP): Psychiatric Symptoms Visitors to this site will find an article originally published in *American Family Physician* (November 1998), on screening for psychiatric symptoms. Hosted by the American Academy of Family Physicians, the article examines the Psychiatric Review of Symptoms (PROS) as a screening tool for family practitioners. General interviewing techniques for psychiatric symptoms are explained, along with specific recommendations for mood disorders, borderline personality disorders, substance abuse, anxiety, somatization disorders, eating disorders, dementia, and psychotic disorders. A bibliography is provided.
http://www.aafp.org/afp/981101ap/carlat.html

Mental Health of Adolescent Girls Sponsored by medEmall.com, this site reports on the results of the Commonwealth Fund Survey of the Health of Adolescent Girls._ According to the survey, many adolescent girls have signs of poor mental health. The news story details the results, including topics such as depression and lack of self-confidence. The symptoms were also rated by ethnicity, race, and income. Future needs are outlined.
http://www.medemall.com/children/mentalfax-adolescentgirls.htm

Screening for Mental Health, Inc.: Symptoms and Risk Factors Screening for Mental Health, Inc. is a nonprofit organization that coordinates national screening events and programs for alcohol abuse, anxiety disorders, depression, and eating disorders. Symptoms and risk factors for these conditions are described through articles, sample screening tests, and fact sheets on the site. In addition, there is information on telephone and online screening in the workplace, and for healthcare organizations. Information on ordering the *Harvard Medical School Guide to Suicide Assessment and Intervention* is also posted on the site.
http://www.mentalhealthscreening.org/

Surgeon General: Overview of Cultural Diversity and Mental Health Part of a larger report on mental health from the Surgeon General, this section discusses race as a factor associated with poor mental health. Cultural identity is examined as it relates to coping styles, including the use of family and community as resources. There is also a discussion of utilization of resources among African Americans, Asian Americans, Hispanics, and Native Americans. Barriers to receipt of treatment are covered, including typical help-seeking behavior, mistrust, stigma, cost, and clinician bias. Suggestions for improvement of treatment for minorities are provided. In addition, there are links to other sections of this comprehensive Surgeon General report.
http://www.surgeongeneral.gov/library/mentalhealth/chapter2/sec8.html

6.3 DIAGNOSTICS

ASSESSMENT AND TESTING

American Academy of Child and Adolescent Psychiatry (AACAP): Summary of the Practice Parameters for the Psychiatric Assessment of Infants and Toddlers   This full-text article includes an abstract, considerations in the assessment of infants and toddlers, assessment techniques, diagnostic formulation, treatment planning, and detailed guidelines for a suggested infant and toddler mental status exam.
http://www.aacap.org/clinical/infntsum.htm

Australian Transcultural Mental Health Network: Research Literature on Multilingual Versions of Psychiatric Assessment Instruments
Bibliographic information is available at this site for articles describing research evaluating or utilizing specific psychiatric assessment instruments. There is an order form on the site for the bibliography.
(fee-based) http://www.atmhn.unimelb.edu.au/library/services/specialist_reports/mhi.html

Educational Resources Information Center (ERIC): AE Test Locator
The test collection covers a broad array of tests, including educational and managerial fields of testing. The site allows users to search test databases from the site's sponsors: the ERIC Clearinghouse on Assessment and Evaluation, the Library and Reference Services Division of the Educational Testing Service, the Buros Institute of Mental Measurements at the University of Nebraska in Lincoln, the Region III Comprehensive Center at George Washington University, and Pro-Ed test publishers.
http://ericae.net/testcol.htm

Educational Testing Service: Test Database   A search tool is provided on this site for the Educational Testing Service's database of more than 9,500 tests and research instruments. Each test offers information such as author, publication date, and source, as well as an abstract describing the test, its intended population, and uses. A search tool in the center of the site allows for searches of reviews of educational and psychological tests that the Buros Institute of Mental Measurements and Pro-Ed have included in their directories.
http://ericae.net/testcol.htm#ETSTF

Mental Health Net: Assessment Resources   This address lists more than 50 sources and online locations of psychiatric assessment tests, providing descriptions and ratings with site links. Resources include tools for assessing depression, mania, emotional intelligence, childhood behavioral problems, and sexual disorders, as well as links to sites providing catalogs of assessment resources. Resources are available for both professionals and nonprofessionals searching for self-assessment tools. Links to newsgroups, journals, publications and research papers, professional organizations and centers, additional assess-

ment resources, product suppliers, and software companies are also available. Users can subscribe to mailing lists for e-mails of specific news and information at the site.
http://mentalhelp.net/guide/pro01.htm

Neuropsychology Central A comprehensive listing of Internet resources related to neuropsychology is featured on this Web page. Topics include psychiatric assessment, forensics, geriatrics, neuroimaging, neuromedical and neuropsychology literature, organizations, pediatric resources, assessment and treatment centers, software, and training. Brief descriptions of each site are provided.
http://www.neuropsychologycentral.com/interface/
content/links/links_interface_frameset.html

New York University: Assessment and Testing Designed to provide psychiatric information to the general public, this site offers links for resources on diagnostic assessment, screening, and treatment. Users can complete online screening tests for depression, anxiety, sexual disorders, attention deficit disorder, and personality disorders. In the "Diagnosis" section, there is detailed information defining psychiatric disorders, along with information on depression. In addition, there are links for further information on a variety of treatment options. http://www.med.nyu.edu/Psych/public.html

New York University: Department of Psychiatry: Psychiatry Information for the General Public This site provides links to general online psychiatry resources for the general public, including NIMH information; online screening tests for depression, anxiety, sexual disorders, attention deficit/hyperactivity disorder, and personality disorders; and resources for the diagnosis of psychiatric disorders and depression. Treatment resources are available, with topics including psychotherapy, medications, group psychotherapy, psychoanalysis, and cognitive behavioral therapy. Links are also included to self-help resources, advocacy groups, fact sheets, articles and other publications, and search engines.
http://www.med.nyu.edu/Psych/public.html

Psychiatric Assessment of Infants and Toddlers Originally published in the *Journal of the American Academy of Child & Adolescent Psychiatry* (1997), this full-text article offers recommendations for the psychiatric assessment of infants and toddlers (0-36 months), courtesy of Web site developer Barbara C. Johnson, Esq. The article details the family interview, including the importance of establishing a working alliance with the family, identifying reason for referral, taking a developmental history of the child, a family relational history, and clinical observation. In addition, there is information on the infant and toddler mental status exam, standard instruments for assessment, interdisciplinary assessment, and treatment planning. References are provided.
http://falseallegations.com/evaluat2.htm

CLASSIFICATIONS

BehaveNet: APA DSM-IV Diagnostic Classification   Diagnostic classifications and categories of psychiatric disorders and associated conditions are listed. Specific disorders are listed by category. Ordering information is available for the American Psychiatric Association DSM-IV, related publications, and books and other media through Amazon.com.
http://www.behavenet.com/capsules/disorders/dsm4classification.htm

International Classification of Diseases: Psychiatry   Primarily for clinicians and other professionals, this site offers an organized list of psychiatric disorders, according to the International Classification of Diseases, from the World Health Organization. This reference manual allows searches by disorder categories, alphabetical lists, and keywords. A basic description of the disorder or group of related disorders is presented, as well as links to additional psychiatry sites.
http://www.informatik.fh-luebeck.de/icd/welcome.html

CLINICAL DIAGNOSIS

Clinical Disease Management for Psychiatric Disorders   This site offers links to chapters in the *Merck Manual* and to other clinical sources for diagnosis and treatment of specific disorders, including libraries of pathology images, clinical practice guidelines, and clinical management resources. Links take the visitor to relevant sections of the Collaborative Hypertext of Radiology (CHORUS), CliniWeb, Internet Mental Health, *Family Practice Handbook,* National Guideline Clearinghouse, and other Internet information sources.
http://www.slis.ua.edu/cdlp/WebDLCore/clinical/psychiatry/index.htm

Internet Mental Health: Diagnosis and Disorders   A comprehensive resource for concise diagnostic information regarding most of the more common mental health disorders, this Web site provides descriptive information for the physician or patient. A life quality analysis is available through a questionnaire that gives the patient or physician a summary of characteristics and an associated numerical measurement. American and European descriptions of more than 35 disorders and online diagnostic screenings for each are available. Additionally, research, treatment, and related Internet links are provided for each condition. Personality disorders, anxiety disorders, and substance-related disorders are included.
http://www.mentalhealth.com/p71.html

Merck Manual of Diagnosis and Therapy: Psychiatric Disorders
Topics available through this portion of the *Merck Manual* include psychiatry in medicine, somatoform disorders, anxiety disorders, dissociative disorders, mood disorders, suicidal behavior, personality disorders, psychosexual disorders, schizophrenia and related disorders, psychiatric emergencies, drug use and de-

pendence, and eating disorders. Specific disorders under these headings are described, and resources on each subject typically include etiology, symptoms and diagnosis, prognosis, and treatment.
http://merck.com/pubs/mmanual/section15/sec15.htm

University of Iowa: Family Practice Handbook   The psychiatry chapter of the *University of Iowa Family Practice Handbook* explores mood disorders, anxiety disorders, substance-use disorders, acute psychosis, schizophrenia, and eating disorders. Each section has extensive clinical practice guideline and treatment information.
http://www.vh.org/Providers/ClinRef/FPHandbook/15.html

Using DSM-IV Primary Care Version: A Guide to Psychiatric Diagnosis in Primary Care   As a courtesy of the American Academy of Family Physicians, this article reviews the *Diagnostic and Statistical Manual of Mental Disorders,* primary care version (DSM-IVPC), examining the methods by which it accommodates the family physician in clinical practice. A comparison between the DSM-IV and DSM-IVPC is made in regard to the diagnostic features unique to DSM-IVPC as well as unresolved clinical issues regarding the primary care algorithms and other limitations to the family physician model with respect to hard-to-diagnose disorders.
http://www.aafp.org/afp/981015ap/pingitor.html

MENTAL STATUS EXAMINATION

Indiana University: Mental Status Examination   This Indiana University lecture on the mental status examination provides a comprehensive resource for this important diagnostic tool. There is significant detailed information on every aspect of the examination, such as utility, method, procedure and focal issues, and findings.
http://php.iupui.edu/~flip/g505mse.html

Psychiatry LectureLinks   This online lecture and tutorial contains an introduction to psychiatry and the behavioral sciences. There is a mental status exam as well as a cognitive exam. Disorders and illnesses that are discussed include dementia, mood disorders, schizophrenia, childhood autism, and substance abuse. Many other topics are discussed and introductions to the various sections are also provided.
http://omie.med.jhmi.edu/LectureLinks/PsychiatryLinks.html

ONLINE DIAGNOSIS

Internet Mental Health: Online Diagnosis   This site allows visitors to use interactive question and answer programs for provisional diagnoses of mental disorders, including anxiety disorders, childhood disorders, eating disorders, mood disorders, personality disorders, schizophrenia, and substance-related

disorders. Descriptions, treatment, research, educational booklets, articles, and links to additional resources are available for each disorder.
http://www.mentalhealth.com/fr71.html

6.4 PSYCHOTHERAPIES

GENERAL RESOURCES

Health Center.com: Therapy   Devoted to providing information on all aspects of psychological therapy, this site provides consumers and professionals with links to resources on therapy, assistance in obtaining therapy, the different types of therapy, and specific mental disorders, as well as an overview of symptoms and treatments. Access to discussion boards and a Spanish version of the site are also available.
http://www4.health-center.com/mentalhealth/therapy/default.htm

Medscape: Psychiatry: Treatment Updates   A list of treatment updates, some with CME credit, is provided on this Web page, courtesy of Medscape. Fifteen treatment updates can be accessed after completing a free registration on the site.
(free registration) http://psychiatry.medscape.com/
Home/Topics/psychiatry/directories/dir-PSY.TreatUpdate.html

PSYweb.com: Psychotherapy   Visitors to this site will find short descriptions of many psychotherapy schools, including Adlerian, behavior, existential, Gestalt, person-centered, psychoanalytic, rational-emotive, reality, and transactional analysis therapies. These short overviews may be useful to both consumers and professionals.
http://www.psyweb.com/psywebsub/MentalDis/AdvPsych.html

Society for the Exploration of Psychotherapy Integration (SEPI)   This site provides information on the society's mission, conference information, a list of influential books, training opportunities in psychotherapy integration, an online article, and links of interest.
http://www.cyberpsych.org/sepi/

Surgeon General: Psychotherapy   Part of a larger publication, *Mental Health: A Report of the Surgeon General,* this section focuses on psychotherapy. An overview of psychotherapy is provided, along with a review of major approaches to psychotherapy such as psychodynamic therapy, behavior therapy, and humanistic therapy. Additional sections of the report can be navigated through hyperlinks on the left side of the page.
http://www.surgeongeneral.gov/library/mentalhealth/chapter2/sec6.html#psycho

ALTERNATIVE THERAPIES

Alternative Therapy: Focus on Herbal Products This article from Pediatric Pharmacotherapy offers a discussion of several popular herbal products. The National Institutes of Health alternative therapy criteria, FDA regulations, and current statistics on the use of alternative therapies are available, as well as discussions of Echinacea, St. John's wort, and ginseng. The article identifies active ingredients in each featured herbal product, contraindications, possible side effects, and history of use. Clinical studies of herbal products are referenced and a list of sources for information on herbal therapies is provided. (free registration) http://www.med.virginia.edu/cmc/pedpharm/v4n5.htm

Knowledge Exchange Network: Alternative Treatment Links at this site provide users with access to centers and other organizations offering information on music therapy, drama therapy, and other alternative approaches to mental wellness.
http://www.mentalhealth.org/links/alternative.htm

National Coalition of Arts Therapies Associations (NCATA) This alliance of professional associations dedicated to the advancement of art therapy represents six organizations. Art therapy, dance/movement therapy, drama therapy, music therapy, psychodrama, and poetry therapy are defined and discussed at this site. Information on upcoming conferences and contact details for professional organizations are available.
http://www.ncata.com/home.html

National Institute of Mental Health (NIMH): Questions and Answers about St. John's Wort Visitors to this site can read answers to questions about the use of St. John's wort in the treatment of depression.
http://www.nimh.nih.gov/publicat/stjohnswort.cfm

BEHAVIOR THERAPY

Association for Advancement of Behavior Therapy (AABT) The Association for Advancement of Behavior Therapy Web page offers professionals information on the organization; information on special interest groups, such as those concerned with addictive behaviors, anxiety, and trauma; and access to abstracts from AABT publications, namely *Behavior Therapy, The Behavior Therapist,* and *Cognitive and Behavioral Practice.* Also available are details concerning the AABT annual convention, a list of free patient fact sheets, and a list of related Internet resources. A section for the public describes careers in behavior therapy. Patients may also find the "Find a Therapist" service useful. http://www.aabt.org/

Association for Behavior Analysis The Association for Behavior Analysis, an international organization based at Western Michigan University, promotes

experimental, theoretical, and applied analysis of behavior. Visitors to the site can access a job placement service, lists of affiliated chapters, student committees, special interest groups, annual convention details, membership details, a member directory, association publications, and links to related Web sites.
http://www.wmich.edu/aba/contents.html

Behavior Analysis Located within the University of South Florida, this site has a number of links to Web pages, associations, journals, and other resources related to behavior analysis. In addition, educational training resources, graduate program information, and related Web sites are listed.
http://www.coedu.usf.edu/behavior/behavior.html

Behavior Online This is a professional site providing a structured forum for discussion of over 25 behavioral therapies and topics such as anxiety disorders, evolutionary psychology, legal issues for therapists, online clinical work, and behavioral medicine, and primary care. Described as an online gathering place for mental health and behavioral science professionals, this site offers numerous discussion forums, in addition to links to obtain conference information, home pages for related organizations and institutes, and other related Web sites.
http://www.behavior.net

Behavior Therapy Links Behavior therapy resources at this site include links to general information sources, associations, newsgroups, journals, and sources for psychological tests and software information. Most resources found at the site are technical and are not for untrained audiences.
http://home.planet.nl/~tgth/links_en.htm

Cambridge Center for Behavioral Studies Offering information to the public about the range of applications of behavioral technology, this site includes information on the fields where a positive difference has been made with behavior analysis applications. Details about these programs as they apply to autism, behavioral safety, and education are included, and visitors are encourage to explore the complete Behavior Analysis Webring, which links several major Internet resources in the field. http://www.behavior.org

Encyclopedia.com: Behavior Therapy A concise definition of behavior therapy is offered at this site, including links to explanations of related terms. Links to additional suggested resources are provided with some related terms.
http://encyclopedia.com/printable/01275.html

Journal of the Experimental Analysis of Behavior This psychology journal primarily publishes findings "relevant to the behavior of individual organisms." The site provides subscription information, instructions on preparation of manuscripts, a history of the journal, a table of contents and abstracts of current and archived issues, selected electronic reprints of articles, commentaries, audio presentations, video clips, and links to related journals and organizations. Visitors can search abstracts for relevant material by keyword.
http://www.envmed.rochester.edu/wwwrap/behavior/jeab/jeabhome.htm

BRIEF SOLUTION-FOCUSED THERAPY

Brief Solution-Focused Therapy   This site offers access to a mailing list that provides an ongoing therapy discussion, which can serve as a resource to professionals interested in brief therapy, solution-focused therapy, strategic, structural, and related models. Visitors can subscribe to the list, find links to several related sites, access an online bookstore, read an article on brief therapy and managed care, and find a reference list of related articles.
http://inetarena.com/~bneben

Brief Therapy   Written by Jill Aubuchon and Candace Crosby of Valdosta State University, Georgia, this Web page offers information and resources on brief therapy. The length and types of brief therapy are outlined. Five myths on this kind of therapy are addressed, including the misconception that brief therapy doesn't treat the "real" problem, is only for minor problems, and was only developed in response to limited financial resources. The site also contains Internet links for more information, as well as a comprehensive recommended reading list.
http://teach.valdosta.edu/dtwasieleski/brief.htm

Brief Therapy Institute of Sydney: Solution-Focused Brief Therapy
An overview of brief solution-focused therapy is provided on this Web page. Topics covered include the duration of the therapy, types of problems addressed, and studies reporting the effectiveness of the method.
http://www.brieftherapysydney.com.au/referrers/brief/aboutbrief.html

Community Health Network: Brief Solution-Focused Therapy
Visitors to this site will find a concise description of brief solution-focused therapy. The differences between solution-focused therapy and other psychotherapies are discussed, as well as the efficacy of the method.
http://www.commhealthnet.co.uk/solfocused.html

Depth Oriented Brief Therapy (DOBT)   Designed for professionals interested in brief solution-focused therapy, the Depth Oriented Brief Therapy's methodology and concepts are available via literature, the DOBT video series, and training seminars for psychotherapists and other healthcare professionals. Professional references and links to DOBT case studies can be accessed.
http://www.dobt.com

New Therapist: Brief Solution Therapy   A full-text article on brief solution therapy is presented on this Web page, originally published in *New Therapist* magazine. The article examines the disorder paradigm, based on traditional psychotherapy approaches, and the coherence paradigm, based on newer therapies such as depth-oriented brief therapy, family themes, dialectical constructivism, and traumatic incident reduction. Old and new assumptions between the two paradigms are discussed. A list for further reading is provided.
http://www.newtherapist.com/ecker6.html

CLIENT-CENTERED THERAPY

Carl Rogers: Founder of Client-Centered Therapy Hosted by Shippensburg University, this Web site offers a brief biography of Carl Rogers, along with a description of client-centered therapy, also known as Rogerian therapy. The theory behind the therapy is explained, including incongruity, defenses, and perceptual distortion. Qualities in the therapist necessary for successful implementation of this type of therapy are also discussed.
http://www.ship.edu/~cgboeree/rogers.html

Client-Centered Therapy Written by a student therapist, this Web page offers a short description of client-centered therapy. The nondirective approach to therapy is described, along with the theory behind it. Links to related Web resources are provided, as well as an index of client-centered therapy papers.
http://portents.ne.mediaone.net/~matt/cct.html

COGNITIVE-BEHAVIOR THERAPY

Academy of Cognitive Therapy Professionals will find information on workshops, conferences, and certification in cognitive therapy on the academy's Web page. For consumers there is a worldwide directory of cognitive therapists.
http://www.academyofct.org/

American Institute for Cognitive Therapy This site describes the process and concepts of cognitive therapy, lists psychiatric problems addressed at the institute, and provides common questions, answers, and transcripts of recent news articles related to cognitive therapy and the institute. Suggested readings, staff member biographies, fact sheets, an online newsletter, links to related sites, and fellowship details are also available.
http://www.cognitivetherapynyc.com

Beck Institute for Cognitive Therapy and Research The Beck Institute for Cognitive Therapy and Research, under the direction of the founder of cognitive therapy, Aaron T. Beck, M.D., Emeritus Professor of Psychiatry, University of Pennsylvania School of Medicine, and Director Judith S. Beck, Ph.D., Clinical Assistant Professor of Psychology in Psychiatry at the University of Pennsylvania, offers cognitive therapy training programs for mental health and medical professionals. Details of training programs, certification information, an online bookstore, an online newsletter, Dr. J. S. Beck's speaking schedule, and links to related sites are all available at this address. Visitors can also download an application for training programs at the site.
http://www.beckinstitute.org

Center for Cognitive Therapy This center was founded by request from the founder of cognitive therapy to open a center in southern California. The center offers consultation, therapy for therapists, licensing preparation services for Ph.D.-level psychologists in California, and training workshops. The site provides information on upcoming workshops, links to details of workshops worldwide, suggested readings with ordering links, conference news, and membership information.

http://www.padesky.com

International Association for Cognitive Psychotherapy This site offers visitors information about the International Association for Cognitive Psychotherapy and its activities. In addition, abstracts are available online for their *Journal of Cognitive Psychotherapy*. A list of related Internet resources around the world is also provided.

http://iacp.asu.edu/

MindStreet: Cognitive Therapy An introduction to cognitive therapy is provided on this Web page. A definition is provided, along with the research background of the technique and how it is conducted. A suggested reading list is provided. In addition, there is a link for a multimedia learning program on cognitive therapy, along with ordering information.

http://www.mindstreet.com/aboutcg.html

MindStreet: Cognitive Therapy: A Multimedia Learning Program
This site describes the first computer program to combine interactive multimedia with psychiatric techniques of cognitive therapy. The program consists of a full-screen, full-motion video and a take-home manual with customized patient homework assignments. The program is designed to help patients cope with emotional problems, assist therapists in reaching treatment goals, and reduce healthcare costs. The site includes a program synopsis, an introduction to cognitive therapy, and a description of the learning environment and training applications. Additional features include ordering information, comments and reviews, author information, credits, system requirements, and general information about MindStreet.

http://mindstreet.com

National Association of Cognitive-Behavioral Therapists Up-to-date information and news is provided at the official site of the National Association of Cognitive-Behavioral Therapists, including back issues of the *Rational News* newsletter. A referral database sends you to the organization's national database of certified cognitive-behavioral therapists. Professional certifications offered by the organization are outlined, and a professional and self-help resources store is provided online. Products for professionals include home study courses, books, and audiovisual materials. Self-improvement courses and multimedia materials are available to the lay community.

http://www.nacbt.org

Social Cognition Paper Archive and Information Center In addition to the fact sheets, presentations, articles, and abstracts about social cognition and related subjects that are available for both professionals and consumers, information can be obtained through the many related links that are provided as

well. Details concerning various researchers working in the field of social cognition are also available.
http://www.psych.purdue.edu/~esmith/scarch.html

University of Pennsylvania: Health System (UPHS): Department of Psychiatry: Center for Cognitive Therapy The Center for Cognitive Therapy offers tertiary care, therapy, education, clinical training, and research programs. The site provides a staff listing, information on educational programs, answers to FAQs, links to related sites, information on the center's case consultation service, employment listings, and a referral list of cognitive therapists. http://www.med.upenn.edu/~psycct

DIALECTICAL BEHAVIORAL THERAPY (DBT)

Behavioral Technology Transfer Group: Dialectical Behavior Therapy The Behavioral Technology Transfer Group offers workshops, training, and consulting related to DBT. This site offers an overview that covers the origins of DBT; behavioral targets and stages of treatment; movement, speed, and flow; and randomized clinical trials of DBT. There are also links to DBT literature, DBT research data, and abstracts of published randomized controlled trials.
http://www.dbt-seattle.com/basics.html

Dialectical Behavioral Therapy An overview of DBT is provided on this site. The theory behind DBT is described, along with how it works.
http://www.palace.net/~llama/psych/dbt.html

Mental Health Net: Dialectical Behavior Therapy An article on dialectical behavior therapy in the treatment of borderline personality disorder, originally published in 1995 in *Psychiatry Online,* is featured on this Web page. Borderline personality disorder is briefly described, along with patient characteristics. Dialectical behavior therapy is explained, and the important characteristics in the therapist and patient are examined. The four primary modes of treatment in DBT are covered; namely, individual therapy, group skills training, telephone contact, and therapist consultation. In addition, stages of therapy and treatment targets, as well as treatment therapies, are covered. Empirical evidence for the effectiveness of this form of therapy is provided.
http://mentalhelp.net/articles/dbt1.htm

EYE MOVEMENT DESENSITIZATION AND REPROCESSING (EMDR)

Eye Movement Desensitization and Reprocessing Europe Association Information related to eye movement desensitization and reprocessing is featured on the EMDR Europe Association Web page. Visitors will find an overview of EMDR, along with information on the association, their annual conference, and a bibliography of research studies (with abstracts). There is also

a workshop schedule on the site for practitioners, a directory of EMDR consultants in Europe, and a short list of related links.
http://www.emdr-europe.net/

Eye Movement Desensitization and Reprocessing Institute EMDR, a treatment for depression and other pathologies, is described at this site for both consumers and professionals. The site also describes training at the institute and offers faculty profiles, publications and controlled studies, information on humanitarian assistance by the institute, discussion groups, study groups, and a system for ordering books and other products. Contact information for clinician referrals is also available.
http://www.emdr.com

GESTALT THERAPY

Association for the Advancement of Gestalt Therapy (AAGT) Visitors to the AAGT Web site will find information on the organization and its activities. Additionally, the site contains an article on the theory of Gestalt therapy. Conference information and a newsletter are also found on the site.
http://www.aagt.org/

Gestalt Therapy Center: A Brief Summary of Gestalt Therapy For those interested in Gestalt therapy, this Web page offers an overview. The origins of Gestalt therapy and its existential roots are also described. There is also a short list of related links.
http://www.gestaltcenter.net/info.htm

GROUP THERAPY

American Group Psychotherapy Association The American Group Psychotherapy Association works to enhance the practice, theory, and research of group therapy. The association offers information about group therapy, a directory of group therapists for interested patients, news, a meetings and events calendar, and publications details at this site. Specific resources for group therapists and students include ethical guidelines for group therapists, training opportunities information, certification details, government reports, advanced principles of psychotherapy, and links to affiliated societies.
http://www.groupsinc.org

American Psychological Association (APA): Group Psychology and Group Psychotherapy (Division 20) The Group Psychology and Group Psychotherapy Division offers a history of the division, committee lists, general awards information, a directory of officers, details of publications, membership details, news, and an e-mail mailing list. Links are available to related sites, including research centers, online journals, and other professional associations.
http://www.pitt.edu/~cslewis/GP2/Hello.html

American Society of Group Psychotherapy and Psychodrama (ASGPP) For those interested in group psychotherapy, psychodrama, and sociometry, the ASGPP Web site offers information on practitioner certification requirements, a list of training programs, a list of regional chapters, and information on the *International Journal of Action Methods*. In addition, there is general information on sociometry, as well as psychodrama. A bibliography of more than 4,000 citations related to psychodrama is provided. Visitors can also join a LISTSERV and read about the upcoming ASGPP conference.
http://asgpp.org/

Association for Specialists in Group Work (ASGW) The ASGW presents a resource starting point for practitioners of group therapy. The ASGW Web site describes the organization's primary mission of establishing standards for professional practice and for the support and dissemination of research knowledge in the field. Descriptions of core group work skills are illustrated in the "Group Work Rainbow" and core group work training standards are established and prepared for counselors and other professionals. Access to the ASGW products, including publications, audiovisual materials, and software is available. A calendar of events and links to further resources are provided.
http://www.psyctc.org/mirrors/asgw

Children's Group Therapy Association (CGTA) Information on the CGTA is provided on this Web page, intended for professionals. Annual conference information is provided, and the most recent newsletter is posted, with full-text articles.
http://www.cgta.net/

Group Psychotherapy Dedicated to group psychotherapy, this site offers a resource guide developed by group psychotherapist, Haim Weinberg. The guide offers an introduction to psychotherapy, along with information on group therapy conferences around the world, courses, jobs, research grants, several full-text articles, a bibliography, and a list of related Internet sites. Professionals are invited to join an e-mail discussion group.
http://www.group-psychotherapy.com/

Interactive Group Therapy This Web address includes listings of articles, books, and training opportunities for the professional psychotherapist involved in group therapy work, in addition to information for the general public on interactive group therapy. Annotated transcripts of group therapy sessions, articles for therapists, and handouts for group members that encourage interactive work are all available. A professional publication on the pattern system as it applies to group therapy may be accessed online, and a host of professional group therapy organizations and e-mail lists can be found.
http://www.earley.org/Group%20Therapy/group_therapy_frame.htm

International Association of Group Psychotherapy The association is dedicated to the development of group psychotherapy by means of international conferences, publications, and other forms of communication. The Web page

consists of membership information and a directory of the executive committee and board of directors. The site also offers links to conference information, an electronic forum, and links to other sites of interest.
http://www.psych.mcgill.ca/labs/iagp/IAGP.html

Psyche Matters: Group Therapy, Group Dynamics, and Analysis Links   This site lists links to institutes, organizations, publications, conference details, and general resources related to group therapy. Short descriptions are available with some site links.
http://psychematters.com/group.htm

Shame and Group Psychotherapy   This site offers a discussion of shame and group psychotherapy, as well as patient education booklets, links to related sites, references on shame, and references on scapegoating, bullying, cruelty, and persecution.   http://members.tripod.com/~birchmore/index.html

HYPNOTHERAPY

American Board of Hypnotherapy   The American Board of Hypnotherapy supports over 4,000 members located in the United States and throughout the world. The site offers an explanation of the organization's purpose, membership information, and registration and certification details.
http://www.abh.cc/

American Psychotherapy and Medical Hypnosis Association (APMHA)   The APMHA was founded in 1992 for state board licensed and certified professionals in the disciplines of medicine, psychology, social work, family therapy, alcohol and chemical dependency, professional counseling, dentistry, and forensic and investigative hypnosis. The site provides a description of hypnosis, membership information and application, professional referrals, training and certification program information, links to related sites, and ordering information for professional video training tapes.
http://apmha.com/

Hypnodirect.com: Official Hypnotists Directory of the United States
Visitors to this site will find a directory of hypnosis that can be searched by name, specialty, or location. Access is also provided to a chat room, a bulletin board, training information, hypnosis schools, products, related organizations, access to the newsletter, and information about hypnosis itself. Links to related sites are also available.   http://www.hypnodirect.com

Hypnosis, Brief Therapy, and Altered States of Consciousness Web Site Links   This personal Web page provides links to sites providing resources on hypnosis and related topics, altered states of consciousness, parapsychology, brief therapy, and lucid dreaming. Personal notes from recent hypnosis conferences are available.
http://www.inmet.com/~dlb/hypnosis/hypnosis.html

Hypnotherapy and Clinical Hypnosis Links Links to professional journals, United Kingdom - based organizations and hypnotherapy providers, discussion sites, and personal sites related to hypnotherapy are found at this address. http://easyweb.easynet.co.uk/~dylanwad/morganic/links.htm

 Professional Board of Hypnotherapy, Inc. The Professional Board of Hypnotherapy Web page offers information about their organization, a list of hypnotherapy schools, and a "Find a Hypnotherapist" service that includes domestic and international professionals. There is also a discussion board, as well as a chat room and a list of related Web sites, and counseling links. http://www.hypnosiscanada.com/

INTERPERSONAL PSYCHOTHERAPY (IPT)

 American Psychological Association (APA): Interpersonal Psychotherapy Taken from *The Clinical Psychologist*, this article examines the use of interpersonal psychotherapy for depression. A description of treatment, summary of supporting studies, references, and resources for training are featured. There are also links to other empirically supported treatments. http://www.apa.org/divisions/div12/rev_est/ipt_depr.shtml

 International Society for Interpersonal Psychotherapy Information on the history of interpersonal therapy in addressing issues in depression, its early guiding principles, and theoretical assumptions of its practice are discussed at this site's links. Specific interpersonal problems are outlined, and techniques used in IPT are reviewed. Additional connections provide details on specific applications of the technique, and a variety of training information and research findings are offered. http://www.interpersonalpsychotherapy.org/

MARRIAGE AND FAMILY THERAPY

 American Association for Marriage and Family Therapy (AAMFT) The American Association for Marriage and Family Therapy represents the professional interests of more than 23,000 marriage and family therapists throughout the United States, Canada, and abroad. This site offers a directory of therapists and provides information on the association in addition to clinical updates on various marriage and family mental health issues. A link for practitioners lists information on conferences and conference highlights, resources, a referral section, publications, education, training, licensing links, and membership information. (some features fee-based) http://www.aamft.org

 American Family Therapy Academy This nonprofit professional organization fosters an exchange of ideas among family therapy teachers, researchers, and practitioners. The site presents the organization's objectives, policy and press releases, membership details, a membership directory, excerpts of the or-

ganization's newsletter, and lists of recent awards with recipients. The site also offers links to related professional organizations.
http://www.afta.org

American Mental Health Counselors Association (AMHCA)   The professional resources available at this Web site include information on the AMHC Annual conference, a publications catalog, and workshop information for continuing education. In addition, there is information on public policy and malpractice insurance, as well as a list of related links. A "Find a Therapist" directory is also provided.
http://www.amhca.org/home.html

Family Therapy Net: Online Counseling   Visitors to this site can e-mail a professional for advice concerning marriage, relationships, family, and stepfamilies, and access facts about parenting, divorce, abuse, and children. Personal online counseling sessions are available, and visitors can also read recent mailings with professional responses. Links are provided to Internet resources related to family therapy, mental health, addiction and recovery, codependency, and stepfamilies.
http://www.familytherapynet.com/index.htm

Family Therapy Web Sites   This site contains links to family therapy resources on the Internet, including associations, journals, home pages of practitioners and groups, and sites offering general resources. Short site descriptions are provided with most links.
http://www.abacon.com/famtherapy/links.html

Marital and Family Therapy Pathfinder Directory   California Lutheran University (CLU) offers this helpful directory of marital and family therapy Internet resources. Categories of resources include periodicals, databases, electronic journals, CLU journals, reference sources, encyclopedias, assessment tools, statistical information, Web directories, newsgroups, associations and organizations, and universities and institutes. Resources are also listed alphabetically. Some material is available only to CLU students, faculty, and staff.
(some features fee-based) http://www.clunet.edu/iss/path/therapy/thleft.html

National Council on Family Relations (NCFR)   The NCFR is composed of family researchers, educators, policy makers, and practicing professionals. Site visitors can access membership details, register for monthly teleconferences, and peruse job listings. There are also discussion forums. Families will find tips for handling different aspects of family life, such as infants, parenting, adolescents, and divorce.
http://www.ncfr.com/

OCCUPATIONAL THERAPY

American Occupational Therapy Association, Inc. This organization offers information on occupational therapy, membership conferences, products and services, academic accreditation resources, continuing education resources, publications, and academic and fieldwork education. Student resources include journals and information on educational programs, fieldwork, and careers. Consumers can access information on occupational therapy, fact sheets, case studies, a directory of practitioners, news updates, and links to related sites.
http://www.aota.org

American Occupational Therapy Foundation (AOTF) Professionals will find a variety of resources in the field of occupational therapy on this Web site. Abstracts from current and past issues of the *Occupational Therapy Journal of Research* are available online. The Wilma L. West Library, a national repository for occupational therapy literature, offers an online bibliographic database with more than 27,000 citations. There is also a database of organizations, as well as a comprehensive listing of related Web links. In addition, the site offers information on occupational therapy scholarships, research grants, and postdoctoral fellowships. The most recent issue of the AOTF newsletter is also provided. For those studying for a doctoral degree, the Doctoral Network offers programs and a directory of members.
http://www.aotf.org/

National Board for Certification in Occupational Therapy Occupational therapists will find information on certification in the field on this Web page. Examination and certification information is the primary focus of the site. Candidate handbooks and applications are available online. News on workshops, study guides, and fact sheets on certification are also provided.
http://www.nbcot.org/

Occupational Therapy Resources This site catalogs links to Internet resources in occupational therapy and rehabilitation by topic. Associations, organizations, general information sites, and online forums are included in the list. Some of the topics covered include disability, schizophrenia, attention-deficit/hyperactivity disorder, arthritis, AIDS, and carpal tunnel syndrome.
http://www.qldnet.com.au/tvhs/occ-ther.htm

PLAY THERAPY

Association for Play Therapy Resources at this Web page offer professionals information on registration designations such as "Registered Play Therapist" and "Supervisor," annual conference details, and a continuing education provider directory. Also available for download in MSWord format are play therapist practice guidelines and a research compilation of more than 80 play therapy

studies and more than 20 filial therapy studies. A bookstore, as well as discussion boards, is also featured.
http://www.iapt.org/

International Board of Examiners of Certified Play Therapists Information on certification in child psychotherapy and play therapy is presented on this Web page by the International Board of Examiners of Certified Play Therapists. There are also links to information on certification standards, membership application, and the Canadian Play Therapy Institute.
http://www.playtherapy.org/pti/history.htm

PRIMAL PSYCHOTHERAPY

Primal Psychotherapy For those interested in regressive deep feeling psychotherapies, this personal Web site contains important information regarding the theory of primal therapy, links to other primal therapy Web sites, and related reference material. Topical material such as Reiki techniques and primal parenting can be found. Links to primal centers worldwide and sites connecting the user with primal discussion groups and book reviews are offered.
http://planet.nana.co.il/temichev

Primal and Regression Therapy This comprehensive resource offers a broad array of information on primal and regression therapy. There are numerous articles on primal therapy and on topics such as death and dying, birth trauma, and adoption. The site also features book reviews, a bibliography, related organizations, primal and regressive therapy centers, and personal stories.
http://www.geocities.com/HotSprings/Spa/7173/

Primal Psychotherapy A discussion of primal psychotherapy is provided on this personal Web page, written by Frederick Michael Farrar. Intending to provoke discussion, the author has posted his articles on primal psychotherapy that include a critique of early primal theory, primal theory and liberation, a reappraisal of the early primal model, and primal pain and narcissism.
http://www.users.globalnet.co.uk/~straus/Topic1.html

Primal Psychotherapy This useful site offers news, book reviews, a list of centers specializing in primal psychotherapy, questions and professional answers, links to related sites, articles, a newsletter, chat forums, articles on birth trauma, and special program information. Primal psychotherapy is discussed, including a description of conditions benefiting from this form of therapy.
http://home.att.net/~jspeyrer

PSYCHOANALYSIS

Academy for the Study of the Psychoanalytic Arts This site provides professionals with free online access to program papers, articles, and other ref-

erence materials on the topic of psychoanalysis and related fields. The organization's background, meeting, and membership information is also provided.
http://www.academyanalyticarts.org

 American Academy of Psychoanalysis The American Academy of Psychoanalysis offers links to the *Journal of the American Academy of Psychoanalysis,* selected articles from the *Academy Forum,* information on related meetings, a member roster, organization information, publications, and research details. http://aapsa.org

 American Psychoanalytic Association The American Psychoanalytic Association is a professional organization of psychoanalysts throughout the United States. Press releases, a calendar of events and meetings, general information about psychoanalysis, fellowship details, an online book store, a directory of psychoanalysts, *Journal of the American Psychoanalytic Association* abstracts, and an online newsletter are all available at the site. An extensive catalog of links to related online journals, institutes, societies, organizations, libraries, museums, and general sites is offered through the site. The Jourlit and Bookrev databases are also available in the "Online Bibliography" section, offering bibliographies of psychoanalytic journal articles, books, and book reviews. Information on obtaining journal reprints is supplied.
http://apsa.org

 American Psychoanalytic Association: Psychoanalysis A fact sheet on psychoanalysis, directed to consumers, is featured on this Web page. An overview is provided, along with a discussion of child and adolescent psychoanalysis, the origins and history of the method, and who can benefit from it. The term psychoanalyst is defined, and patients can access an online directory of psychoanalysts with membership in the American Psychoanalytic Association.
http://www.apsa.org/pubinfo/about.htm

 American Psychoanalytic Association: Psychoanalytic Literature More than 30,000 bibliographic citations are featured in this database of psychoanalytic journal articles, books, and book reviews. Visitors can search the database, view a list of included journals, and order reprints online.
http://www.apsa.org/lit/

 American Society of Psychoanalytic Physicians This society and Web site were created to provide a forum for psychoanalytically oriented psychiatrists and physicians. The purpose of the society, as well as a list of the officers and editorial board, is available.
http://pubweb.acns.nwu.edu/~chessick/aspp.htm

 Association for Psychoanalytic Medicine (APM) The non-profit Association for Psychoanalytic Medicine is an affiliate society of both the American Psychoanalytic Association and the International Psychoanalytic Association. Most members are graduates of the Columbia University Center for Psychoanalytic Training and Research. An extensive list of association-

sponsored lectures is provided, publications, such as *The Bulletin,* the journal of the APM, and *Shrink Ink,* the association's newsletter. There is information on awards, as well as a membership roster. Other links include postgraduate education information and mental health resources.
http://theapm.org

Center for Modern Psychoanalytic Studies The Center for Modern Psychoanalytic Studies is dedicated to training and research in psychoanalysis. Within this Web site, professionals will find reference materials, including online access to the table of contents to the journal, *Modern Psychoanalysis,* workshop bulletins, a book list, and conference listings.
http://www.cmps.edu

Cyberpsych.org This site offers descriptions and links to professional psychoanalytical societies and psychoanalytical forum discussions.
http://www.cyberpsych.org

International Psychoanalytical Association (IPA) Described as the world's primary psychoanalytic accrediting and regulatory body, the IPA offers numerous links at its Web site to the various conferences and congresses organized by the association, as well as links to special committees' synopses, a message forum, access to IPA newsletters, and other related links.
http://www.ipa.org.uk

Mental Health Net: Psychoanalysis and Psychodynamics A comprehensive listing of more than 80 Web resources on psychoanalysis and psychodynamic topics is provided here. Topics covered include theory, therapy, Jungian and Adlerian resources, Gestalt, and dream analysis. In addition to these topics, there are newsgroups, mailing lists, journals, and links to professional organizations. http://mentalhelp.net/guide/pro11.htm

National Psychological Association for Psychoanalysis (NPAP) Both professionals and patients will find useful information related to psychoanalysis on this Web page. For professionals, there is information on the NPAP Training Institute, including course descriptions and an online application. A "Virtual Lounge" offers discussion boards and a directory of psychoanalysts. There is also information on professional workshops, seminars, and conferences, as well as the table of contents from the NPAP journal, *The Psychoanalytic Review.* FAQs about psychotherapy and psychoanalysis and a list of related links are also available. http://www.npap.org/

New York University Medical Center: NYU Psychoanalytic Institute NYU Psychoanalytic Institute educates qualified individuals from a variety of professional backgrounds in the theory and practice of psychoanalysis. The site describes psychoanalysis, educational programs provided by the institute, and consultation and treatment services at the institute. Several links to related sites are available.
http://www.westnet.com/~pbrand

Psychoanalytic Therapy FAQ This Web site contains brief answers to over 30 questions about psychoanalytic therapy, with topics including benefits, role of the therapist and patient, dreams, the unconscious, different schools, length of treatment, cost, and choosing a therapist.
http://users.erols.com/henrywb/Psyan.html

TRANSACTIONAL ANALYSIS

European Association for Transactional Analysis (EATA) The professional resources available at this site include information on membership to the EATA, upcoming conferences, an online discussion forum, and reprints from articles in the EATA newsletter. In addition, there is a list of related Internet links.
http://www.eatanews.org/

International Transactional Analysis Association Created to provide information about transactional analysis, the International Transactional Analysis Association site offers a fact sheet on transactional analysis, along with a comprehensive list of related Web sites. Under the "News and Events" section, there is an exam calendar, as well as conference information. A publications catalog is also found.
http://www.itaa-net.org/

United States of America Transactional Analysis Association This organization is a community of professionals utilizing transactional analysis in "organizational, educational, and clinical settings, and for personal growth." A history of the organization, membership details, events notices, and articles are available at the site. Links are provided to transactional analysis associations, online publications, and educational sites. http://www.usataa.org/

6.5 SOMATIC THERAPIES

BIO- AND NEUROFEEDBACK

Association for Applied Psychophysiology and Biofeedback (AAPB) This nonprofit organization of clinicians, researchers, and educators is dedicated to advancing the knowledge of applied psychophysiology and biofeedback to improve health and the quality of life. General information at the site includes a description of biofeedback and psychophysiology, a list of common health problems helped by biofeedback, meetings and workshop information, membership information, a bibliography of recent research articles related to biofeedback and psychophysiology, links to related sites, an online bookstore, and content lists of AAPB publications. The site offers a directory of biofeedback practitioners and a forum for asking questions of biofeedback experts.
(fee-based) http://www.aapb.org

Bio Research Institute: Biofeedback An overview of biofeedback is offered on this site. The process is described, along with a typical session, and monitoring tools are examined, including temperature, the electromyograph, electrodermal activity, heart rate, respiration, and the electroencephalograph. The many applications of biofeedback are outlined, such as anxiety disorders, depression, and stress.
http://www.7hz.com/what.html

Biofeedback Network This online network of biofeedback and neurofeedback resources offers access to a wide variety of related sites, including association listings, equipment training and technology, treatment centers, practitioners, and employment and equipment-related classified ads.
http://www.biofeedback.net

EEG Spectrum International: Neurofeedback Research and Clinical Services Neurofeedback research and clinical services are the subject of this encyclopedic site, which offers separate menus for the public and professional audiences. General resources pertaining to specific disorders for which neurofeedback may assist functioning are compiled and easily accessed. Articles on the origins of biofeedback and current applicable analysis are included. The site also contains information on training courses for professionals, a site-specific search engine, and additional helpful resources.
http://www.eegspectrum.com

Neurofeedback Yellow Pages Worldwide At Neurofeedback Yellow Pages Worldwide, the user may click anywhere inside a country's border to view a listing of neurofeedback practitioners in that region. Neurofeedback practitioners may add, modify, or remove information as necessary.
http://www.thegrid.net/dakaiser/nfyp

Self-Improvement Online: Biofeedback Sites This site contains a listing of Web sites offering information on biofeedback and related therapies. Online articles, organizations, prevention and self-help resources, and institutes are included at the site.
http://www.selfgrowth.com/biofeedback.html

Society for Neuronal Regulation (SNR) This organization consists of professionals interested in neurofeedback training and research. Site resources include a glossary, a reference center, a listing of neurofeedback providers, conference information, and a neurofeedback archive of online abstracts and papers from selected SNR meetings. Information on the society's *Journal of Neurotherapy* and the opportunity to download full-text articles directly from the site are available.
http://www.snr-jnt.org

ELECTROCONVULSIVE THERAPY (ECT)

American Academy of Family Physicians (AAFP): Electroconvulsive Therapy for Severe Depression This site answers important questions about ECT. Visitors will find a list of conditions treated with ECT, a description of the procedure, common precautions and preparations for the procedure, a description of the ECT session, and a discussion of possible side effects and outcome. http://familydoctor.org/handouts/058.html

American Psychiatric Association (APA): Electroconvulsive Therapy Written in easy-to-understand terms, this consumer brochure offers information on how ECT works, indications for its use, and possible effectiveness. Risks associated with treatment, side effects, and myths about brain damage are addressed. http://www.psych.org/public_info/ect~1.cfm

Electroshock Both a patient and professional center are available from this site's main page, which provides research reports on ECT efficacy and use in a variety of clinical situations. Patient and professional questions and answers, fact sheets for healthcare consumers, information on ECT training, and details on a variety of useful publications and multimedia materials are provided. http://www.electroshock.org/

University of Pennsylvania: Health System (UPHS): Commonly Asked Questions Concerning Electroconvulsive Therapy The site answers common questions on ECT, discussing the process of ECT, safety, common side effects, risks and benefits, number of treatments, when to stop ECT, testing prior to treatment, the treatment plan, therapeutic strategies after the initial course of treatments, and maintenance ECT. http://www.med.upenn.edu/ect/ectfaq.htm

What You Should Know about Electroconvulsive Therapy This site, presented by the Committee for Truth in Psychiatry, attempts to warn visitors of possible dangers associated with ECT. A prototype informed consent statement, a description of shock therapy, and articles discouraging this form of therapy are available at the site. http://www.harborside.com/~equinox/ect.htm

EXERCISE THERAPY

American Psychological Association (APA): Exercise Therapy A full-text article on exercise therapy for psychiatric patients is provided on this Web page. Originally published in *Professional Psychology: Research and Practice,* this article reviews research on the use of exercise therapy for a variety of disorders, including depression, anxiety, developmental disabilities, and schizophrenia. Recommendations are made for future research needs and for clinicians interested in using exercise therapy with their patients. A bibliography is included. http://www.apa.org/journals/pro/pro303275.html

Exercise Against Depression Originally published in the October 1998 issue of *The Physician and Sports Medicine,* this full-text article examines the use of exercise to combat depression. The article covers the exercise-depression link and the physiological reasons for why exercise works. Recommendations are made for establishing an exercise program that includes realistic expectations, integrating exercise with other therapies, and maintaining vigilance. References are provided.

http://www.physsportsmed.com/issues/1998/10Oct/artal.htm

 President's Council on Physical Fitness and Sports (PCPFS): Exercise and Mental Health The influence of exercise on mental health is explored in this article, originally published in the *PCPFS Research Digest*. The article examines anxiety reduction following exercise, exercise and depression, and other variables associated with mental health such as positive mood, self-esteem, and restful sleep. A bibliography is provided, along with a glossary of terms.

http://www.fitness.gov/activity/activity4/mentalhealth.htm

LIGHT THERAPY

 Enviro-Med: Articles on Bright Light Therapy for Seasonal Affective Disorder A collection of approximately 10 articles related to seasonal affective disorder and bright light therapy is featured on this Web page. Half of the articles have hyperlinks leading to the full-text article. Topics include the use of light therapy for premenstrual depression, sleep and mood disorders, and seasonal affective disorder.

http://www.bio-light.com/articles.html

 Light Therapy Center Information is provided at this Web address on the use of light therapy for premenstrual syndrome, migraines, and seasonal affective disorder. The site offers articles on light therapy, as well as scientific studies of photic stimulation, and a bibliography.

http://www.lightmask.com/

PSYCHOSURGERY

 Massachusetts General Hospital: Psychosurgery A full-text article on psychosurgery is provided on this Web page. Topics covered include a historical background on psychosurgery, the anatomic and physiologic rationale for psychosurgery, and the careful selection of patients. Four surgical procedures are described: anterior cingulotomy, subcaudate tractotomy, limbic leucotomy, and anterior capsulotomy. Indications, results, and complications associated with each procedure are discussed. A bibliography is included.

http://neurosurgery.mgh.harvard.edu/psysurg.htm

mylifepath.com: Psychosurgery A patient guide to psychosurgery is presented on this Web page. The guide offers a definition, along with the purpose of psychosurgery and precautions. Lobotomy and bilateral cingulotomy are described. Preparation, after care, risks, and normal results from cingulotomy are explained. A glossary of key terms, recommendations for further reading, and organizations for additional information are provided.
http://www.mylifepath.com/article/gale/100266450

TRANSCRANIAL MAGNETIC STIMULATION (TMS)

Transcranial Magnetic Stimulation An online movie demonstrating the spread of cortical electrical brain activity following transcranial magnetic stimulation is shown, and numerous links to detailed information regarding the principles and safety of this new technique are found. Terminology, journal articles, current research, and further Internet connections are provided.
http://www.biomag.helsinki.fi/tms

Transcranial Magnetic Stimulation in Psychiatry The principles of transcranial magnetic stimulation are described and the safety and efficacy of extracranial techniques are examined at this page, which details new potentials for its use in the treatment of mental illness.
http://www.musc.edu/tmsmirror/intro/layintro.html

Transcranial Magnetic Stimulation: Its Potential in Treating Neuropsychiatric Disorders A detailed description of TMS is explored at this Web site, and recent clinical studies are outlined, including the results of patients found to be refractory to other treatments. Published reports of the use of TMS in posttraumatic stress disorder patients and the limited research on the therapy as applied to TMS and Parkinson's disease are mentioned. Side effects and the future of TMS are discussed, and references to additional reading for clinicians are also included. http://www.mcleanhospital.org/psychupdate/psyup-l-4.htm

6.6 PSYCHOPHARMACOLOGY/DRUG THERAPY

GENERAL RESOURCES

Internet Mental Health: Medications An A-to-Z listing of psychiatric medications is provided at this Web site, developed by the Canadian-based Internet Mental Health. Each drug listing provides information on its pharmacology, indications, contraindications, precautions while taking the drug, adverse effects, proper dosage, and symptoms and treatment for overdose. Visitors to the site will find a useful translation feature, which offers English to Spanish, Italian, French, and German language conversions. In addition, a link is pro-

vided for current research on the drug. At the bottom of the left-side column of drugs are links for related articles, booklets, and Internet links.
http://www.mentalhealth.com/fr30.html

ANTICHOLINERGICS/ANTICONVULSANTS

Bandolier: Anticonvulsants   From the *Bandolier,* this article provides information about the use of anticonvulsants in the treatment of head injury patients. The site describes studies and results. Graphics and references are included. http://www.jr2.ox.ac.uk/bandolier/band51/b51-3.html

Healthnotes: Anticonvulsants   This site provides information about anticonvulsants, a class of drugs used to prevent seizures in people with epilepsy. The site provides drug and brand names and details possible interactions with dietary supplements. Supplements discussed include biotin, carnitine, folic acid, melatonin, vitamin D, and vitamin K.
http://www.puritan.com/healthnotes/Drug/Anticonvulsants.htm

Healthwell.com: Anticonvulsants   The interactions of anticonvulsants with dietary supplements is described on this Web page. Depletion of biotin, carnitine, folic acid, vitamin B12, melatonin, vitamin D, and vitamin K is discussed in relation to several anticonvulsant drugs. References are provided.
http://www.healthwell.com/healthnotes/Drug/Anticonvulsants.cfm

How Anticholinergics Work   A hypothesis regarding anticholinergic activity of antipsychotics is presented at this Web site. Also outlined is the normal anatomy and physiology of chemical brain cell communication and excess dopamine activity that produces the symptoms of psychosis. Synapses, neurotransmitter functions, and symptoms of malfunction are reviewed. Examples of drugs that increase dopamine activity and possibly produce symptoms of anxiety or psychosis are discussed, as are the Parkinsonian or extra-pyramidal side effects common in those treated with dopamine receptor blockade. A summary of adjunct therapy with anticholinergics to prevent muscular rigidity and tremor is presented. http://www.nmhc.co.uk/moa-proc.htm

Lithium and the Anticonvulsants in Bipolar Disorder   Lithium and the anticonvulsants for use in treatment of bipolar disorder are discussed on this site, hosted by the American College of Neuropsychopharmacology. Treatment with lithium is examined in detail, including its antidepressant effects, predictors of response, and adverse effects. A similar analysis is provided for treatment of bipolar disorder with carbamazepine (CBZ), valproate, and lamotrigine.
http://www.acnp.org/G4/GN401000106/CH.html

Louisiana State University: Anticonvulsants   This site contains a lecture on anticonvulsants that may be downloaded.
http://www.toxicology.lsumc.edu/ahpharm/anticonv.htm

MEDLINEplus: Anticholinergics/Antispasmodics (Systemic) Covering the group of medicines of anticholinergics/antispasmodics, this site offers information on the drugs. Brand names, the purpose of the medications, dosage forms, and considerations before taking the medicine are outlined. Possible drug interactions and other medical conditions that may affect the use of anticholinergics/antispasmodics are described. Proper dosing, what to do if one misses a dose, precautions, and possible side effects are explained.
http://www.nlm.nih.gov/medlineplus/druginfo/anticholinergicsantispasmodics202049.html

MEDLINEplus: Anticonvulsants Intended for consumers, this site offers detailed information on anticonvulsants. The site lists the brand names of the drugs, explains how the drug works, and the risks associated with it. Proper use of the drug is also explained, along with precautions while taking the drug and the drug's side effects.
http://www.nlm.nih.gov/medlineplus/druginfo/anticonvulsantshydantoinsystem202052.html

MEDLINEplus: Dione (Systemic) A consumer's guide to the anticonvulsant drug dione is provided on this site. The drug is not commercially available in the United States or Canada. A description of the drug's use and purpose is provided, along with proper dosage, risks, side effects, and precautions to take while using the medicine.
http://www.nlm.nih.gov/medlineplus/druginfo/anticonvulsantsdionesystemic202051.html

MEDLINEplus: Valproic Acid Detailed information on valproic acid is provided on this site for consumers. A description of the drug and its purpose is provided, along with a list of brand names in the United States and Canada. In addition, proper use of the medicine, risks associated with taking it, proper dosage, and precautions while taking the drug are covered. Side effects are also described.
http://www.nlm.nih.gov/medlineplus/druginfo/valproicacidsystemic202588.html

PainCarePlus: Anti-Convulsant Medications Indications of anticonvulsants in seizure disorders and special instructions and precautions for the most commonly prescribed anticonvulsant therapies are described at the Web address. For further physician knowledge and patient information, an adverse event list is included. http://www.paincareplus.com/anti-convulsant_meds.html

ANTIDEPRESSANTS

American Academy of Family Physicians (AAFP): Antidepressants A patient fact sheet on antidepressants is provided on this site. The fact sheet explains the purpose of antidepressants, how they work, and how long to take one. Brief descriptions of the different types of antidepressants are offered, including tricyclics, SSRIs (selective serotonin reuptake inhibitors), and MAOIs (monoamine oxidase inhibitors). Potential interactions of antidepressants with other medications are also explained.
http://familydoctor.org/handouts/012.html

Selective Serotonin Reuptake Inhibitors (SSRIs) This site contains several interrelated abstracts. An update on SSRIs is provided that summarizes the safety, efficacy, and common side effects. In addition, the selection of SSRIs as the treatment of choice in instances of eating disorders, premenstrual dysphoria, panic disorder, depression, and obsessive-compulsive disorder is discussed. Links to additional article abstracts highlighting the progress made with specific SSRIs, further information on mechanism of action, and SSRI selection recommendations are found.
http://www.biopsychiatry.com/ssrispec.htm

Serotonin and Judgment By selectively restoring serotonin's activity level in patients with depression, researchers hope to prevent impulsive and destructive behaviors that often lead to suicide. This online *Brain Briefing* from the Society for Neuroscience outlines current study that may lead to the use of brain imaging techniques for identification of those at greatest risk for destructive behavior. An explanation of possible new insights into the mechanisms of serotonin and the identification of components that play a role in defective serotonin processing are presented.
http://www.sfn.org/briefings/serotonin.html

ANTIPSYCHOTICS/NEUROLEPTICS

Dopamine Receptor Blockade: Antipsychotic Drugs The chemical structure of various typical and atypical antipsychotics and their properties allowing them to block dopamine receptors are discussed at the Web site. Features of typical antipsychotics, helpful in alleviating the positive symptoms of schizophrenia, are discussed, as well as the atypical antipsychotics, which lack the undesirable side effects present with the traditional antipsychotics. A page summarizing the clinical application of dopamine discusses the splitting of cognitive function in schizophrenia, symptoms hypothesized to be from dopaminergic dysfunction, and the DSM-IV categories of schizophrenia.
http://www.williams.edu/imput/synapse/pages/IIIB5.htm

Duke University Medical Center: Antipsychotics A patient fact sheet on neuroleptics, also called antipsychotics, is offered on this site. The purpose of the medications is described, as well as brand names, side effects, and when to call the doctor.
http://psychiatry.mc.duke.edu/CMRIS/ED/Medication/Neuroleptics.htm

Neuroleptics Information regarding formulations, dosage, and pharmacologic considerations of administration of neuroleptics is outlined at this Neuroland Web site. Phenothiazines, thioxanthenenes, butyrophenones, and heterocyclics are all included categories.
http://neuroland.com/psy/neuroleptics.htm

Newer Generation Antipsychotic Drugs Limitations to traditional antipsychotics and an introduction to the more novel drug treatments in schizo-

phrenia are reviewed, with a focus on effectively treating both the positive and negative symptoms of the illness. Extrapyramidal, anticholinergic, anti-adrenergic, and other side effects of traditional neuroleptics are summarized, in addition to the recent advances in the improvement of adverse event profiles.
http://www.nlpra.org.hk/1stSymposium/NGAD.html

University of Iowa: Virtual Hospital: Atypical Antipsychotics A clinical discussion of atypical antipsychotics is provided on this site. The term is defined, and characteristics of the atypical antipsychotics are outlined. Receptors and antipsychotic effects are discussed, along with receptors and adverse effects. Detailed information on clozapine, risperidone, olanzapine, quetiapine, ziprasidone, and sertindole (awaiting FDA approval), including their pharmacokinetics, efficacy, use with schizophrenia, adverse effects, and drug interactions, is featured. A full bibliography is included.
http://www.vh.org/Providers/Conferences/CPS/04.html

ANXIOLYTICS

Benzodiazepines A listing of the most commonly prescribed benzodiazepines is offered, with additional information regarding duration of action, detection in urine, psychological and physical effects, and symptoms of withdrawal.
http://www.adhl.org/benzodi.html

Future Directions in Anxiolytic Pharmacotherapy This article abstract, an excerpt from a major psychiatric medical journal, offers summary format information on the current state of development regarding new anxiolytic alternatives to benzodiazepines in the treatment of anxiety. Mention of their beneficial targeting of neurotransmitter receptors and citing of partial antagonists with beneficial clinical profiles are found. Serotonin receptor subtype targeting and simultaneous targeting of multiple receptor sites in future treatment are discussed. Additional therapies and the future of the neurobiological regulation of anxiety are summarized.
http://www.biopsychiatry.com/anxfut.html

Medication Profiles: Benzodiazepines (BZs) This Web page, courtesy of Anxieties.com, provides information on the benefits, side effects, and disadvantages of benzodiazepine usage. A chart outlining the possible symptoms associated with drug withdrawal, suggestions for dosage tapering, and individual profiles of the more commonly prescribed benzodiazepines are provided.
http://www.anxieties.com/8Meds/panic_medication_BZs.htm

CLINICAL PHARMACOLOGY

American College of Neuropsychopharmacology (ACNP) To further education and research in the field, the American College of Neuropsychopharmacology provides information on panel, poster, and study-group abstract submissions; the Archives dedicated to psychopharmacology at Vanderbilt University; and the organization's annual meeting. Current and archived issues of the online *ACNP Bulletin* are available in Adobe Acrobat format, and the site's scientific link directs visitors to a searchable, online version of the ACNP professional publication, *Neuropsychopharmacology*. Related advocacy affiliates and scientific links are provided.

http://www.acnp.org

Harvard University: Psychopharmacology Algorithms Project This site allows professionals to view and download the computerized algorithms created by this project. The depression and schizophrenia algorithms are complete, and these programs provide advice and guidance on drug therapy in various psychoses. Confidence ratings inform as to the quality of research evidence to fortify each step of the algorithm. A publications bibliography is also included. http://www.mhc.com/Algorithms

MedWebPlus: Psychopharmacology MedWebPlus supplies links to journal titles, abstracts, and some full-text articles, listing articles by subject. Full journal information is also provided. Psychopharmacology topics include bibliographies, consumer health, history of medicine, internship and residency resources, neurology, neuropharmacology, patient education, periodicals, pharmacology, psychiatry, psychophysiology, religion and medicine, societies, scientific societies, and substance-related disorders.

http://www.medwebplus.com/subject/Psychopharmacology.html

Neurology Pharmacotherapeutics This online medicinal chemistry tutorial provides information on general and local anesthetic agents, opioid analgesics, and antiseizure agents. Stages of general anesthesia, specific agents, and chemical structural components are examined.

http://wizard.pharm.wayne.edu/medchem/pha422.html

Psychopharmacology Links Resources provided at this site include links to psychopharmacology forums, search tools, substance abuse resources, basic pharmacology information related to antidepressants, publications, journals, articles, associations, and pediatric psychopharmacology information.

http://www.links.co.nz/culture/drugs/psycho.htm

Psychopharmacology Tips Visitors to this site will find general information on the psychopharmacological treatment of psychiatric disorders based on a chat forum of therapists at the site. Specific drugs and psychiatric disorders can be chosen to include in a site search, and users can also search by keyword. Links are available to another chat forum, Internet resources in psychiatry and psychopharmacology, and a list of answers to questions posted by patients and caregivers. http://www.dr-bob.org/tips/

University of Iowa: Clinical Psychopharmacology Nearly 50 major topics related to clinical psychopharmacology are explored through this menu

provided by the University of Iowa College of Pharmacy, such as specific disorder treatments, dosing, primary therapeutic action, and side effects.
http://www.vh.org/Providers/Conferences/CPS/contents.html

University of Iowa: Pharmacological Management of Organic Agitation   This peer-reviewed, clinical psychopharmacology seminar reviews the pharmacologic management of behavioral disturbances secondary to delirium. Antipsychotics, treatment of acute and chronic delirium, studies comparing benzodiazepines to antipsychotics, and summaries on lithium and anticonvulsants are all included. An outcome table for measurement of efficacy of treatment with non-neuroleptics is provided.
http://www.vh.org/Providers/Conferences/CPS/02.html

Drug Databases

Clinical Pharmacology   At this electronic drug reference site, professionals and laypersons can search the database for drug information, available as a brief summary or mini-monograph.
(free registration) http://www.cponline.gsm.com

Internet Mental Health: Medications   Resources on more than 150 psychiatric medications are available at this site. Information on each drug, taken from Canadian monographs, includes pharmacology, indications, contraindications, warnings, precautions, adverse effects, overdose, dosage, supplied dose, and any details on current research related to the drug. The site also offers links to sites containing additional drug information and an online medical dictionary. http://www.mentalhealth.com/fr30.html

National Institute of Mental Health (NIMH): Medications   This address offers an online Medications booklet from the National Institute of Mental Health, designed to help patients understand how and why drugs can be used as part of the treatment for mental health problems. An introduction to drugs and their use in the treatment of mental illnesses, important considerations about drug therapy, and important questions for a patient's doctor are found at the site. Detailed information is available on antipsychotic, anti-manic, antidepressant, and anti-anxiety medications. A discussion of medications in children, the elderly, and pregnant or nursing women is available, as well as an index of medications listing generic and trade names and a bibliography of reference articles. http://www.nimh.nih.gov/publicat/medicate.cfm

Neuro Med: Pharmacology   Dosage information on neuropharmacotherapies is provided at this Neuroland Web site. With more than 30 medication categories including antidepressants, anticonvulsants, muscle relaxants, and spasticity treatments, practitioners can quickly scan administration and adverse event information. For each pharmaceutical choice, alternative treatments and related readings may be obtained.
http://www.neuroland.com/neuro_med/index.htm

Project Inform: Psychoactive Drugs Taken from the *HIV Drug Book,* this site contains concise explanations of drugs used to treat more common psychiatric disorders, such as anxiety, depression, insomnia, psychosis, and mania. Drug categories and specific drugs are listed, and links to fact sheets describing the type of drug, treatment information, and side effects are provided. http://www.thebody.com/pinf/drugbkix.html

Psychopharmacology and Drug References This site offers users the opportunity to locate drug information by generic name, including pharmacology, indications, contraindications, warnings, precautions, adverse effects, overdose information, typical dosages, supplied dosages in typical pill forms, and research information. Visitors can also access links to newsgroups, mailing lists, journals, publications, research papers, professional organizations and centers, and other Internet resources. http://www.mentalhelp.net/guide/pro22.htm

Drug Interactions

drkoop.com: Drug Checker This site features a very useful tool for researching information about one or more drugs and checking for interactions between them. Research results offer hyperlinks for additional information on each drug and the option to check the listed drugs for interactions with each other. The information provided written in laymen's terms, includes a brief description, who should not take the drug, how to take the drug, side effects, and interactions. Additional clinical information can be found through links at the top of the page for warnings, side effects, pharmacology, lactation, and pregnancy. http://www.drugchecker.drkoop.com/apps/drugchecker/DrugSearch?cob=drkoop

McMaster University: Drug Interactions Drug interaction information specific to psychoactive drugs is provided on this site. More than 75 tables are provided indicating interactions between selective serotonin reuptake inhibitors (SSRI), monoamine oxidase inhibitors (MAOI), reversible inhibitors of monoamine oxydase (RIMA), tricyclic antidepressants (TCA), other (such as nefazodone), and mood stabilizers. Each table describes the evidence for the combination, the structural and biochemical mechanisms involved in the interaction, and the clinical implications of interactions. http://www-fhs.mcmaster.ca/direct/phys/pydit.html

Mood Stabilizers

Internet Mental Health: Lithium Carbonate A Canadian monograph for lithium carbonate is provided on this site by Internet Mental Health. Information presented on the site includes the drug's brand names, pharmacology, indications, contraindications, precautions while taking the drug, drug interactions,

and adverse effects. Proper dosage, along with symptoms and treatment for overdose is also described.
http://www.mentalhealth.com/drug/p30-l02.html

Pharmacology Links to information on six mood stabilizing drugs are offered at this site of the HealthCentral Rx Online Pharmacy. Visitors will find complete warnings and prescribing information, with access to clinical pharmacology, inactive ingredients, mechanisms of action, indications, precautions, patient information, and a pregnancy risk category. The links also feature drug interactions, a system-by-system guide to side effects, and dosage and administration tables for all included drugs.
http://www.walkers.org/noframes/stabilizers.htm

6.7 Clinical Practice

Clinical Guidelines and Practice

American Academy of Child and Adolescent Psychiatry (AACAP): Clinical Practice This site describes activities of the American Academy of Child and Adolescent Psychiatry aimed at improving clinical practice for both professionals and patients. Practice parameters and systems of care developed by the academy, information on managed care issues, resources on current procedural terminology (CPT) codes, and efforts to preserve psychotherapy as the core of child and adolescent psychiatry are described at the site.
http://www.aacap.org/clinical

American Psychiatric Association (APA): Clinical Practice This site links users to APA resources, including those for early-career psychiatrists. Other sections of the site include links to professional development resources, as well as a final report from the APA Task Force on Quality Indicators. Resources are provided on mental retardation and developmental disabilities, the APA Practice Research Network, APA delivery systems and special-interest caucuses, and cross-cultural APA resources. Connections to many resources for practice management, the Federation of State Medical Boards, and a worldwide directory of psychiatric organizations are also available from the site.
http://www.psych.org/pract_of_psych/index.cfm

American Psychiatric Association (APA): Practice Guidelines Practice guidelines from the American Psychiatric Association are available at this site including those for the treatment of patients with delirium, panic disorder, bipolar disorder, eating disorders, substance abuse disorders, Alzheimer's disease and other dementias, schizophrenia, nicotine dependence, and major depressive disorder. Guidelines also cover psychiatric evaluation of adults. Users can also access quick reference guides on treating delirium and schizophrenia, patient

and family guides related to delirium and smoking cessation, and ordering information for print guidelines.
http://www.psych.org/clin_res/prac_guide.cfm

American Psychiatric Association (APA): Practice Research Network (PRN)   The Practice Research Network is composed of psychiatrists cooperating in the collection of data and conduct of research studies on issues relating to clinical and health services delivery. The site offers a mission statement, research objectives, details of study collaborations, information on joining the PRN, details concerning PRN activities, and connections to psychiatric news updates and related resources.
http://www.psych.org/res_res/background.cfm

Expert Consensus Guidelines   Visitors to this site can download expert consensus guidelines for the treatment of posttraumatic stress disorder, schizophrenia, agitation in older persons with dementia, obsessive-compulsive disorder, and bipolar disorder. Guidelines for psychiatric and behavioral problems in mental retardation, attention deficit/hyperactivity disorder, and the treatment of depression in women are available. A description of methodology used in developing the guidelines, patient and family guides, conference details, and links to related sites are also available at this address. These guidelines have been supported by unrestricted educational grants from Abbott Laboratories, Bristol-Myers Squibb, Eli Lilly and Co., Janssen Pharmaceutical, Inc., Novartis Pharmaceuticals Corporation, Ortho-McNeil Pharmaceutical, Pfizer, Inc., Solvay Pharmaceuticals, and Zeneca Pharmaceuticals.
http://www.psychguides.com

National Guideline Clearinghouse (NGC): Mental Disorders   Close to 90 guidelines are available for a variety of mental disorders, courtesy of the National Guideline Clearinghouse. Categories include sleep disorders; eating disorders; mood disorders; anxiety disorders; substance-related disorders; delirium, dementia, amnestic, and cognitive disorders; sexual and gender disorders; mental disorders diagnosed in childhood; and schizophrenia and other disorders with psychotic features. Users may opt to view brief summaries, complete summaries, or the complete text of the chosen guidelines and practice parameters.
http://www.guideline.gov/FRAMESETS/search_fs.asp?view=disease

National Guideline Clearinghouse (NGC): Mental Health Treatment and Intervention   With over 70 clinical practice guidelines individually accessible, this page of the National Guideline Clearinghouse offers guidelines regarding behavioral health treatment and interventions. Parameters specific to mental health services, personality assessment, psychological techniques, psychiatric somatic therapies, behavioral sciences, psychotherapy, and psychological tests may be accessed. Users may opt to view brief summaries, complete summaries, or the complete text of the chosen guidelines and practice parameters.
http://www.guideline.gov/FRAMESETS/search_fs.asp?view=treatment

National Guideline Clearinghouse (NGC): Nervous System Diseases
Eighty clinical guidelines relating to nervous system diseases are available at this site. Visitors can also access guidelines on related subconcepts of nervous system diseases, including neuromuscular diseases, neurological manifestations, nervous system neoplasms, mental retardation, nervous system abnormalities, central nervous system diseases, and peripheral nervous system diseases.
http://www.guideline.gov/FRAMESETS/search_fs.asp?view=disease

University of Groningen: Department of Psychiatry: Schedules for Clinical Assessment in Neuropsychiatry (SCAN) Schedules for Clinical Assessment in Neuropsychiatry, developed within the World Health Organization, offers tools and manuals for "assessing, measuring, and classifying psychopathology and behavior associated with the major psychiatric disorders in adult life." This site offers a list of SCAN training centers worldwide, a bibliography of SCAN publications, answers to frequently asked questions, and a link to the World Health Organization SCAN home page. A discussion of SCAN includes a detailed description of methods used in assessment, SCAN software, suggested reference materials, a list of advisory committee members, and a short description of SCAN training courses.
http://www.psychiatry.nl/?4

MANAGED CARE

American Psychiatric Association (APA:) Managed Care Practice Management More than 20 links are available at this address, offering access to federal agencies, associations, education resources, institutes, organizations, and other information sources related specifically to mental health and/or managed care. The site serves as a comprehensive source of information on managed care. http://www.psych.org/pract_of_psych/managed_care.cfm

Knowledge Exchange Network: Managed Care This Web page features more than 20 links related to managed care. Topics covered include government agencies, organizations, and various publications on mental health and managed care. Each link has a short description of the site.
http://www.mentalhealth.org/links/managedcare.htm

Psychotherapy Finances and Managed Care Strategies This Web site was created to aid behavioral health providers with the financial issues in practice and managed care. Updated news items relating to managed care, social work, and other mental health related topics are provided. Articles from the *Psychotherapy Finances* newsletter are available online. There is an online store, conference information, links to other therapists' Web sites, a provider directory, and a link to a fact sheet on strategies related to mental health provision and finances. http://www.psyfin.com

Other Topical Resources for Psychiatry

7.1 Abuse, Neglect, and Domestic Violence

About.com: Abuse/Incest Support About.com offers current news and policy information related to domestic abuse, as well as a guide to Internet resources related to domestic abuse and violence. Articles, therapy and professional resources, information and support for survivors of domestic abuse, hotline numbers, prevention resources, statistics, and general information on different forms of abuse are cataloged at this site.
http://incestabuse.about.com/health/incestabuse/?once=true&

Administration on Aging: National Elder Abuse Incidence Study The final report of the National Elder Abuse Incidence Study, dated September 1998, is posted on this Web page. The report can be read online or downloaded in Adobe Acrobat PDF format. The study design and methods are enumerated, as well as the findings including a comparison of reported and unreported abuse and neglect, and characteristics of victims. References are provided.
http://www.aoa.gov/abuse/report/default.htm

American Bar Association (ABA): Commission on Domestic Violence This support site offers a directory of nationwide coalitions against domestic violence, abuse screening information, a link to publications on news and educational materials for affected persons, information on events, national support groups, and a fact sheet presenting statistics on violence against women. Also included is a bibliography on various aspects of sexual assault, as well as discussions of men and women's issues, psychosocial, elderly and medicolegal topics, a list of related sites, and general information about the ACOG.
http://www.abanet.org/domviol/home.html

American College of Obstetricians and Gynecologists (ACOG): Violence Against Women This support site offers a directory of nationwide coalitions against domestic violence, abuse screening information, a link to publications on news and educational materials for affected persons, information on events, national support groups, and a fact sheet presenting statistics on violence against women. Also included is a bibliography on various aspects of sexual assault; discussions of men and women's issues; information on psy-

chosocial, elderly, and medicolegal topics; a list of related sites; and general information about the ACOG.
http://www.acog.org/from_home/departments/dept_web.cfm?recno=17

American Professional Society on the Abuse of Children (APSAC)
The mission of APSAC is to ensure that everyone affected by child maltreatment receives the best possible professional response. This professional society's site provides information on the society itself, membership information, legislative activities, professional education, state chapters, and public affairs, as well as current news. Information on the society's publications, such as the *APSAC Advisor,* and the *APSAC Guidelines for Practice,* the *APSAC Handbook on Child Maltreatment* is available online. There is also information for those interested in donating to the society.
http://www.apsac.org

Association for the Treatment of Sexual Abusers (ATSA) The
Association for the Treatment of Sexual Abusers is an international organization focused specifically on the prevention of sexual abuse through effective management of sex offenders. The site provides membership information, the table of contents for the journal *Sexual Abuse,* graduate research awards and ATSA research grants, position statements, conference information, internship and fellowship opportunities, employment opportunities, and book lists.
http://www.atsa.com

Center for Mental Health Resources (CMHR): Abuse Resources As a
service of the CMHR, this site provides a variety of links related to abuse-specific topics. Comprehensive site connections include the National Clearinghouse on Child Abuse and Neglect Information, Abused Children with Disabilities, and the Borderline Personality Disorder Sanctuary. Links at this site offer information on topics that range from forming one's own self-help group to communicating via real-time with other victims of abuse. This is a notable site for abuse survivors.
http://www.mentalhealth.org/links/abuse.htm

Child Abuse Prevention Network This site offers resources for reporting
child abuse, as well as links to sites offering discussions of survivors' issues and childhood violence, newsgroups, federal resources, and organizations engaged in prevention activities. Parenting resources, the National Data Archive on Child Abuse and Neglect, and general child abuse Web sites are accessible from this site. http://child.cornell.edu/capn.html

Domestic Violence Internet links to domestic violence resources are
provided on this site, courtesy of the nonprofit organization, Safe Horizon. There are more than 150 sites listed for resources categorized as international, domestic, and state and local. There are also police domestic violence resources within the United States. Short descriptions of each site are provided.
http://www.dvsheltertour.org/links.html

Elder Abuse Prevention Hosted by Elder Abuse Prevention, this Web site offers an information and resource guide. The guide offers detailed explanations of what constitutes elder abuse, how to recognize it, who must report it, and what to do.
http://www.oaktrees.org/elder/

Family Violence and Sexual Assault Institute (FVSAI) FVSAI is a nonprofit resource center offering a clearinghouse of categorized references and unpublished papers related to all aspects of family violence and sexual assault. Information is available on conferences, training, publications, and membership. Services listed at the site include a categorized reference database; program development, consultation, and assistance; a speaker database; and professional workshops and certified training. Some resources are only available to those with a current membership, which requires an annual fee.
http://www.fvsai.org

Feminist Majority Foundation: Violence Against Women Internet Resources This list of Internet resources offers links to sites presenting general information, emotional abuse resources, research, organizations, shelters, and information on stalking and self-defense. Each link is accompanied by a short paragraph providing a description of the site.
http://www.feminist.org/gateway/vs_exec2.html

Men and Domestic Violence Index Chat transcripts, quotes, and other information sources on issues relating to men and domestic violence are available at this site. Topics include husband battering, child abuse, other domestic violence, other male abuse, and links to related references.
http://www.vix.com/pub/men/domestic-index.html

National Center for Missing and Exploited Children (NCMEC) The National Center for Missing and Exploited Children, a nonprofit organization, is the nation's resource center for child protection. Organizational resources include program and activity details, new technology descriptions, and contact information. Visitors can search for child photos, report a possible sighting of a missing child, find donating and volunteering information, read success stories, and access news and events details. Information at the site is available in both English and Spanish.
http://www.missingkids.org

National Clearinghouse on Child Abuse and Neglect This organization provides information, advocacy, and support for sexual assault. Within this site are links to conference and advocacy news, membership information, legal advice and court case summaries, and articles on sexual assault and violence. There is also a section on sexual assault myths and facts, as well as a list of related Web sites.
http://www.calib.com/nccanch

National Coalition Against Domestic Violence A broad array of information related to domestic violence is provided on this site. There is a fact sheet on domestic violence, guidelines for starting a community shelter, and a registry of women who have died from domestic violence. A "Getting Help" section offers a hotline, local organizations, and fact sheets related to developing a personal safety plan, getting support, workplace guidelines, and legal guidelines. Under the "Resources" section, there is contact information for organizations at the state, international, and national levels. There are also suggested readings, a comprehensive listing of links, and a product catalog, which includes some free publications.
http://www.ncadv.org/

National Coalition Against Sexual Assault This organization provides information, advocacy, and support for sexual assault. Within this site are links to conference and advocacy news, membership information, legal advice and court case summaries, and articles on sexual assault and violence. There is also a section on sexual assault myths and facts, as well as a list of related Web sites.
http://dreamingdesigns.com/other/indexncasa.html

National Data Archive on Child Abuse and Neglect Sponsored by the Family Life Development Center of Cornell University, this site offers research data on child abuse and neglect. Data sets, available for a fee, cover topics such as adoption and foster care, runaway and homeless youth, the maltreatment of children with disabilities, and family violence. Some data can be viewed online for free. There are also free publications such as a newsletter, an investigator's handbook, and a conference summary on child welfare. Information on researcher training, as well as an Internet discussion group can be found on the site. (some features fee-based) http://www.ndacan.cornell.edu/

National Institute of Mental Health (NIMH): Helping Children and Adolescents Cope with Violence and Disasters This site offers a definition of trauma, a discussion of how children and adolescents react to trauma, suggestions on helping a victim, information on posttraumatic stress disorder, and treatment of this disorder. A discussion of current research and a resource list for support and additional information sources are also offered.
http://www.nimh.nih.gov/publicat/violence.cfm

Prevent Child Abuse America As its name implies, this nonprofit organization is dedicated to preventing child abuse. The Web page offers information on their programs, such as Healthy Families America, a home visiting program; the National Center on Child Abuse Prevention Research; and their chapter network. Advocacy and prevention education are also featured. The public can access online materials such as reports, surveys, fact sheets, tips for parents, information for children, and position statements. There is also a large list of related links, with descriptions of each site.
http://www.preventchildabuse.org/

Rape, Abuse, and Incest National Network (RAINN) This support site offers a directory of rape crisis centers and hotline numbers, facts about the network, including contact information, and basic information on rape and related abuse statistics. Fact sheets on what to do if sexually assaulted, current news, and access to the RAINN newsletter and its archive are also available to visitors.
http://www.rainn.org

Recovered Memories of Sexual Abuse: Scientific Research and Scholarly Resources This comprehensive Web site contains information about the author, research data, controversy and theories, a great number of research articles on recovered memories, related reference materials and legal information. The articles address various topics including false memory syndrome, the psychiatry of dissociation and memory, and other related topics. In addition, there are links to the psychiatric diagnosis of dissociative amnesia, support information, and related Web sites.
http://www.jimhopper.com/memory

Safer Society Foundation This national nonprofit organization provides advocacy, referrals, and research for the prevention and treatment of sexual abuse. At this site, professionals and consumers can find news updates, learn about the foundation's information and referral services, obtain training and consulting information, research resources, and order books and other reference materials provided by the Safer Society Press. Links to related organizations are also provided.
http://www.safersociety.org

Sexual Assault Information (SAIP) This site serves as a clearinghouse for fact sheets, articles, links to Web sites, organizations, and other types of resources related to sexual assault, rape, sexual abuse, sexual harassment, and other related topics. There is a section answering FAQs, as well as online access to previous issues of the *SAIP Newsletter*. Resources are divided into sections that include type of sexual abuse or assault, domestic violence, legal issues, men's issues, professional and university resources, trauma-related issues, rape and rape crisis centers, and newsgroups.
http://www.cs.utk.edu/~bartley/saInfoPage.html

Substance Abuse and Mental Health Services Administration (SAMHSA): Women, Co-occurring Disorders and Violence Study Program structure, principal investigators, and study sites are described at this address. Links are available to Web addresses associated with study sites and principal investigators.
(some features fee-based) http://www.prainc.com/wcdvs/index.html

Useful Victimology Links Supported by the School of Nursing at the University of Pennsylvania, this site contains resources related to the study of victims and victims' issues, including numerous links to organizations, articles, Web sites, documents, and support groups. The resources are divided into four

categories: forensic resources, rape and child abuse, government and Pennsylvania resources, and domestic violence issues.
http://www.nursing.upenn.edu/Victimology

7.2 ACADEMIC PSYCHIATRY

Association for Academic Psychiatry The Association for Academic Psychiatry is devoted to psychiatry education issues and provides a forum for members to discuss teaching techniques, curriculum, and other related topics. Visitors to the site can access online newsletters, membership details, teaching resources, and annual meeting information. Table of contents, abstracts, full-text articles, and archives of the association's journal, *Academic Psychiatry,* are also available through this site.
http://www.hsc.wvu.edu/aap/

Association for the Advancement of Philosophy and Psychiatry The mission of the Association for the Advancement of Philosophy and Psychiatry is to encourage interdisciplinary activity in philosophy and psychiatry and to advance knowledge, promote research, and facilitate understanding in both fields. The association's mission statement is provided at the site, as well as links to the officers and executive council members, meetings and conferences, local and special interest groups, and free access to the official journal of the association, *Philosophy, Psychiatry, and Psychology.*
http://www3.utsouthwestern.edu/aapp/

7.3 ADOPTION

Adopt: Assistance Information Support Organization departments include current news about adoption, online support forums, a state-by-state adoption resource directory, and 24-hour chats for adoptive parents and adoptees. Complete adoption resources include a listing of licensed agencies, assistance in finding children, and international adoption information. Novel features of this site include photo listings of available children and birth family search information.
http://www.adopting.org/ar.html

Adoption Network The Adoption Network is a volunteer-operated general information resource for the adoption community. Links to live chat rooms, an Internet-based classified ad service, information and support for birth parents and adoptees, and a list of FAQs round out this informative, well-organized site.
http://www.adoption.org

National Adoption Information Clearinghouse This site offers a wealth of information related to adoption for professionals, adoptees, birth relatives, and parents. Professionals will find abstracts of outcome studies and information on kinship care, open adoption, recruitment, transracial adoption, and training resources. Adoptees will find information on accessing adoption and vital records, as well as ordering information for a brochure on search and reunion Web sites. There are also bibliographies of adoption-related books for children. Birth relatives can find information on the adoption option, and access to records. For parents, there are fact sheets on the adoption process, open adoption, transracial adoption, financial assistance, and international adoption. The site also features statistics, adoption law summaries, a listing of related links, and databases of adoption abstracts, agencies, support groups, and organizations. In addition, there are hundreds of free online publications that include fact sheets, federal statutes, international adoption statistics, and legal resources. http://www.calib.com/naic/

Support-Group.com Adoption At Support-Group.com Adoption, local listings of support groups and organizations may be accessed by state/country. An adoption bulletin board is available and a Usenet group, alt.adoption, may be accessed with proper Web browser configuration.
http://www.support-group.com/cgi-bin/sg/get_links?adoption

7.4 ADVOCACY, PUBLIC POLICY, AND LAW

Advocacy and Protection The Center for Mental Health Services, a division of the Federal Substance Abuse and Mental Health Services Administration, has drawn together more than 30 organizations and programs covering advocacy for patients, consumers, and survivors. Each of these entries is a hot link to the primary organization and will be helpful to any individuals who are concerned about the problems of mental illness and the individuals and families who are affected.
http://www.mentalhealth.org/links/advocacy.htm

Advocacy Unlimited, Inc. This Connecticut-based group promotes self-determination for individuals suffering or recovering from psychiatric disabilities. The site describes the organization's philosophies and goals, provides information on advocacy education, offers online application to education programs, lists special events and announcements, and contains employment opportunities, featured articles, a resource center for other publications, and an online bookstore. Links to related sites include other advocacy groups, associations, legal sites, and other consumer resources.
http://www.mindlink.org/

American Academy of Child and Adolescent Psychiatry (AACAP): Legislation Visitors to this address will find legislative alerts, as well as links to information on current regulatory issues, state legislative issues, and important federal agency Web sites. Information about the State Children's Health Insurance Program (SCHIP) includes updates, benefit information by state, archived alerts, and CHIP state contact numbers. Visitors can also send specific messages to Congress, selecting congressional recipients by zip code or member name. http://www.aacap.org/legislation

American Academy of Psychiatry and the Law (AAPL)   Dedicated to forensic psychiatry, the organization's Web site provides links to information about the organization and membership; publications, including the AAPL journal, newsletter, and ethics code; meetings, training programs, and fellowships in forensic psychiatry; information on board certification; other forensic resources and links; and a question forum.
http://www.emory.edu/AAPL

American Psychiatric Association (APA): Public Policy Advocacy
This site offers information for psychiatrists on writing members of Congress, contacting the APA district branch in each state, and joining the APA's Grassroots Network. Information sources include action alerts and announcements, current issue briefs and fact sheets, transcripts of APA testimony, articles presenting current federal legislative and regulatory issues, APA regulatory comments, information on confidentiality issues, state law fact sheets, state testimony on mental health coverage and other issues, and newsletters offering state and federal policy updates.
http://www.psych.org/pub_pol_adv/index.cfm

Bazelon Center for Mental Health Law   This nonprofit legal advocacy organization provides legislative and law case updates at its Web site as well as a variety of online publication excerpts and ordering ability. Fair housing issues, children's rights, aging issues, mental health care, advance directives, and Americans with Disabilities Act resources are provided for attorneys and other advocates in the legal system.
http://www.bazelon.org

Center for Mental Health Services (CMHS): Advocacy/Consumers /Survivors   An extensive listing of mental health advocacy Web sites is presented at this CMHS page. Useful links include Internet support groups, a bilingual mental health discussion list, and the consumer-run Justice in Mental Health Organization (JIMHO), which provides consumer-run alternatives for the mentally ill such as community drop-in centers. Links to information for health advocates and an online mental health magazine, *1st Person,* are notable.
http://www.mentalhealth.org/links/advocacy.htm

Center for the Study of Issues in Public Mental Health   Dedicated to improving public mental health outcomes, the Center for the Study of Issues in Public Mental Health site offers information on their research programs. Primary research programs include promoting recovery in target populations, systems integration, examining the care and livelihood of people with severe mental illness, and methods for mental health services research. The site also contains a newsletter, a listing of related resources, statistical methods and computer programs, and seminar information. A bibliography of the center's publications is also provided. http://www.rfmh.org/csipmh/

Consortium for Citizens with Disabilities (CCD)   The Consortium for Citizens with Disabilities is made up of approximately 100 national disability organizations that are dedicated to advocacy on behalf of people with physical and mental disabilities. Visitors to the site will find information on the task forces and legal issues currently being addressed by the consortium, including child care, developmental disabilities, education, employment and training, fiscal policy, and health. Additional issues include housing, long-term services, rights, social security, and transportation. There is also a list, with contact information, of member organizations.
http://www.c-c-d.org/

Council for Disability Rights   The Council for Disability Rights is an advocacy organization that advances the rights of people with disabilities. Their site offers practical information for the disabled community such as a detailed guide to the Americans with Disabilities Act, written in laymen's terms. There is also a Guide to Disability Rights that covers employment, free medication, social security benefits, special education, and tax benefits for families. In addition, there is a guide for parents to enroll their children in special education programs, as well as tips on taking action against structural barriers. Voting resources and election information are also provided on the site.
http://www.disabilityrights.org/

Council for Exceptional Children (CEC)   The Council for Exceptional Children is an international professional organization dedicated to improving educational outcomes for exceptional children. The Web site highlights the organization's current research endeavors and outlines its public policy positions. Current legislative information is provided directly and updated frequently. The professional development section tells of upcoming events and assists with software selection for developing individualized education programs (IEPs). A link is provided to the Educational Resources Information Center (ERIC), which contains over 900,000 citations of educational documents and articles.
http://www.cec.sped.org/

Council of Parent Attorneys and Advocates   The Web site of this independent, nonprofit organization of attorneys, advocates, and parents outlines its mission and highlights many of the resources offered. Advocacy training program development, information resources for parents of children with disabilities, and a complete annual conference synopsis are included. The membership brochure and application are available online.
http://www.copaa.net

Department of Justice: Americans with Disabilities Act (ADA)
Hosted by the Department of Justice, this site offers detailed information on the Americans with Disabilities Act. The "Technical Assistance" section offers ADA legal documents, along with publications for individuals, business and nonprofit service providers, and state and local governments. The "Enforcement" section offers status reports on the ADA, instructions on how to file a complaint, and

settlement information. There is also information on certification of state and local building codes.
http://www.usdoj.gov/crt/ada/adahom1.htm

Disability Rights Education and Defense Fund (DREDF), Inc.   The DREDF is a national law and policy center dedicated to advancing the civil rights of people with disabilities through legislation, litigation, and advocacy. Resources available at the site include pertinent Court decisions and legislative information, a complete publication listing that includes comprehensive documents on the Americans with Disabilities Act (ADA), and information on the ADA Technical Assistance Hotline, which provides businesses, governmental agencies, and consumers with informational materials regarding rights and responsibilities under Title II and III of the ADA.
http://www.dredf.org

Federation of Families for Children's Mental Health   The Federation of Families for Children's Mental Health is a parent-run organization focusing on the needs of children with emotional, behavioral, or mental disorders. An in-depth mission statement along with links to further information are found at the Web site including local chapters and affiliates, details on managed care and children's health, and conference and membership material.
http://www.ffcmh.org/Eng_one.htm

Knowledge Exchange Network: Advocacy/Consumers/Survivors   Visitors to this site will find links providing access to organizations, consumer groups, support groups, and advocacy resources related to mental health. Nearly 40 sites are currently listed at the address.
http://www.mentalhealth.org/links/advocacy.htm

MacArthur Research Network on Mental Health and the Law   Part of the University of Virginia's Institute of Law, Psychiatry, and Public Policy, the Macarthur Research Network on Mental Health and the Law focuses on mental competence, risk of violence, and coercion. Research summaries and publication bibliographies are available on the site for the network's studies on adjudicative competence, violence risk, coercion, and treatment competence. The Macarthur FTP archive offers downloadable research instruments and manuals. Contact information for researchers is also provided.
http://macarthur.virginia.edu/

National Alliance for the Mentally Ill (NAMI)   The National Alliance for the Mentally Ill is the preeminent advocacy voice for those facing mental illness. The NAMI Web site provides comprehensive, up-to-date information on the latest developments in national mental health public policy initiatives and current legislation. Pertinent medical and legal information is reviewed and access is provided to an array of position papers. Also available are book reviews, NAMI research information, and local NAMI affiliates.
http://www.nami.org

National Association for Rights Protection and Advocacy (NARPA)
The NARPA exists to expose abuses and promote real alternatives to the current mental health system. The organization's Web site provides readings on mental health advocacy including current case decisions and legislative information, excerpts from the NARPA's annual conferences and an online version of the *Rights Tenet* newsletter. Interesting links such as the history of mental health advocacy are available. Online membership information and application are provided.
http://www.connix.com/~narpa

National Association of Mental Health Planning and Advisory Councils (NAMHPAC) Targeted towards members of mental health planning and advisory councils, this Web page offers information on NAMHPAC, along with a discussion board and a LISTSERV. Users can also download booklets on planning councils, evidence-based herbal therapies, managed care, and mental health and homelessness from the "Resources" section. Technical assistance is offered to councils; after completing a self-assessment form, follow-up with a NAMHPAC staff member will be arranged. The site also has a short list of related links.
http://www.namhpac.org/

National Association of Protection and Advocacy This site offers information related to the protection and advocacy of people with mental and physical disabilities. The "Disability Rights" section offers information on abuse and neglect, advance directives, community integration, employment, and healthcare. There is also contact information for state protection and advocacy agencies. Professionals will find training opportunities, job announcements, and a publication catalog. There is also a comprehensive list of Internet resources for disability-related organizations and LISTSERVs.
http://www.protectionandadvocacy.com/

National Association of Psychiatric Health Systems (NAPHS) The National Association of Psychiatric Health Systems advocates for health systems providing mental health and substance abuse services. The site provides a description of the organization, links to sites offering consumer information, details of marketing opportunities, membership details, and news articles. A resource catalog offers information on publications, conferences, and services of the organization, including advocacy materials and projects, clinical resources and projects, behavioral health events, financial resources, administrative resources, directories, and mailing lists. One section is restricted to registered members. (some features fee-based) http://www.naphs.org

National Center for Kids Overcoming Crisis KidsPeace, the National Center for Kids Overcoming Crisis, is a not-for-profit organization that serves more than 2,000 children, providing a comprehensive continuum of mental health treatment programs. KidsPeace advocates for intervention services and educates children and parents around the globe on how to avert crisis. Information on round-the-clock telephone counseling and the National Referral Net-

work database are available at the KidsPeace Web site. Other site features include an electronic version of the semiannual *Healing* magazine, topical index of articles for kids in crisis, a virtual cybermuseum, and a multimedia, bilingual, interactive presentation of the KidsPeace Continuum of Care.
http://www.kidspeace.org

National Coalition of Mental Health Professionals and Consumers, Inc.   The National Coalition of Mental Health Professionals and Consumers is dedicated to addressing the problems of managed mental health care. Their site offers FAQs, papers on alternatives to managed care, and excerpts from the *Mental Health Consumer Protection Manual*. In addition, there is a collection of articles on mental health treatment and managed care, as well as full-text articles from their newsletter. A bibliography of recommended reading and links to related resources are provided.
http://www.nomanagedcare.org/foyer.htm

National Empowerment Center (NEC)   This nonprofit self-help organization describes its workshop offerings and provides a list of interesting articles on the explanations of mental illness via the empowerment vision of recovery. The NEC newsletter, with articles past and present, is available online as is the NEC chat room with a full schedule of live discussions. Articles, books, booklets, and videos are available for ordering online.
http://www.power2u.org

National Health Law Program (NHeLP)   NHeLP is a public interest law firm dedicated to improving healthcare for working and unemployed poor, minority, elderly, and disabled Americans. Resources at this site include staff rosters, employment and internship listings, news, NHeLP publications, links to organizations and federal sites, and legal research resources. Topical resources are located under headings including private and federal advocacy, Medicaid, Medicare, public accountability, child health, racial/cultural issues, consumer resources, reproductive health, immigrant health, state and regional resources, managed care, and technology. Visitors can also subscribe to a mailing list alerting members about site updates.
http://www.healthlaw.org

National Information Center for Children and Youth (NICHCY) with Disabilities   NICHCY is a national referral center providing information on disabilities and related issues for families, educators, and other professionals with a special focus on children and youth. The organization's award-winning Web site describes its referral services and offers online publications in text-only or PDF format. (Acrobat Reader is downloadable from the Web site.) Publications include *Basics for Parents* and *Education Rights,* as well as parent guides, research briefings, and multiple fact sheets. Materials are also available in Spanish. http://www.nichcy.org

National Mental Health Association   The National Mental Health Association works to increase tolerance and awareness, improve mental health

services, prevent mental illness, and promote mental health. Resources available at the site include updates on state and federal legislative actions, employment opportunities, an events calendar, and an information center providing links to referrals and educational materials. Links to discussions of topics including mental health disorders, advocacy issues, public education, and healthcare reform are found at the site, as well as links to the association's affiliate and membership network.

http://www.nmha.org/index.cfm

National Mental Health Consumers Self-Help Clearinghouse The National Mental Health Consumers Self-Help Clearinghouse on the Web provides consumers with the ability to plan, provide, and evaluate mental health and community support services. Information about starting self-help groups, political material, and organization conference announcements are available. An online newsletter as well as several technical assistance guides are downloadable from the Web site after a brief registration process.

(free registration) http://www.mhselfhelp.org

Psychiatry and the Law This site, created by the medical director of the Taylor Hardin Secure Medical Facility in Alabama, is devoted to the disciplines of psychiatry and law. There are links to the National Forensic Hospital Database, general information regarding legal issues and psychiatry, links to mental health experts and attorneys, conference information, the American Psychiatric Association's relevant position papers, and other related Web pages.

http://mentalhelp.net/law

Psychiatry.com: Mental Health Advocacy Links are provided at this site to advocacy resources for patients with amyotrophic lateral sclerosis (ALS), AIDS/HIV, and other disabilities.

http://www.psychiatry.com/directory/ment_health_advoc.html

Rights—A Service of the Center for Mental Health Services Included in this list of Web sites are links to various organizations and agencies focusing exclusively on the rights of the mentally ill. Included are the National Association for Rights Protection and Advocacy (NARPA), the National Mental Health Association, and the Bazelon Center for Mental Health Law. All are dedicated to improving the lives of those affected by mental illness by advocating for patient rights, providing legal information, and promoting real alternatives to coercive or dangerous practices. http://www.mentalhealth.org/links/rights.htm

State Advocacy and Assistance Organizations The Center for Health Services, a federal agency, has assembled an extremely important and useful guide to state agencies that focus on issues of mental health advocacy and assistance. Hundreds of agencies across the country are profiled with complete descriptions, names of directors, addresses, telephone numbers, fax numbers, and statewide or national toll-free numbers. Many of the agencies within each state have their own Web sites.

http://www.mentalhealth.org/publications/stateresourceguides.cfm

State Protection and Advocacy Agencies for Persons with Developmental Disabilities   Contained at this Web site is a state-by-state, comprehensive listing of contact information for advocacy programs around the country. Assistance program entries encompass those for people with disabilities, as well as for the mentally ill, and include address, fax, e-mail, and Web sites where applicable.

http://www.protectionandadvocacy.com/atoh.htm

Surgeon General: Mental Health Reports   Full-text reports from the Surgeon General are available on this site. Reports include: *Youth Violence: A Report of the Surgeon General, Surgeon General's Conference on Children's Mental Health,* and *Mental Health: A Report of the Surgeon General 1999.*

http://www.mentalhealth.org/specials/surgeongeneral/index.htm

University of Pittsburgh: Center for Mental Health Services Research   Research "to improve access to services and quality of care for underserved populations" is the primary focus of the Center for Mental Health Services Research. Their Web site briefly describes research training, classes, faculty, and postdoctoral fellowship opportunities at the center. In addition, there are links to related sites.

http://server.socialwork.pitt.edu/~cmhsr/

University of Virginia: Institute of Law, Psychiatry, and Public Policy   Research activities at this University of Virginia institute include community and clinic-based programs on mental health issues, such as adjudicative competence; the human genome project and its ethical, legal, and social ramifications; serious juvenile offenders and their assessment; and violence in the workplace and on campus. Links to each program include faculty, related organizations, and comprehensive summaries of the program. Additional resources include a mental health law bibliography, online access to the publications of the institute, including *Developments in Mental Health Law,* and links to fact files on forensic evaluation services available at the institute.

http://www.ilppp.virginia.edu/index.html

7.5   ANTIPSYCHIATRY

Antipsychiatry Coalition   Articles at this site were written by psychiatrists and a lawyer representing former psychiatric patients. The publications offer criticisms of biologic psychiatry, psychiatric drugs, Ritalin and attention deficit hyperactivity disorder, electroconvulsive therapy, psychotherapy, and involuntary psychiatric commitment. Additional articles attempt to refute the existence of schizophrenia and biological depression. News, announcements, links to related sites, and a mailing list for messages from other site visitors are also found at this site. http://www.antipsychiatry.org

Antipsychiatry Reading Room   This address presents links to Web sites and articles related to psychiatric errors, psychiatric drugs and adverse effects,

psychiatric practice and patients' rights, evidence of abuse, and electroconvulsive therapy. Poetry, illustrations, and other non-informational materials are also found at the site.
http://home.kscable.com/madpride/idx_main2.html

 Citizens Commission on Human Rights   The Citizens Commission on Human Rights, established in 1969, is an antipsychiatry site based upon the work of the Church of Scientology. The organization claims to expose psychiatric abuse and document crime by mental health professionals. Additional information revealing its opposition to psychiatry is found at the page, including explanation of their philosophy and details on taking action against psychiatric abuse. http://www.cchr.org

 Mental Health Facts   This Web site is described as a "source of comprehensive information on mental heath, mental illness, and treatment options." There are links to articles on mental health, psychiatry, and related topics. Most articles are composed as antipsychiatric editorials, but there are a few links to articles and Web sites that may prove informative to both professionals and the public. http://www.mentalhealthfacts.com

 What You Should Know About Psychiatry and Psychiatric Drugs
Books reviewed at this site offer criticism of psychiatric drugs and the psychiatric profession. Links are also available to related sites.
http://www.geocities.com/HotSprings/3568/index.html

7.6 Brain Banks

 Brainbanks.org   The home page of the American Brain Banking Network provides background information about the organization, its goals, and research purposes. Brain banks throughout the world are listed at the site, with entries offering links to individual Web sites, demographic information on specimens, and additional information on specific brain banks.
http://www.brainbanks.org/index.htm

7.7 Certification and Licensure

 American Board of Psychiatry and Neurology, Inc.   The American Board of Psychiatry and Neurology certifies physicians in psychiatry and neurology. Their Web page offers professionals information on certification requirements, examinations, recertification, and FAQs. Consumers will find fact sheets on what certification means and can also request, for a fee, the certification status of their physician.
(some features fee-based) http://www.abpn.com/

 Mental Health Licensure Resources   Professionals will find resources related to licensure for psychologists, marriage and family therapists, professional counselors, and social workers on this Web page, hosted by Tarleton State University. Links to Web sites on state licensure boards, current issues in the field, licensure exam preparation, and specific state board information are provided. http://www.tarleton.edu/~counseling/coresour/lllpc.htm

7.8 CHILD AND ADOLESCENT PSYCHIATRY

American Academy of Child and Adolescent Psychiatry (AACAP) Providing educational materials to patients and their families, this site offers information on child depression awareness, current legislation activities, and coverage of hot topics, such as children and psychiatric medication. A fact sheet for families is accessible from the home page, in addition to an assortment of professional resources. Clinical practice, research, and training pages are included, as is a Web page builder especially for physician members.
(some features fee-based) http://www.aacap.org

American Society for Adolescent Psychiatry (ASAP) Primarily for professionals, the ASAP Web page offers recent ASAP newsletters, book reviews, and the table of contents from *Annals of Adolescent Psychiatry*. Fact sheets on depressed adolescents, teen suicide, and risk behaviors are also offered. Information on membership and the society's annual meeting is provided on the site. http://www.adolpsych.org/

Association for Child Psychoanalysis (ACP) The ACP is an international not-for-profit organization providing a forum for the interchange of ideas and clinical experience in order to advance the psychological treatment and understanding of children and adolescents and their families. This site was designed to promote the association and its programs. Links to a searchable roster, referral information, the ACP archives, psychoanalysis-related sites, and a comprehensive list of programs developed by ACP members are available at the site.
http://www.westnet.com/acp

Child and Adolescent Bipolar Foundation (CABF) Intended primarily for parents of children with bipolar disorder, this Web page offers a broad array of education and support information. In the "Learning Center" section, there are online publications on topics such as early onset bipolar disorder, and educating your child, as well as new research findings, journal articles, and personal stories. The "Community Center" section offers message boards, online support groups, chat rooms, a "Find a Doctor" service, and a creative art and literature gallery of children's work. Related links are provided. http://www.cabf.org/

Child and Adolescent Psychiatry Online Resources at this site are mainly for patients and caregivers, and include articles on specific topics, professional articles, a database of residential treatment units in the United Kingdom, a bulletin board, and links to additional sites offering child and adolescent psychiatry information, reviewed by *Psychiatry Online* editors.
http://www.pol-it.org/psychild.htm

Child Psychiatry Pamphlets   This Web site, created by a pediatric psychiatrist, provides access to psychiatric pamphlets providing in- depth information on the diagnosis and treatment of many child and adolescent psychiatric disorders, including attention deficit/hyperactivity disorder, conduct disorder, bipolar disorder, social phobia, panic, depression, and oppositional defiant disorder.
http://www.klis.com/chandler

Childswork/Childsplay   This site is for teachers, parents, and others involved in helping children cope with their psychological disorders. There are lists of links to sites for parents, presenting topics such as divorce issues and learning problems, and for teachers, with topics on multiple intelligence and conflict issues. There are also links to current newsgroups, books, discussion groups, and sites related to children's mental health. Included are links to information on common childhood disorders, a list of products, and training resources.
http://www.childswork.com

Glossary of Symptoms and Mental Illnesses Affecting Teenagers
Common mental illnesses and emotional problems affecting teenagers are listed at this site, including alcohol and drug abuse, anorexia nervosa, attention deficit/hyperactivity disorder, bulimia nervosa, conduct disorder, depression, obsessive-compulsive disorder, physical abuse, posttraumatic stress disorder, psychosis, schizophrenia, sexual abuse, suicide, and Tourette's disorder. Descriptive information and symptoms are available for each problem.
http://www.aacap.org/Web/aacap/about/glossary/index.htm

Indiana University: Adolescence Directory Online   A service of the Center for Adolescent Studies at Indiana University, this award-winning site serves as an online directory of Internet resources on adolescent issues. Topics include conflict and violence, mental health issues, health and health risk issues, resources for counselors, and resources for teens.
http://education.indiana.edu/cas/adol/adol.html

Indiana University: Mental Health Risk Factors for Adolescents
Internet resources listed at this site include abuse, adolescent development, alcohol and other drugs, attention deficit/hyperactivity disorder, autism, bipolar disorder, conduct disorder, depression, eating disorders, grieving, obsessive-compulsive disorder, panic disorder, retardation, sexual abuse, stress, and suicide. General resources and support groups are also found through the site. Short site descriptions are provided with each link.
http://education.indiana.edu/cas/adol/mental.html

Maternal and Child Health Bureau   This bureau is dedicated to improving the health of mothers and children in the United States. This site offers a history and mission of the organization, directories of staff and regional offices, grant resources, newsletters and other publications, and links to specific divisions within the bureau and to related sites.
http://www.mchb.hrsa.gov/index.html

National Conference of State Legislatures: Adolescent Mental Health An article on school-based mental health services for adolescents is provided on this site. Adolescent mental health statistics are described, along with federal and state legislative initiatives for school-based mental health services. Funding for these services is also examined. There is a table of state laws on school-based mental health services that contains the citation and provision of each law. References are provided.
http://www.stateserv.hpts.org/hpts2000/issueb2000.nsf/cd5fe
07d402115ac852564f0007cb093/0cbf250cc509837a85256784004e1328?OpenDocument

National Foundation for Abused and Neglected Children Information on childhood abuse and neglect is provided on this site. A child abuse fact sheet offers a definition, what to look for, and how to report it. There are also detailed fact sheets on shaken baby syndrome, as well as on gangs. Tips for children and teens and their parents on avoiding gang activity are found. A comprehensive listing of related resources offers links on child welfare, sites for children, drugs and violence, and parents' sites.
http://www.gangfreekids.org/index.html

Online Psych: Children's Issues Resources available through links at this site include a list of questions to ask prior to hospital treatment of children and adolescents, information related to attention deficit/hyperactivity disorder, adolescent depression, adolescent violence, anxiety disorders, Asperger's syndrome, autism, bedwetting, child abuse, schizophrenia, sleep apnea, and many other topics. Many additional resources are offered concerning child and adolescent mental and physical health. Visitors can also order related books through Amazon.com at the site.
http://www.onlinepsych.com/public/Childrens_Issues/

Pediatric Psychiatry Page A board-certified child and adolescent psychiatrist developed this home page, which describes professional interests, provides bibliographies for pediatric psychiatry topics, offers information on workshops and conferences, and includes links to related sites.
http://pubweb.acns.nwu.edu/~gjw569/pedpsych/homepage.htm

Portland State University: Research and Training Center on Family Support and Children's Mental Health This research center aims to improve services for families of children with serious mental, emotional, or behavioral disabilities. The site describes current projects, and training activities, at the center. Specific research themes include family participation in services, family participation at the policy level, families and out-of-home care, evaluation of family organizing efforts, and interventions in professional education. Publications, including an online newsletter, mailing lists, faculty and staff directories, employment opportunities, and conference details are also found at the address.
http://www.rtc.pdx.edu

Stanford University: Child and Adolescent Psychiatry This site offers information on current projects in the Stanford University Child and Adolescent

Psychiatry Department. Subjects include neuroimaging, behavioral neurogenetics, violence prevention, eating disorders, autism, mood disorders, pediatric posttraumatic stress disorder, and anxiety disorders. Recruitment information is available for those wishing to volunteer in current research studies, with responsibilities including data coding, transcription, observations, and interviews. Additional information on patient services, training, and research, as well as a staff listing is also available. http://www-cap.stanford.edu

The Child Advocate   Children's rights are the focus of the Child Advocate, a nonprofit organization. The "Subjects" section of their Web page offers information such as national and state child advocacy resources, sexual abuse evaluation methods, and a protocol for admission of children to psychiatric treatment facilities. Under the "Contents" section, articles, publications, and Internet resources are provided for children's rights in regard to mental health, education, medical and psychiatric conditions, and the legal system.
http://www.childadvocate.net/

TLTP Project: Child Development   At this site, downloadable Windows and Macintosh versions of this program displaying the key stages of development from birth to six years are available. Topics introduced and discussed include motor and speech development, play, communication, and social behavior development. Users can access information either by selecting an age, which displays milestones typically achieved by that age, or by selecting an individual subject area, chronologically displaying different milestones in that subject area.
http://www.ccc.nottingham.ac.uk/~mczwww/tltp/child.htm

University of Virginia: Curry School of Education: Office of Special Education   This address contains directories of site links related to attention deficit/hyperactivity disorder, autism, cerebral palsy, communication disorders, hearing impairment, learning disorders, mental retardation, serious emotional imbalance, traumatic brain injury, and visual impairment. Visitors can find organizations, educational resources, information on medications, conference and forum details, and general resources related to each topic through this site.
http://curry.edschool.virginia.edu/go/cise/ose/categories

University of Wisconsin: Madison: Waisman Center: Child Neurology   Many valuable Internet resources can be found through this online directory. Resource categories include academy sites, online books, clinical service information, continuing medical education online, mailing lists for child neurologists, journals, MEDLINE search engines, parent information, pharmaceutical information, professional information, research in child neurology, teaching resources, general medical Web portals, and online courses. Major sources for information are also listed, including PubMed, full-text online journals, government resources, and professional organizations.
http://www.waisman.wisc.edu/child-neuro/index.html

Virtual Hospital: Patient Information by Department: Child Psychiatry   Interested professionals and consumers can access resource materials from

informative links, including topics in attention deficit/hyperactivity disorder, Tourette's disorder, trichotillomania, and children and family moves.
http://www.vh.org/Patients/IHB/Psych/Peds/PedsPsychiatry.html

World Association for Infant Mental Health (WAIMH) WAIMH is an interdisciplinary and international association promoting education and research on all aspects of infant mental health. Included are links to the association's mission statement and membership information, conference listings, and affiliates. Internet resources include training information and online access to the table of contents for the *Infant Mental Health Journal*.
http://www.msu.edu/user/waimh

7.9 COMMUNITY SUPPORT

Knowledge Exchange Network: Community Support Information on the Community Support program of the Center for Mental Health Services is featured on this site. Short descriptions of the center's programs are provided for activities related to employment intervention, criminal justice, managed care, and women and violence. Toolkits and publications in support of research and evaluation are provided. There are also state resource guides for local support. Guides for mental health planning and advisory councils are available for evidence-based assertive community treatment and for mental health and homelessness. Links for further information on accessibility, employment, support, and rights are also found.
http://www.mentalhealth.org/cmhs/communitysupport/index.htm

7.10 COMMUNITY-BASED PSYCHIATRIC TREATMENT

See also Inclusion and Integration.

American Association of Community Psychiatrists The American Association of Community Psychiatrists promotes excellence in in-patient mental healthcare, solves common problems encountered by psychiatrists in a community setting, establishes liaisons with related professional groups for advocacy purposes, encourages psychiatrist training, improves relationships within community settings between psychiatrists and other clinicians and administrators, and educates the public about the role of the community mental health system in the care of the mentally ill. This site provides information on the mission of the association, board members, and membership information. The present and previous issues of *Community Psychiatrist* are available, as well as links to relevant training and research programs in the discipline.
http://www.comm.psych.pitt.edu/find.html

Assertive Community Treatment Association (ACTA) Assertive community treatment (ACT), a specific approach providing community-based psychiatric treatment, rehabilitation, and support, is described in detail at this

site. Topics include a description of people served by ACT and minimum qualifications a service must meet to be considered an ACT provider.
http://www.actassociation.com/

Knowledge Exchange Network: Community Support Programs

Community Support Programs of the Center for Mental Health Services facilitate the effective delivery and implementation of mental health services in local
communities. The site offers state resource guides, publications, Program of Assertive Community Treatment standards, archived activity updates, a program
fact sheet, and specific community support program summaries. Links are
available to sites offering resources related to accessibility issues, employment,
self-help/support groups, and patients' rights.
http://www.mentalhealth.org/cmhs/communitysupport/index.htm

National Council for Community Behavioral Healthcare   The National
Council for Community Behavioral Healthcare conducts advocacy and educational activities for community behavioral healthcare organizations. Resources
at the site include a description of membership benefits, current advocacy issues
and initiatives, recent letters to Congress, news, and conference details. Educational materials include books available to order, an online newsletter highlighting recent legislation, an online journal of educational articles, and a detailed
discussion of behavioral health statistics and the impact of behavioral disorders
on society. Services and employment opportunities are listed at the site. Paid
membership allows access to current public policy reports, news, online communications, and a networking directory.
(some features fee-based)   http://www.nccbh.org

7.11 CRIME AND MENTAL ILLNESS

BehaveNet: Insanity Defense   This Web page offers terms, and their
explanations, for "not guilty by reason of insanity" pleas. Terms include wild
beast, Durham rule, irresistible impulse, and cognitive arm. Several books related to the insanity defense are listed on the site.
http://www.behavenet.com/capsules/forensic/insanitydefense.htm

Coping with Mental Illness in Prisons   A full-text article, originally
published in the October 1998 issue of *Family and Community Health,* on coping with mental illness in prisons is featured on this Web page. The article examines why people with mental illness are a criminal justice problem, the treatment of mental illness in prisons, and a new kind of residential program for
prisons. References are provided.
http://www.findarticles.com/m0FSP/3_21/53578841/p1/article.jhtml

Insanity Defense   The subject of the insanity defense, including medical
definitions and legal aspects, is explored at this American Psychiatric Association (APA) site. The article is an in-depth examination of the issues, the position

of different states, the frequency of use, and other relevant topics related to the insanity defense.
http://www.psych.org/public_info/insanity.cfm

Jail Suicide and Mental Health The full-text of a newsletter (Spring 2000) on jail suicide and mental health, issued jointly by the National Center on Institutions and Alternatives and the National Institute of Corrections, is posted on this Web page. Articles in the newsletter include: current suicide prevention efforts and future needs, a national survey of juvenile suicide in jail, jail mental health service initiatives, the mentally ill in jail, and an investigation into the suicide of a prison inmate. Resources for additional information are provided.
http://www.igc.org/ncia/spring2000update.html

National Alliance for the Mentally Ill (NAMI): Criminalization The criminalization of symptomatic behavior is examined at this site, and connections to a listing of resources from NAMI are provided. A position paper on the subject, NAMI's public policy on criminalization, and guidelines geared toward state government that address the need to establish jail diversion programs and legislation are found. Recently enacted law, an amicus brief on the subject, and an online publication describing how Texas criminal law applies to alleged offenders with mental illness are offered.
http://www.nami.org/legal/crim.html

National Center for Policy Analysis: Juvenile Crime and Mental Illness A fact sheet on juvenile crime and mental illness is presented on this site. Drawn from an article in the *New York Times,* it examines the growing number of people with mental illness and/or mental retardation that are in the juvenile justice system. A link to the full text of the article is provided, as well as a link for additional information on juvenile crime.
http://www.ncpa.org/hotlines/juvcrm/pd120500b.html

National Schizophrenia Fellowship: Schizophrenia and Violence Information on schizophrenia's weak connection with violence against others is presented at this fact sheet, as well as research findings on the subject by the Royal College of Psychiatrists and several other sources.
http://www.nsf.org.uk/news_views/briefings/violence.html

Soros Foundation: Mental Illness in U.S. Jails An article on mental illness in U.S. jails, originally published by the Center on Crime Communities & Culture of the Open Society Institute, is provided on this Web page. The article examines why mentally ill individuals end up in jail, what criminal justice administrators think about mental health services, and the need to divert mentally ill offenders from jail. The high rate of suicide in jail is also discussed. A bibliography is included.
http://www.soros.org/crime/research_brief__1.html

7.12 CROSS-CULTURAL MENTAL HEALTH

Bryn Mawr College: Serendip Mental Health: Cultural/Sociological Considerations A variety of links are available at this site, including connections to articles that advocate a cross-cultural perspective in diagnostic mental health settings. Cultural conceptions of mental health in relation to alcoholism, psychopathology, and factors that may lead to a social stigma toward mental illness are among the topics. Additional cross-cultural subject matter is available, with coverage of culture as an etiological factor in mental health and socioeconomic status as it relates to mental health.
http://serendip.brynmawr.edu/sci_cult/mentalhealth/sociocultural.html

International Association for Cross-Cultural Psychology Syllabi for a variety of undergraduate and graduate courses in cross-cultural behavior and mental health are available in PDF format from this site. Information on the organization's publications, the *Journal of Cross-Cultural Psychology* and the *Cross-Cultural Psychology Bulletin,* is found at the site, with online access to the current issue and archives of the latter. An extensive list of related cross-cultural Web resources and an online discussion group are offered.
http://www.fit.edu/CampusLife/clubs-org/iaccp/

7.13 CULTISM

American Family Foundation (AFF): Cults and Psychological Manipulation Sponsored by the American Family Foundation, a professional organization devoted to public education about cults, this Web site provides consumers and professionals with links to online journals and their articles, essays, support and research information, a directory of specialized professionals, guides on cults and related topics, and meeting information. Links are provided to information about specific cult organizations by group or topic type. Topic listings assist in finding information for specific uses or audiences, including children, educators, psychology, social influence, civil rights, medical, recovery, substance abuse, women, and others. Consumer information, media, educational, mental health, government, religious studies, and law enforcement agencies are listed at the site for additional resources. In addition, current news and information about the organization is included.
http://www.csj.org

Social Psychology of Cults This psychology resource contains detailed links regarding the powerful social forces associated with cults and the social psychological effects that these groups have had and can produce. Obedience and conformity, alterations in personality, and posttraumatic stress disorder are examined. Journals covering the impact of cults, anti-cult organizations, and interesting article abstracts discussing sects and cults are all found in addition to an index of cult and anti-cult movements and cult-specific news coverage.
http://www.fmdc.calpoly.edu/libarts/cslem/Cults/Cults.html

7.14 DEINSTITUTIONALIZATION

Deinstitutionalization: What will it Really Cost? This article on deinstitutionalization appeared in the *Schizophrenic Digest*. It is an editorial by a schizoaffective patient who compares the quality of life in an institution to the quality of life in a community. He finds the former more conducive to the health and well-being of the patient and articulates his reasons.
http://www.mentalhealth.com/mag1/p51-sc02.html

InterActivist Network: Deinstitutionalization A discussion of deinstitutionalization and the homeless mentally ill is featured on this Web page. The article offers a brief history of deinstitutionalization, a look at what happened to the patients, and an examination of the phenomenon of the homeless mentally ill. Other issues addressed include liberty, and criminalization.
http://www.interactivist.net/housing/deinstitutionalization_2.html

National Program Office on Self-Determination A program of the Robert Wood Johnson Foundation, the National Program Office on Self-Determination works for the self-determination of individuals with disabilities. The site offers a description of self-determination, along with the *Common Sense* newsletter, and online publications, such as *Making Self-Determination Work*. There is also a brief list of related resources.
http://www.self-determination.org/index.htm

National Resource Center on Community Integration The integration of people with developmental disabilities into communities is the mission of the National Resource Center on Community Integration. Their Web page offers online publications and resources related to positive practices, community supports, family supports, friendships, gender and disability, and housing. Additional topics covered include multiculturalism and disability, inclusion, recreation, self-advocacy, supported employment, and supported living.
http://web.syr.edu/~thechp/nrc.htm

University of Minnesota: Institute on Community Integration The Institute on Community Integration works to improve services and support for people with developmental and other disabilities. The site describes their programs related to early childhood, school-age, transition, and adults. There is also information on professional training programs, as well as a catalog of newsletters, resource guides, curricula, reports, brochures, and videos. A comprehensive list of related Web resources is provided that covers topics such as developmental disabilities, funding sources, education, employment, health, and policy. http://ici.umn.edu/

7.15 DISABILITIES AND REHABILITATION

About.com: Parenting Special Needs This Internet directory contains links to sites offering information on parents' special needs for children with physical, mental, or emotional disorders, including AD/HD, autism, cerebral palsy, cystic fibrosis, Down syndrome, epilepsy, muscular dystrophy, reactive attachment disorder, spina bifida, visual impairment, and many related disorders. Special articles are available on featured topics, and the site also offers a chat forum, a newsletter, and an online bookstore and video store.
http://www.specialchildren.about.com/home/specialchildren

Administration on Developmental Disabilities This government agency, part of the Department of Health and Human Services, offers information on their programs directed to people with developmental disabilities. Programs include state councils on developmental disabilities, state protection and advocacy agencies, university centers, and national associations. Program highlights and outcomes are featured. In addition, policy and announcements are posted on the site including the full text of the Developmental Disabilities Assistance and Bill of Rights Act of 2000. There are also links to state disability Web sites.
http://www.acf.dhhs.gov/programs/add/

American Association of People with Disabilities (AAPD) Primarily for people with disabilities, the AAPD Web page emphasizes membership in their association and its benefits. Benefits include access to life insurance, prescription drug plans, and viatical benefits. In addition, there is a list of related Internet links covering advocacy, the Americans with Disabilities Act, organizations, independent living, and products.
http://www.aapd.com/

Americans with Disabilities Act Document Center More than 55 full-text documents of the Americans with Disabilities Act statutes, regulations, and technical assistance manuals are posted on this Web page, created by Duncan C. Kinder. There is also a comprehensive listing of related links covering disability, medical issues, legal concerns, government agencies, employment, and newsgroups. A link to the Job Accommodation Network provides information on job accommodations for people with disabilities.
http://janweb.icdi.wvu.edu/kinder/

Center for Information Technology Accommodation (CITA) The Center for Information Technology Accommodation works with a network of public and private sector partners to create "a nationally recognized model demonstration facility influencing accessible information environments, services, and management practices." The site provides information on services and partnerships, current projects, the Universal Access Working Group, people with disabilities and the national infrastructure, resources for hearing-impaired and deaf persons, federal accommodation programs and initiatives, legislation and policies, assistive technology providers, and upcoming conferences. Infor-

mation is also available on creating a more universally accessible Web site. Users can access a staff directory, the CITA Handbook, and the Department of Justice federal agency self-evaluations and checklists.
http://www.itpolicy.gsa.gov/cita

Consortium for Citizens with Disabilities (CCD) This consortium is made up of approximately 100 national disability organizations. The Web page offers contact information and announcements for a broad array of legislative issues handled by the CCD, including child care, developmental disabilities, education, employment, fiscal policy, health, and long-term services. There is also a list of CCD task forces, as well as links and contact information for all member organizations.
http://www.c-c-d.org/

Department of Justice: Americans with Disabilities Act (ADA)
Resources at this site include sources and instructions for obtaining publications, the toll-free telephone number for an information line, new or proposed regulation documents, information on certification of state and local building codes, and details of other ADA mediation activities. Enforcement information includes status reports, settlements, details of the ADA Litigation Project, and instructions on filing complaints. Visitors can search the site, the Freedom of Information Act ADA Information, and the Department of Justice press releases for additional resources.
http://www.usdoj.gov/crt/ada/adahom1.htm

Disability and Medical Resource Mall This directory contains links to over 400 companies offering disability and medical products, resources, and services. Categories include augmentative communication computers and electronics; assistance animals products and services, vehicles, and services for the blind and visually impaired; deaf, hearing, and speech-impaired; books, magazines, brochures, and catalogs; canes, crutches, and walkers; medical equipment; pharmaceuticals; and other related products and services.
http://www.coast-resources.com

Disability Resources Monthly Guide to Disability Resources on the Internet This colorful Web site, available also in text-only version, is a comprehensive Internet resource for disability-related material and was developed to promote awareness and accessibility to independent living. Departments include a "State of the Week" in which disability organizations and resources in a particular locale are reviewed, in addition to its regional resource directory, updated topics of the week, disability news, past features, a list of FAQs, and an award-winning online newsletter, *Disability Resources Monthly* (DRM), which reviews resources for independent living. A variety of disability resources on the Internet are reviewed at the DRM Webwatcher and favorite pages can be accessed. New visitors are encouraged to read the online user guide, in order to take full advantage of all the site has to offer.
http://www.disabilityresources.org/

Disabled Peoples' International: Links Disability resources found in the links section at this address include many national and international organizations support services and information, disability studies, and personal pages and stories. Topical sites are included under equal rights and advocacy, sports and leisure, travel, independent living and housing, and employment and education. All sites are listed by host country.
http://www.dpi.org/links.html

Educational Resources Information Center (ERIC): Clearinghouse on Disabilities and Gifted Education Sponsored by the U.S. Department of Education, Office of Educational Research and Improvement, and administered by the National Library of Education, ERIC EC "gathers and disseminates the professional literature, information, and resources on the education and development of individuals of all ages who have disabilities and/or who are gifted." The ERIC database, available through this site, offers journal articles, conference proceedings, papers, speeches, research reports, teaching guides and curricula, and books related to educational issues. This site also offers instructions on submitting documents to ERIC and information on special projects, research details, fact sheets, answers to frequently asked questions, mailing lists, links to similar information resources, conference calendars, and access to the National Parent Information Network and the "AskEric" question-answering service.
http://ericec.org

Educational Resources Information Center (ERIC): Clearinghouse on Disabilities and Gifted Education The ERIC Clearinghouse on Disabilities and Gifted Education Web page offers a wealth of information, maintained by the Council for Exceptional Children. The ERIC database contains abstracts of education-related journal articles, conference proceedings, and research reports. The Exceptional Child Education Resources (ECER) database, offered by subscription, contains similar information for special and gifted education. The site also contains information on grants and research findings of federally funded special education research, through the ERIC/OSEP special project. A comprehensive listing of links covers topics such as advocacy, attention deficit disorder, autism, Down syndrome, and mental health. In addition, there are digests (short overviews), fact sheets, FAQs, and bibliographies related to disabilities and gifted education. Visitors can sign up for e-mail discussion lists. Parents will find articles on education through a link to the National Parent Information Network.
(some features fee-based) http://ericec.org/

Equal Access to Software and Information (EASI) Equal Access to Software and Information is a group committed to providing resources to the education community on access-to-information technologies. Specific activities include seminars and online workshops, an electronic journal, mailing lists, and other publications and videos. The site offers links to information and sources for adaptive resources, libraries, distance learning, science and math education,

and other related sites. The group's journal and other publications are available from the site.
http://www.isc.rit.edu/~easi

Integrated Network of Disability Information and Education (INDIE)
Available in text-only and French versions, the INDIE site may be searched for links by keyword or by clicking on any one of 15 available categories relating to disability information and education. Disability subtopics include rehabilitation, transportation, employment, organizations, recreation, and social development and legislation. Web addresses and direct connections are provided along with brief descriptions of the sites.
http://laurence.canlearn.ca/english/learn/accessguide/indie/index.html

International Center for Disability Resources on the Internet   A large collection of disability-related Internet resources is available at this site where assisting the disability community is the primary mission. The latest in news, accessible travel resources, Internet guides, and disability publications can be viewed and important ramifications of the Americans with Disabilities Act regarding Internet usage are discussed.
http://www.icdri.org

Job Accommodation Network (JAN) on the Web: Americans with Disabilities Act (ADA) Links   Links at this site provide valuable resources on ADA law, accessibility guidelines, ADA technical assistance manuals, ADA enforcement, and other ADA materials and Web sites.
http://janweb.icdi.wvu.edu

Kansas Commission on Disability Concerns   This site lists numerous resources, including more than 25 links to sites offering specific information on assistive technologies. Public service groups, companies providing assistive technologies, software sources, and state-based programs are included at the site. Over 20 links to general disability resources on the Internet are also provided. Specific topical resources are found on assistance dogs, independent living, and particular disabilities.
http://adabbs.hr.state.ks.us/dc

Knowledge Exchange Network: Assistive Technology   This site lists more than 15 valuable Internet sources for information, products, and support related to assistive technology. Resources include personal sites, databases of information, government organizations, state and international organizations, and research centers.
http://www.mentalhealth.org/links/assistive.htm

Knowledge Exchange Network: Disabilities   More than 20 Internet links related to disabilities are provided on this Web page. Topics include abused children with disabilities, the Americans with Disabilities Act, assistive technology, psychiatric disabilities, and learning disabilities. Brief descriptions of each site are provided. http://www.mentalhealth.org/links/disabilities.htm

National Association of Developmental Disabilities Councils (NADDC)   A coalition of state developmental disabilities councils, the NADDC offers a catalog of their publications, profiles of state council accomplishments, and a list of state council Web sites. In addition, there are legislative updates, related Internet resources, and an Internet index containing links to sites for people with a variety of disabilities. There is also a link to the Administration on Developmental Disabilities.
http://www.naddc.org

National Early Childhood Technical Assistance System   This technical assistance consortium provides services and information on and for children with disabilities and their families. Information on related organizations is available, as well as current news items, legal information, archives, government links, such as a link to the Americans with Disabilities Act and the Department of Education, and a publications list. Of interest to professionals is a project database, searchable by a variety of methods, and a link to resources on developmental delay in children, which includes project information, state and national support information, scientific articles on the subject, and a concept paper. Links to related sites are also included.
http://www.nasdse.org/national_early_childhood_techn.htm

National Information Center for Children and Youth (NICHCY) with Disabilities   This national referral center serves professionals and nonprofessionals by providing information on children and adolescents with disabilities. At this site, one can access the center's publications, including fact sheets, summaries, news articles, parent and student guides, reference lists, and other information. There are links to state resource documents, FAQs, training information, a newsletter, related organizations and centers, and conference information. http://www.nichcy.org

National Institute on Disability and Rehabilitation Research (NIDRR)   The National Institute on Disability and Rehabilitation Research "conducts comprehensive and coordinated programs of research and related activities to maximize the full inclusion, social integration, employment, and independent living of disabled individuals of all ages." The site offers information about the organization, projects, research topics, programs, the institute's Switzer Fellowship Program, and a calendar of events. Specific programs include model spinal cord injury systems, Rehabilitation Engineering Research Centers (RERC), Rehabilitation Research Training Centers (RRTC), and traumatic brain injury model systems. Research topics include assistive/adaptive technologies, burn rehabilitation, disability and health, emerging disability, employment, transition to post secondary school for students with disabilities, universal design, and women with disabilities.
http://www.ed.gov/offices/OSERS/NIDRR

University of Minnesota: Disability Services: Disability-Specific Web Sites   More than 150 categories are available in this directory of Internet sites

offering information, support, legal, and product services related to a wide range of disabilities. A short description accompanies each site link.
http://disserv.stu.umn.edu/disability/

University of Wisconsin: Trace Research and Development Center
This research center aims to make computers, the Internet, and information kiosks more accessible to everyone through universal (accessible) design. The site offers information about the center, project areas and activities, collaborators, and research and development history. Specific descriptions are available of the center's projects in underlying technologies research, applied research and development, transfer and industry support, and dissemination, education, and user support. Links are provided to sites of academic and industry collaborators. http://trace.wisc.edu/about

Virtual Assistive Technology Center
Visitors to this address will find articles and links to Internet sources for general information, commercial vendors, projects, and research related to assistive technologies. Shareware for Macintosh, Windows, and DOS operating systems can also be found through the site. Related books can be ordered at the site through Amazon.com.
http://www.at-center.com

Weaver's Web Site for Parents of Children with Brain Disorders
Hosted by the mother of a child with mental disabilities, this site offers parents in similar situations valuable suggestions for coping with mental illness in a child. Each of nearly 20 suggestions is offered with links to Internet resources for further information. Suggested coping strategies relate to self-education about the disorder, communication with the child, therapy, stress reduction, and support sources. http://www.ioa.com/~d-g-weaver

World Association of Persons with Disabilities
The purpose of this site is to offer resources for people with disabilities and their caregivers. There are discussion boards, a chat room, and a free weekly newsletter. Hundreds of links are categorized in the "Resources" section under topics such as aids to daily living, ADA, cognitive disabilities, grant resources, disability research, and rehabilitation. A listing of assistive devices and a marketplace are also available. The site can be read in French, German, Italian, Portuguese, and Spanish.
http://www.wapd.org/

7.16 DIVORCE

Children of Divorce: Psychological, Psychiatric, Behavioral Problems, and Suicide
This section of the Divorce Statistics Collection from Americans for Divorce Reform highlights the major aspects of the psychological effects of a broken family on children. Links to literature from the National Institute of Mental Health and the *Journal of Marriage and Family* are accessible, as is material and citations derived from major researchers in the field.
http://www.divorcereform.org/psy.html

Divorce Online Resources on divorce at this site include articles related to financial, legal, psychological, ownership, and other issues common to the process of divorce. Recent articles offer advice on child custody, choosing a matrimonial lawyer, dating, and other relevant topics. A bulletin board and professional referral directory are also available for use by site visitors. Professionals can list a practice in the referral section. Consumers confronting divorce will find this site a valuable reference.
http://www.divorceonline.com/ffindex.html

 Divorce Source Visitors can search the "Divorce Research Center" database for links to thousands of articles, case law, case analysis, and Web pages. Alternatively, the site can be browsed by topic, such as child and spousal support, custody and visitation, financial issues and assets, and general divorce information. There are also a directory of divorce professionals, finance calculators, divorce laws by state, cases of interest, discussion boards, and chat rooms. Available for purchase on the site are divorce forms, state divorce guidebooks, child support calculation reports, and a missing person search.
(some features fee-based) http://www.divorcesource.com/

 Divorce, Clinical Disorders, Childhood Depression This site examines the distinction between depressed mood and clinical disorders and offers suggestions on recognizing the important differences. Links to divorce articles, professional contact listings, psychological testing information, and the site's discussion/message board can be found.
http://www.divorcedoc.com/depressio.htm

7.17 DREAM RESEARCH

 Association for the Study of Dreams This nonprofit organization is dedicated to the "pure and applied investigation of dreams and dreaming." Conference information, a magazine, education resources, discussion forums, membership details, an online bookstore, details of current projects, and a membership directory are found at the site. Abstracts of articles and other details of the association's journal, *Dreaming,* are available at the site, as well as some full-text articles.
http://www.asdreams.org

 Dreamgate.com: Dream Resources Both offline and online dream resources are provided at this Web address, of interest to professionals and consumers. Offline resources include regional dream centers, groups, organizations, and newsletters. Online resources are comprehensive and include discussion lists, newsgroups, and Web sites. The sites are organized by category such as dream sharing, magazines and journals, organizations, dream journals, religion, lucid dreaming, research organizations, books and articles, Jung and dreams, and Freud and dreams.
http://www.dreamgate.com/dream/resources/

International Institute for Dream Research   From the University of California at Santa Cruz, technical information regarding methodology and findings via a method of objective and quantitative dream research is explained. Discoveries pertaining to cross-cultural similarities, gender influences, and age differences are analyzed with the approach, and the consistency and continuities between waking life and dreams lead the researchers to conclude that accurate predictions about the dreamers' concerns and interests may be made with the method. Content analysis, representative samples, and statistical approach are completely explained, and a spreadsheet for quantitative dream data may be downloaded. Scientists and students with further interest in the field may find links to additional information regarding quantitative dream study.
http://psych.ucsc.edu/dreams

Lucidity Institute   This Web site, dedicated to the understanding of lucid dreaming, research in the area, and the application of the research to the betterment of human health, offers resources for lucid dreaming via an online catalog that includes scientific publications, books, and tapes. Lecture and workshop listings and practical excerpts from lucid dreaming literature are accessible. Research articles and abstracts may also be viewed, and the institute discussion forum and mailing list keep visitors up-to-date regarding the physiology and philosophy of lucid dreaming, new Web sites, events, and dream experiments. http://www.lucidity.com

Psych Web: Freud: The Interpretation of Dreams   The full text of the third edition of Sigmund Freud's *The Interpretation of Dreams* is provided on this Web page. The book covers the scientific literature dealing with dreams, dream interpretation, dreams as wish-fulfillment, distortion in dreams, material and sources of dreams, "dream-work," and the psychology of the dream processes. The bibliography, before the publication of the first German edition in 1900, is included.
http://www.psychwww.com/books/interp/toc.htm

7.18 EMOTIONS

Cornell University: Emotions and Emotional Intelligence   An online bibliography on emotions and emotional intelligence is provided on this page, courtesy of a Cornell University professor. The site also offers a fact sheet defining emotional intelligence, its importance, and tests of emotional intelligence. Affect, mood, and emotions are also discussed, along with the neuropsychology of emotions. Methods for researching emotions are also discussed.
http://trochim.human.cornell.edu/gallery/young/emotion.htm

Ethics and Emotions Portal   This personal Web page, developed by Michael D. Speer, offers more than 100 links related to ethics and emotions. The links are organized as general information, drawn primarily from encyclopedias

and dictionaries, papers, articles, and abstracts; a bibliography; and a miscellaneous selection of related articles.
http://www.michaelspeer.com/emotions/

Forsyth's Motivation and Emotion Page   Subjects such as nonverbal expressions, personal motivation, happiness, anger, autonomic nervous system and emotions, emotional intelligence, and related sexual topics are discussed in comprehensive and detailed documents available at this site. In addition, there are links to resources on various aspects of psychology, such as intelligence, learning, personality, social psychology, and other related sites.
http://www.vcu.edu/hasweb/psy/psy101/forsyth/zmoemo.htm

Limbic System: The Center of Emotions   This Web site reviews the anatomy and function of the limbic system, offers a review of different theories on limbic system function and emotions, explains the evolution of emotions, and provides detailed information on specific brain structures and emotions. Informative illustrations are present.
http://www.healing-arts.org/n-r-limbic.htm

7.19 ETHICS AND PSYCHIATRY

Abuse, Memory, Science, Therapy Ethics, and Malpractice   Full-text articles, book reviews, tables of research findings, research studies, and peer-reviewed article abstracts are found at this site devoted to issues of therapy ethics. Users can request free reprints of more than 25 selected articles from the site. http://www.idealist.com/memories/sitemap.shtml

American Psychiatric Association (APA): Guidelines for Inpatient Facilities   Guidelines for psychiatric practice in public sector psychiatric inpatient facilities are featured on this Web page, courtesy of the American Psychiatric Association. Approved in 1993, the guidelines offer model job descriptions for the chief medical officer and staff psychiatrist. In addition, there are guidelines for psychiatric evaluation and treatment, emergencies, psychiatric staffing, psychiatric signatures, and psychiatric ethics.
http://www.psych.org/pract_of_psych/public_prac.cfm

American Psychiatric Association (APA): Principles of Medical Ethics with Annotations Especially Applicable to Psychiatry   This site provides the current Principles of Medical Ethics with Annotations Especially Applicable to Psychiatry. Many of the current annotations are based on the American Medical Association's Principles of Medical Ethics. Resources include the full-text Principles with Annotations, as well as procedures for handling complaints of unethical conduct. Addendums offer guidelines for ethical practice in organized settings, and answers are provided to questions about procedures for handling complaints of unethical conduct.
http://www.psych.org/apa_members/ethics_index.cfm

Forensic Psychiatry and Medicine: Professional Ethics This site offers a short discussion of professional ethics, as well as links to relevant professional associations, court rulings, articles, and major sites offering professional ethics resources. http://www.forensic-psych.com/articles/catProfEthics.html

7.20 FORENSIC PSYCHIATRY

American Academy of Psychiatry and the Law (AAPL) Intended for professionals, the American Academy of Psychiatry and the Law Web page offers information on forensic psychiatry. The site offers tables of contents and abstracts, dating back to 1973, from the *Journal of the American Academy of Psychiatry and Law.* There are also full-text articles from their newsletter, ethical guidelines, and a fellowship directory. Information on meetings and certification is also found. Related links connect to legal resources, government information, and organizations. Visitors can also send questions, by e-mail, to members of the academy. http://www.emory.edu/AAPL/

Forensic Psychiatry Online Presented by *Psychiatry Online,* this site offers full-text professional articles relating to forensic psychiatry. *Psychiatry Online* provides brief and case reports, an archive of professional documents, transcultural mental health resources, news, a bulletin board, current research articles, CME materials, a forum for students, a side-effect registry, and links to worldwide psychiatry resources and other related sites. Users can search the site for specific information and order books and other products at the site. This site is supported by an unrestricted educational grant from AstraZeneca. http://www.priory.com/forpsy.htm

Forensic Psychiatry Resource Page This site, created by a professor and medical director of the Taylor Hardin Secure Medical Facility, offers links to a wide range of forensic psychiatry resources. Visitors can access a database comparing forensic facilities, general psychiatry, and legal information for attorneys and psychiatrists, information on forensics in countries outside of the United States, position statements from the American Psychiatric Association, meeting and conference calendars, literature searches through MEDLINE, summaries of landmark cases in mental health law, and legal databases. http://mhnet.org/law/about.html

Forensic Psychiatry Resources A board-certified psychiatrist compiled this list of Internet resources related to forensic psychiatry. Professional associations, additional Internet directories, legal resources, sites hosted by psychiatrists, institutes, professional services resources, and educational materials are included. http://www.umdnj.edu/psyevnts/forensic.html

Forensic Psychiatry: Medicine and Psychiatry Expert This site is hosted by the co-director of the Program in Psychiatry and the Law at Harvard Medical School. Subjects discussed at the site include managed healthcare and medical malpractice, employment issues, emotional and physical damages, im-

portant court rulings on standards for experts, product liability, criminal justice and public safety, family and custody issues, professional ethics, trial consulting, organizational consulting, and risk management. Discussions are accompanied by general and professional articles. Links are available to Internet resources and articles related to telemedicine and other related sites.
http://www.forensic-psych.com

New York Center for Neuropsychology and Forensic Behavioral Science   This center, a combination of two New York mental health centers, offers diagnostic, assessment, treatment, and consulting services to patients, as well as to medical and judicial professionals. Services include clinical evaluations and psychological testing; individual, group, couples, and family therapy; psychological and legal testimony; diagnostic services; sexual offender treatment; and corporate consultations. In addition, the center offers workshops and seminars.   http://www.nyforensic.com

Ultimate Forensic Psychology Database   This site is home to a large database of different types of forensic psychology resources, including a library of books on various related topics, a journals list, a news bulletin, educational information, events index, consulting directory, employment, FAQ section, related links, and a large article database. An online newsgroup and information on forensic psychology are also provided.
http://flash.lakeheadu.ca/~pals/forensics/index.html

University of Virginia: Institute of Law, Psychiatry, and Public Policy   This institute at the University of Virginia is an interdisciplinary program in mental health law, forensic psychiatry, and forensic psychology. The institute offers academic programs, forensic clinical evaluations, professional training, empirical and theoretical research, and public policy consultation and review. Information at the site includes a description of the institute, teaching programs, research activities, clinical evaluations and other services, and fellowship programs. Faculty biographies, publications, a directory of forensic evaluators in Virginia, and registration forms for conferences, training programs, and symposia are also found at the site.
http://www.ilppp.virginia.edu

7.21 GENETICS AND PSYCHIATRY

Genetics of Depressive Illness   Archived article links available at this site cover the recent agenda in the field of genetics and psychiatry, heredity versus environment as a cause of depression, and the genetics of seasonal affective disorder, affective and schizophrenic disorders, and bipolar depression.
http://www.psycom.net/depression.central.genetics.html

Human Behavioral Genetics   Originally published in the *American Journal of Human Genetics,* a full-text article on human behavioral genetics is posted on this Web page, hosted by the Federation of American Societies for Experi-

mental Biology. The article examines traditional methods of behavioral-genetic analysis through family, twin, and adoption studies. New approaches are then discussed such as quantitative-trait loci analysis and biometric model fitting. Ethical and social issues are also addressed, especially in terms of the responsibilities of the scientist. A bibliography is included.
http://www.faseb.org/genetics/ashg/policy/pol-28.htm

International Behavioural and Neural Genetics Society (IBANGS)
Formerly the European Behavioural and Neural Genetics Society (EBANGS), this international society supports research in the field of neurobehavioral genetics. Membership information, society information, a member directory, meeting details, links to member societies, and past meeting transcripts are available at the site. Links are also available at the site to sources for meeting information, societies and networks, institutions and databases, and publications of interest in neurobehavioral and neural genetics.
http://www.ibngs.org

International Society of Psychiatric Genetics   The International Society of Psychiatric Genetics promotes and facilitates research, education, and communication in the genetics of psychiatric disorders, substance abuse, and related traits. This address offers a board of directors listing, information on upcoming meetings, society bylaws and mission statement, and links to several related sites. http://www.ispg.net

National Institute of Mental Health (NIMH): Genetics and Mental Disorders   The full text of the *Report of the National Institute of Mental Health's Genetics Workgroup* is offered on this Web page. The report examines current knowledge of mental disorders and genetics, status of research programs, and recommendations for future research. Specific disorders addressed include schizophrenia, bipolar disorder, and early-onset depression. An extensive bibliography is included.
http://www.nimh.nih.gov/research/genetics.htm

National Institute on Drug Abuse (NIDA): Genetics Web Resources
This address offers a comprehensive list of Internet sites related to human genetics and mental health. Links are included to major government and private sources for resources related to human genetics, genetics of animals used in research, quantitative methods, organizations, journals, and publishers.
http://www.nida.nih.gov/genetics/genetics6.html

Psychiatric Genetics   A comprehensive listing of links to genetic databases and projects seeking to reveal the genetic basis of diseases influenced by multiple genes can be found at this Web site. Current mathematical models that go beyond the standard segregation linkage research paradigm may demonstrate further insights into genetic etiology of psychiatric illness. The actual projects explore familial syndrome patterns, genetic maps, polynucleotide markers, and genotype-phenotype associations. More than 30 genetic databases from promi-

nent national and international laboratories and institutes are directly accessible. http://www.unizh.ch/bli/BLI/Subhome/geneti.html

7.22 GERIATRIC PSYCHIATRY AND GERONTOLOGY

American Association for Geriatric Psychiatry (AAGP)   Professional resources on this Web page include funding opportunities and the "Stepping Stones" program, which educates residents on fellowship training and assists fellows in career planning. There is also information on scholarships and the activities of the Geriatric Mental Health Foundation. Advocacy information is also provided. A section for patients and caregivers offers fact sheets on dementia, depression, and the role of the geriatric psychiatrist.
http://www.aagpgpa.org/

American Geriatrics Society (AGS)   The American Geriatrics Society Web page offers information for patients and professionals on geriatric mental and physical health issues. Professionals will find information on Alzheimer's research grants, fellowships, certification exams, and CME opportunities. Patient educational materials cover topics such as depression, Alzheimer's disease, dementia, and memory loss.
http://www.americangeriatrics.org/

American Psychological Association (APA): Division 20   This division of the American Psychological Association studies the psychology of adult development and aging. The site offers information about the division, including research and employment opportunities, programs of study, awards, and a directory of members. Educational resources include videotape and book lists, graduate and undergraduate syllabi, and curriculum suggestions. Students can access a guide to graduate and postdoctoral study, as well as a list of student awards offered by the institute. Conference details, including those offering continuing medical education credits, and links to related sites are also found at this address. http://aging.ufl.edu/apadiv20/apadiv20.htm

American Society on Aging (ASA)   The American Society on Aging provides information resources on gerontology through educational programming, publications, and training. General resources at this site include membership and contact details, meeting information, conference and training schedules, and awards listings. Links are available to information on publications, including *Aging Today* and *Generations*. Visitors can also access news, links to related sites, job banks, and information on specific ASA networks, including business and aging; environments, services, and technologies; healthcare and aging; lesbian and gay aging issues; lifelong education; mental health and aging; multicultural aging issues; religion and spirituality; and aging. Databases containing information on conferences, training events, and resources on aging issues are available for members, as well as a chat forum, special offers, and member directories. (some features fee-based) http://www.asaging.org

CanWest Therapeutics: Geriatric Institute   Visitors to this site, presented by CanWest Therapeutics, can access a calendar of upcoming conferences, chat forums, patient education materials on anxiety and depression, links to related sites, and an online bookstore. Articles, presentations, case studies, and other resources are available only to professional members.
(free registration) http://www.geriatricinstitute.com/messenger.htm

ElderWeb   Primarily for patients and their caregivers, this site offers information and resources on elder care. Visitors will find articles on topics such as Alzheimer's disease, medications, mental health, and senior activities, under the "Body and Soul" section. There are also articles related to finance, law, housing, and care. An associations section offers lists of associations and agencies that offer elder care. An "Eldercare Locator" enables users to search for services such as an attorney, financial planner, or nurse, by region.
http://www.elderweb.com/

Gerontological Society of America   The Gerontological Society of America promotes research and disseminates information related to gerontological research. Site sections list awards, annual meeting details, press releases, employment opportunities, news, publications, society divisions, and links to related sites. Related foundations, a referral service, useful sources for information, student organization details, and membership details are also found through the site. A discussion is available on social security and women.
http://www.geron.org

GeroWeb Virtual Library on Aging   A database of Web sites related to aging and older individuals is featured on this site, maintained by Wayne State University. The database can be searched by keyword or browsed by topic, such as Alzheimer's, grants and funding, mental health, social services, support groups, and women's issues. Search results offer a list of Web sites with short descriptions of each.
http://www.iog.wayne.edu/GeroWebd/GeroWeb.html

International Psychogeriatric Association (IPA)   Dedicated to psychogeriatrics, this Web page offers useful information for professionals. There are full-text articles on psychogeriatrics and on the behavioral and psychological symptoms of dementia. There is also a guide to the diagnosis and assessment of Alzheimer's disease, along with downloadable presentations. The association's newsletter is available on the site, as well as tables of contents and abstracts from their journal, *International Psychogeriatrics*. Information on joining IPA is also found. http://www.ipa-online.org/

National Aging Research Institute, Incorporated   This Australian institute for gerontology and geriatric medicine research offers general information about the institute, current projects, research publications, educational resources, and links to related sites at this address. Visitors have access to some full-text articles from official publications of the institute.
http://www.mednwh.unimelb.edu.au

National Institute on Aging (NIA) The National Institute on Aging promotes healthy aging and supports public education and biomedical, social, and behavioral research. Press releases, employment opportunities, program announcements, and program updates are found at the site. The site describes extramural and intramural aging research programs, as well as an international program, and provides news from the National Advisory Council on Aging. Researchers can access funding training information. For the general public, there are resources on Alzheimer's disease, public education booklets, brochures, fact sheets, press releases, and public service advertisements. Assorted publications for health professionals are available on issues related to the care of older people. http://www.nih.gov/nia

Senior Sites Hosted by the California Associations of Homes and Services for the Aging, this site serves as a directory for senior citizens searching for information on nonprofit housing communities and other resources on the Internet. Resources at the site include a discussion on the benefits of choosing nonprofit housing, a calendar of upcoming events of interest to seniors by state, a directory of national and state associations, and links to other useful sites. Visitors can conduct detailed searches of the site's directory of nonprofit housing facilities, choosing from a wide range of options to include in the search. http://www.seniorsites.com

U.S. Administration on Aging: Web Sites on Aging This site contains links to resources specific to aging and general mental health. Specific topics include state agencies, federal agencies, and megasites. There are also related resources on the Administration on Aging site, including a resource directory, retirement and financial planning, statistical data, and an eldercare locator. http://www.aoa.dhhs.gov/agingsites/default.htm

7.23 GRIEF AND BEREAVEMENT

American Association of Retired Persons (AARP): Grief and Loss Created to provide information about grief and loss, this Web page offers information for widows and widowers, family members, and professionals. Widows and widowers will find articles on common reactions to loss, FAQs, and types of help available. For family members, there is information on understanding parent's grief and on depression. Professionals will find statistics on widowhood, grief in the workplace, and information on beginning a bereavement program. Additional resources on the site include a list of grief organizations, brochures, professional organizations, and journals. http://www.aarp.org/griefandloss/

Compassionate Friends Compassionate Friends is a national nonprofit organization helping families cope with the death of a child of any age, from any cause. Visitors to the site can access chapter directories, brochures, conference details, links to chapter Web sites, news, and links to related Internet re-

sources. An online catalog of publications and videotapes, general information about the organization, chat forums, and subscription information for the organization's magazine are also available at the site.
http://www.compassionatefriends.org

Crisis, Grief, and Healing This site is hosted by a psychotherapist and author of several popular books on male grieving patterns. General information about the grieving process, book excerpts, an online bookstore, chat forums, and suggestions on grieving from other site visitors are all found at this address. Information about the site host, Tom Golden, LCSW, includes a description of his private practice, speaking schedule, workshops, and consultations.
http://www.webhealing.com

Death and Dying Primarily a support site, Death and Dying offers such resources as a chat room and message boards, links to grief support articles, newsletters, and other related sites and organizations. Also, there are planners, many fact sheets on grief support and bereavement, near-death experience articles, terminal illness issues, legal subjects, and sites for online support, expert advice, and child and adolescent related subjects.
http://www.beyondindigo.com

GriefNet GriefNet, supervised by a practicing clinical psychologist, offers online grief support through more than 30 e-mail support groups. Visitors can join e-mail support groups for children or for those suffering the loss of a spouse or partner, child, parent, sibling, or friend. Special groups are devoted to losses due to health problems, support for men, losses of pets, deaths due to violence, suicide, and spiritual aspects of loss. One group offers discussion and support to professional counselors. Visitors can also access a companion site for children, an online bookstore, memorials, an online newsletter, and links to related resources, including suicide prevention and survivors' resources.
http://rivendell.org

State University of New York (SUNY) University at Buffalo Counseling Center: Coping with Death and Dying Targeted to college students, this fact sheet offers information on typical reactions to death and dying. The site discusses stages of grief, including denial and shock, anger, bargaining, guilt, depression, loneliness, acceptance, and hope. Suggestions on coping with death and dying, as well as helping bereaved students, are available, and contact information is provided for University sources of help.
http://ub-counseling.buffalo.edu/process.shtml

Teenage Grief (TAG) This nonprofit organization is composed of professionals who train school personnel, health professionals, law enforcement officials, and organizations serving at-risk youth in grief support. The site discusses why ongoing support is necessary for grieving teens, in addition to grief and the adolescent, the spiritual dimension of grief, and anger. News, an online store for publications, and links to related sites are also available at this address.
http://www.smartlink.net/~tag/index.html

University of Baltimore: Grief Support Groups A listing of grief support groups is provided on this Web page, organized by state. Each state has several kinds of groups, for pregnancy/infant loss, parent, children, widow/widower, suicide loss, homicide loss, automobile death loss, general bereavement, and hospice support.
http://www.ubalt.edu/bereavement/states.htm

7.24 HOMELESSNESS

Department of Health and Human Services (HHS): Homelessness
Resources related to homelessness are featured on this Department of Health and Human Services Web page. Under the "Profile of Homelessness" section, visitors can view the results from a national survey of homeless assistance providers and homeless persons, as well as an excerpt from *Priority Home!: The Federal Plan to Break the Cycle of Homelessness* (1994). Many links are provided on the site to homeless resources within the Department; such as programs, publications, and funding, links to other government agencies; a non-profit organization search engine; and a list of news resources.
http://aspe.os.dhhs.gov/progsys/homeless/

Health Care for the Homeless (HCH): Information Resource Center
This resource center provides technical assistance and information to providers and program staff in an effort to improve the delivery of healthcare services to homeless individuals. Site resources include annotated bibliographies; clinical tools, including clinical intake, assessment, and screening topics; a video lending library; a quarterly bulletin; conference details; a directory of current HCH grantees and subcontractors; and a directory of organizations providing services to homeless individuals.
http://www.prainc.com/hch/index.html

Knowledge Exchange Network: Homelessness Several sites are listed at this address, offering access to the home pages of nonprofit organizations, government agencies, and service providers. Short site descriptions are provided with each link.
http://www.mentalhealth.org/links/homelessness.htm

National Alliance to End Homelessness The National Alliance to End Homelessness is made up of public, private, and nonprofit organizations working together to end homelessness. Their site offers facts on homelessness, policy and action alerts, and profiles of related programs. The publications section offers many online fact sheets, reports, and *The Alliance* newsletter. There are also fact sheets for children, categorized by grade level for kindergarten through high school age. Links to related organizations are found.
http://www.endhomelessness.org/

National Coalition for the Homeless (NCH) This national organization is an advocacy network of individuals, activists, and service providers working

to end homelessness through public education, policy advocacy, grassroots organizing, and technical assistance. Visitors to the site will find facts and statistics on homelessness, including a discussion of homelessness and mental health, legislation and policy resources, news alerts, organization directories, information on NCH projects, a calendar of events, links to related Internet resources, an online newsletter, and NCH publications. The NCH online library offers a bibliographic database with references to research on homelessness, housing, and poverty.
http://www.nationalhomeless.org/

National Law Center on Homelessness and Poverty   Dedicated to eliminating homelessness in America, the National Law Center on Homelessness and Poverty offers fact sheets on homelessness and poverty that examine the causes and solutions. In addition, there is a publications catalog of reports, articles, and their newsletter. The site index offers information organized by topic, such as the Earned Income Credit, the education of homeless children, food stamp information, civil and legal rights of homeless people, and vacant federal property acquisition.
http://www.nlchp.org/

National Resources Center on Homelessness and Mental Illness   The National Resource Center on Homelessness and Mental Illness provides policy makers, service providers, researchers, consumers, and other interested parties with technical assistance and research findings related to homelessness and mental illness. Resources offered at the site include a description of technical assistance services, directories of organizations and assistance resources, annotated bibliographies by subject, a periodic bulletin, events notices, monographs and papers, and links to related sites. Visitors can also submit information requests by e-mail or phone.
http://www.prainc.com/nrc

University of Colorado: Homelessness   More than 500 links are provided on this site with information on homelessness. The sites are categorized under topics such as discussion lists; academic courses, education, articles, and fact sheets; art; children and youth; health and medical services; homeless newspapers; shelters; resources; laws and rights; and service providers. There are also links to national and international government agencies.
http://csf.colorado.edu/homeless/

7.25 INCLUSION AND INTEGRATION

See also Community-Based Psychiatric Treatment.

National Program Office on Self-Determination   Dedicated to the rights of people with disabilities, the National Program Office on Self Determination works for the freedom to exercise rights, authority over money used for support, support from other resources, and responsibility towards their community. The site offers a publication catalog, some full-text articles from their newsletter, *Common Sense,* and an e-mail discussion list. Links to related resources are provided. http://www.self-determination.org/index.htm

Syracuse University: National Resource Center on Community Integration   Visitors to this site will find bulletins, research reports, and articles related to the integration or inclusion of people with disabilities, especially those who are mentally retarded and developmentally disabled. Topics include positive practices, community supports, family supports, friendship, gender and disability, and housing. Additional topics cover inclusion, multiculturalism and disability, recreation, self-advocacy, supported employment, and supported living. http://web.syr.edu/~thechp/nrc.htm

7.26 INFERTILITY

Infertility Counseling and Support   This online fact sheet, courtesy of the American Society for Reproductive Medicine, outlines the emotional stresses associated with infertility and provides a checklist for depression and information on finding counseling and support. Adobe Acrobat reader is needed for viewing this PDF file.
http://www.asrm.org/Patients/FactSheets/Counseling-Fact.pdf

Psychological and Coping Information   Included at this Web site are educational tools designed to assist those coping with infertility. An in-depth article and online guide written by infertility specialists offers advice to family members and friends to aid in understanding the emotional difficulties associated with infertility, and a list of FAQs attempts to explain when psychological counseling may be useful as well as the general impact that infertility has on emotional well-being.
http://www.thelaboroflove.com/forum/infertility/coping.html

Psychological and Social Issues of Infertility   Encouraging a balanced approach to infertility, this Internet resource guide to the psychological and social issues provides useful strategies for managing the complex emotions associated with infertility. Survey results offer insight into depression and infertility and the stress of infertility compared to other factors and conclude that the Internet has great potential to help people faced with infertility. An article summarizing ways in which to balance infertility treatment and work-related responsibilities and an online brochure for preferred responses to insensitive family and friends are some of the features found.
http://www.ihr.com/infertility/psychosocial.html

7.27 INFORMATICS

An Informatics Curriculum for Psychiatry This in-depth research article on the current state of information technology and its relation to the field of psychiatry outlines the components of medical informatics principles as applied to the field. Patient care, communication, education, and practice management are stressed. Assessment of resources and other issues affecting program implementation are also discussed.
http://www.psych.med.umich.edu/Web/Umpsych/staff/mhuang/papers/infocurric.htm

National Library of Medicine (NLM): Research Programs Visitors to this site will find links to National Library of Medicine centers for research; computational molecular biology resources, including molecular biology databases and other online molecular tools; and medical informatics resources. Additional materials available through this site are relevant to digital computing and communications, digital library research, interactive multimedia technology, and medical informatics training. The Visible Human Project and details of extramural funding opportunities are also available.
http://www.nlm.nih.gov/resprog.html

Psychiatric Society for Informatics The home page of the Psychiatric Society for Informatics serves to increase the understanding and use of informatics related to the field of psychiatry. Information on the organization, its current news and upcoming meetings, online membership information and benefits, and the organization's electronic newsletter are all presented.
http://www.psych.med.umich.edu

7.28 INSTITUTIONALIZATION

University of Minnesota: Institutionalization A booklet for parents, dated March 1995, on the long-term effects of institutionalization on children from Eastern Europe and the former Soviet Union is featured on this Web page. Intended to help newly adopting parents, the booklet describes the environment for infants and toddlers, as well as pre-school and school-age children, in institutions. Research findings on institutionalization are outlined, and the importance of early intervention and appropriate services emphasized. Diagnostic classifications of mental health and developmental disorders are also discussed. A recommended reading list is provided.
http://www.cyfc.umn.edu/Adoptinfo/institutionalization.html

7.29 MANAGED CARE

American Psychiatric Association (APA): APA Handbook for the Development of Public Managed Care Systems Prepared by the APA's Managed Care Committee, this online publication offers its viewers chapters on

program development, patient and clinician rights, and cultural competence for effective healthcare delivery in cross-cultural situations. Additional requirements of effective public managed care systems are reviewed, including those for service access, education of the public, community outreach, and quality improvement programs.
http://www.psych.org/pract_of_psych/handbook.cfm

American Psychiatric Association (APA): Health Policy, Economics, and Practice Management Resources   A glossary of managed care technical terms, an online guide to health and medical economics resources on the Web, and managed care articles from Medscape are provided at this site. Visitors will also find a health plan performance measurement link from an organization dedicated to providing information on the quality of the nation's managed care plans.
http://www.psych.org/other_orgs/health_econ.cfm

Medscape: Psychiatry: Managed Care   Several articles related to the practice of psychiatry in a managed care environment are featured on this Web page. The articles cover topics such as medication costs, treatment of depression and bipolar disorder, short-term dynamic psychotherapy, and the future of the profession. (free registration)   http://psychiatry.medscape.com/ Home/Topics/psychiatry/directories/dir-PSY.ManagedCare.html

National Institute of Mental Health (NIMH): Research Center on Managed Care for Psychiatric Disorders   Sponsored by the National Institute of Mental Health, the NIMH Research Center on Managed Care for Psychiatric Disorders is a joint program of UCLA and RAND. Research programs center around policy, clinical services, and vulnerable populations. Brief descriptions of the research projects for each of these core areas are provided. Abstracts from the center's journal publications, working papers, and books are offered. Community updates—brief articles on research findings—are also found.
http://www.hsrcenter.ucla.edu/NIMHcenter.html

7.30 MARRIAGE

Coalition for Marriage, Family, and Couples Education   In addition to links that provide general statistics about marriage and divorce rates, this site has links to fact files on divorce predictors, a large number of online articles both scholarly and popular, a directory for counseling and training programs, and conference information. A fact sheet on the coalition itself, a directory of children's courses, books, conference tapes, and other products are available as well. http://www.smartmarriages.com

Latest Research on Marital Adjustment and Satisfaction   This report of the American Psychological Association briefly outlines the recent research regarding the relationship between psychological type and a couple's satisfac-

tion with each other. Also presented is a summary on recent findings and overall trends related to marital adjustment and detachment from parents.
http://www.apa.org/releases/marital.html

Marital Problems   A listing of Web sites, with descriptions and ratings, on marital problems is provided on this Web page, maintained by the ABC's of Parenting. More than 15 sites are listed on topics such as divorce, marriage therapy, father's rights, and trial separation.
http://www.abcparenting.com/index.cfm?cat=49

Psychology: Marriage and Family   This Web site describes current films, courtesy of the American Psychiatric Association, American Psychological Association, and other organizations, that document universal difficulties and themes within the context of marriage. Insightful explanations as to whom people fall in love with and why couples argue are addressed in these family relations documentaries that may be ordered online.
http://www.filmakers.com/MARRIAGE.html

WholeFamily Marriage Center   A consumer-oriented site, the WholeFamily Marriage Center Web site provides real-life situations and offers therapeutic coping formulas for couples. The crisis center presents difficult dilemmas encountered within the marital relationship and offers responses and opportunities for visitors to contribute their own advice. Self-tests, exercises, and surveys help partners to understand each other more completely. "Real Life Dramas" and "Family Soap Opera" both deal with a variety of marital issues including money, sensitivity, communication, fighting fairly, alcohol, children, and the secrets to successful marriages.
http://www.wholefamily.com/aboutyourmarriage/index.html

7.31 MEN AND MENTAL HEALTH

Mind: Men's Mental Health   This U.K.-based mental health charity has devoted a significant portion of its site to the specific mental health concerns of men. General information on men and their use of the healthcare system, recent study summaries of the occurrence of depression and other mental disorders in men, and details on gender differences in the expression and course of schizophrenia, substance abuse, personality disorders, and other mental health problems are introduced, as well as some specific social causes of men's mental distress.
http://www.mind.org.uk/information/
factsheets/M/mental/MEN%27S_MENTAL_HEALTH1.asp

7.32 MENTAL HEALTH POLICY

Mental Health: A Report of the Surgeon General The full text of a report on mental health, from the Surgeon General's office, is featured on this page. It is the first report of its kind from the Surgeon General's office, and it aims to review the scientific advances in the study of mental health and mental illnesses. The report consists of eight chapters covering the fundamentals of mental health and mental illness, children and mental health, adults and mental health, older adults and mental health, organization and financing of services, confidentiality, and a vision for the future. The report is also available in Adobe Acrobat PDF format.
http://www.surgeongeneral.gov/library/mentalhealth/toc.html

7.33 METHODOLOGY AND STATISTICS

American College of Neuropsychopharmacology: Methodology and Statistics An article, written by a statistician, is featured on this site on the methodological and statistical progress in psychiatric clinical research. Issues covered include diagnosis and disorder, the importance of validity, and meta-analysis. In addition, the value and importance of longitudinal research is discussed. Abuse of biometric language, in particular risk and causal factors, is examined. Fitting mathematical models to the real world and the need for exploratory research are also discussed.
http://www.acnp.org/G4/GN401000178/CH174.html

Lancaster University Centre for Applied Statistics: Statistics Glossary Basic definitions of statistics terminology are presented at this site's links, as well as pages offering definitions related to sampling, probability, and hypothesis testing. Pages of terminology for categorical data, non-parametric methods, and time series data are also found, as well as an alphabetical index of all included entries.
http://www.cas.lancs.ac.uk/glossary_v1.1/main.html

Mental Health Net: Statistics and Research Design The collection of links at this site contains an assortment of statistical information in the mental health field. Clinical research trial listings, a pamphlet regarding library research in psychology, a tutorial addressing experimental design, and a publication addressing the pitfalls of data analysis are included. Visitors will also find related newsgroup access, mailing lists on psychological statistics and research design, research papers links, and related professional organization site connections. http://www.mentalhelp.net/guide/pro16.htm

Society for the Quantitative Analyses of Behavior The Society for the Quantitative Analyses of Behavior Web page offers annual conference information, as well as abstracts from conference papers dating back to 1994. There are

also video presentations for sale, a short list of mathematical Web resources, and an e-mail discussion list. http://sqab.psychology.org/

7.34 NON-TREATMENT CONSEQUENCES

ApplesForHealth.com: Mental Illness In America The societal and economic costs of not treating mental illness are briefly discussed in this fact sheet. Disorders such as depression, manic-depressive illness, suicide, schizophrenia, obsessive-compulsive disorder, and posttraumatic stress disorder are covered. http://www.applesforhealth.com/illamerica1.html

Non-Treatment Consequences Consequences of untreated mental illness are explored at this informative site, which offers statistics on homelessness, incarceration, episodes of violence, victimization, and suicide. The costs and community impact of untreated mental illnesses are included in this survey. http://www.psychlaws.org/GeneralResources/Fact1.htm

7.35 NUTRITION AND MENTAL HEALTH

Mental Health and Nutrition Journal The *Mental Health and Nutrition Journal* is an online publication presenting information from recent studies investigating links between nutrition and several mental disorders, including schizophrenia, bipolar disorder, depression, Alzheimer's disease, and other dementias. Articles, notices of upcoming events, tutorials, links to related sites, and a glossary of relevant terms are all available at this address. Both professionals and consumers will find the articles presented at the site interesting and informative. http://www.mhnj.com/

Nutrition Science News Online: Natural Remedies for Depression A report on altering the brain's chemistry through dietary changes is presented in this online issue of *Nutrition Science News*. The possible roles of amino acid supplementation, vitamin and mineral therapy, and herbal additions to the diet are explored in terms of boosting neurotransmitters and elevating mood. http://www.healthwellexchange.com/ nutritionsciencenews/NSN_backs/Feb_99/depression.cfm?path=ex

7.36 OCCUPATIONAL PSYCHIATRY

Academy of Organizational and Occupational Psychiatry (AOOP) The Academy of Organizational and Occupational Psychiatry provides a forum for communication between psychiatric professionals and personnel in the workplace. The site offers annual meeting details, general academy news items, and a description of the organization and its goals. Research papers, bulletins,

membership details, descriptions of previous annual meetings, and links to related sites are found at this address.
http://www.aoop.org

Society for Industrial and Organizational Psychology   Professionals interested in industrial and organizational (I-O) psychology can read the online version of the society's journal, *The Industrial-Organizational Psychologist,* on this site. Additional features of the site include conference information, graduate training programs, a job database, and a publications catalog. Related links offer information on grants, I-O groups, and I-O related sites.
http://www.siop.org/

7.37 PATIENT EDUCATION AND SUPPORT

ABC's of Internet Therapy   This consumers guide to online counseling provides links to fact sheets on online therapy and its related issues, therapists' credentials, information on teletherapy, its ethics, confidentiality, legal aspects, and effectiveness. The kinds of services available, a therapist directory, and a newsroom are provided. http://www.metanoia.org/imhs

About.com: Mental Health Resources   More than 700 sites related to mental health are found in the About.com directory, intended for consumers. The sites are organized by subject and cover anxiety and panic, depression, personality disorders, schizophrenia, stress management, and obsessive- compulsive disorder. Other topics include medications, services online, self-help, online journals, and psychotherapy. There are also links to search tools, government resources, and a glossary.
http://mentalhealth.about.com/health/mentalhealth/

American Self-Help Clearinghouse: Self-Help Sourcebook Online   Supported by Mental Health Net, this site primarily serves those persons affected by mental health disorders who are searching for support groups and information. Resources available include FAQs; support group research; information on starting support groups; and local, national, and international self-help clearinghouses and phone numbers. Links to various disorders and online purchase of this guide are available. http://mentalhelp.net/selfhelp

Concerned Counseling   At this Web address, consumers can interact with counselors, access online support groups, view the events calendar, get information on eating disorders, and access fact sheets on over 40 psychiatric disorders and topics. Chat rooms, bulletin boards, and extensive support information are present. http://www.concernedcounseling.com/

Coping with Serious Illness   Written by a clinical psychologist, this article gives answers to common questions about medical illness and mental health. Topics include the importance of mental health, psychological therapy, emotional support, coping issues, support information, and how to choose the best therapy. http://helping.apa.org/mind_body/haber.html

CYFERnet: Children, Youth, and Families Education and Research Network   Part of the National Children, Youth, and Families at Risk Initiative, this site has links to scientific information on children, adolescents, families, and the community. Each subject area contains a number of links to additional support and information resources. Available at this site are chat room and a section for professionals that contains links to databases, funding information, and training information. This site also provides resources for children, current events, and a number of links to community project information. http://www.cyfernet.org

Focusing on Bodily Sensations   This page on biofeedback and the theory of emotional feedback in psychology was created by a psychologist and provides facts on these topics, as well as links to related sites, links to an electronic book on biofeedback, scientific research studies on emotions, and information on the theory of emotions and biofeedback equipment. http://www.netvision.net.il/php/gshalif/

Handling Your Psychiatric Disability in Work and School   Dedicated to supplying information about the Americans with Disabilities Act for people with psychiatric disabilities, this site provides consumers and professionals with links to fact sheets on accommodations, legal support for affected persons, discrimination in school and work, mental illness and work issues, disclosing your disability, learning and mental illness topics, documenting your disability, and other resources. http://www.bu.edu/sarpsych/jobschool

Internet Mental Health: Booklets   Online patient education booklets and related resources are listed at this informative site. Links are listed by topic, including anxiety disorders, childhood disorders, eating disorders, impulse-control disorders, mood disorders, personality disorders, schizophrenia, sleep disorders, substance disorders, medications, treatment and therapy, and general interest. http://www.mentalhealth.com/book/fr40.html

Mental Health InfoSource   Resources related to mental health are provided on this site, primarily for consumers. The "MH Interactive" section offers discussion forums, chat rooms, and an ask-the-expert column. The site also features an A-to-Z listing of disorders, including attention deficit disorder, bipolar disorder, and schizophrenia. Each disorder entry contains articles and related sites. The "Healthier You" section offers links to resources, support, associations, and online articles. Professionals will find continuing education opportunities. http://www.mhsource.com/

Mental Help: Procedures to Avoid   Primarily for consumers, this document, written by a clinician, lists more than 10 therapies of dubious merit and reviews their therapeutic procedures and scientific value. References are provided. http://www.quackwatch.com/01QuackeryRelatedTopics/mentserv.html

Mentalwellness.com In addition to providing resources for finding support groups and therapists, this site has links to mental illness and economic issues, support issues, books, mental health definitions and fact sheets on various psychiatric disorders.
http://www.mentalwellness.com

National Network of Adult and Adolescent Children Who Have Mentally Ill Parent(s) Created by adult children of mentally ill parents, this Web site offers many links to articles and other documents that provide information and support, as well as to other Internet sources of information.
http://home.vicnet.net.au/~nnaami

Patient UK This site lists a large number of links (mostly for resources in the United Kingdom) to organizations, personal pages, Web sites, fact sheets, and support groups related to mental health topics. In addition, information on diseases, medicine, books, alternative treatments, and self-help topics can be found. http://www.patient.co.uk

Self-Help Magazine This site offers a large number of links to questions and answers for a range of mental health issues, such as children's behavior, dreams, depression, stress disorders, addiction, grief, divorce, Internet psychology, men's and women's topics, relationships, aging, and seasonal issues. There are links to discussion forums, online products, lists of related articles on various topics, telehealth resources, a newsletter for professionals, and other Web sites of interest.
http://www.shpm.com

Support-Group.com Support-Group.com allows people with health, personal, and relationship issues to share their experiences through bulletin boards and online chats and provides a wide variety of links to support-related information on the Internet. The A-to-Z listing offers hundreds of connections to disease-related support, bereavement assistance, marriage and family issue groups, and women's and men's issues, to name a few. The "Bulletin Board Tracker" lists the most recent messages and provides a complete cross-reference of topics. By visiting the Support-Group.com chat schedule page, dates, times, and group facilitators for upcoming chat events can be viewed.
http://www.support-group.com

World Federation for Mental Health This international organization is devoted to preventing mental illness, promoting mental health, and providing education and support to those affected by mental illness. There are links to conference information, the Eastern Mediterranean branch of the federation, programs sponsored by the federation, their newsletter, related organizations, and consumer and survivor information. General information about the federation and membership is also included. http://www.wfmh.com

7.38 PATIENT EXPLOITATION

A Thin Line: Patient/Therapist Sexual Contact   Sexual misconduct in medical settings is a major ethical issue that is explored through this Dateline NBC discussion. Statistical incidence, warning signs, and methods of filing complaints are all discussed.
http://www.ect.org/shame/dateline.html

Patient Exploitation   Patient/therapist sexual conduct is explored at this American Psychiatric Association (APA) site, which explores issues related to medical ethics and the position of the APA. A listing of state psychiatry associations is provided to report incidences of sexual exploitation by therapists.
http://www.psych.org/public_info/patient_&_fam.cfm

Sexual Abuse in Professional Relationships   Ethical and legal aspects of patient sexual exploitation are explored at this site which examines the extent of the problem, issues of ethical conduct, and warning signs.
http://www.kgrs.com/info/abuse.htm

7.39 PSYCHIATRIC EMERGENCIES

Crisis Intervention Resource Manual   This manual, developed for the Bartow County School System (Georgia), offers counselors, principals, and other school staff a resource for dealing with a variety of crisis situations, including suicide, death/grief, and natural disasters. Crisis team handouts, parent/teacher handouts, and sample letters and memoranda are available at the site. A list of suggested reading resources, emergency telephone numbers (for Bartow County), reference citations, and links to sites offering resources on crisis intervention are also found at this address.
http://www.bartow.k12.ga.us/psych/crisis/crisis.htm

Federal Emergency Management Agency: Response and Recovery
The Federal Emergency Management Agency describes crisis counseling services available to survivors of Presidentially-declared major disasters at this address. Hotline numbers and a link to additional resources are also available.
http://www.fema.gov/r-n-r/counsel.htm

Merck Manual of Diagnosis and Therapy: Psychiatric Emergencies
Information is available at this site for physicians treating patients with psychiatric symptoms in an emergency situation. The general nature of this situation is discussed, followed by a list of emergencies requiring a general medical evaluation, hospitalization or other institutional support, minimal pharmacologic intervention, and more comprehensive intervention. For each condition, a list of medical conditions presenting the mental condition, possible causes (when known), and suggested therapies are included.
http://www.merck.com/pubs/mmanual/section15/chapter194/194a.htm

University of Iowa: Emergency Psychiatry Developed by the University of Iowa Hospitals and Clinics, this site features an emergency psychiatry service handbook. The handbook covers suicidal patients, agitated and violent patients, medical emergencies in psychiatry, and alcohol related emergencies. For treatment of suicidal patients, there are basic facts, risk factors, when to admit to a psychiatric hospital, and crisis intervention techniques. General approach and treatment for agitated patients is examined. In addition, medical emergencies such as delirium due to life threatening conditions, neuroleptic malignant syndrome, lethal catatonia, serotonic syndrome, and monamine oxidase inhibitor/tyramine reactions are discussed. Alcohol related emergencies are also briefly covered.

http://www.vh.org/Providers/Lectures/EmergencyMed/Psychiatry/TOC.html

7.40 PSYCHOPHYSIOLOGY

Neuroscience and Psychophysiology More than 55 links are provided on this site for neuroscience and psychophysiology, courtesy of the Social Psychology Network. For neuroscience, there are links for general resources, social neuroscience, brain imaging, and neuromedicine. Psychophysiology links include general resources and psychophysiology laboratories. There are also teaching resources, professional organizations, journals, and newsletters.

http://www.socialpsychology.org/neuro.htm

7.41 PSYCHOSOMATIC MEDICINE

Academy of Psychosomatic Medicine Professionals interested in studying medical and psychiatric illness and the interaction between them may find the Academy of Psychosomatic Medicine Web site of interest. Practice guidelines, resident guidelines, fellowship standards, and a list of fellowship training programs are provided. There are also position papers on managed care and end-of-life care. The most recent newsletter is posted, along with job opportunities and a short list of related links. In addition, visitors can search a member directory.

http://www.apm.org/

International Society of Psychosomatic Obstetrics and Gynecology
Objectives of the organization are discussed at this page, and a link to the *Journal of Psychosomatic Obstetrics and Gynecology* is provided, offering visitors information on the purpose of the publication and links to online abstracts.

http://ispog.org/

Merck Manual of Diagnosis and Therapy: Psychosomatic Medicine
Drawn from the *Merck Manual of Diagnosis and Therapy,* this Web page provides an overview of psychosomatic medicine. Written in clinical terms, the overview examines the relationship between physical and mental illness, along

with physical symptoms reflecting psychic states. Psychological reactions to a physical disorder are also discussed.
http://www.merck.com/pubs/mmanual/section15/chapter185/185c.htm

7.42 REFUGEE MENTAL HEALTH

Knowledge Exchange Network: Refugee Mental Health   A wide variety of links are provided on this Web site for refugee mental health. Sites are primarily from nonprofit organizations and government agencies in the United States. Short descriptions of each site are provided.
http://www.mentalhealth.org/links/refugee.htm

7.43 RELIGION AND MENTAL HEALTH

American Association of Pastoral Counselors (AAPC)   For those interested in pastoral counseling—certified mental health professionals with in-depth religious training—the AAPC Web site offers information on the profession. Visitors will find a fact sheet on the history and practice of pastoral psychology, along with an in-depth article on pastoral counseling. Professionals will find employment opportunities, conference information, a code of ethics, and training programs. Consumers can use "Find a Counselor" directory. Internet resources for pastoral counseling are comprehensive and include discussion forums, general information, professional journals, conferences, and promoting one's practice on the Internet.
http://www.aapc.org/

Psychology and Religion Pages   Pages accessible at this site were developed as a resource for those interested in the psychological aspects of religious belief and behavior. This general introduction to the psychology of religion describes all that psychologists have learned regarding the influence of religion. Conference listings, a message board, information on the future of the field, and an essay from a psychoanalytically trained psychiatrist are provided, along with feature books, organizations, and an index of primary journals in the field.
http://www.psywww.com/psyrelig/index.htm

7.44 RUNAWAYS

National Runaway Switchboard   The National Runaway Switchboard provides crisis intervention and referrals to youth and their families. Teens will find anonymous discussion boards, FAQs about calling the switchboard, success stories, and information on the Home Free program, which offers a free Greyhound bus ticket home. For parents, there are FAQs, parent success stories, information and referrals, and a message relay service to get in touch with their runaway teen through the switchboard. Educators can participate in "Kids Call"

by having their classroom call the switchboard with their questions, or they can download a teacher's guide to runaway prevention. There are also statistics, and a comprehensive list of links for regional resources as well as national resources such as agencies, organizations for missing children, services for parents, and services for youth. http://www.nrscrisisline.org/

7.45 SELF-HELP AND EMPOWERMENT

Mental Health Net: Self-Help Research   This site features brief research reviews of studies on the effectiveness of self-help groups. More than 35 studies are covered, for groups dedicated to mental health, weight loss, addiction recovery, bereavement, diabetes, caregivers, the elderly, cancer, and chronic illness.
http://www.mentalhelp.net/articles/selfres.htm

National Empowerment Center (NEC)   This organization offers information and resources for the empowerment of people with mental illness. The Web site provides a toll-free information and referral line, as well as full-text articles on empowerment, recovery, self-help, trauma, cross-disabilities, and managed care. There is also information on their speakers program. Links to related sites are provided.
http://www.power2u.org/

National Mental Health Consumers Self-Help Clearinghouse   Part of the consumer self-help movement, the National Mental Health Consumers' Self-Help Clearinghouse describes themselves as a consumer-run national technical assistance center. Visitors to the site will find a technical assistance catalog, online articles, and information on starting a self-help group. A "Freedom Self-Advocacy" workshop curriculum is also available on the site. In addition, political issues, legislative alerts, and position papers are found.
(free registration) http://www.mhselfhelp.org/

7.46 SEXUALITY

About.com: Sexuality   Hundreds of Web sites related to sexuality are featured on this Web page. Organized by topic, the sites cover advocacy, bisexuality, homosexuality, safer sex, sex education, sexual health, sexual abuse, sexual disorders, and therapy. There are also how-to guides, a guide to contraceptives, an STD library, and archives of over four years of articles.
http://sexuality.about.com/health/sexuality/mbody.htm

American Psychological Association (APA): Homosexuality   A fact sheet on sexual orientation and homosexuality is offered on this Web site, written by the American Psychological Association. The fact sheet explains sexual orientation, theories on the causes of a particular sexual orientation, and the fact that homosexuality is not a mental illness. The reasons that gay men and lesbians tell people about their sexual orientation are discussed, as well as the fact that lesbians and gay men can be good parents. There is also a detailed discussion of why therapy can not change sexual orientation. Resources for additional information are provided.

http://www.apa.org/pubinfo/orient.html

Classification of Gender and Sexual Orientation An article on the classification of gender and sexual orientation in American psychiatry is featured on this Web site, hosted by Priory Lodge Education. The article examines the inconsistency in deleting homosexuality from the *Diagnostic and Statistical Manual of Mental Disorders* while keeping the terms "gender identity disorder" and "transvestic fetishism." The article discusses etiology, inherent distress and impairment in sexual orientation and gender orientation, and experienced distress and impairment. A bibliography is included.

http://www.priory.com/psych/disparat.htm

Kinsey Institute for Research in Sex, Gender, and Reproduction
This nonprofit corporation is affiliated with Indiana University and "promotes interdisciplinary research and scholarship in the fields of human sexuality, gender, and reproduction." Information about the institute, an online library catalog, descriptions of archives and art collections at the institute, details of special events and exhibitions, reference services, links to related sites, and lists and ordering information for recent institute publications are available through the site. Information on the institute's Sexual Health Clinic and Menstrual Cycle Clinic is also found at this address.

http://www.indiana.edu/~kinsey/index.html

Mental Health Net: All About Sexual Problems Resources related to sexual problems are found at this site, including lists and descriptions of symptoms and related diagnoses. Links are available to many related resources, including patient education brochures, commercial sites, support resources, information sources, newsgroups, articles, publications, and organizations.

http://mentalhelp.net/sexual

Resources in Sexuality This Web site, a service of the Sexual Health Network, comprehensively covers the area of sexuality in relation to physical and mental health including plenty of fundamental and unique information. Sexuality following disability, antidepressants and sexual functioning, discussions on love, libidos, and possible physical and mental obstacles to sexual fulfillment are discussed. A special "Sex Over 40" section, a chat room, and the complete Sexual Health Network library are all available online for professionals, students, teachers, and anyone interested in further exploring hundreds of topics in the area of sexual health.

http://www.sexualhealth.com

Sexual Health InfoCenter Everything from sexual difficulties to sexual techniques is covered at the Sexual Health InfoCenter. Articles and links to additional information are provided on a broad array of topics, including safer sex, sex and aging, or better sex. http://www.sexhealth.org

Sexuality Information and Education Council of the United States (SIECUS) A broad range of information related to sexuality is provided on this Web site, with sections specifically directed to schools, parents, teens, policymakers and advocates, religious institutions, and international initiatives. The school section offers a guide to coordinated school health programs. Parents will find audio clips from the SIECUS radio program, as well as publications on topics such as HIV/AIDS and talking with your pre-teen. In the teen section, there are many publications related to sexual choices, risks, pregnancy, and sexual orientation. Policymakers and advocates will find policy updates, state sexuality laws, and related links. Information for religious institutions includes fact sheets and a sexual education course for faith communities. International sexuality education, training, and conferences are also found. There are also more than 50 publications described in the "Publications" section, many available online. In addition, a hyperlink for "Other Organizations" at the top of the Web page leads to a comprehensive listing of related links covering activism, facts and statistics, foundations, government, health, HIV/AIDS and STDs, libraries, sexuality issues, parents and teens, religion, and organizations. http://www.siecus.org/

Society for the Scientific Study of Sexuality An international organization, the Society for the Scientific Study of Sexuality offers conference information, awards and research grants, a job bank, and an online guide to educational opportunities in human sexuality on its Web site. The "Publications" section features the society's newsletter, as well as the tables of contents for the annual review of sexual research and the society's journal. Fact sheets are also found on compulsive sexual behavior, rape, and pornography. A link to the Foundation for the Scientific Study of Sexuality offers additional information on research. http://www.sexscience.org

ThriveOnline: Sexuality Primarily for consumers, this site offers articles related to sexuality, organized by categories such as sex and society, reproductive health, sexual empowerment, and sexual healing. The site also offers advice for parents and interactive tools, such as a contraceptive chooser and an STD symptom checker. There are also chat rooms and discussion boards on a variety of topics. http://thriveonline.oxygen.com/sex/

University of Maryland: Sexual Orientation Links to resources on sexual orientation are featured on this site. The sites are categorized as art, bibliographies, media reviews, conferences, government and politics, history, Internet metasites, issues specific to sexual orientation, library resources, and non-government organizations. In addition, there are full-text articles, LISTSERVs and chatrooms, and employment opportunities. A brief description of each site is provided. http://www.inform.umd.edu/EdRes/Topic/Diversity/Specific/Sexual_Orientation/

7.47 SOCIAL WORK

 Clinical Social Work Federation, Inc. Primarily for clinical social workers, this Web page offers information on the Clinical Social Work Federation and its activities. The site also contains legislative updates, an e-mail mailing list, and a description of the *Clinical Social Work Journal*. There are related Web resources, with a description of each, and a list of links to schools of social work. http://www.webcom.com/nfscsw/

 National Association of Social Workers (NASW) Directed to social workers, the NASW Web page offers information on the association and its activities. A catalog of books, journals, reference materials, and magazines from the NASW press is provided. There are also NASW professional standards, clinical indicators, and career information. Continuing education, job opportunities, credential information, and a clinical social worker directory are offered. A comprehensive listing of links features NASW state chapters and related organizations, as well as information on government and advocacy, child welfare, and mental health. http://www.naswdc.org/

7.48 SOFTWARE

 Catalyst: Computers and Psychology Dedicated to computers and psychology, this site offers a broad range of information. The site is best navigated through the "Contents" section on the left side of the page. Under "Features" there are more than 100 articles on research and issues of psychology and computers. The articles are also organized by topic at the top of the site; topics include net addiction, hackers, online behavior, online therapy, and research. There are also online research surveys in psychology, mental health software, conference information, a message board, and a list of computer and psychology organizations. http://www.victoriapoint.com/catalyst.htm

 Computers in Mental Health As a subsection of the Internet Mental Health Web site, this site provides the latest news and technological advances in software and mental health. Software information is divided into lists such as diagnosis, child psychology, clinical education, medical records, and disorders. Also available are a discussion forum, online access to articles relating to software and mental health, a list of reference materials, and links to other related sites. http://www.ex.ac.uk/cimh

 Psychiatry Software PsychWrite Pro, a clinical case management software program, may be downloaded directly from the Web site and is designed for psychiatrists and other clinicians who wish to easily maintain clinical records and have access to medication and managed care databases. Information on voice recognition programs to be used in conjunction with the software is available, and an online help screen answers FAQs and provides a forum for e-mail support. http://psychwrite.com/rx.html

7.49 State Mental Health Resources

Center for Mental Health Services (CMHS): Services Locator Visitors to this Web page can access mental health statistics, resources, and services for their state, by clicking on the map of the U.S. or selecting their state from the drop-down menu. http://iservices.cdmgroup.com/cmhsdata/cmhsdata.cfm

National Association of State Mental Health Program Directors Intended for professionals, information on the National Association of State Mental Health Program Directors is provided on this site. Descriptions of its divisions and councils for areas such as adult services, forensics, older persons, and state psychiatric hospitals are provided. Also available are a member directory, policy information, meeting information, staff contacts, and position statements. Links are provided to the association's research institute and to the National Technical Assistance Center for State Mental Health Planning. http://www.nasmhpd.org/

7.50 Stigma/Mental Illness

Canadian Mental Health Association: Stigma A fact sheet on stigma and mental health is provided on this Web site. The term "stigma" is defined, along with an explanation of why stigma exists, the effects on people with mental disorders, and tips on eliminating stigma. http://www.cmhawrb.on.ca/stigma.htm

National Mental Health Association: Stigma Watch A description of the Stigma Watch program is provided on this Web site. The National Mental Health Association, in cooperation with the National Stigma Clearinghouse, works to identify and eliminate stigmatizing media depictions of people with mental health issues. The site offers information on reporting a stigmatizing incident and an alert on current inappropriate media images. http://www.nmha.org/newsroom/stigma/index.cfm

National Stigma Clearinghouse Dedicated to advocating on behalf of people with mental disorders, this organization offers at this Web address positive stories of survivors, a fact sheet on promoting accuracy and sensitivity in the media, and news stories dating back to 1999. Links are provided to international organizations, along with links of interest to activists. http://community-2.webtv.net/stigmanet/STIGMAHOMEPAGE/index.html

Report from Stigma Plank: National Summit of Mental Health Consumers At this site, the Report on the Stigma Plank is presented by panelists from the University of Chicago who shared information about internalized stigma as well as external stigma. Stigma Plank goals, 10 action steps, and steps for overcoming internal and external stigma are outlined. http://www.mhselfhelp.org/rstigma.html

7.51 SURROGACY

 Psychological and Emotional Aspects of Surrogacy Links to nine articles regarding the psychological and emotional aspects surrounding surrogacy are available at this address including material on the motivations of surrogate mothers as well as the psychological experiences of recipients. A personal experience synopsis concerning the components of a successful surrogate arrangement is outlined, and the grief and shame linked to the infertility experience are examined. This site is provided by the American Surrogacy Center. http://www.surrogacy.com/psychres/article/index.html

 Surrogacy-Related Viewpoints The Organization of Parents Through Surrogacy, Inc.'s Web site offers extensive information surrounding the psychological components of the surrogacy experience. The "Surrogate's Point of View" contains personal thoughts and discussions regarding the decision to become a surrogate mother, and the family stories section describes common conceptions and misperceptions on the decision to pursue a gestational carrier. The "Counselor's Corner" contains articles by specialists in the field regarding the emotional insights of surrogacy. A special section on the experiences of siblings and adopted children is included. http://www.opts.com/articles.htm

 The American Surrogacy Center (TASC) Primarily for consumers, the TASC site offers information on surrogacy and egg donation. There are online support groups, as well as discussion boards, some with ask-the-expert forums to ask agencies, lawyers, doctors, or psychologists questions. There are also a professional directory, a catalog of related books and videos, and a comprehensive list of related links. Along with personal stories, there are articles on medical, legal, agency, and psychological issues. http://www.surrogacy.com/

7.52 THEORETICAL FOUNDATIONS

 Albert Ellis Institute Previously listed as the Institute for Rational-Emotive Therapy, this nonprofit educational organization's Web site provides background information on the institute and its founder, provides access to papers by Dr. Ellis, and has professional services, educational training, and product information. Consumer information available includes workshops and lectures for the public, therapist referrals, and self-help and support. The institute's publications and products are cataloged for sale at this site. http://www.rebt.org

 Alfred Adler Institute of San Francisco This site describes in detail the approaches and concepts behind classical Adlerian psychology and also discusses how this system differs from other psychological approaches. More detailed information is available on basic principles of classical Adlerian psychology, the 12 stages of classical Adlerian psychotherapy, and the institute's professional training program and seminars. Access to several related articles is provided. http://ourworld.compuserve.com/homepages/hstein/

Association for the Advancement of Gestalt Therapy (AAGT) The Association for the Advancement of Gestalt Therapy provides a professional forum dedicated to the preservation and advancement of Gestalt therapy. This site describes the association and its special interest groups and offers a simplified summary of gestalt therapy, conference information, an online newsletter, and several links to related sites. http://www.aagt.org/

B. F. Skinner Foundation The B. F. Skinner Foundation publishes literary and scientific works in behavioral analysis and educates professionals and the public about behavioral science. The site describes continuing and upcoming activities and offers a brief autobiography of Skinner, reviews of books by Skinner and others, and a full bibliography of Skinner's publications. http://www.bfskinner.org/index.asp

C. G. Jung Institute of Boston Dedicated to the discipline of analytical psychology, the C.G. Jung Institute of Boston is chartered by the New England Society of Jungian Analysts. Descriptions and admissions criteria for the Analyst Training Program are available, as well as information on public education programs, a directory of members, and a calendar of events. http://www.cgjungboston.com/

C. G. Jung Page This page, created to encourage education and dialogue, offers an introduction to Jung, chat forums and bulletin boards, Jungian articles, an editorial page, news, seminars. Links are available to psychology and psychiatry sites, general Jungian sites, Jungian training institutes, collected works, institutes, professional ethics resources, and sources for books and other publications. Jungian essays on psychology and culture are also found at this comprehensive site, offering psychological commentaries on technology and film. http://www.cgjungpage.org/

Gestalt Growth Center of the San Francisco Bay Area This site describes the center and director, offers general information on Gestalt therapy, and provides contact information for the center. http://www.gestaltcenter.net

Gestalt Therapy Page This Web page, a joint project sponsored by *The Gestalt Journal* and the International Gestalt Therapy Association, offers a catalog of books, conference information, academic articles, and information for ordering a copy of the Web site on CD-ROM. A worldwide directory of Gestalt therapists in private practice is also available. http://www.gestalt.org

Glossary of Freudian Terminology This site, compiled by a professor of psychology at Haverford College, offers detailed explanations and definitions of terms used or developed by Freud in his published works. Links to additional Internet resources on Freud and assorted publications are also available. http://www.haverford.edu/psych/ddavis/p109g/fgloss.html

Jungian Psychology For those interested specifically in Jungian psychology, this Web site offers a number of links to resources on Jungian conferences and workshops, national and international organizations, related forums, Web sites devoted to Jungian psychology, related articles and Jungian links, and many links to information on dreams and personality. http://www.onlinepsych.com/public/Jungian_Psychology/

Philosophy of Psychiatry Bibliography This site contains a bibliography of psychiatry publications, covering many specific topics, with links to Amazon.com ordering information. Topics include ethics and philosophy, law, gender and antipsychiatry, psychoanalysis, criminal responsibility, genetics, classification, and antipsychiatry and critical theory. http://www.uky.edu/~cperring/PPB4.HTM

Sigmund Feud and the Freud Archives This site provides links to Internet resources related to Freud and his works. Biographical materials, museum sites, general information about Freud, Freud texts on the Internet, transcripts of Freud letters, and writings on Freud are all available through the links at this site. http://plaza.interport.net/nypsan/freudarc.html

7.53 UNDERSERVED POPULATIONS

Association of Clinicians for the Underserved Established by former members of the National Health Service Corps, the Association of Clinicians for the Underserved offers this Web site for information and resources. Visitors can read the association's newsletter, dating back to 1997. In addition, there are discussion boards, conference information, student training opportunities, and links to related organizations. (some features fee-based) http://www.clinicians.org/

7.54 WOMEN AND MENTAL HEALTH

National Institute of Mental Health (NIMH): Women's Mental Health Consortium This government-sponsored division makes available its research on the impact that mental illness has on both genders, with epidemiological differences between men and women highlighted. Strategic goals of the consortium and links to current news, funding opportunities, publications, and conference summaries of the division are provided. A research bibliography of women's mental health and an assortment of fact sheets addressing specific women's mental health concerns are offered. http://www.nimh.nih.gov/wmhc/index.cfm

8

ORGANIZATIONS AND INSTITUTIONS

8.1 ASSOCIATIONS AND SOCIETIES

DIRECTORIES OF ASSOCIATIONS

Mental Health InfoSource: Association Address Book This site contains a directory of professional associations related to mental health. Information includes a street address, telephone number, and a Web site address if available. Visitors can also find annual association meetings listed by date. http://www.mhsource.com/hy/address.html

Mental Health Net: Professional Associations and Organizations Links to home pages of more than 350 professional associations and organizations related to mental health are available at this address. A short summary and rating is available for each listed address. Organizations include professional societies, academies, support groups, research institutes, and other groups. http://mentalhelp.net/guide/pro80.htm

Mental Health Services Database This database includes information on over 1,800 organizations and government offices that provide mental health services. The database, searchable by keyword, organization, state, or city, returns contact information, abstracts, and additional keywords to help the visitor find similar organizations. http://www.cdmgroup.com`/Ken/kenindexnew.htm

INDIVIDUAL ASSOCIATION WEB SITES

Below are profiles of more than 80 associations and societies in the field of psychiatry. Those organizations that have a specific focus appear a second time in this volume under the "Diseases" section or under an appropriate topical heading.

Academy for the Study of the Psychoanalytic Arts This site provides professionals with free online access to program papers, articles, and other reference materials on the topics of psychoanalysis and related fields. The organization's background, meeting, and membership information is also provided. http://www.academyanalyticarts.org

Academy of Eating Disorders This multidisciplinary professional organization focuses on anorexia nervosa, bulimia nervosa, binge eating disorder, and related disorders. Divisions of the Academy specialize in Academic Sciences, Human Services, Primary Medicine, Psychiatry, Psychology, Dietetics, Nursing, and Social Work. Visitors to the site can access membership information, annual conference details, facts on all eating disorders, and a bibliography of information sources. Specific topical discussions include the prevalence and consequences of eating disorders, courses and outcome of eating disorders, etiology, and treatment.

http://www.acadeatdis.org/

Academy of Organizational and Occupational Psychiatry (AOOP) The Academy of Organizational and Occupational Psychiatry provides a forum for communication between psychiatric professionals and personnel in the workplace. The site offers annual meeting details, general Academy news items, and a description of the organization. Research papers, bulletins, membership details, descriptions of previous annual meetings, and links to related sites are all found at this address.

http://www.aoop.org

Academy of Psychological Clinical Science The Academy of Psychological Clinical Science is an alliance of leading and scientifically oriented doctoral training programs in clinical and health psychology in the United States and Canada. The site includes links to the various academic members, a list of officers, a mission statement, membership information, a history of the Academy and a link to related Web sites.

http://w3.arizona.edu/~psych/apcs/apcs.html

Al-Anon/Alateen Organization Al-Anon and Alateen are part of a worldwide organization providing a self-help recovery program for families and friends of alcoholics. Resources available at this official site include meeting information, the 12 steps, traditions, and concepts of the programs, information on Alateen, pamphlets, suggested readings and videotapes, an online newsletter, a calendar of events, and information on a television public service announcement developed by the organization. Professional resources include information on the organization, reasons people are referred to Al-Anon/Alateen, a description of group activities and how they help, and details of how Al-Anon/Alateen cooperates with professionals.

http://www.al-anon.org

Alzheimer's Association The Alzheimer's Association offers information and support on issues related to the disease. Patients and caregivers can access general facts about Alzheimer's disease, and detailed discussions of medical issues, diagnosis, expected lifestyle changes, treatment options, clinical trial participation, planning for the future, and contact information for special programs and support. Caregiver information and professional resources are also available. Resources for investigators include a summary of current research, lists of

grant opportunities, lists of past grant awards, progress report forms, and information on the Reagan Institute. The Association also offers news, program, and conference calendars; publications; and information on advocacy activities at this site.
http://www.alz.org

Alzheimer's Disease Society   Created to provide information about Alzheimer's disease and other dementias, this site has links to descriptive fact sheets on these disorders, their symptoms, and physical causes and consequences, treatment and prognosis. In addition, there are summaries of current research theories on these dementias. For caregivers, there is general support advice and related topics, as well as current news, information about the society itself, as well links to other related societies.
http://www.alzheimers.org.uk

American Academy of Addiction Psychiatry   Informational links on the academy and membership, as well as the different committees and policy statements are provided. Links to previous, present, and future annual meetings, Accreditation Council for Graduate Medical Education (ACGME) information, as well as a Web store for reference tapes and other materials are present.
http://www.aaap.org

American Academy of Child and Adolescent Psychiatry (AACAP)   The home page of the American Academy of Child and Adolescent Psychiatry welcomes users to its Web site with information about current legislative activities and an online fact sheet for families. Other departments include press releases, legislation, journals, and clinical practice information. An online Web Builder Program allows members to create their own advertisement-free site.
(some features fee-based) http://www.aacap.org

American Academy of Clinical Neuropsychology (AACN)   This site presented by the American Academy of Clinical Neuropsychology allows users to search the AACN directory of members, view the articles and bylaws of the Academy, view current AACN news, and access continuing education materials. Links to other neuropsychology sites are present.
http://www.med.umich.edu/abcn/aacn.html

American Academy of Experts in Traumatic Stress   American Academy of Experts in Traumatic Stress membership includes health professionals, as well as professionals from emergency services, criminal justice, forensics, law, and education committed to the advancement of intervention for survivors of trauma. The Academy's Web site provides extensive informational links for professionals in the field. A description of the academy, links to membership information, credentials, certifications, education credits, searching the national registry, the administration, board of advisors are present. Free access to selected articles from Trauma Response is provided. Also, ordering instructions for the Practical Guide for Crisis Response in Our Schools (3rd edition) are available. http://www.aaets.org

American Academy of Psychoanalysis   The American Academy of Psychoanalysis represents the National Academy of Professional Medical Psychoanalysists. Informative links to the Journal of the American Academy of Psychoanalysis, selected articles from the Academy Forum, related meetings, member roster, organization information, publications, and research details are available at the site.
http://aapsa.org

American Academy of Sleep Medicine (AASM)   The professional section of the site provides links to information on membership, AASM history and goals, directory of accredited centers, educational products, ASDA staff, accreditation information and policy, board certification, funding opportunities, position papers, professional education, free online access to publications from the National Center on Sleep Disorders (NCSDR), abstracts from the 1998 meeting, and the journal *Sleep*. Links to other sleep-related sites are included. The patient and public area provides links to answers of common questions about sleep disorders, diagnoses and treatment, patient support groups, resources from (NCSDR) and other related links.
http://www.asda.org

American Anorexia Bulimia Association   The American Anorexia Bulimia Association is a national nonprofit organization dedicated to the prevention and treatment of eating disorders. This site contains a number of links to informative pages on eating disorders, such as anorexia, bulimia, and binge eating. Information on symptoms, support, medical consequences, risk factors, a list of references about these disorders, as well as membership information is included.
http://www.aabainc.org

American Association for Geriatric Psychiatry (AAGP)   The AAGP Web site includes numerous links to various issues of interest for both professionals and interested laypersons. There are news reports, the AAGP bookstore, meeting information, consumer information, including brochures and a question/answer section, advocacy and public policy section, a link to the American Journal for Geriatric Psychiatry, a health professional bulletin, member meeting place, staff listing, and a link to the AAGP Education and Research Foundation. (some features fee-based) http://www.aagpgpa.org

American Association for Marriage and Family Therapy (AAMFT)   The American Association for Marriage and Family Therapy is the professional association for the field of marriage and family therapy, representing the professional interests of more than 23,000 marriage and family therapists throughout the United States, Canada and abroad. This site allows professionals and other interested parties to search directories for therapist listing and provides information on the Association. General information includes clinical updates on various marriage and family mental health issues; the link for practitioners lists information on conferences and conference highlights, resources, a referral section, publications, education, training, licensing links, and membership information. (some features fee-based) http://www.aamft.org

American Association of Community Psychiatrists The American Association of Community Psychiatrists promotes excellence in inpatient mental healthcare, solves common problems encountered by psychiatrists in a community setting, establishes liaisons with related professional groups for advocacy purposes, encourages psychiatrist training, improves relationships within community settings between psychiatrists and other clinicians and administrators, and educates the public about the role of the community mental health system in the care of the mentally ill. This site provides information on the mission of the Association, board members, and membership information. The present and previous newsletters and issues of Community Psychiatrist are available, as well as links to relevant training and research programs in the discipline. http://www.comm.psych.pitt.edu/find.html

American Association of Psychotherapists The American Association of Psychotherapists is a national nonprofit, multidisciplinary professional organization of certified clinicians dedicated to the support and development of psychotherapy. This Web site was created to provide networking opportunities for professionals. The site provides a message board, chat room, and online membership application. (fee-based) http://www.angelfire.com/tx/Membership/index.html

American Association of Suicidology This nonprofit organization is dedicated to the understanding and prevention of suicide. The Web site includes information regarding the Association, conference information, links to other relevant sites, internship information, and a directory for support groups and crisis centers. In addition, there are links to sources for books and other printed resources, links to legal and ethical issues, treatment, assessment and prediction, and certification/accreditation manuals. http://www.suicidology.org

American Association on Mental Retardation (AAMR) AAMR promotes global development and dissemination of progressive policies, sound research, effective practices, and universal human rights for people with intellectual disabilities. Site resources include information about the AAMR, current news, bookstore, membership information, reference materials from the annual meeting, free access to the American Journal on Mental Retardation and Mental Retardation, a list of the divisions of the AAMR, and links to the discussion group and chat rooms. http://www.aamr.org

American Family Therapy Academy This nonprofit professional organization fosters an exchange of ideas among family therapy teachers, researchers, and practitioners. The site presents the organization's objectives, policy and press releases, membership details, a membership directory, excerpts of the organization's newsletter, and lists of recent awards with recipients. http://www.afta.org

Don't type in long URLs – add the site number to the eMedguides URL: www.eMedguides.com/**G-1234**.

American Group Psychotherapy Association   The American Group Psychotherapy Association works to enhance the practice, theory, and research of group therapy. The Association offers information about group therapy, a directory of group therapists for interested patients, news, contact information, a meetings and events calendar, and publications details at this site. Specific resources for group therapists and students include ethical guidelines for group therapists, training opportunities information, certification details, government reports, advanced principles of psychotherapy, and links to affiliated societies.
http://www.groupsinc.org

American Hyperlexia Association   The American Hyperlexia Association is a nonprofit organization comprised of parents and relatives of children with hyperlexia, speech and language professionals, education professionals, and other concerned individuals with the common goal of identifying hyperlexia, promoting and facilitating effective teaching techniques both at home and at school, and educating the general public as to the existence of the syndrome called hyperlexia. This Web site includes links to pages describing hyperlexia and treatment options, as well as links to the mailing list, membership information, materials order list, organizations and therapist directories, other hyperlexia sites, and a guestbook.
http://www.hyperlexia.org

American Neuropsychiatric Association (ANPA)   Resources offered by the ANPA at this site include program and registration information for the group's 2000 Annual Meeting, contact information, membership applications, an e-mail news subscription service, a directory of members, an online newsletter, journal information, and links to related sites of interest to neuroscientists. Internet access for this site is made available by Butler Hospital, and the site is supported by an unrestricted educational grant from Hoechst. A list of ANPA officers is also provided.
http://www.neuropsychiatry.com/ANPA/index.html

American Occupational Therapy Association, Inc.   This organization offers information on occupational therapy, news, membership details, details of events, products and services, academic accreditation resources, continuing education resources, publications, and information on academic and fieldwork education. Student resources include journals and information on educational programs, fieldwork, and careers. Consumers can access information on occupational therapy, fact sheets, case studies, a directory of practitioners, and links to related sites. Conference details and links to related sites are also found at this address.
http://www.aota.org

American Professional Society on the Abuse of Children (APSAC)   The mission of APSAC is to ensure that everyone affected by child maltreatment receives the best possible professional response. This professional society's site provides information on the society itself, membership information, legislative

activities, professional education, state chapters, and public affairs, and current news. Information on the society's publications, such as the APSAC Advisor, the APSAC Guidelines for Practice, the APSAC Handbook on Child Maltreatment and Child Maltreatment are available online. There is also information for those interested in donating to the society.
http://www.apsac.org

American Psychiatric Association (APA)   The American Psychiatric Association is a national and international association of psychiatric physicians. The site includes updates, public policy and advocacy information, clinical and research resources, membership information, medical education, related organizations, governance, library and publications, events schedule, psychiatric news, APA catalog, and a link to APPI (APA Press, Inc.).
http://www.psych.org

American Psychiatric Nurses Association   The American Psychiatric Nurses Association is devoted to providing leadership to psychiatric and mental health nursing professionals. This Web site has links to information on membership, conferences, the association, advocacy updates, legislative news, APNA chapters, and a calendar of events. With respect to publications, there is access to the table of contents to the APNA journal, as well as position papers, APNA news articles, graduate programs in psychiatric nursing, and other related links.
http://www.apna.org

American Psychoanalytic Association   The American Psychoanalytic Association is a professional organization of psychoanalysts throughout the United States. Press releases, a calendar of events and meetings, general information about psychoanalysis, fellowship details, an online book store, a directory of psychoanalysts, Journal of the American Psychoanalytic Association abstracts, and an online newsletter are all available at the site. An extensive catalog of links to related online journals, institutes, societies, organizations, libraries, museums, and general sites are offered through the site. The Jourlit and Bookrev databases are also available, together constituting a formidable bibliography of psychoanalytic journal articles, books, and book reviews. Information on obtaining journal reprints is supplied.
http://apsa.org

American Psychological Association (APA)   The American Psychological Association Web site provides numerous links including reference materials, publications, national and international research sites, education, conferences, government information, and help centers. Comprehensive information regarding the Association itself is present.
(fee-based) http://www.apa.org

American Psychological Society (APS)   The American Psychological Society aims to provide a forum for research and application to the science of psychology. The site offers information regarding membership, current news,

conventions, and APS publications. Updates on funding opportunities and legislative events relevant to psychology are provided.
http://www.psychologicalscience.org

American Psychotherapy and Medical Hypnosis Association (AP-MHA)   The APMHA was founded in 1992 for State Board Licensed and Certified Professionals in multi-disciplines of Medicine, Psychology, Social Work, Family Therapy, Alcohol and Chemical Dependency, Professional Counseling, Dentistry, and Forensic and Investigative Hypnosis. The site provides a description of hypnosis, membership information and application, professional referrals, training and certification program information, links to related sites, ordering information for professional video training tapes, and contact details.
http://apmha.com

American Society of Addiction Medicine (ASAM)   Offering educational opportunities to physicians and improving the quality of care available to those dealing with addiction, this organization provides addiction medicine news, scheduled trainings in the field, and information on behavioral and pharmacologic interventions under study. Pain management in addiction medicine and an online professional forum are offered. An assortment of additional departments and topics can be accessed from the menu at the left side of the page, including patient placement criteria, practice guidelines, and updates on AIDS and addiction.
http://www.asam.org

American Society of Psychoanalytic Physicians   This Society and Web site were created to provide a forum for psychoanalytically-oriented psychiatrists and physicians. The purpose of the Society, as well as a list of the officers and editorial board are available.
http://pubweb.acns.nwu.edu/~chessick/aspp.htm

American Society on Aging (ASA)   The American Society on Aging provides information resources on gerontology through educational programming, publications, and training. General resources at this site include membership and contact details, meeting information, conference and training schedules, and awards listings. Links are available to information on publications, including *Aging Today* and *Generations*. Visitors can also access news, links to related sites, job banks, and information on specific ASA networks, including business and aging; environments, services, and technologies; healthcare and aging; lesbian and gay aging issues; lifelong education; mental health and aging; multicultural aging issues; and religion, spirituality; and aging. Databases containing information on conferences, training events, and resources on aging issues are available for members, as well as a chat forum, special offers, and member directories. (some features fee-based) http://www.asaging.org

Angelman Syndrome Association   The Australian Angelman Association provides general information at its Web site pertaining to the diagnosis, research, and treatment of the rare, neuro-genetic disorder. The Angelman syn-

drome LISTSERV is provided for communication via e-mail as are past issues of the Association's newsletter.
http://www.angelmansyndrome.org/

Anxiety Disorders Association of America (ADAA)   General information about anxiety disorders, additional consumer resources, and a professional department are all part of this organization's home page. Psychiatrists and other interested clinicians will find details about continuing education credits, the organization's report on childhood anxiety disorders, and information on therapists recognized by the association. Publications, events, and an online bookstore are found, as are special sections addressing unproven treatments and patient advocacy.
http://www.adaa.org

Association for Academic Psychiatry   This Association focuses on education in psychiatry. The Web site includes links to the Association's officers, full online access to the bulletin and *Academic Psychiatry,* membership information, teaching resources, annual conference information, and a link to Collaborative Academic Resources (CAR).
http://www.hsc.wvu.edu/aap/

Association for Applied Psychophysiology and Biofeedback (AAPB) This nonprofit organization of clinicians, researchers, and educators is dedicated to advancing the "development, dissemination and utilization of knowledge about applied psychophysiology and biofeedback to improve health and the quality of life through research, education, and practice." General information at the site includes a description of biofeedback and psychophysiology, a list of common health problems helped by biofeedback, meetings and workshop information, membership information, a bibliography of recent research articles related to biofeedback and psychophysiology, links to related sites, an online bookstore, and content lists of AAPB publications. The site offers a directory of biofeedback practitioners and a forum for asking questions of biofeedback experts. (fee-based) http://www.aapb.org

Association for Behavior Analysis   The Association for Behavior Analysis, an international organization based at Western Michigan University, promotes experimental, theoretical, and applied analysis of behavior. Visitors to the site can access a job placement service, lists of affiliated chapters, student committees, special interest groups, annual convention details, membership details, a member directory, Association publications, and links to related Web sites.
http://www.wmich.edu/aba/contents.html

Association for Child Psychoanalysis (ACP)   The Association for Child Psychoanalysis (ACP) is an international not-for-profit organization providing a forum for the interchange of ideas and clinical experience in order to advance the psychological treatment and understanding of children and adolescents and their families. This site was designed to promote the association and its programs. Links to a searchable roster, referral information, the ACP archives, psy-

choanalysis related sites, and a comprehensive list of programs developed by ACP members are available at the site.
http://www.westnet.com/acp

Association for Medical Education and Research in Substance Abuse
The Web site for this multidisciplinary organization of professionals interested in substance abuse has links to the mission statement, organization and membership information, conference information, an online discussion group, and a link to the table of contents for the journal, Substance Abuse.
http://www.amersa.org

Association for Psychoanalytic Medicine
The Association for Psychoanalytic Medicine (APM) is a nonprofit organization, and is an affiliate society of both the American Psychoanalytic Association and the International Psychoanalytic Association. Most members are graduates of the Columbia University Center for Psychoanalytic Training and Research, participating in professional development and community outreach activities. An extensive list of the association-sponsored lectures, held at the New York Academy of Medicine, as well as online access to publications, such as The Bulletin—the Journal of the APM, and The Shrink. There is information on awards, and a membership roster. Other links include postgraduate education information, and mental health resources. http://theapm.org

Association for Research in Nervous and Mental Disease (ARNMD)
The Association for Research in Nervous and Mental Disease is the oldest society of neurologists and psychiatrists. The site provides links to the history and mission of ARNMD, the board of trustees, ARNMD publications from 1920, an events calendar, 1998 meeting abstracts, and a list of program speakers and talks from the 1998 annual course.
http://www.arnmd.org

Association for the Advancement of Gestalt Therapy (AAGT)
The Association for the Advancement of Gestalt Therapy provides a professional forum dedicated to the preservation and advancement of gestalt therapy. This site describes the Association and its special interest groups, and offers a simplified summary of gestalt therapy, conference information, an online newsletter, and several links to related sites.
http://www.aagt.org

Association for the Advancement of Philosophy and Psychiatry
The mission of the Association for the Advancement of Philosophy and Psychiatry is to encourage interdisciplinary activity in philosophy and psychiatry and to advance knowledge, promote research, and facilitate understanding in both fields. The Association's mission statement is provided at the site, as well as links to the officers and executive council members, meetings and conferences, local and special interest groups, and free access to the official journal of the Association, Philosophy, Psychiatry, and Psychology.
http://www3.utsouthwestern.edu/aapp/

Association for the Study of Dreams This nonprofit organization is dedicated to the "pure and applied investigation of dreams and dreaming." Conference information, a magazine, education resources, discussion forums, membership details, on online bookstore, details of current projects, a membership directory, and contact details are all found at the site. Abstracts of articles and other details of the Association's journal, Dreaming, are available at the site, as well as some full-text articles. A search engine is available for more specific information.
http://www.asdreams.org

Association for the Treatment of Sexual Abusers (ATSA) The Association for the Treatment of Sexual Abusers is an international organization focused specifically on the prevention of sexual abuse through effective management of sex offenders. The site provides membership information, Sexual Abuse journal table of contents, graduate research awards and ATSA research grants, position statements, conference information, internship and fellowship opportunities, employment opportunities, and book lists.
http://www.atsa.com

Association for Treatment and Training in the Attachment of Children This coalition of parents and professionals exchanges information on attachment and bonding issues. Information on healthy attachment, membership details, events and training notices, a newsletter, recommended reading lists, book reviews, assessment instrument reviews, and clinical notes are found at this address. Details of the organization's structure, research reviews, links to related sites and contact details for non-Internet resources, and lists of suggested professional resources are also available.
http://www.attach.org

Association of Traumatic Stress Specialists (ATSS) This international nonprofit organization provides professional education and certification to those actively involved in crisis intervention, trauma response, management, treatment, and the healing and recovery of those affected by traumatic stress. The site provides information on the organization, membership benefits, certification as a trauma specialist, an events calendar, links to other trauma-related sites, and a resource guide.
http://www.atss-hq.com

Autism Society of America (ASA) The mission of the Autism Society of America is to promote lifelong access and opportunities for persons within the autism spectrum and their families, to be fully included, participating members of their communities through advocacy, public awareness, education, and research related to autism. This site contains a large amount of information and links pertaining to all aspects of autism. There are links to advocacy and government action alerts, the ASA and membership information, legislative action news, conference information, and a searchable directory of the Web site and mailing list. A link to research in autism, including articles from autism research professionals, and numerous links including reference materials, glossary, treatment and diagnosis, medical and insurance information, and links to other related organizations and sites are provided.

http://www.autism-society.org

Canadian Psychiatric Association This voluntary professional association for psychiatrists encourages communication and collaboration both within psychiatry and with other professions, consumers, and government agencies. Visitors to the site will find links to associated academies (including the Canadian Academy of Geriatric Psychiatry and the Canadian Academy of Psychiatry and the Law), continuing professional development, annual meeting and other program details, employment listings, membership information, and news releases. A chat forum is available to members and registered users. Full-text articles from the *Canadian Journal of Psychiatry,* position papers, guidelines and statements, newsletters, annual reports, and patient education brochures are all found at the site.

(free registration) http://www.cpa-apc.org/

Cyclic Vomiting Syndrome Association This organization's site provides basic information about the disorder, lists upcoming events and conferences, provides information about membership, and offers a list of related links to Web sites. In addition, there is ample research information, as well as support resources. http://www.beaker.iupui.edu/cvsa/index.html

Depression and Related Affective Disorders Association (DRADA)
This site provides information about DRADA, links to research reports and other reference materials, book reviews, an online store for videos and books, support groups and other related organizations, as well as a link to clinical research studies seeking participants.

http://www.med.jhu.edu/drada

Dyslexia—The Gift: Davis Dyslexia Association International The Davis Dyslexia Association International offers workshops and training to teachers and professionals on helping individuals with dyslexia and other learning disabilities. A resource library at the site includes articles, questions and answers about dyslexia, book excerpts, and links to other information sources. Educational materials, professional resources, chat forums, a Davis Program provider directory, and workshop calendars are all found at the site. Resources are provided in English, Spanish, German, French, Dutch, and Italian.

http://www.dyslexia.com

Gerontological Society of America The Gerontological Society of America promotes research and disseminates information related to gerontological research. Site sections list awards, annual meeting details, press releases, employment opportunities, news, publications, Society divisions, and links to related sites. Related foundations, a referral service, useful sources for information, student organization details, and membership details are also

found through the site. A discussion is available on social security and women. Visitors can search the site by keyword for specific information.
http://www.geron.org

Harry Benjamin International Gender Dysphoria Association, Inc.

This professional Association is committed to the understanding and treatment of gender identity disorders, with members from the fields of Psychiatry, Endocrinology, Surgery, Psychology, Sociology, and Counseling. Site resources include general information about the Association, details of the Association's biennial conference, membership information, the full text of the Benjamin Standards of Care for Gender Identity Disorders (5th version), links to related sites, and contact details for those seeking more specific information.
http://www.hbigda.org/

International Angelman Syndrome Association (IASO)

The organization's mission and member countries are enumerated at this site along with information on joining the IASO electronic mailing list. The Web site's conference announcements are also available and may be viewed in English, French, Spanish, or German.
http://www.asclepius.com/iaso

International Association of Eating Disorders Professionals (IAEDP)

The International Association of Eating Disorders Professionals offers a certification process for health professionals seeking specialized credentials in the treatment of patients with eating disorders. The Web site provides information regarding the Association, membership and certification information, and registration details for symposium events.
http://www.iaedp.com

International Association of Group Psychotherapy

The Association is dedicated to the development of group psychotherapy as a field of practice, training, and scientific study and by means of international conferences, publications, and other forms of communication. The Web page consists of membership information and a directory of the executive and board of directors. The site also offers links to conference information, an electronic forum, and links to other sites of interest. Upcoming links include abstracts of scientific articles relating to group psychotherapy.
http://www.psych.mcgill.ca/labs/iagp/IAGP.html

International Behavioural and Neural Genetics Society (IBANGS)

This international Society supports research in the field of neurobehavioral genetics. Membership information, Society information, rules, a member directory, meeting details, links to member societies, and past meeting transcripts are available at the site. Links are also available at the site to sources for meeting information, societies and networks, institutions and databases, and publications of interest in neurobehavioral and neural genetics.
http://www.ibngs.org

International Dyslexia Association This nonprofit Association is devoted to the study and treatment of dyslexia. Site resources include information about the organization, position papers, descriptions of branch services, membership details, conference and seminar calendars, an online bookstore, technology resources, legal and legislative information, research discussions, press releases, and a bulletin board for site visitors. The site also offers a detailed discussion of dyslexia, including information and links to Internet resources for adolescents, college students, parents, adults, and educators and other professionals.
http://www.interdys.org

International Psychoanalytical Association (IPA) Described as the world's primary psychoanalytic accrediting and regulatory body, the Association's Web site has numerous links to the various conferences and congresses organized by the Association, as well as links to special committees' synopses, a message forum, access to IPA newsletters, and other related links.
http://www.ipa.org.uk

International Society for the Study of Dissociation (ISSD) This nonprofit professional organization advocates research and professional training in the diagnosis, treatment and education of dissociative disorders, as well as serving to promote international communication among scientists and professionals working in this area. There are links to conference information, membership and society information, a link to the *Journal of Trauma and Dissociation,* the ISSD newsletter, education resources, including articles on related topics, and a list of dissociation disorder treatment guidelines. In addition, there is a set of professional and self-help links, and contact information.
http://www.issd.org

International Society for Traumatic Stress Studies (ISTSS) A professional society created for the sharing of scientific information and strategies on traumatic stress, this Web site has links to conference information, other affiliates of the ISTSS, membership information, related links, and access to articles from the *Journal of Traumatic Stress,* as well as critical reviews and treatment guide. http://www.istss.org

International Society of Psychiatric Genetics The International Society of Psychiatric Genetics promotes and facilitates research, education, and communication in the genetics of psychiatric disorders, substance abuse, and related traits. This address offers a Board of Directors listing, information on upcoming meetings, Society bylaws and mission statement, and links to several related sites. http://www.ispg.net

International Society of Psychosomatic Medicine, Obstetrics, and Gynecology The International Society of Psychosomatic Obstetrics and Gynaecology promotes the study and education of the psychobiological, psychosocial, ethical, and cross-cultural problems in the fields of Obstetrics and Gynecology. This site presents the objectives of the Society, as well as a newsletter and links to local chapters. Free online access to the abstracts of the *Journal of Psy-*

chosomatic Obstetrics and Gynecology is available, as well as links to information on international meetings and congresses. Related links and a keyword search engine are available.   http://www.ispog.org

Learning Disabilities Association (LDA)   This nonprofit organization advances the education and general welfare of children and adults with learning disabilities. Visitors to the site will find a mission statement, resources on specific conditions, position statements, suggested reading lists, news, a calendar of upcoming events, membership information, contact details, links to state affiliates, fact sheets, an online bookstore, and contact information for support organizations, educational resources, and publication sources.
http://www.ldanatl.org

Mood Disorders Association of British Columbia   This association's Web site has links to general information about certain mood disorders, and offers an information request form and links to related sites.
http://www.mdabc.ca

National Association for Rights Protection and Advocacy (NARPA)
The NARPA exists to expose abuses and promote real alternatives to the current mental health system. The organization's Web site provides readings on mental health advocacy including current case decisions and legislative information, excerpts from the NARPA's Annual Conference and Annual Rights Conference, and an online version of Rights Tenet newsletter are available. Interesting links such as the history of mental health advocacy are easily accessed. Online membership information and application is provided.
http://www.connix.com/~narpa

National Association of Anorexia Nervosa and Associated Disorders
This national nonprofit organization helps eating disorder victims and their families through hotline counseling, support groups, and referrals to healthcare professionals. The site offers information about the organization, eating disorder definitions, fact sheets, warning signs, therapy information, statistics and demographics, and suggestions on confronting someone with an eating disorder. Visitors will also find information on insurance discrimination and eating disorders, legislative alerts, and links to related useful sites.
http://www.anad.org

National Association of Cognitive-Behavioral Therapists   Up-to-date information and news is provided at the official site of the National Association of Cognitive-Behavioral Therapists, including back issues of the Rational News newsletter. A referral database sends you to the organization's National Database of Certified Cognitive-Behavioral Therapists. Professional certifications offered by the organization are outlined, and a professional and self-help resources store is provided online. Products for professionals include home study courses, books, and audiovisual materials. Likewise, self-improvement courses, and multimedia materials are available to the lay community.
http://www.nacbt.org

National Association of Psychiatric Health Systems (NAPHS)   The National Association of Psychiatric Health Systems advocates for health systems providing mental health and substance abuse services. The site provides a description of the organization and services, links to NAPHS and other sites offering consumer information, details of marketing opportunities, membership and contact details, and news articles. A resource catalog offers details of publications, conferences, and services of the organization, including advocacy materials and projects, clinical resources and projects, behavioral health events, financial resources, administrative resources, directories, and mailing lists. One section is restricted to registered members.
(some features fee-based) http://www.naphs.org

National Association of Social Workers (NASW)   This international organization of professional social workers is devoted to the professional growth of its members, the creation and maintenance of professional standards, and the advancement of social policies. Membership details, chapter listings, publications information, a directory of social workers, continuing education resources, employment notices, an online store, news, and advocacy activities are listed at the site. Links are available to state chapters, professional organizations, government and advocacy resources, child abuse prevention and child welfare resources, health, mental health, substance abuse resources, and commercial partners.
http://www.naswdc.org

National Attention Deficit Disorder Association   The National Attention Deficit Disorder Association helps people with AD/HD lead happier, more successful lives through education, research, and public advocacy. Membership information, conference details, articles, news, guiding principles for diagnosis and treatment, and a directory of professionals treating AD/HD are available at the site. Research, treatment, and general information about AD/HD is offered, as well as links to sites offering resources on work, family, education, and legal issues associated with AD/HD. Support group sites and sites for children and teens are also listed. Visitors can read personal stories and interviews, and search the site by keyword.
http://www.add.org

National Coalition of Arts Therapies Associations (NCATA)   This alliance of professional associations dedicated to the advancement of art therapy represents six organizations. Art therapy, dance/movement therapy, drama therapy, music therapy, psychodrama, and poetry therapy are defined and discussed at this site. Information on upcoming conferences and contact details for professional organizations are available.
http://www.ncata.com/home.html

National Depressive and Manic-Depressive Association   The National Depressive and Manic-Depressive Association strives to educate patients, families, professionals, and the public concerning the nature of depressive and bipolar disorders as treatable medical disorders, foster self-help, eliminate discrimination, improve access to care, and promote research. The site contains extensive information on the Association and links to general information on depression and bipolar disorder and related issues. Links to support groups, patient assistance programs, education, advocacy, clinical trials, and reference materials are listed. http://www.ndmda.org

National Mental Health Association   The National Mental Health Association works to increase tolerance and awareness, improve mental health services, prevent mental illness, and promote mental health. At this site, interested individuals will find updates on state and federal legislative actions, employment opportunities, an events calendar, and an information center providing links to referrals and educational materials. Informative links to discussions of topics including mental health disorders, advocacy issues, public education, and healthcare reform are found at the site, as well as links to the Association's affiliate and membership network.
http://www.nmha.org/index.cfm

New England Society for the Treatment of Trauma and Dissociation
This Society, an affiliate of the nonprofit International Society for the Study of Dissociation (ISSD), serves professional members from Connecticut, Maine, Massachusetts, New Hampshire, Rhode Island, and Vermont. Quarterly meetings offer professional presentations, discussion groups, consultation clinics, networking opportunities, and the Society sponsors educational workshops on the treatment of dissociative disorders and other topics. This site provides visitors with a mission statement, membership information, a calendar of events, recent newsletter articles, a bulletin board, and links to related sites.
http://www.nesttd.org

Psychiatry Society for Informatics   The home page of the Psychiatric Society for Informatics serves to increase the understanding and use of informatics related to the field of psychiatry. Information on the organization, its current news and upcoming meetings, online membership information and benefits, and the organization's electronic newsletter are all presented.
http://www.psych.med.umich.edu

Safer Society Foundation   This national nonprofit organization provides advocacy, referrals, and research for the prevention and treatment of sexual abuse. At this site, professionals and consumers can find news updates, learn about the Foundation's information and referral services, training and consulting information, research resources, and order books, and other reference materials provided by the Safer Society Press. Contact information and links to related organizations are also provided.
http://www.safersociety.org

Social Phobia/Social Anxiety Association Home Page   The purposes and goals of the Social Phobia/Social Anxiety Association (SP/SAA), informational articles, and current news are enumerated at the Association's Web site.

Social anxiety links, fact sheets, and mailing lists may be accessed. The Anxiety Network bookstore page allows users to choose and order books securely over the Internet. Professional literature and a subscription to the quarterly publication, SP/SAA Journal is available through a mail-in registration process.
http://www.socialphobia.org

Society for Neuronal Regulation (SNR)   This organization consists of professionals interested in neurofeedback training and research. Site resources include a glossary, a reference center, a listing of neurofeedback providers, conference information, and a neurofeedback archive of online abstracts and papers from selected SNR meetings. There is also free access to the *Journal of Neurotherapy*.   http://www.snr-jnt.org

Society for the Autistically Handicapped   The Society exists to bring an increased awareness of autism and expand patient's exposure to well-established and newly developed approaches in the diagnosis, assessment, education, and treatment of the disease. This site has many links describing autism, its treatment and diagnosis, including updated news on the latest research and treatment. There are large news and fact files, as well as informative links to topics such as sexuality, the culture and treatment of autism, and a list of worldwide conferences, workshops, and seminars relating to autism. There is also access to Europe's largest autism library, a message board, and related links. This site is a very informative resource for professionals and the public.
http://www.autismuk.com

Society for the Exploration of Psychotherapy Integration (SEPI)
The primary objective of SEPI is to explore the interface between differing approaches to psychotherapy. This site provides information on the society's mission, conference information, a list of influential books, training opportunities in psychotherapy integration, an online article, and links of interest.
http://www.cyberpsych.org/sepi/

Society for the Study of Ingestive Behavior   This professional society's site includes links to current news and information on ingestive behavior topics, relevant journals, calendar of events, membership information, employment, access to the newsletter, awards and grants and links to related organizations and other sites. This site is searchable by keyword.
http://www.jhu.edu/~ssib/ssib.html

Society of Behavioral Neuroendocrinology   This Society targets research professionals in the fields of behavior and neuroendocrinology. The site includes conference information, membership information, society officers, goals and bylaws of the Society, a link to related meetings. Publications resources include access to the official journal of the Society, *Hormones and Behavior,* and related journals, namely the *Journal of Neuroscience* and *Neuropeptides.*
http://www.sbne.org

Stress and Anxiety Research Society (STAR) This professional multidisciplinary organization of researchers promotes the exchange of information on anxiety and stress. At this site, the society's mission and history is presented, as well as membership information, STAR members, conference information, national and international representatives, and a list of publications from STAR. A list of related organizations, academic departments, journals, databases, employment opportunities, and online newsgroups and mailing lists is also provided. http://star-society.org

Tourette's Syndrome Association (TSA), Incorporated Described as the only national organization dedicated to providing information on Tourette's syndrome (TS), the Tourette's Syndrome Association's Web site includes links to public service announcements and a chat room. The site contains numerous general facts about TS, as well as scientific links, such as a publications list, research grant awards and TS diagnosis and treatment. Interested persons will find links to national chapters of the association, and international contacts. There are links to order TSA publications, and online access to selected relevant articles. http://www.tsa-usa.org

United States of America Transactional Analysis Association This organization is a community of professionals utilizing transactional analysis in "organizational, educational, and clinical settings, and for personal growth." A history of the organization, membership details, events notices, and articles are available at the site. Links are provided to transactional analysis associations, online publications, and educational sites.
http://usataa.org

World Association for Infant Mental Health (WAIMH) WAIMH is an interdisciplinary and international association promoting education and research on all aspects of infant mental health. Included are links to the association's mission statement and membership information, conference listings, and affiliates. Internet resources include training information and online access to the table of contents for *Infant Mental Health Journal*.
http://www.msu.edu/user/waimh

World Psychiatric Association (WPA) This organization of professional psychiatric societies is devoted to the advancement of psychiatric and mental health education, research, clinical care, and public policy initiatives. Proceedings and conclusions of the most recent general assembly, ethical guidelines related to psychiatric practice, and descriptions of official Association publications are available at the site. Educational activities of the Association are presented at the site, with a calendar of upcoming educational events, information on Continuing Medical Education and general public education, and links to other psychiatry education sites. A list of WPA scientific sections and chairs, a calendar of general meetings, and a description of the organization's structure are also found at the address.
http://www.wpanet.org

8.2 RESEARCH ORGANIZATIONS

DIRECTORIES OF RESEARCH CENTERS

Centerwatch: Profiles of Centers Conducting Clinical Research This site is ordered geographically by state. It provides an in-depth profile of hundreds of clinical institutions and research centers engaged in psychiatric research. The contact information of each center is provided along with an overview, research experience description, information on facilities, staff expertise, and patient demographics.
http://www.centerwatch.com/professional/profglst.html

Laboratories at the National Institute of Mental Health (NIMH), Division of Intramural Research Programs Connections to more than 28 laboratories/branches may be accessed at the National Institute of Mental Health's Intramural Research site. The research roles of each section and its subdivisions are enumerated as are key division personnel and contact information. Research divisions include the Laboratory of Neurochemistry, the Behavioral Endocrinology Branch, the Laboratory of Brain and Cognition, and the Section on Pharmacology.
http://intramural.nimh.nih.gov/research

Research, Training, and Technical Assistance Centers These research, training, and technical assistance centers are supported by the Center for Mental Health Services. Services may include technical assistance, information and referrals, on-site consultation, training, library services, publications, and annotated bibliographies, among other resources. Contact information on individual research centers as well as brief outlines of the information, conferences, and other services they provide are included.
http://www.mentalhealth.org/publications/allpubs/KEN95-0010/KEN950010.htm

INDIVIDUAL RESEARCH CENTERS

Center for Mental Health Policy and Services Research A component of the University of Pennsylvania's Health System, this Center provides general overviews of the ongoing and completed research projects in topics including aging, forensics, serious mental illnesses, homeless issues, substance abuse, and prevention. A list of the Center's publications, presentations, and managed care consensus reports, a faculty, staff, fellows, and student directory, as well as fellowship information are included.
http://www.med.upenn.edu/~cmhpsr

Center for Mental Health Research on AIDS Part of the National Institute of Mental Health, the Center for Mental Health Research on AIDS offers information on their research programs on this site. Research programs include HIV/STD prevention and translational research, HIV-1 infection of the central nervous system, HIV and AIDS among the severely mentally ill, and AIDS mental health services research. The site also offers related news, publications, and a link to the CRISP (computer retrieval of information on scientific projects) database for information on federally funded biomedical research projects. http://www.nimh.nih.gov/oa/

Center for Mind-Body Medicine   This educational organization promotes the recognition and study of all aspects of health and illness, including mental, emotional, social, and physical. The Center encourages new paragons in care, including education of professionals and students and service-oriented personnel. Current programs include research in mind-body awareness, school wellness, and professional and community education. A variety of workshops, comprehensive conference information, references, staff information, and other links are included.
http://www.healthy.net/clinic/therapy/mind/index.asp

Center for the Study of Issues in Public Mental Health   This Center exists as a collaboration of various New York State mental health organizations and institutes. The Center's mission is to research severely mentally ill adults in a community and multidisciplinary fashion. Projects of the Center include studies that focus on the development, organization, finance, and evaluation of assistance to adults with severe mental illness. Overviews of specific projects are provided, in topics such as homelessness, managed care, drug abuse, recovery, and innovative treatment. Online access to the Center's newsletter, current events, links to faculty and research partner sites, and references to other related publications are included.
http://www.rfmh.org/csipmh

Chicago Institute for Psychoanalysis   This Web site features information on the Institute's clinic and offers answers to common questions about psychoanalysis. There is also information on the Child and Adolescent Clinic, the Barr-Harris Clinic, and the Fluency Readiness Program. Information on the various educational programs offered at the Institute, conferences, current news, and links to other related Web sites are provided.
http://www.chicagoanalysis.org/

Crisis Prevention Institute's Violence Prevention Resource Center   This Center provides training information and other resources in violence and crisis intervention. Intervention techniques and information are provided in the areas of education, healthcare, mental health, security, corrections and police, business, human service and government, and youth services.
http://www.crisisprevention.com

Dana.org   Described as "the site for brain information," this Web page offers a broad array of resources. The "BrainWeb and Brain Information" section offers full-text articles and links to related resources for diseases such as Alzheimer's, Parkinson's, addiction, head/brain injury, and mental illness. Informa-

tion on research grants, books, publications, and broadcasts are found. The BrainyKids section offers games and more than 90 animated shorts on health, science, and technology. In addition, the kids section offers interactive laboratories, as well as lesson plans for teachers.
http://www.dana.org/

Indiana University: Institute of Psychiatric Research For those interested in the genetics of bipolar disorder, the Institute of Psychiatric Research describes their research on the topic. Information on the site includes how to participate in the study, articles, contact information on the research staff, and a short list of related Internet links.
http://ipr.iupui.edu/

Institute for Behavioral Genetics Located within the University of Colorado, Boulder, this multidisciplinary Institute focuses on performing research on the genetic and environmental factors that contribute to individual differences in behavior. At this site, lists of publications from the Institute are available, and computer programs written by and courses taught by the faculty are listed. Faculty, staff, scientists, and students home page links are included at the site. http://ibgwww.colorado.edu

Institute for Behavioral Healthcare This California-based Institute, a division of the Institute for the Advancement of Human Behavior, provides continuing medical and general education to professionals in the mental health fields. The site contains clinical workshop information, and home study courses on various topics such as substance abuse, pain control, and attention-deficit/hyperactivity disorder.
http://www.ibh.com

Institute for Mathematical Behavioral Sciences Located at University of California, Irvine, the Institute's mission is to facilitate communication between scientists interested in creating and testing human behavior theories. There is a comprehensive faculty list, information on the doctoral program and students, online access to technical report abstracts, and information on the upcoming workshop. A list of related university sites is also available.
http://aris.ss.uci.edu/mbs

Institute for Psychological Study of the Arts This University of Florida Institute site provides links to seminars, in topics such as psychoanalytic psychology and criticism, a staff list and brief summaries of their interests, online abstracts and bibliography of the Institute, and a link to the *Journal for the Psychological Study of the Arts*. The site also offers links to relevant sites and other associations, as well as conference information.
http://www.clas.ufl.edu/ipsa/intro.htm

Institute of Psychiatry and the Department of Psychiatry and Behavioral Sciences Located within the Medical University of South Carolina in Charleston, this Institute provides psychiatric and drug abuse treatment, rehabilitation, and prevention assistance. Clinical psychiatric services include adult, general, and special services, such as eating disorders, crime victims research and treatment, family bonding, and geropsychiatry programs. In addition, there are programs designed for youth, such as the Tic and Tourette's Program, eating disorders treatment, and the adolescent dual diagnosis program. Alcohol and drug rehabilitation programs are also offered. Research program information is available at the site in topics including Alzheimer's research, anxiety, drug and alcohol abuse, clinical psychopharmacology, and more. A referral service as well as other general information about the Institute are also available. http://www.musc.edu/psychiatry

Los Angeles Institute and Society for Psychoanalytic Studies The Los Angeles Institute and Society for Psychoanalytic Studies is a division of the Society of the International Psychoanalytical Association. At this site, the latest publications of the Institute are available in full, as well as a bibliography of publications by the Institute's members. Seminar and workshop information, as well as extension courses and training program details are present. http://www.laisps.org/

Louis de la Parte Florida Mental Health Institute A component of the University of South Florida, this Institute is described as the primary research and training center for mental health services in Florida. Current research focuses on various issues regarding aging and mental health, such as cognitive aging, and mental health needs of senior citizens. In addition, there is a link to research that examines the mental health of children and families, such as autistic children, special risk children, and families with children that have serious emotional disturbances. There are also projects that focus on the law and mental health, including criminal competence assessment, child abuse, substance abuse in prisons, and drug court programs. A comprehensive list of publications by the faculty at the center is available in abstract and full text form. Information on educational opportunities and upcoming events are also present at this site. http://www.fmhi.usf.edu

Mental Health Research & Training Agencies Twenty separate government agencies focused on mental health research, training, and technical assistance are profiled at this useful site established by the Center for Mental Health Services, a federal agency. The agencies cover children's mental health, family support, psychiatric disabilities, psychiatric rehabilitation, empowerment, consumer self-help, homelessness, government planning, transitional assistance, networking in the field of mental health, and technical assistance in many forms. http://www.mentalhealth.org/publications/allpubs/KEN95-0010/KEN950010.htm

Nathan Kline Institute for Psychiatric Research This Institute, a constituent of New York State's Office of Mental Health, is described as one of the nation's foremost centers of excellence in mental health research. Each link to a research topic provides an overview of the topic, ongoing studies, collaborators, achievements, and a publications list. Research topics include Alzheimer's disease, analytical psychopharmacology, basic neuroimaging, cellular and molecular neurobiology, clinical neuroimaging, issues in public mental health, cognitive neuroscience and schizophrenia, co-occurring disorders, dementia, movement disorders, homelessness research, addiction and dual diagnosis, neurobehavioral and genetics, neurochemistry and neurobiology, quantitative EEG, violence and the mentally ill, and others. A description of the Institute's facilities, a faculty list, upcoming events, and other related links are provided. http://www.rfmh.org/nki

National Alliance for Research on Schizophrenia and Depression A nonprofit organization, the National Alliance for Research on Schizophrenia and Depression (NARSAD) is devoted to the scientific research of brain and behavior disorders. Visitors to the site will find information on research grants for basic and/or clinical research in neurobiology, as well as recent articles from the NARSAD Research Newsletter. A Brain Disorders section offers fact sheets, information on NARSAD-funded research, and a publication order form for disorders such as schizophrenia, depression, and bipolar disorder. Participation opportunities in ongoing studies are also described. In addition, there is a publication catalog, and a list of recommended reading.
http://www.mhsource.com/narsad/

National Center for American Indian and Alaska Native Mental Health Research (NCAIANMHR) Affiliated with the University of Colorado, the NCAIANMHR focuses on evaluating the presence of alcohol, drug, and mental disorders in Native populations, and examining the effectiveness of intervention. The site contains program goals, methods, and measures for 14 research projects, such as Suicide Among American Indians, American Indian Pathways to Abstinence, and the Role of Attachment in Child Social-Emotional Outcomes. Descriptions of past research, and associated publications, are also found. In addition, there is a staff directory, online issues of the NCAIANMHR journal, a list of staff publications, training opportunities, and related Internet resources. http://www.uchsc.edu/sm/ncaianmhr/

National Center for Stuttering This Center performs research studies in many different aspects of stuttering. The mission of the Center is to provide facts about stuttering, offer a hotline, conduct research, provide treatment, and supply continuing education for professionals. An overview of the research findings, as well as the treatment programs, and a summary of the Center's model of stuttering are provided.
http://www.stuttering.com

National Technical Assistance Center for State Mental Health Planning This Center provides technical aid and training to professionals. The site provides information on its meetings, research, and publications. Users can search for information on specific projects by topic or state. There are over 30 topics, from advocacy and support, to telecommunications technology. Selected project highlights, a comprehensive resource list, links to state assistance

centers, current events, and online access to the Center's publications are all available at this comprehensive site.
http://www.nasmhpd.org/ntac

New Hampshire-Dartmouth Psychiatric Research Center   The Psychiatric Research Center describes their program as specializing in developing interventions in research conditions and translating them to practice. Brief descriptions of their research projects are found, covering the areas of vocational rehabilitation, dual diagnosis and homelessness, aging services, children and adolescents, and knowledge dissemination and application. There is also information on the faculty, including biographies, vita, and links to publications. A list of the Center's publications and books is provided, along with an ordering form. Downloadable tools are provided on the site including an alcohol and drug use screen, clinician-rated alcohol and drug use scales, and model fidelity rating scales.
http://www.dartmouth.edu/dms/psychrc/

New York State Psychiatric Institute   Described as the nation's first psychiatric research institute, over 300 psychiatry-related studies are currently performed at this center. Links to research areas provide professionals with a comprehensive project background and summaries, as well as extensive information about the involved faculty and departments. Research areas include psychiatric genetics, neuroscience, depression evaluation, clinical pharmacology, anxiety disorders (such as phobias and panic disorder), developmental psychobiology (such as maternal deprivation), molecular neurobiology, child psychiatry, epidemiology, and mental illness in children. Links are offered to details of current treatment programs for a variety of psychiatric disorders. Information on education and training opportunities is available, as well as details of clinical services. http://www.nyspi.cpmc.columbia.edu

Perceptual Science Laboratory   Part of the University of California, Santa Cruz, this Laboratory performs research in the areas of perception and cognition. A major focus of research is on speech perception by ear and eye, as well as facial animation, and professionals and other interested individuals can access research news and updates on this research. Links to the faculty home pages, a publications list, and downloadable demonstrations of current research are provided. There are numerous links to related sites, in topics such as facial animation and analysis, speech reading, and computer graphics.
http://mambo.ucsc.edu

Psychiatric Research Institute   Affiliated with the Via Christi Health System in Kansas, the Psychiatric Research Institute conducts research for all stages of clinical drug trials designed for the treatment of disorders such as anxiety, panic disorder, schizophrenia, and Alzheimer's disease. Research participants can find information on outpatient studies and phase I studies.
http://www.via-christi.org/pri/

Psychoanalytic Institute of New England, East The mission of this Institute is to study psychoanalysis and its evolution over time, especially in reference to current theory and treatment. Educational information, current programs and seminars, and a list of faculty are provided at the site.
http://www.analysis.com/pine

San Francisco Psychoanalytic Institute and Society This nonprofit Institute provides educational and training services for professionals, conducts seminars for consumers and professionals, and provides psychoanalytic services for the public. Included are links to introductory information on psychoanalysis, an events calendar, clinic information, and a referral service, as well as links to child development programs, such a child psychotherapy and divorcing parents support groups.
http://www.sfpi.org

Southeastern Rural Mental Health Research Center Hosted by the University of Virginia (UVA), this Web site offers a brief description of the mission of the Southeastern Rural Mental Health Research Center. The Center is dedicated to research that will facilitate mental health service delivery to high-risk rural minority and impoverished people. There is a staff directory, and related Internet links. A link to the UVA Health System, UVA School of Nursing, and the University is also provided.
http://www.virginia.edu/~srmhrc/

University of California: Los Angeles: Center for Research of Treatment and Rehabilitation of Psychosis This research center conducts experiments, and provides consulting and technical support to other professionals interested in severe psychiatric illnesses, like schizophrenia. Research activities and laboratories at the Center study topics including cognition, psychophysiology and neuropsychology, diagnostic and psychopathology assessment, psychopharmacology, and psychosocial assessment and treatment. Detailed overviews of these programs, summaries of important findings of the Center, and a faculty directory are offered at the site.
http://www.npi.ucla.edu/irc

University of California: Mental Health Clinical Research Center Staff at the University of California San Diego Mental Health Clinical Research Center are primarily focused on the neurobiology of affective disorders. Their site offers program descriptions and abstracts of papers related to the neurobiology of depression. The programs cover the themes of sleep and chronobiology, psychoimmunology, neuropharmacology, molecular genetics, brain imaging, and premenstrual depression. The site also contains fellowship/training information, staff biographies and abstracts of their papers, and a short list of related links. Patients will find information on participating in the Center's studies. http://varesearch.ucsd.edu/gillin/mhcrc/default.htm

University of Maryland: Maryland Psychiatric Research Center Examining schizophrenia is the primary mission of the Maryland Psychiatric

Research Organizations

Research Center. Their site offers information on their research programs, faculty biographies, Internet links on schizophrenia, and information on their clinical training program. Their inpatient programs consist of a Residential Research Unit that focuses on new treatments, new imaging techniques, and building social and life skills, and the Treatment Research Unit for people who do not respond to traditional treatment. The Schizophrenia Related Disorders outpatient program examines motor disorders, first episode psychosis, eyetracking, family studies, and children at high risk. In addition, there is an outpatient program focused on new treatment and imaging. Program goals, staff expertise, and eligibility for program participation for all of the programs are described.
http://www.umaryland.edu/mprc/

University of Michigan: Mental Health Research Institute   The Mental Health Research Institute focuses on biological psychiatry and molecular neuroscience. Staff interests are outlined briefly and include brain imaging, mapping of genes related to psychiatric disorders, schizophrenia, neuropeptides, and depression. There is a link to the Department of Psychiatry that offers more detailed information on education programs, clinical services, and research at the University.   http://www.med.umich.edu/mhri/

University of North Carolina: Mental Health Systems and Services Research   Current research projects are described on this site including the "Impacts of Managed Care on Substance Abuse Service Linkages," and the "Utilization of Public Sector Behavioral Health Systems and Jails." The results of prior projects are also described. The site also contains faculty contact information, training opportunities, a description of the post-doctoral fellowship program, and related Web sites.
http://www.schsr.unc.edu/research_programs/Mental_Health/MHSection.html

University of Southern Mississippi: Psychophysiology Research Laboratory   This Laboratory performs research in the area of human psychophysiology, with primary emphasis on visceral perception and related topics. Site resources include complete texts of conference presentations, overviews of current research projects, recent and upcoming publications lists, and abstracts and presentations. A reference list for visceral perception articles and links to other related sites are included at the site.
http://ocean.st.usm.edu/~gejones/psyphylab.html

Yale University: Psychiatry Research Clinics   Yale University's Psychiatry department is studying and operates clinics in the areas of affective disorders, anxiety, prevention, post-traumatic stress disorder, repetitive transcranial magnetic stimulation, schizophrenia, and winter depression. Links on the left side of the page offer detailed information on the clinic, diagnosis and treatment, as well as other basic information.
http://info.med.yale.edu/psych/clinics/intro.html

8.3 SELECTED MEDICAL SCHOOL PSYCHIATRY DEPARTMENTS

Many of the medical school departments listed below are affiliated with hospitals that are profiled in the hospital departments section. Numerous hospital and medical school departments overlap considerably relative to faculty, hospital staff, and research activities.

P-1275
Baylor College Department of Psychiatry and Behavioral Science
http://www.bcm.tmc.edu/psych

P-1276
Boston Graduate School of Psychoanalysis School of Psychoanalysis
http://www.bgsp.edu

P-1277
Boston University: Department of Psychiatry
http://www.bumc.bu.edu/Departments/HomeMain.asp?DepartmentID=68

P-1278
Columbia University: Department of Psychiatry and Neurology
http://cpmcnet.columbia.edu/dept/pi/psych.html

P-1279
Cornell University: Department of Psychiatry
http://www.nycornell.org/psychiatry

P-1280
Dartmouth Medical School Department of Psychiatry
http://www.dartmouth.edu/dms/psychtry/

P-1281
Duke University Department of Psychiatry
http://psychiatry.mc.duke.edu

P-1282
Emory University: Department of Psychiatry and Behavioral Sciences http://www.emory.edu/WHSC/MED/PSYCHIATRY/home.htm

P-1283
Florida Mental Health Institute Department of Community Mental Health http://www.fmhi.usf.edu/cmh/statement.html

P-1284
Georgetown University Department of Psychiatry
http://www.dml.georgetown.edu/schmed/depts/psychiatry.html

P-1285
Harvard University: Department of Psychiatry
http://www.hmcnet.harvard.edu/psych/index.html

P-1286
Indiana University: Department of Psychiatry
http://www.iupui.edu/~psych

P-1287
Johns Hopkins University:
Department of Psychiatry and Behavioral Sciences
http://www.med.jhu.edu/jhhpsychiatry/master1.htm

P-1288
Medical College of Ohio Department of Psychiatry
http://www.mco.edu/depts/psych

P-1289
Medical College of Virginia Department of Psychiatry
http://views.vcu.edu/views/psych

P-1290
Medical College of Wisconsin:
Department of Psychiatry and Behavioral Medicine
http://www.mcw.edu/psych

P-1291
Michigan State University Department of Psychiatry
http://www.com.msu.edu/dept/departments.html#anchor1751341

P-1292
Mount Sinai: Department of Psychiatry
http://www.mssm.edu/psychiatry/

P-1293
New York University: Department of Psychiatry
http://www.med.nyu.edu/Psych/NYUPsych.Homepage.html

P-1294
Northwestern University Medical School Department of Psychiatry
and Behavioral Sciences
http://www.nums.nwu.edu/psychiatry/

P-1295
Southern Illinois University Department of Psychiatry
http://www.siumed.edu/psych/main/SIUpsych.htm

P-1296
Stanford University:
Department of Psychiatry and Behavioral Sciences
http://www.stanford.edu/dept/PBS

P-1297
Texas A&M University
Department of Psychiatry and Behavioral Science
http://www.sw.org/depts/psych/dept.htm

P-1298
Tufts University/
New England Medical Center Department of Psychiatry
http://www.nemc.org/psych/

P-1299
Tulane University: Department of Psychiatry and Neurology
http://www.mcl.tulane.edu/departments/psych_neuro/psnra01.htm

P-1300
University of Alabama, Birmingham Department of Psychiatry
http://www.uab.edu/psychiatry

P-1301
University of California: Davis: Department of Psychiatry
http://neuroscience.ucdavis.edu/psychiatry

P-1302
University of California: Los Angeles: Department of Psychiatry and
Biobehavioral Sciences
http://www.MentalHealth.ucla.edu/psychiatry

P-1303
University of California: San Francisco: Department of Psychiatry
http://www.ucsf.edu/psych/home.htm

Don't type in long URLs – add the site number to the eMedguides URL: www.eMedguides.com/**G-1234**.

P-1304 **University of Chicago: Department of Psychiatry**
http://psychiatry.uchicago.edu

P-1305 **University of Cincinnati: Department of Psychiatry**
http://psychiatry.uc.edu

P-1306 **University of Colorado: Department of Psychiatry**
http://www.uchsc.edu/sm/psych/dept/index.htm

P-1307 **University of Connecticut: Department of Psychiatry**
http://marvin.uchc.edu

P-1308 **University of Florida: Department of Psychiatry**
http://www.med.ufl.edu/psych

P-1309 **University of Iowa: Department of Psychiatry**
http://www.uihealthcare.com/depts/med/psychiatry/

P-1310 **University of Louisville:**
Department of Psychiatry and Behavioral Sciences
http://www.louisville.edu/medschool/psychiatry

P-1311 **University of Massachusetts: Department of Psychiatry**
http://www.umassmed.edu/psychiatry/

P-1312 **University of Miami:**
Department of Psychiatry & Behavioral Sciences
http://www.med.miami.edu/psychiatry/main.html

P-1313 **University of Michigan: Department of Psychiatry**
http://www.med.umich.edu/psych

P-1314 **University of Minnesota: Department of Psychiatry**
http://www.med.umn.edu/psychiatry

P-1315 **University of North Carolina: Department of Psychiatry**
http://www.med.unc.edu

P-1316 **University of Pennsylvania: Department of Psychiatry**
http://www.med.upenn.edu/psych

P-1317 **University of Pittsburgh: Department of Psychiatry**
http://www.wpic.pitt.edu

P-1318 **University of Rochester: Department of Psychiatry**
http://www.urmc.rochester.edu/smd/Psych

P-1319 **University of South Florida: Department of Psychiatry and Behav-**
ioral Medicine
http://www.med.usf.edu/PSYCH/psychome.html

Don't type in long URLs – add the site number to the eMedguides URL: www.eMedguides.com/G-1234.

P-1320
**University of Southern California:
Department of Psychiatry and Behavioral Sciences**
http://www.usc.edu/schools/medicine

P-1321
**University of Texas: Galveston:
Department of Psychiatry and Behavioral Sciences**
http://psychiatry.utmb.edu

P-1322
University of Texas: Southwestern: Department of Psychiatry
http://www3.utsouthwestern.edu/psychiatry/

P-1323
University of Utah: Department of Psychiatry
http://www.med.utah.edu/psychiatry

P-1324
University of Virginia: Department of Psychiatric Medicine
http://www.med.virginia.edu/medicine/clinical/psychiatric/home.html

P-1325
**University of Washington:
Department of Psychiatry and Behavioral Sciences**
http://depts.washington.edu/psychweb/index.html

P-1326
University of Wisconsin: Madison: Department of Psychiatry
http://www.psychiatry.wisc.edu

P-1327
Virginia Commonwealth University Department of Psychiatry
http://views.vcu.edu/psych/

P-1328
**Wake Forest University
Department of Psychiatry and Behavioral Medicine**
http://www.wfubmc.edu/psychiatry

P-1329
Washington University: Department of Psychiatry
http://www.psychiatry.wustl.edu

P-1330
**Wayne State University:
Department of Psychiatry and Behavioral Neurosciences**
http://psychiatry1.med.wayne.edu

P-1331
Yale University Department of Psychiatry
http://info.med.yale.edu/psych/

P-1332
**Yeshiva University (Albert Einstein)
Department of Psychiatry and Behavioral Sciences**
http://quark.aecom.yu.edu/psychlab

8.4 SELECTED HOSPITAL PSYCHIATRY DEPARTMENTS

P-1333
HOSPITAL

Barnes-Jewish Hospital, Washington University Medical Center The site provides a general overview of facilities available, hospital statistics, support groups, events, contact information, and specific hospital services and programs. **Research:** A wide range of techniques were pioneered at the Hospital, including the first double-lung transplant and the first laparoscopic nephrectomy. Specialized techniques include multiple organ transplantation, in-vitro fertilization, osteoporosis treatment, lung volume reduction surgery, minimally invasive surgery, diabetes treatment, eye treatment, cancer treatment, and cardiology. Services related to psychiatry include research and care for sleep disorders and Alzheimer's disease, electroconvulsive therapy, and a full range of behavioral health services, including a crisis response center and individual, group, and family therapy. **Patient Resources:** Lodging suggestions, general information about St. Louis, physician referral service, and health risk appraisal will be of interest to patients. **Location:** St. Louis, Missouri
http://www.bjc.org

P-1334
HOSPITAL

C. F. Menninger Memorial Hospital Detailed information about the types of services offered for children and adults with learning disorders are provided. Guidelines are listed for parents to help determine if their child suffers from a learning disorder. Information about the Institute's Summer Teacher Training program, and development and educational services offered to public and private schools, clinics, professional organizations and families is also given. **Research:** Research carried out at the Child and Family Center includes delineating patterns of psychological and behavioral disturbance in infants, designing interventions to foster the bonding of fathers to their newborn infants, and designing interventions with parents of disturbed infants. The research department of Menninger provides links to a large variety of additional projects targeting new knowledge across a wide variety of mental illnesses in young children, adolescents, and adults. **Patient Resources:** The site contains referral information and a comprehensive list of psychiatric services offered to adults, children and adolescents, as well as corporations. The various programs of the hospital that have been described in detail are the Child and Family Center, Center for Learning Disabilities, Institute for Psychoanalysis, continuing education, Center for Clinical Research, and training programs for mental health professionals. General information about the hospital including history, location, governance and staff, mission statement, clinical staff, employment opportunities and benefits, news releases, telephone directory, library, bookstore, and subscription information for the hospital's bulletin are provided. **Location:** Topeka, Kansas
http://www.menninger.edu

P-1335
HOSPITAL

Children's Hospital, Boston Children's Hospital, Boston is the pediatric teaching hospital of Harvard Medical School. Patient care services, research activities, training opportunities, contact information, employment opportunities, community services, department Web sites, and directions for visitors are offered at this site. Users can find specific information with a site search engine. **Research:** Research news, administration, and facilities information, and links to departments and laboratories are offered for details of current research. Research and services of psychiatric interest in Neurology are offered through the Behavioral Neurology Program, the Mental Retardation Research Center, and the Division of Clinical Neurophysiology and Epilepsy. The Department of Psychiatry integrates cognitive, behavioral, psychoeducational, psychodynamic, family, group, developmental, and biological methods in the treatment of disorders and preventative interventions. The Division of Psychology provides patient evaluation, education, psychodiagnostic testing, and therapy. **Patient Resources:** The site provides detailed informational resources from each division, department, and program, inpatient hospital visit details, explanations of a patient's healthcare team at the hospital, hospital resources, international patient services, and associated specialty and primary care locations. **Location:** Boston, Massachusetts

http://www.childrenshospital.org

P-1336
HOSPITAL

Duke University Medical Center Department of Psychiatry and Behavioral Sciences
Research: Current areas of research include behavioral medicine, biological psychiatry, child and adolescent psychiatry, medical psychology, geriatric psychiatry, community psychiatry, and personality disorders. **Patient Resources:** Detailed information is presented about the department's administrative structure and Grand Rounds conferences. Links are provided for psychiatrically oriented institutions, online journals, newsgroups, and other Internet resources. Information about continuing medical education and educational programs for physicians, medical residents, and psychologists is presented. Several clinical programs and their descriptions and an alphabetical listing of research activities is presented. **Location:** Durham, North Carolina

http://psychiatry.mc.duke.edu/

P-1337
HOSPITAL

Johns Hopkins University: Department of Psychiatry and Behavioral Sciences
Information on depressive disorder and bipolar disorder is well presented. Research reports, books and video information, support group information, and links to other organizations are provided. Book reviews are also available at this site. **Research:** Obsessive-compulsive disorders, child and adolescent psychiatry, neuropsychiatry and memory, genetics of schizophrenia, and psychiatric neuroimaging are the main foci of investigation. Specific psychiatric disorders being studied in the child and adolescent psychiatry division include attention-deficit/hyperactivity disorder, anxiety disorders, major depression and bipolar disorder, autism, developmental disorders, and fragile X-linked mental retardation. The neuropsychiatry group's investigation mainly involves the study and treatment of Alzheimer's disease and its related illnesses. The epidemiology and genetics program is involved in the identification of schizophrenia susceptibility genes. **Patient Resources:** Information is provided about the hospitals clinical services, fellowships and training programs, educational programs, faculty, research programs, patient resources, and directions and parking at the hospital.

Links to other Johns Hopkins Web sites are also provided. **Location:** Baltimore, Maryland

http://www.med.jhu.edu/jhhpsychiatry/master1.htm

Massachusetts General Hospital Information is available for participation in several research programs in the areas of women's mental health and depression. Several links to depression resource centers are provided. **Research:** Studies are being conducted in the areas of clinical pharmacology and psychotherapy, drug abuse behavioral pharmacology, neuroimaging, substance abuse epidemiology, bipolar mood disorders, alcohol and drug dependence, eating disorders, gerontology, HIV infection, pediatric psychopharmacology, psychiatric oncology and trauma, neurobiology, and schizophrenia. Research studies carried out at the Center for Women's Mental Health include identification of effective treatments for women suffering from premenstrual dysphoric disorder, postpartum psychiatric illness, and menopause-associated depression. **Patient Resources:** The site provides extensive information about the various departments in the psychiatry division of the Massachusetts General Hospital. These departments include Analytic Psychotherapy, Center for Women's Mental Health, a child and adolescent psychiatry residency training program, a depression clinical and research program, an obsessive-compulsive disorders clinic and institute, pediatric psychopharmacology, psychotic disorders, telepsychiatry, and a law and psychiatry service. Information about psychiatry fellowships and psychiatry residency training programs is also provided. A physician location service is also featured at this site. **Location:** Boston, Massachusetts

http://www.mgh.harvard.edu/depts/allpsych/HomePage.html

Mayo Clinic This site provides details of services offered at the Clinic, including care by specialty, educational programs, and typical procedures for patient testing and treatment. The site also presents general information on lodging, directions, and amenities available to patients and visitors. **Research:** All major areas of medicine are investigated at the Clinic, including research in Psychiatry and Psychology, but information on this program is not provided at the site. **Patient Resources:** Detailed descriptions of services offered to patients and families during treatment are found at the site. **Location:** Rochester, Minnesota

http://www.mayo.edu/mcr

McLean Hospital Information about participation in research studies of Alzheimer's, attention deficit hyperactivity disorders, depression and other psychiatric disorders is provided for patients and their families. **Research:** The McLean Hospital's research program in neuroscience and psychiatry is the largest of private psychiatric hospitals in the United States. Research is being carried out in drug and alcohol abuse, bipolar and psychotic disorders, schizophrenia-related changes in brain microcircuitry, psychotic depression, treatment of adult survivors of childhood trauma, degenerative diseases of the nervous system including Alzheimer's, Parkinson's, and Huntington's diseases. Research at the brain-imaging center involves the monitoring of changes in brain chemistry to document the course of illness or the effects of medication. The Brain Bank at

McLean collects and distributes human brain tissue for research. **Patient Resources:** The McLean Hospital is a teaching facility of the Harvard Medical School and an affiliate of the Massachusetts General Hospital. The site contains detailed information about the hospital's clinical programs, research, educational and professional training programs, and library resources and services. Extensive links to other psychiatric organizations, institutes, information centers, and libraries are also provided. Employment opportunities at the hospital are listed. **Location:** Belmont, Massachusetts

http://www.mcleanhospital.org

P-1341
HOSPITAL

Mount Sinai: Department of Psychiatry **Research:** Extensive research is being conducted in Alzheimer's disease, autism, mood and personality disorders, post-traumatic stress disorders, schizophrenia, anxiety disorders, molecular neurobiology and neurogenetics, neuroinflammation, molecular neuropsychiatry, psychopharmacology, neuropathology, neurochemistry, neuroscience positron emission tomography, and neuroanatomy and morphometrics. **Patient Resources:** This page offers information about the various research programs and laboratories in psychiatry and clinical programs and services available for patients including emergency services, electro-convulsive therapy, and psychological and neurological testing. Training information for psychiatric residents is also presented in detail. **Location:** New York, New York

http://www.mssm.edu/psychiatry/

P-1342
HOSPITAL

New York Presbyterian Hospital Columbia University Campus Important links to several psychiatric organizations and hospitals are provided at this site for patient perusal. **Research:** More than 300 biological, behavioral and social research studies are being conducted at the psychiatric institute. Studies in neuroscience, depression evaluation, clinical psychopharmacology, bulimia, anxiety disorders, developmental psychobiology, molecular neurobiology, and child psychiatry are currently in the forefront of research at the psychiatric institute. **Patient Resources:** This Web page contains a profile of the Psychiatry Department, its administrative structure, list of faculty members, and description of clinical, research, and affiliated centers training programs. Departmental components including the Presbyterian Hospital psychiatric services, departmental clinical services, and the New York State Psychiatric Institute are described in detail. Links to the Columbia University home page and affiliated institutions, namely, the Harlem Hospital Center, the Creedmoor Psychiatric Center, and St. Luke's Roosevelt Hospital are provided. Links can also be found to other psychiatry departments in the U.S., and psychiatric associations, institutes, and agencies. In addition, a long list of psychiatric references including journals, Internet resources, and the National Library of Medicine may be accessed. **Location:** New York, New York

http://cpmcnet.columbia.edu

P-1343
HOSPITAL

UCLA Neuropsychiatric Hospital Two online resource directories are available: 1) The California Developmental Disabilities Netlink provides information about services and programs for children and adults with developmental disabilities 2) The Women with Developmental Disabilities link provides several informative resources on housing, health and wellness, books, and links to related Web sites for women. **Research:** Studies are aimed at understanding the biological mechanisms of and treatment of anxiety disorders. Specific projects in the child and adolescent anxiety program focus on selective mutism, Tourette's disorder, and other Tic disorders. Severe mental illnesses such as schizophrenia are under investigation at the UCLA Center for Research on Treatment and Rehabilitation of Psychosis. Other research areas include mental retardation and managed care for psychiatric disorders. **Patient Resources:** This Web site offers information about the various psychiatric departments and their programs, the Women's Life Center, which offers mental health treatment during pregnancy, menopause, etc., and presents a guide to literature on qualitative research methods and qualitative and quantitative research integration methods. Links are provided to other UCLA departments and UCLA related Web sites as well as other neuropsychiatric and healthcare related Web sites. **Location:** Los Angeles, California

http://www.npi.ucla.edu

P-1344
HOSPITAL

UCSF Stanford Health Care This site offers general health information for patients and the public, links to associated hospitals and clinics, and specific information on services offered at the general and children's hospitals. **Research:** Continuing Medical Education information, and clinical highlights are available at the site. Specialty services in Psychiatry and Behavioral Sciences are offered through the Aging Clinical Research Center, Bipolar Disorders Clinic, Center for Narcolepsy, Child and Adolescent Psychiatry Program, Eating Disorders Research Studies, Psychosocial Treatment Laboratory, and the Stanford/VA Alzheimer's Center. **Patient Resources:** Health and medical news, health tips, and clinical highlights are available for patients. Overviews of medical services available for adults and children, international patient resources, and referral resources are also found at the site. **Location:** Stanford, California

http://www-med.stanford.edu

P-1345
HOSPITAL

University of California: San Francisco: Medical Center Langley Porter Psychiatric Institute **Research:** Studies are focused on innovative treatments for substance abuse, and the pharmacology, physiology, and psychology of commonly abused drugs in humans. **Patient Resources:** This site provides extensive information about the hospital's clinical services, training programs, research divisions, and links to affiliated sites. Insurance and intake and referral information is provided. **Location:** San Francisco, California

http://www.ucsf.edu/psych/home.htm

P-1346
HOSPITAL

University of Chicago: Hospitals & Health System The site provides an introduction and history of the Health System, location and directions, patient checklist, news releases, events, community outreach programs, resources for physicians, employment opportunities, links to departments and specialties, online video presentations, and contact information. **Research:** The Department of Psychiatry offers assessment and treatment programs for disorders of mood,

emotion, cognition, perception, memory, intellect, and behavior. A full range of child and adolescent psychiatry services is also provided at the System's facilities. News releases, online hospital publications, and contact details are available for additional research information. **Patient Resources:** A section of the site is devoted to patients, and provides suggestions for appointment preparations, directions to the hospitals, resources available during a visit, and additional issues to consider before an appointment. **Location:** Chicago, Illinois
http://www.uchospitals.edu

P-1347
HOSPITAL

University of Michigan: Medical Center Department of Psychiatry
Information is presented on electroconvulsive therapy and women's health and anxiety issues. The Schizophrenia Consultant, a quarterly newsletter of the schizophrenia program containing information for patients, families, and providers is also accessible. **Research:** Under research scrutiny in the ambulatory and hospital services division are areas such as evolutionary biology, unconscious processes, women's health, mood disorders, schizophrenia, Cushing's disease, and adrenergic psychoneuroendocrinology. Basic science research includes regulation of signal transduction in the nervous system, noninvasive studies in the human brain using positron emission tomography, biochemical correlates of regeneration, molecular and integrative studies of stress, opioids and dopaminergic systems, mapping of genes that cause neurological and psychiatric disorders, regulation of inositol lipid hydrolysis and calcium signaling in human neurotumor cells, neurochemical imaging, etc. **Patient Resources:** This site provides information concerning research and links to information on postdoctoral, residency, and fellowship training in the Department of Psychiatry. Links are also provided to helpful Web resources. **Location:** Ann Arbor, Michigan
http://www.med.umich.edu/psych

P-1348
HOSPITAL

University of Missouri: Health Sciences Center
General information about the Center and its recent acquisition of Columbia Regional Hospital, clinic information and locations, a physician directory, links to specific hospital information, patient care details, research information, and information on education programs are available at this site. **Research:** The Missouri Institute of Mental Health in St. Louis is associated with the Center, offering the Policy Information Exchange online (at pie.org), a source of materials on issues affecting mental health policy in North America. Links to additional research information are available at the site, offering details of research facilities, current clinical trials, grants information, and other resources. **Patient Resources:** Patients can access information on clinical programs and services at the Health Sciences Center through an alphabetical listing of topics. General facts about the Center, maps, and contact details are also provided. **Location:** Columbia, Missouri http://www.hsc.missouri.edu

P-1349
HOSPITAL

University of Pennsylvania: Health System (UPHS)
Resources at this site include visitor information, news, a description of medical services offered, a physician referral service, an events calendar, and basic health information. **Research:** Research and services are offered by UPHS in addiction, geriatrics,

mood and anxiety disorders, bipolar disorders, depression, neuropsychiatry, schizophrenia, sleep disorders, and weight and eating disorders. Specialty research and treatments are provided through the Center for Mental Health Policy and Services Research, the Center for Neurobiology and Behavior, and the Center for Psychotherapy Research. **Patient Resources:** Health topics are presented at the site, including discussions in preventative medicine, general health information, and managing chronic conditions. Other information useful to patients includes a physician referral service, educational seminars and support groups details, and a list of health insurance plans accepted at the facility. **Location:** Philadelphia, Pennsylvania http://www.med.upenn.edu/psych/

P-1350
HOSPITAL

University of Pittsburgh: Medical Center Western Psychiatry Institute and Clinic Information is presented for those interested in rendering volunteer service in the field of mental health care, research, and elementary education. **Research:** Work is being done in the areas of bipolar disorder, child and adolescent depression and anxiety, eating disorders, schizophrenia, alcohol research, and autism. **Patient Resources:** This site features information about education and training opportunities at the Medical Center, programs for mental health providers, a faculty directory, and information about educational conferences and upcoming events. Extensive information about the clinical programs including those in child psychiatry and development, adult mood and anxiety disorders, schizophrenia, geriatrics, and eating disorders. Several important Internet links to libraries, journals, government organizations, and the University of Pittsburgh are also provided. **Location:** Pittsburgh, Pennsylvania http://www.wpic.pitt.edu

P-1351
HOSPITAL

University of Washington: Medical Center Department of Psychiatry and Behavioral Sciences **Research:** The Department has nationally recognized research programs in neurosciences, molecular biology, molecular genetics, endocrinology, neuroimaging, physiological psychology, as well as in psychosocial and socio-cultural areas, epidemiology, and health services. **Patient Resources:** Information is available about the department's academic, clinical and research programs, and its faculty, lectures, and grand rounds. **Location:** Seattle, Washington http://depts.washington.edu/psychweb/index.html""/pbsw.html

P-1352
HOSPITAL

Yale/New Haven Hospital Department of Psychiatry Contact and referral information for various psychiatric services is offered. **Research:** The Alzheimer's research unit conducts clinical trials for investigational treatments for Alzheimer's disease and age-related cognitive impairment. Clinical studies in the neuroscience research unit are designed to determine the neurobiological mechanisms underlying depressive, bipolar, obsessive-compulsive, and pervasive developmental disorders. Research on trauma and anxiety disorders is also under investigation. **Patient Resources:** This Web page offers information about the various psychiatric services available for patients in the Adolescent, Adult, and Geriatric Psychiatry program, Substance Abuse Program, and the Psychiatry/Medical Comorbidity Program. Contact information is listed. **Location:** New Haven, Connecticut http://info.med.yale.edu/psych/

PSYCHIATRIC DISORDERS

9.1 ADJUSTMENT DISORDERS

P-1353

Adjustment Disorder By clicking on "Adjustment Disorder" on the left side of the page, visitors can access descriptions, treatment, and research findings on the chosen condition. More than 50 disorders are included in this alphabetical listing, with each initial connection bringing visitors a variety of resources. Both American and European diagnostic criteria are offered, in addition to online booklets and magazine articles on the topics.
http://www.mentalhealth.com/fr20.html

P-1354

Adjustment Disorder with Anxiety HealthInformatics.com offers this online information sheet regarding adjustment disorder with anxiety, which includes its etiology, symptoms, and diagnostic criteria. Spontaneous resolution of symptoms is explained, as well as several useful relaxation strategies.
http://www.healthinformatics.com/docs/english/BHA/adjdsanx.bha.asp

P-1355

Adjustment Disorder with Depressed Mood This online fact sheet on adjustment disorder with depressed mood provides information on its etiology, symptoms, and treatment. Symptoms occurring in reaction to life stressors are explained, and the feelings of sadness and hopelessness specific to this adjustment disorder are reviewed. Differentiation of this condition from major clinical depression is made, and a link to the more serious symptoms of the latter are found. http://www.healthinformatics.com/docs/english/BHA/adjdsdep.bha.asp

P-1356

Help for Families: Stress-Related Problems Help for Families is an interactive parenting guide developed by a clinical psychologist. Topics of discussion include family communication, discipline, and school problems. This address offers descriptions of adjustment and anxiety disorders in children. Therapy and parental communication suggestions are available to help alleviate these problems, and parents can follow links discussing specific communication strategies. http://www.helpforfamilies.com/stress1.htm

P-1357

PSYweb.com: Adjustment Disorders Adjustment disorders are discussed at this site, including a definition, diagnostic criteria (DSM-IV), and common specifiers and subtypes. Links to descriptions of different schools of psychotherapy are available.
http://www.psyweb.com/Mdisord/adjd.html

What Are Adjustment Disorders? The many different categories of adjustment disorders are reviewed at an online table, courtesy of Health-Center.com. Adjustment disorder with depressed mood, anxiety, mixed anxiety and depressed mood, disturbance of conduct, mixed disturbance of emotions and conduct, and unspecified disturbances are differentiated.
http://www3.health-center.com/mentalhealth/adjustment/default.htm

9.2 ANXIETY DISORDERS

GENERAL RESOURCES

About.com: Panic/Anxiety Disorders Many quality sites are found through links at this site, including professional organizations, personal home pages, and patient education resources. Sites are organized by topics, which include agoraphobia, generalized anxiety disorder, obsessive-compulsive disorder, panic disorder, posttraumatic stress disorder, social phobia, medications, anger management, stress management, cognitive-behavioral therapy, therapist directories, international resources, information for women, and youth anxiety. Feature articles and news items, support forums, online stores, subscription information for an online newsletter, and answers to FAQs are also available at the site. http://panicdisorder.about.com/health/panicdisorder

American Society for Adolescent Psychiatry (ASAP): Dictionary of Anxiety and Panic Disorders This site provides basic definitions for psychological and clinical terms related to anxiety disorders, including hormones, therapies and support mechanisms, alternative medications, phobias, and anxiety disorders. Other resources include a separate listing of definitions of related disorders, basic information on medications and drug treatments, abbreviations, a chronology, statistics, and a list of references.
http://www.netaxs.com/people/aca3/AD-ENG.HTM#Home

Anxiety Disorders Association of America (ADAA) As a service of the National Institute of Mental Health, the site of the Anxiety Disorders Education Program provides information on its national campaign to increase awareness among the public and healthcare professionals regarding anxiety disorders. Links to disorder information including panic disorder, phobias, and posttraumatic stress disorder, pertinent news, and the Anxiety Disorders Education Program Library are all readily accessible. A professional section supplies a list of scientific books, articles, and educational videotapes, a list of professional meetings, and ordering information for patient brochures.
http://www.adaa.org

Anxiety Disorders Education Program As a service of the National Institute of Mental Health, the site of the Anxiety Disorders Education Program provides information on its national campaign to increase awareness among the public and healthcare professionals regarding anxiety disorders. Links to disorder information including panic disorder, phobias, and posttraumatic stress disorder; pertinent news; and the Anxiety Disorders Education Program Library are all readily accessible. A professional section supplies a list of scientific books, articles, and educational videotapes; a list of professional meetings; and ordering information for patient brochures.

http://www.nimh.nih.gov/anxiety/anxiety/whatis/objectiv.htm

Anxiety Disorders in Children and Adolescents Short descriptions of generalized anxiety disorder, obsessive-compulsive disorder, panic disorder, posttraumatic stress disorder, separation anxiety disorder, social phobia, and specific phobias in children and adolescents are presented at this site. Visitors can also find information on the treatment of anxiety disorders at the site.

http://www.adaa.org/aboutanxietydisorders/childrenadolescents/

Anxiety Disorders Report This online report was written primarily for consumers and provides general information about anxiety, panic, phobic, obsessive-compulsive, and posttraumatic stress disorders. Included are descriptions of symptoms, consequences of the disorder, personal descriptions of the disorder, treatment details, and information about support groups. This report is provided by the National Institute of Mental Health.

http://www.hoptechno.com/anxiety.htm

Anxiety Network International The Anxiety Network home page provides information, support, and therapy for the three largest anxiety disorders: social anxiety, panic/agoraphobia, and generalized anxiety disorder. Over 100 individual articles are available, and the resources of the Anxiety Network bookstore add to the already broad base of information, with some individual publication ratings provided. The "Social Anxiety Mailing List," along with recovery programs, anxiety help links, and multimedia materials is available.

http://www.anxietynetwork.com

Anxiety Panic Internet Resource (tAPir) The Anxiety Panic Internet Resource (tAPir) is a self-help network dedicated to the overcoming and cure of debilitating anxiety. Support, information, and the tools of self-empowerment and recovery are available from this grassroots anxiety resource. Information about tAPir, treatment information, and an online discussion group are available. An extensive index of anxiety resource links is also provided.

http://www.algy.com/anxiety/index.shtml

Anxiety-Panic-Stress.com Dedicated to serving the needs of those suffering from symptoms related to stress and anxiety, this Web site provides concise, case descriptions of anxiety disorder, panic disorder, obsessive-compulsive disorder, social phobia, and posttraumatic stress disorder. General resources and referrals, excerpts from PRNewswire released by the National Mental Health Association, and a list of FAQs are presented.

http://anxiety-panic-stress.com

Anxiety-Panic.com   Anxiety-Panic.com offers a comprehensive Web guide to information on such topics as anxiety, panic, phobia, trauma, stress, obsession, and depression. The wide variety of resources available include books, journals, chats, mail lists and newsgroups, organizations, medications, and spiritual alternatives. Visitors can access an educational anxiety-panic trivia game to test their knowledge of anxiety, panic, and related disorders.
http://www.anxiety-panic.com

 Anxiety.com   Created primarily for consumers, this site offers general summaries of the more common anxiety conditions, such as fear of flying, generalized anxiety disorders, social phobias, and panic attacks. Additional resources include a fact sheet on anxiety medication, self-help books, a personal assessment link, and information about online consultation provides instructions and a fee schedule for online consultations.
http://anxieties.com/home.htm

 Anxiety/Panic Resource Site   The Anxiety/Panic Resource Site offers information on the signs and symptoms of panic attacks and a comprehensive list of medications commonly prescribed for panic attacks, obsessive-compulsive disorder, depression, and generalized anxiety. Information is also offered on the understanding of the disorders, as well as the potential dangers of aspartame. A message board provides visitors with an opportunity to post their personal experiences. Featured books of the month may be ordered online.
http://www.anxietypanic.com

 Center for Anxiety and Related Disorders   Located within Boston University, the center treats anxiety disorders such as panic disorder, generalized anxiety disorder, specific phobias, depression, obsessive-compulsive disorder, and sexual disorders. At this site, links to a disorder provide fact files on the disorder, the center's program of treatment, and other symptom and treatment information. The center also has information on their different programs, divided into areas for the adult, the adolescent/child, sexuality, and general information. A link to recent and upcoming events at the center is also present.
http://www.bu.edu/anxiety

 Center for Anxiety and Stress Treatment   This Web site provides reviews for related publications, information on programs for anxiety and stress reduction and management, online personal stories, symptoms checklist, a question and answer forum, and other related workshops and publications.
http://www.stressrelease.com

 CyberPsych Anxiety Disorders Links   Links are available at this site to resources related to panic disorder, phobias, obsessive-compulsive disorder, social phobia, generalized anxiety disorder, posttraumatic stress disorder, and childhood phobias. Sites include home pages of patients' groups, parenting resources, professional associations, and general information sources.
http://www.cyberpsych.org/anxlink.htm

National Anxiety Foundation   This nonprofit organization provides fundamental information on all aspects of anxiety disorders, including describing the different anxiety disorders, such as panic, and generalized anxiety disorders, their differential diagnosis, treatment information, a reading list, and support organization information. Also available are a case history and a description of panic disorder, including symptoms, and physical and psychological consequences and treatment.
http://lexington-on-line.com/nafmasthead.html

National Institute of Mental Health (NIMH): Anxiety   At this site, both professionals and consumers can obtain information on the most common types of anxiety disorders, such as panic or obsessive-compulsive disorders, phobias, generalized anxiety, and posttraumatic stress disorders. Consumers can get basic information on the symptoms, treatment, and treatment centers for these anxiety disorders. Professionals can view the latest research findings, literature references, and NIMH news advisories related to anxiety.
http://www.nimh.nih.gov/anxiety/anxietymenu.cfm

National Mental Health Association: Anxiety Disorders   An overview of anxiety disorders is featured on this site. Hyperlinks are provided for further information on generalized anxiety disorders, obsessive-compulsive disorder, posttraumatic stress disorder, panic disorder, and social phobia. Each disorder is described, along with its causes, treatment, and resources for additional information.
http://www.nmha.org/camh/anxiety/index.cfm

Panic and Anxiety Education Management Services (PAEMS)   This comprehensive site provides information to the professional and lay person alike on anxiety disorders and related research and treatment. With a focus on recovery from anxiety and panic, the site offers stories of personal experiences with panic/anxiety, the PAEMS panic and anxiety chat room, and interviews with experts in the anxiety/panic field.
http://www.paems.com.au

Social Anxiety Network   This online network provides fundamental information on social anxiety, symptoms, and treatment. In addition, there are personal examples of social anxiety, a list of support and professional organizations, an explanation of the difference between social anxiety and other psychological disorders, links to related Web sites, references and other products for support and information about social anxiety, and news updates.
http://www.social-anxiety-network.com

Support-Group.com: Anxiety/Panic Disorders   Support-Group.com provides an overview of general resources available to those coping with anxiety/panic disorders. In addition to the site's comprehensive, state-by-state listing of support groups and organizations, one will also find links to an anxiety/panic disorder bulletin board, national and international organizations, gov-

ernmental agencies and information sites, and information for healthcare professionals from the National Institute of Mental Health.
http://www.support-group.com/cgi-bin/sg/get_links?anxiety_panic

Update on Potential Causes and New Treatments for Anxiety Disorders Supported by the National Alliance for Research on Schizophrenia and Depression, this document provides an overview of the types of anxiety disorders, including their frequency of occurrence; treatments; diagnosis issues; possible causes, including genetics; comorbidity; and psychotherapy. Information on specific drugs is included, as well as references.
http://www.mhsource.com/narsad/anxiety.html

Agoraphobia

Agoraphobics Building Independent Lives Agoraphobics Building Independent Lives is a nonprofit organization dedicated to helping those with anxiety and panic disorders. Their Web site offers full-text articles and book reviews on anxiety. In addition, there is information on self-help groups.
http://www.anxietysupport.org/b001menu.htm

Internet Mental Health: Agoraphobia Resources related to agoraphobia are presented on this site. There are American and European definitions of the condition, an online diagnostic tool, and treatment information. Research on anxiety disorders is also described. Booklets, related Internet links, and full-text articles are provided.
http://www.mentalhealth.com/dis/p20-an02.html

Generalized Anxiety Disorder

Internet Mental Health: Generalized Anxiety Disorder Generalized anxiety disorder descriptions found at this site include the American description, European description, and links to the United States Surgeon General reviews of the condition. Access to papers on the future of treatment and research of anxiety disorders is offered, as well as several booklets on the condition from reputable organizations. An online diagnostic tool assists patients and practitioners in making accurate assessments.
http://www.mentalhealth.com/dis/p20-an07.html

Obsessive-Compulsive Disorder (OCD)

Anxiety-Panic Attack Resource Site: Obsessive-Compulsive Disorder
Visitors to this site will find a thorough definition of obsessive-compulsive disorder (OCD). Additional discussion addressing the difference between normal compulsions and actual OCD, as well as information on other disorders that

may accompany the OCD are found. Discussion of therapies available is provided. http://www.anxietypanic.com/ocd.html

Awareness Foundation for Obsessive-Compulsive Disorder and Related Disorders This foundation works to increase professional, educational, and public understanding of obsessive-compulsive disorder and related disorders through workshop speakers and films. The site provides general information about OCD and the organization, contact details for film and video resources, a downloadable brochure, and links to related sites.
http://www.ocdawareness.com/

Expert Consensus Guidelines: Obsessive-Compulsive Disorder This document provides useful information for consumers on the specific symptoms, time course of action for the disorder, heritability, etiology, differential diagnosis, treatment, educational information, support information, and sections on specific therapies and drugs used to treat this disorder. Related reading materials and organizations are listed.
http://www.psychguides.com/oche.html

HealthGate: Obsessive-Compulsive Disorder This site offers a general description of obsessive-compulsive disorder and answers questions related to causes, symptoms, diagnosis, treatment, duration, self-care, and when to contact a physician.
http://home.nbci.com/form/redirect/1,355,,00.html?tag=p-hl.to.s-303.p-hl.fs

Obsessive-Compulsive Foundation This comprehensive Web site serves to provide information for all interested groups with respect to obsessive-compulsive disorder. There are links to the description of OCD and related disorders, treatment and medication details, and a screening test. There are links to support groups, a message board, research awards, newsletters, conference information, an online bookstore, membership information, a research digest listing, and a variety of other sites related to OCD of interest to both professionals and the public.
http://www.ocfoundation.org

Panic Disorder

Answers to Your Questions about Panic Disorder Supported by the American Psychological Association, this informative document offers consumers facts related to panic disorder symptoms, diagnosis, causes, treatment options, and consequences of the disorder.
http://www.apa.org/pubinfo/panic.html

How to Treat Your Own Panic Disorder This site offers basic but comprehensive information on all aspects of panic disorders and their treatment. A self-help menu offers information on panic and hyperventilation, breathing techniques, and exercises. There are also links on diagnosis and

treatment, doctors and therapists, herbal medications, a referral service, and a bibliography. A message board is available, along with self-help books and tapes available for purchase.
http://www.eadd.com/~berta/

Panic Disorder Consensus Statement   This consensus statement is provided by the National Institute of Mental Health and offers comprehensive information on the incidence, causes, assessment, clinical signs, and current treatment practices for panic disorders. Consequences of treatment, future research questions, and concluding thoughts are presented.
http://www.nimh.nih.gov/anxiety/resource/constate.htm

PHOBIAS, ALPHABETICAL

Alphabetical List of Phobias   An A-to-Z listing of more than 250 phobias is presented at this Web address, maintained by Tesarta Online. Each phobia has a brief description.
http://www.tesarta.com/www/resources/phobias/phobias.html

Phobia List   This site contains an alphabetized list of phobias, both common and rare. Included are links to information on phobia nomenclature, categories, treatment of phobias, and links to sites for information and support with respect to phobic disorders.
http://www.phobialist.com

POSTTRAUMATIC STRESS DISORDER (PTSD)

American Academy of Experts in Traumatic Stress   American Academy of Experts in Traumatic Stress membership includes health professionals, as well as professionals from emergency services, criminal justice, forensics, law, and education committed to the advancement of intervention for survivors of trauma. The Web site offers a description of the academy, links to membership information, credentials, certifications, education credits, and the ability to search the national registry. Free access to selected articles from *Trauma Response* is provided. Also, ordering instructions for the *Practical Guide for Crisis Response in Our Schools* (3rd edition) are available.
http://www.aaets.org

Association of Traumatic Stress Specialists (ATSS)   This international nonprofit organization provides professional education and certification to those actively involved in crisis intervention, trauma response, management, treatment, and the healing and recovery of those affected by traumatic stress. The site provides information on the organization, membership benefits, certification as a trauma specialist, an events calendar, links to other trauma-related sites, and a resource guide.
http://www.atss-hq.com

ChildTrauma Academy   Created from a partnership between Baylor College of Medicine and the Texas Children's Hospital, ChildTrauma Academy is dedicated to improving the systems that educate, nurture, protect, and enrich children. The academy's site provides links to scientific articles on child trauma, research projects, and information specific to professionals and caregivers. General information about the academy, the associated clinic, and other resources is also available.
http://www.bcm.tmc.edu/civitas

David Baldwin's Trauma Information Pages   This award-winning site, created by a licensed psychologist, focuses on emotional trauma and traumatic stress, including posttraumatic stress disorder. Links include information on supportive resources, a bookstore, disaster handouts, trauma-related articles, and other trauma resources. A translator provides site content in Spanish, French, and other languages. There is information about Dr. Baldwin, with links to other relevant sites available.
http://www.trauma-pages.com/index.phtml

Gift From Within   This site is the home page for the International Charity for Survivors of Trauma and Victimization, an organization devoted to providing information and support for those affected by posttraumatic stress disorder. Articles and lectures on PTSD, as well as prevention programs, products, support information and other related links, are included.
http://www.sourcemaine.com/gift

International Society for Traumatic Stress Studies (ISTSS)   A professional society created for the sharing of scientific information and strategies on traumatic stress, this Web site has links to conference information, other affiliates of the ISTSS, membership information, related sites, and access to articles from the *Journal of Traumatic Stress,* as well as critical reviews and a treatment guide. http://www.istss.org

Internet Mental Health: Posttraumatic Stress Disorder   Resources on posttraumatic stress disorder are available at this address, including American and European descriptions, access to online diagnostic tools, treatment information from the National Institute of Mental Health, online educational booklets, magazine articles, and links to sites offering additional trauma and anxiety resources. Disorder descriptions include diagnostic criteria, associated features, and differential diagnosis.
http://www.mentalhealth.com/dis/p20-an06.html

National Center for Posttraumatic Stress Disorder (NC-PTSD)   The National Center for Posttraumatic Stress Disorder, a government agency under the U.S. Department of Veteran Affairs, carries out a broad range of multidisciplinary activities in research, education, and training in an effort to understand, diagnose, and treat PTSD in veterans who have developed psychiatric symptoms following exposure to traumatic stress. The site provides information about the organization and its activities, staff directories, employment and training opportunities, a database of traumatic stress portunities, a database of traumatic stress literature, reference literature, tables of contents to *PTSD Research Quarterly* and *NC-PTSD Clinical Quarterly,* assessment instruments, and links to information about the disorder for the public. http://www.ncptsd.org

Sidran Foundation   The Sidran Foundation is a nonprofit organization dedicated to providing education, advocacy, and research related to trauma-related stress in children and adults. Resources include a list of Sidran books, a catalog of related literature, and a trauma resource center, which provides online access to relevant scientific articles and assessment scales. There are also links to several sites for trauma survivors and other related resources. http://www.sidran.org

SOCIAL ANXIETY AND SOCIAL PHOBIA

International Paruresis Association   Resources related to paruresis, or shy bladder, are provided on this site. There is a fact sheet on the condition, with a discussion of the psychology behind it. In addition, there is a discussion forum, a list of support group contacts, workshop information, and related resources. The "Infopedia" offers information on drug therapy, personal stories, and a bibliography.   http://www.paruresis.org/

National Mental Health Association: Social Phobia   A fact sheet on social phobia is presented on this Web page. An overview of the condition is offered, along with its causes, treatment, and related illnesses. A short list of related Internet resources is provided for further information. http://www.nmha.org/camh/anxiety/social.cfm

Open-Mind.org: Social Phobia/Anxiety   In addition to providing a large bibliography of books for professionals and consumers interested in anxiety and panic disorders and phobias, this site also has a searchable archive of related articles, Web sites, support and professional organizations, newsgroups and LISTSERVs, a chat room, and quotations. http://www.open-mind.org/SP

Shyness   This site provides links to online articles on shyness, newsgroups, related organizations, the Shyness Clinic, the Shyness Institute, and other related sites, as well as support information. http://www.shyness.com

Social Anxiety Institute   With the goal of helping people cope and recover from social anxiety, this home page offers visitors general information on social anxiety, details on therapy programs of the institute, and links to a variety of articles and essays on social anxiety. A social anxiety bookstore is also available. http://www.socialanxietyinstitute.org

Social Anxiety Support   Support for people with social anxiety disorder is offered on this Web site. There are numerous discussion forums, a chat room, a comprehensive listing of related Internet links, and recommended reading. A fact sheet on the condition is also provided and includes online screening tests.
http://socialanxietysupport.com/

Social Phobia in Children and Adolescents   In addition to defining this condition, this site offers information on incidence, causes, symptoms, and the most feared social circumstances. Facts on related disorders, consequences of social phobia, treatment options, drug effects, and other drug issues are all found at the site.
http://www.klis.com/chandler/pamphlet/socphob/socphobpamphlet.htm

Social Phobias   This online handout, provided by the Royal College of Psychiatry, reviews what social phobias are, different types of social phobias, symptoms, related psychological disorders, self-esteem issues, incidence, consequences and causes, self-help advice, behavioral therapies, drug treatments, and supportive contacts.
http://www.rcpsych.ac.uk/info/help/socphob/index.htm

STRESS DISORDERS

American Institute of Stress   Information on the nonprofit organization, the American Institute of Stress, is featured on this site. The organization is dedicated to examining the role of stress in health and disease. The site offers information packets related to topics such as job stress, stress management, and stress and cancer. There is also a description of their newsletter.
http://www.stress.org/

International Critical Incident Stress Foundation (ICISF)   The International Critical Incident Stress Foundation is dedicated to the prevention and mitigation of disabling stress. Their site offers information on events, conference agenda, and a short list of related links. There is also detailed information on courses and training programs, as well as a fact sheet on critical incident stress management.
http://www.icisf.org/

International Stress Management Association   The International Stress Management Association, based in the United Kingdom, offers selected full-text articles from their newsletter, *Stress News,* on their Web site. Additional resources include a bibliography of suggested reading on topics such as anger, anxiety, relaxation, and stress management. Also available are a calendar of events, a list of related links, and fact sheets on coping with stress.
http://www.isma.org.uk/

Job Stress Network   This site serves as the home page for the Center for Social Epidemiology. Many fact sheets, articles, and other resources are available in the subjects of job strain, risk factors, health outcomes, prevention, and related research projects. Links to relevant references, news and events, are available. http://www.workhealth.org

Stress and Anxiety Research Society (STAR)   This professional multidisciplinary organization of researchers promotes the exchange of information on anxiety and stress. At this site, the society's mission and history are presented, as well as membership information, STAR members, conference information, national and international representatives, and a list of publications from STAR. A list of related organizations, academic departments, journals, databases, employment opportunities, and online newsgroups and mailing lists is also provided.
http://star-society.org

Stress Management and Emotional Wellness   Dedicated to those interested in managing stress, maximizing performance, and enhancing emotional health, this Web site offers a comprehensive list of links, a discussion forum, the Optimal Health Concepts Bookstore online, and stress management lecture information.
http://imt.net/~randolfi/StressPage.html

9.3 ATTENTION DEFICIT AND DISRUPTIVE BEHAVIOR DISORDERS

ATTENTION DEFICIT/HYPERACTIVITY DISORDER (AD/HD)

ADD and Addiction.com   Provided by a specialist in the field, ADD and Addiction.com is dedicated to informing visitors of the relationship between attention-deficit/hyperactivity disorder and co-occurring conditions such as substance abuse, eating disorders, behavioral addictions, and criminal behavior. Current articles and books, recent news, helpful links, and ordering information on the publication by the site-author are included.
http://www.addandaddiction.com

ADD/ADHD Categorized Links   Links to sites offering resources related to attention-deficit/hyperactivity disorder are offered at this site. Site categories include AD/HD experiences, adult AD/HD, children's sites, education, support groups, humor, law, marriage, medications, organizations, parenting, personal finance, personal stories, relationships, time management, treatments, women's issues, and workplace issues.
http://user.cybrzn.com/~kenyonck/add/Links/links_categories_stories.html

Adders.org   This attention-deficit/hyperactivity disorder online support group offers links to worldwide sources for information, support, news, personal stories, and general self-help resources on the Internet. Educational re-

sources, research articles, natural remedies, chat forums, freeware, and children's resources are listed at the site.
http://www.adders.org

ADDvance   An award-winning site, ADDvance is dedicated specifically to the understanding of AD/HD in females. Selected articles, books, tapes, support group information, and valuable AD/HD links, including subscription information for *ADDvance* magazine, are all available online.
http://www.addvance.com

ADHDNews.com   Available at this Web site are opportunities to access timely information and articles concerning AD/HD as well as to communicate with others concerned with AD/HD through e-mail discussion groups. With articles contributed by professionals and experts in the field of special education, the online newsletter, *ADDed Attractions* is available free-of-charge after completing a simple, online registration process. E-mail discussion groups include ADDadults, focusing on the particular concerns of the adult diagnosed with AD/HD; ADDtalk, a discussion group for those with educational, advocacy, and parenting concerns; a home schooling group; and a group geared towards alternative treatments.
(free registration) http://www.adhdnews.com

Attention-Deficit Disorder WWW Archive   This archive of sites related to AD/HD contains links to personal Web sites, medical sites, support groups, government resources, and organizations. Some links are listed with short site descriptions.
http://www.geocities.com/tetralogy.geo/add/

Attention-Deficit/Hyperactivity Disorder: A Definition   This fact sheet offered by Plainview Elementary School in Oklahoma offers a definition of attention-deficit/hyperactivity disorder, including DSM-IV subtype definitions, behavioral signals, and difficulties children with these disorders may encounter. Multimedia education programs are discussed as an alternative teaching method and therapy for children diagnosed with AD/HD.
http://www.brightok.net/~dmcgowen/adhd.html

Born to Explore: The Other Side of ADD   The purpose of this site is to provide resources relating to different perceptions of AD/HD. Resources include fact sheets containing information on alternate views of AD/HD; temperament, creativity, and intelligence issues; nutrition; mood changes; support information; books; and links to related sites.
http://borntoexplore.org

Children and Adults with Attention-Deficit/Hyperactivity Disorder (CHADD)   Created principally to provide information for the general public, this site contains background information on CHADD, membership information, disorder fact sheets, legislative information, conference information, news releases, and online access to selected articles from *Attention* magazine. In addition, links to current research synopses on these disorders, government sites, legislative and legal resources, state legislative resources, and international organizations, as well as sites related to coexisting disorders, special education, disability, and health issues, are provided. Links include those specific to attention-deficit/hyperactivity disorder, mental health, anxiety disorders, learning disorders, depression, Tourette's disorder, and pediatrics. http://www.chadd.org

Internet Mental Health: Attention Deficit Hyperactivity Disorder Resources for parents and professionals are provided on this Web page for attention deficit hyperactivity disorder. There are descriptions of the condition, an online diagnostic test, treatment information, and research findings. In addition, there are links to online booklets, magazine articles, and a list of related Internet links. http://www.mentalhealth.com/dis/p20-ch01.html

National Attention Deficit Disorder Association The National Attention Deficit Disorder Association helps people with AD/HD lead happier, more successful lives through education, research, and public advocacy. Membership information, conference details, articles, news, guiding principles for diagnosis and treatment, and a directory of professionals treating AD/HD are available at the site. Research, treatment, and general information about AD/HD is offered, as well as links to sites offering resources on work, family, education, and legal issues associated with AD/HD. Support group sites and sites for children and teens are listed, and visitors can also read personal stories and interviews. http://www.add.org

National Institute of Mental Health (NIMH): Attention Deficit Hyperactivity Disorder A comprehensive brochure on attention deficit hyperactivity disorder is featured on this Web site. An overview of the condition is provided, along with examples of children with the disorder. Symptoms, conditions that produce similar symptoms, and causes of the condition are discussed. Information on getting help covers professionals who make the diagnosis, steps in making the diagnosis, educational options, and treatment. A discussion of medications is emphasized. Current research information, along with a comprehensive list of resources for further information, is included. http://www.nimh.nih.gov/publicat/adhd.cfm

National Institutes of Health (NIH): Consensus Statements: Diagnosis and Treatment of Attention-Deficit/Hyperactivity Disorder This consensus statement on the diagnosis and treatment of AD/HD includes an abstract and an introduction. It describes scientific evidence supporting AD/HD as a disorder; the impact of AD/HD on individuals, families, and society; effective treatments; any risks of medications; diagnostic and treatment practices; barriers to appropriate identification, evaluation, and intervention; and directions for future research. The consensus development panel, speakers, planning committee, lead organizations, and supporting organizations are listed, and users can access a bibliography of references. http://odp.od.nih.gov/consensus/cons/110/110_statement.htm

One A.D.D. Place   A virtual neighborhood of resources relating to attention-deficit/hyperactivity disorder and learning disorders, One A.D.D. Place includes a wide variety of support and management resources. Pertinent research articles, a virtual community library, Internet links, a list of FAQs, and helpful organizations and support groups are included. A professional section offers current information on treatment options, seminars, and programs.
http://www.oneaddplace.com

University of Georgia: Learning Disabilities Research and Training Center   This site describes research and training at the center and offers an information guide for and about adolescents and adults with learning disorders and AD/HD. A detailed discussion of the guide is followed by directories of AD/HD organizations, consumer support groups, general education and adult literacy resources, centers and organizations for general disability information, transition and life management resources, employment, assistive and adaptive technology, government agencies, Internet sites of interest, legal documents and information, publications and books, organizations offering toll-free information services, and learning disabilities research and training center products.
http://www.rit.edu/~easi/easisem/ldnoelbw.htm

DISRUPTIVE BEHAVIOR DISORDERS

AtHealth: Mental Health: Disruptive Behavior Disorders   Useful resources are available at this site devoted to disruptive behavior disorders, including links to related articles, practice parameters, fact sheets, assessment resources, prevention information, and a support site for parents and teachers. General site resources also include an online directory of mental health professionals, a sponsor newsletter, notices of continuing medical education meetings, an online bookstore of relevant materials through Amazon.com, and an extensive directory of mental health resources.
http://www.athealth.com/Practitioner/Newsletter/FPN_3_7.html

Critical Pathways for Disruptive Behavior Disorders   The article found at the site examines the commonalities between oppositional defiant and conduct disorders and their shared roots of origin. The DSM-IV diagnostic criteria for the disorders are listed, and the criteria for severity of the conditions are explained. Relevant clinical features, assessment issues, and coexisting conditions are reviewed, such as hyperactivity and academic deficiencies. Risks coexisting with the disorder, including suicide gestures and depression, are also mentioned. The section "Indicators for Levels of Care" includes explanations of emergent, transitional, and episodic intervention, and the issues associated with residential and custodial environments are explored.
http://pwp.usa.pipeline.com/~fuzzymills/dirupt.htm

MFTSource Treatment: Conduct Disorder   A list of online articles, news, and books (for purchase) related to conduct disorders is provided on this site,

maintained by Marriage and Family Therapy (MFT) Source. More than 30 links are provided for topics such as children with conduct disorders, juvenile crime, and the emotional miseducation of boys.
http://www.mftsource.com/Treatment.conduct.htm

Oppositional Defiant Disorder and Conduct Disorder

ConductDisorders.com   Directed to parents of children with conduct disorders, this Web page offers discussion forums, profiles of children, recommended reading, and several full-text articles. In addition, there is a comprehensive listing of links, with site descriptions, for topics such as attachment disorder, attention deficit disorder, and obsessive-compulsive disorder.
http://www.conductdisorders.com/

Internet Mental Health: Oppositional Defiant Disorder   By clicking on "Oppositional Defiant Disorder" on the left side of the page, visitors will find a description, research, treatment, and educational information pertaining to oppositional defiant disorder. The American and European diagnostic criteria are included as are relevant Internet links.
http://www.mentalhealth.com/fr20.html

Oppositional Defiant Disorder (ODD) and Conduct Disorder (CD) in Children and Adolescents: Diagnosis and Treatment   Oppositional defiant disorder information at this site includes an introduction, definitions, causes, diagnosis, and prognosis for the disorder. A discussion of conduct disorder includes a definition, diagnosis, and prognosis. Coexisting mental conditions are discussed. Information is mainly nontechnical, but both professionals and parents may find the site useful. Strategies for these disorders and possible therapies are also presented.
http://www.klis.com/chandler/pamphlet/oddcd/content.htm

Oppositional Defiant Disorder: Fact Sheet   The New York Hospital-Cornell Medical Center fact sheet on this behavioral disorder concisely defines the disorder; offers information on the symptoms, causes, process, and treatment; and includes self-help advice.
http://www.noah-health.org/english/illness/mentalhealth/cornell/conditions/odd.html

9.4 Catatonia

MedWorks Media: Catatonia in Affective Disorder   Originally published in *CNS Spectrums,* a journal in neuropsychiatry, this article discusses new findings and a review of the literature on catatonia in affective disorder. The article covers a historical background of catatonia, along with contemporary studies. The authors' findings for their study of catatonia are discussed, along with their study method, assessment, data, and statistical analyses. Rec-

ommendations are made for a systematic rating tool for the full spectrum of catatonic motor and behavioral symptoms. A bibliography is included, as well as a quiz for CME credit.
http://www.cme-reviews.com/CMEReviews/catatonia/CNS700_Kruger.html

mylifepath.com: Catatonia A patient fact sheet on catatonia is provided on this Web page. A definition and description of the condition are offered. The possible causes, symptoms, diagnosis, treatment, and prognosis are explained. A glossary of key terms and a short list of further reading are offered.
http://www.mylifepath.com/article/gale/100270403

Virtual Hospital: Medical Emergencies in Psychiatry: Lethal Catatonia This document comes from the *Emergency Psychiatry Service Handbook* and offers detailed information on signs, symptoms, and treatment of lethal catatonia.
http://www.vh.org/Providers/Lectures/EmergencyMed/Psychiatry/MedEmergCatatonia.html

9.5 CODEPENDENCE

Co-Dependents Anonymous A large number of links, meeting information, organizational events and facts, recovery fact sheets, literature resources, and related links are provided at this site. Twelve-step principles, a list of FAQs, employment opportunities, a directory, support information and documents, meeting reports, and international links are included.
http://www.codependents.org/siteindex.html

National Council on Codependence, Inc. (NCC) A fact sheet on codependence is presented on this site. A definition is offered, along with common signs and a discussion of low self-esteem, controlling behaviors, pleasing behaviors, and relationship issues.
http://www.nccod.org/

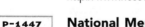

National Mental Health Association: Co-Dependency A fact sheet on codependence is provided at this Web page. The condition is described as well as who it affects, how dysfunctional families cause codependence, and how co-dependents behave. Also available are a questionnaire to identify the signs of codependence, treatment information, and resources for further information.
http://www.nmha.org/infoctr/factsheets/43.cfm

9.6 COMMUNICATION DISORDERS

EXPRESSIVE LANGUAGE DISORDERS

Apraxia A short description and links to information resources are available at this address devoted to apraxia. One link sends users to Amazon.com and a list of books on apraxia, and many autism links are also available through the site. http://www.isn.net/~jypsy/apraxia.htm

Apraxia-Kids: Apraxia of Speech   Frequently asked questions about apraxia of speech in children are featured on this Web page. There are three FAQs: one for parents of a newly diagnosed child, one on therapy, and one for developmental verbal dyspraxia. The FAQ for parents covers the prognosis for children with apraxia of speech, treatment, causes, and finding a good therapist. The therapist FAQ offers resources on apraxia, determining intensity needed for speech therapy, and the relationship between apraxia and other disorders. The developmental verbal dyspraxia FAQ examines the typical presentation, case studies, and progression of the condition over time. http://www.apraxia-kids.org/indexes/indexfaqs.html

Developmental Verbal Apraxia or Developmental Apraxia of Speech This site contains an informative fact sheet on apraxia, including a description, its causes, main symptoms, related dysfunctions, behavioral problems, supportive therapy, and other speech therapies. http://tayloredmktg.com/dyspraxia/das.html

KidSourceOnline: Articulation Problems   Written by the American Speech Language Hearing Association, this fact sheet answers common questions about articulation. The process is described, along with when it is a problem, types of sound errors, causes, and the effect of ear problems. Advice on helping a child with pronunciation, as well as an adult, is provided. Information on speech-language pathologists is also offered. http://www.kidsource.com/ASHA/articulation.html

National Institute on Deafness and Other Communication Disorders (NIDCD): Stuttering   A brief overview of stuttering is provided on this Web page. This fact sheet examines how speech is normally produced, who stutters, the causes of stuttering, and how it is diagnosed. Treatment for the condition is discussed, including stuttering therapy, medications, and electronic devices. Current research is described, and resources for additional information are listed. http://www.nidcd.nih.gov/health/pubs_vsl/stutter.htm

MIXED RECEPTIVE-EXPRESSIVE LANGUAGE DISORDER

American Hyperlexia Association   The American Hyperlexia Association is a nonprofit organization composed of parents and relatives of children with hyperlexia, speech and language professionals, and education professionals, with the common goal of identifying hyperlexia, promoting and facilitating effective teaching techniques; and educating the general public as to the existence of hyperlexia. This Web site includes links to pages describing hyperlexia and treatment options, as well as links to the mailing list, membership information, materials order list, organization and therapist directories, and other hyperlexia sites. http://www.hyperlexia.org

Hyperlexia and Language Disorders   The parent of a hyperlexic child hosts this page devoted to information on hyperlexia. Several articles presenting personal stories and education issues are available in both English and Spanish, and visitors can also access subscription information for a LISTSERV. Many sites offering additional resources are linked through this address. Site link categories include hyperlexia, language disorders, language skills, social skills, study skills, education issues, diet intervention, and commercial sites.
http://www.geocities.com/HotSprings/9402/index.html

Hyperplexia Parent's Page   This forum for parents with hyperlexic children offers articles, examples of story therapy, success stories, parents' letters, chat forums, pen pal resources for children, and links to professional associations. Articles and other resources are nontechnical and offer specific suggestions for dealing with hyperlexia issues in children.
http://www.westwingpublishing.com/hyperlexia.html

WebMD: Mixed Receptive-Expressive Language Disorder   The purpose of this site is to explain mixed receptive-expressive language disorder. A definition is provided, along with incidence, symptoms, and diagnostic tests. Treatment with speech and language therapy, along with psychotherapy, is recommended. Potential complications are also described.
http://my.webmd.com/content/asset/adam_disease_mxreceptvexpressvlangdisordr

9.7 DELIRIUM, DEMENTIA, AMNESTIC, AND OTHER COGNITIVE DISORDERS

GENERAL RESOURCES

Institute of Gerontology   A branch of Wayne State University, this institute conducts research and provides education in the field of gerontology. There are summaries of the research programs at the institute, including family and intergenerational relationships, health and healthcare (including psychological services), human development and expression, and independence and productivity (including cognitive training and aging). A faculty directory and bibliography, are provided, as well as colloquia and conference information.
http://www.iog.wayne.edu

AIDS/HIV DEMENTIA

BETA: AIDS Dementia Complex   From the *Bulletin of Experimental Treatments for AIDS,* this informative document reviews the disorder, its causes, and its symptoms in detail and also provides a useful psychiatric classification of the stages of disorder progression. HIV-related infections and their effect on patient mental health are discussed, along with diagnosis, theories of disease

mechanisms, viral load, treatment, and prophylactic measures. Drug therapies are examined in detail, and current and future research topics are addressed.
http://www.aegis.com/pubs/beta/1996/be963105.html

HIV InSite Knowledge Base   At HIV InSite, documents and abstracts on coping strategies, AIDS-related dementia complex (ADC), psychoactive pharmaceuticals, and the mind-body connection may be accessed. A search engine may be used for browsing current news topics. Also included are HIV prevention and statistical information and a Spanish information section.
http://HIVInSite.ucsf.edu/topics/mentalhealth

Knowledge Exchange Network: HIV/AIDS Resources   Selected for their overall content and quality, the links made available provide the user with a variety of treatment, research, and prevention information. Top sites include the National Institutes of Health *Guide to HIV/AIDS Information Services,* the AIDS Clinical Trials Information Service, and the Centers for Disease Control and Prevention.
http://www.mentalhealth.org/links/hiv.htm

Opportunistic Infections: Neurological Disorders   This site summarizes the possible neurological disorders resulting from HIV infection. It offers links to informative documents on the major effects of HIV on the central nervous system, the AIDS dementia complex, treatment efficacy, peripheral neuropathy, and confounding brain system disorders and HIV infection, as well as a list of references.
http://www.hivpositive.com/f-Oi/OppInfections/4-Neuro/4-NeuroSubMenu.html

Project Inform: AIDS Dementia Complex Hotline Handout   This site provides detailed information on the symptoms of this newly classified dementia, its prevalence, diagnosis and assessment, and the mechanism behind AIDS-caused dementia. In addition, topics such as HIV infection, drug therapy, symptoms of various stages of AIDS-related dementia, and related issues are discussed. Support information is also included.
http://www.projinf.org/fs/dementia.html

Support-Group.com: AIDS/HIV   This Support-Group.com resource page provides links to support groups and organizations nationwide and internationally, governmental agencies and information sites, an AIDS/HIV bulletin board and USENET groups, and online journals. Professional organizations and resources are included as are sites related to AIDS/HIV prevention and alternative treatments.   http://www.support-group.com/cgi-bin/sg/get_links?aids_hiv

The Body: Depression, Anxiety, and Mental Health   Visitors to this address will find interactive questions and answers related to HIV, mental health, and spiritual support, as well as links to sites providing information on a variety of topics. These topics include coping with AIDS and HIV, stress, anxiety, depression, the mind-body connection, psychoactive drugs, relationships

and sexuality, chemical dependency, death and mourning, issues for professionals, and resources for caregivers.
http://www.thebody.com/mental.html

 United Nations Programme on HIV/AIDS HIV/AIDS information by subject or country, publications, press releases, and conference updates are all available at the site of the United Nations Programme on HIV/AIDS. This leading advocate for worldwide action against HIV/AIDS provides past and present issues of its newsletter in PDF and Word format, speech transcripts in English and French, information about its Africa Partnership, and a number of useful links on AIDS education, research, and treatment.
http://www.unaids.org

ALZHEIMER'S DISEASE

 Administration on Aging (AOA): General Resources This site lists links to resources on the Internet for geriatric issues such as Alzheimer's disease and other dementias, as well as general psychology and psychiatry. Resources include metasites, state agencies, federal agencies, and links to information located on the AOA Web site.
http://www.aoa.gov/agingsites/default.htm

 Alzheimer Page Sustained by Washington University Alzheimer's Disease Research Center, this database of information has links to questions and answers on more frequently discussed topics regarding this disease, a searchable archive of the mailing list, and a section on links to support groups, organizations, products, research, jobs, nursing homes, and personal Web sites related to Alzheimer's disease and other dementias.
http://www.biostat.wustl.edu/alzheimer

 Alzheimer Research Forum This Web site's information database consists of a professional and nonprofessional section. The nonprofessional section has links to Web sites on patient care, support groups, commercial products, news, and general information about the disease, as well as associations and disease centers. The professional section contains a keyword searchable database, with links to research findings and treatment guides, online forums and tools, conference information, a drug company directory, and the opportunity to exchange information on specific Alzheimer research topics.
http://www.alzforum.org/

 Alzheimer Web A directory of current Alzheimer's disease research endeavors, links to research laboratories, current papers via PubMed, and a listing of FAQs are included at this Web site, which focuses solely on Alzheimer's disease research. An up-to-date listing of cholinesterase inhibitors and other Alzheimer's drugs and a colorful depiction of the cholinergic pathways affected in the Alzheimer's brain can be viewed.
http://home.mira.net/~dhs/ad3.html

Alzheimer's Association   The Alzheimer's Association offers information and support on issues related to the disease. Patients and caregivers can access general facts about Alzheimer's disease, as well as detailed discussions of medical issues, diagnosis, expected lifestyle changes, treatment options, clinical trial participation, planning for the future, and contact information for special programs and support. Caregiver information and professional resources are also available. Resources for investigators include a summary of current research, lists of grant opportunities, lists of past grant awards, progress report forms, and information on the Reagan Institute. The association also offers news, program, and conference calendars; publications; and information on advocacy activities at this site.
http://www.alz.org

Alzheimer's Disease Education and Referral (ADEAR) Center   This service of the National Institute on Aging offers information on Alzheimer's disease and related disorders. The site describes new features and the ADEAR information and referral telephone services. Fact sheets, research and technical reports, information on training programs, an online newsletter, public service announcements, and online lectures are available at the site. Other features include a bibliographic database of health education materials on Alzheimer's disease, a clinical trials database, and links to related sites.
http://www.alzheimers.org

Alzheimer's Disease Information Directory   The Alzheimer's Disease Information Directory provides an overview of resources for Alzheimer's patients and their caregivers. Links are provided to Alzheimer's Association chapters, worldwide organizations, online discussions lists, and chats geared towards patients as well as caregivers. Information on related dementias, special sites for seniors, and comprehensive research and caregiver information are available. Pages from the Web site may be viewed in English, French, German, Italian, Portuguese, or Spanish via Alta Vista's translator.
http://www.zarcrom.com/users/yeartorem/index4.html

Alzheimer's Outreach: Medical Glossary   More than 50 medical terms related to Alzheimer's disease are available at this address, providing patients and caregivers with a valuable educational resource.
http://www.zarcrom.com/users/alzheimers/w-07.html

Alzheimer's Society   Created to provide information about Alzheimer's disease and other dementias, this site has links to descriptive fact sheets on these disorders, their symptoms, physical causes and consequences, treatment, and prognosis. In addition, there are summaries of current research theories on these dementias. For caregivers, general support advice is provided, with information on related topics, current news, details about the society itself, and links to other related societies.
http://www.alzheimers.org.uk

American Association for Geriatric Psychiatry (AAGP) The AAGP Web site includes numerous links to various issues of interest for both professionals and interested laypersons. There are news reports; the AAGP bookstore; meeting information; consumer information, including brochures and a question and answer section, an advocacy and public policy section; a link to the *American Journal for Geriatric Psychiatry;* a health professional bulletin; and a link to the AAGP Education and Research Foundation.
(some features fee-based) http://www.aagpgpa.org

American Health Assistance Foundation This nonprofit organization is provided to promote research, education, and financial support to those involved in age-related degenerative diseases, such as Alzheimer's disease. There are links to information about the Alzheimer's disease research program and other related resources, including news updates and fact sheets, as well as support resources. There is general information presented on research updates, grants, and upcoming events. http://www.ahaf.org

Baylor College of Medicine: Alzheimer's Disease Research Center As part of Baylor College of Medicine, this center conducts both clinical and scientific research on various aspects of the disease. Links to Alzheimer's related research projects provide overviews of the projects, which include psychosis, language, hemispheric asymmetry, cholinergic dysfunction, and progressive disease studies. A link to clinical drug trials for memory loss provides information on the various FDA-approved drugs for the disease, as well as information on a memory-impairment project. In addition, there are fact files for diagnosis and medical evaluation, advances in diagnosis and treatment, genetic testing, and behavioral changes in the disease. There are also links to educational opportunities and other related sites.
http://www.bcm.tmc.edu/neurol/struct/adrc/adrc1.html

Geropsychology Central This site provides information for seniors, professionals, and consumers interested in issues relating to gerontology and mental health. Included are links to related conferences, literature, journals, organizations, and geropsychology practice qualifications. There are also links for dementia resources, including Alzheimer's and Parkinson's diseases, stroke, mental and quality-of-life assessment materials, and research centers.
http://www.premier.net/~gero/contents.html

Institute for Brain Aging and Dementia Located at the University of California Irving, the institute's research focuses on successful aging, preserving Alzheimer's patient abilities, beta-amyloid research, cell death, exercise and brain well-being, and other related areas. Brief summaries of these research areas are provided. In addition, information on the clinic, which has programs devoted to patient assessment and mental health, as well as their successful aging program, is present. A list of the faculty and their research interests is available, and training opportunities are outlined.
http://maryanne.bio.uci.edu

LewyNet This Web site provides information on Lewy bodies and associated dementias. Informative links include pathological and clinical descriptions of dementias, including figures and diagnostic criteria, consortium and conference information, links to fact files and Web sites on Alzheimer's and Parkinson's diseases, and information on relevant books.
http://www.ccc.nottingham.ac.uk/~mpzjlowe/lewy/lewyhome.html

Memory and Dementia This report offers a review of the problem of memory impairment, common signs, problems related to memory dysfunction, physical causes, and a review of types of dementias, such as Alzheimer's disease. Self-help advice and support information are present.
http://www.rcpsych.ac.uk/info/help/memory/index.htm

Rush Alzheimer's Disease Center This center's research projects focus on risk factors, symptoms and assessment, testing for the disease, examining the neurobiology of Alzheimer's, and devising treatments. There are links to the current clinical trials, which give information on which drugs are tested; a link to educational grants; publications from the faculty; and the Rush Brain Bank, which aids research by providing the materials necessary for basic experiments and also processes, diagnoses, and stores brain specimens and other related materials. There are also a number of links for family support groups and information, as well as educational and training services available at the center.
http://www.rush.edu/patients/radc/

University Alzheimer Center Affiliated with Case Western Reserve University, this center conducts research on memory and aging issues. There are links to current studies being conducted at the center, publications by the center's staff, and articles on research conducted at the center. A fact sheet on Alzheimer's disease, warning signs of Alzheimer's, medication updates, cell division and Alzheimer's, and exercise and Alzheimer's are present. General information about the center, current news, and other related links are also found.
http://www.ohioalzcenter.org/

Washington University: Alzheimer's Disease Research Center Presented by the Washington University Medical Center in St. Louis, this Web site lists the overall research mission of the center, including faculty and staff, and has basic information on the different cores of the center, which include biostatistics, clinical psychometric, and tissue resources. The biostatistics core has numerous links to various statistical and disease-related resources. There is a link to the center's *Horizon Newsletter,* links to related projects, a list of relevant seminars, and a calendar of the center's daily events.
http://www.biostat.wustl.edu/adrc

Amnestic Disorders

Amnestic Disorders This brief introduction to amnestic disorders describes the cognitive impairment involved, lists the amnestic disorder types, and pro-

vides a link to summaries of nearly 10 psychotherapeutic alternatives, including Adlerian therapy, existential therapy, and transactional analysis. The bases, goals, and appropriateness of each theory to specific behaviors and conditions are explained.
http://www.psyweb.com/Mdisord/amnd.html

CREUTZFELDT-JAKOB DISEASE (CJD)

Creutzfeldt-Jakob Disease   This site is presented by the World Federation of Hemophilia. By clicking on "vCJD" on the left side of the federation's home page, visitors will find information on variant Creutzfeldt-Jakob disease and the concerns of the hemophilia community regarding CJD transmission. There are publications on risk assessment, plasma products, research findings, and journal articles.   http://www.wfh.org/

Creutzfeldt-Jakob Disease Fact Sheet   Creutzfeldt-Jakob disease is defined on this site, and discussions include pathology, susceptibility, diagnosis, prognosis, treatment, and research. For those wishing for continued research material, postal and Internet addresses for the Creutzfeldt-Jakob Disease Foundation, National Institute of Neurological Disorders and Stroke, and National Organization for Rare Disorders are provided.
http://members.aol.com/crjakob/brochure.html

Creutzfeldt-Jakob Disease Foundation, Inc.   The Creutzfeldt-Jakob Disease Foundation provides descriptions and fact sheets in an effort to educate the public and give awareness of the research needed to gain a better understanding of this prion disease. Other resources available include information on theories concerning the CJD agent, associated Internet links, current news and statistics, postings of conferences/symposiums, and general information about the Creutzfeldt-Jakob Disease Foundation.
http://cjdfoundation.org/info.html

Neuropathology of Creutzfeldt-Jakob Disease   The characterization of Creutzfeldt-Jakob Disease is made at this Web location, where four neuropathological features are identified. Human prion disease histological investigation and abnormalities are described and illustrated, and classical and other changes associated with the condition are listed. Additional conditions associated with spongiform-like changes in the central nervous system are reviewed including Alzheimer's disease and frontal lobe dementia.
http://www.cjd.ed.ac.uk/path.htm

DELIRIUM

Merck Manual of Diagnosis and Therapy: Delirium   The acute confusional state of delirium is fully reviewed at this page of the online *Merck Manual of Diagnosis and Therapy*. Factors such as coexisting brain disease or sys-

temic illness affecting the brain are discussed, specifically in terms of metabolic, structural, and infectious causes. The rapidly fluctuating symptoms of the disorder, its diagnostic criteria, and the potential for reversibility of symptoms through rapid identification and proper management are summarized.
http://www.merck.com/pubs/mmanual/section14/chapter171/171b.htm

HUNTINGTON'S DISEASE

Dementia in Huntington's Disease A clinical description and diagnostic guidelines for the dementia that occurs as part of the overall brain degeneration of Huntington's disease are offered at the site. Early symptom summaries may be accessed, and a list of differential diagnoses to be considered is presented. Four diagnostic criteria are explained, in addition to the accessible, requisite, general criteria for dementia that must be met. Development of additional extrapyramidal rigidity or spasticity with pyramidal signs is mentioned.
http://www.informatik.fh-luebeck.de/icd/icdchVF-F02.2.html

Huntington's Disease Society of America Geared towards the discovery of a cure for Huntington's disease, this organization is a comprehensive source of information on medical facilities of excellence, research about the disease, and answers to commonly asked questions about the disease. Research guidelines and a calendar of national and chapter events are offered, as are local chapter locations and news and information on clinical trials. http://www.hdsa.org

MULTI-INFARCT DEMENTIA

Internet Mental Health: Multi-infarct Dementia An assortment of resources can be located at this Internet Mental Health site, including both American and European disease descriptions, practice guidelines from the American Psychiatric Association, a variety of cognitive disorder articles from the *Medical Post,* and additional Internet links to cognitive disorder sites.
http://www.mentalhealth.com/dis/p20-or02.html

National Institute of Neurological Disorders and Stroke (NINDS): Multi-Infarct Dementia A brief fact sheet on multi-infarct dementia is provided on this Web site. The condition is explained, along with the importance of prevention. Prognosis for patients is described. A bibliography, along with resources for further information, is included.
http://www.ninds.nih.gov/health_and_medical/disorders/multi-infarctdementia_doc.htm

National Mental Health Association: Multi-infarct Dementia A fact sheet on multi-infarct dementia offers healthcare consumers information on the causes, symptoms, and diagnosis of this common condition. Medical testing, imaging, and prevention of additional damage are emphasized, with links to resources for further information included.
http://www.nmha.org/infoctr/factsheets/102.cfm

PICK'S DISEASE

Pick's Disease of the Brain   Provided for professionals, this document provides clinical information and links to references on case studies, causes of the disease, diagnosis, heritability, neuropathology, and related disorders, such as Alzheimer's and Parkinson's disease. Included are links to medical databases.
http://www.ncbi.nlm.nih.gov/htbin-post/Omim/dispmim?172700

Pick's Disease Support Group   This support organization offers online access to their newsletter, which covers meeting and group information, disease information, personal stories, and scientific articles. In addition, there are links to contact resources, telephone and e-mail directories, articles written by the group's members on this disease, and related sites.
http://www.pdsg.org.uk

PROSOPAGNOSIA (FACE BLINDNESS)

Face Blind! Bill's Face Blindness (Prosopagnosia) Pages   An individual with face blindness hosts this site, presenting an extensive discussion of face blindness in 13 chapters. Topics include physical causes, the importance of recognizing others, how most people recognize others, ways to recognize others without using the face, emotions, sexuality, suggested ways to cope, and other related subjects. Appendixes offer suggestions on finding medical articles related to the condition, diagnosis, and links to related sites.
http://www.choisser.com/faceblind

VASCULAR DEMENTIA

Vascular Dementia: Dementia Caused by Multiple Brain Strokes   Dementia caused by multiple brain strokes is described at this site of Alzbrain.org, with several related diseases and 10 facts about dementia from multiple brain strokes listed. http://www.alzbrain.org/misc/vdementia.html

9.8 DISSOCIATIVE DISORDERS

GENERAL RESOURCES

Colin A. Ross Institute: Diagnosing Dissociative Disorders   The full text and scoring rules for the Dissociative Disorders Interview Schedule, developed by the founder of the Ross Institute, is available for educational purposes at this site. This structured interview is used by professionals for systematic clinical assessment and research of dissociative disorders.
http://www.rossinst.com/dddquest.htm

Don't type in long URLs – add the site number to the eMedguides URL: www.eMedguides.com/**G-1234**.

P-1504 **Dissociative Identity Disorder (DID)/ Trauma/ Memory Reference List** This extensive reference list, composed in 1997, offers citations, sometimes accompanied by quotes or abstracts, related to dissociative identity disorder, trauma, false memory syndrome, amnesia, and related topics. Topics and resources include "Traumatic Amnesia in Holocaust Survivors," "Validity and Diagnosis of DID," "Suggestibility and Hypnotic Pseudomemory," standard of care issues, and statistical references.
http://www.sidran.org/refdid.html

 P-1505 **Healing Hopes, Inc.** This nonprofit organization provides information and support resources for those interested or involved with dissociative identity disorders. There are links to fact sheets on anxiety, panic and anger management, depression, dissociative disorders and their treatment, eating disorders, self-injury and suicide prevention, stress, therapist information, and support group issues. In addition, there are links to related sites.
http://www.healinghopes.org

 P-1506 **International Society for the Study of Dissociation (ISSD)** This nonprofit professional organization advocates research and professional training in the diagnosis, treatment and education of dissociative disorders, as well as serving to promote international communication among scientists and professionals working in this area. There are links to conference information, membership and society information, the *Journal of Trauma and Dissociation,* the ISSD newsletter, education resources, including articles on related topics, and a list of dissociation disorder treatment guidelines. In addition, there is a set of professional and self-help links.
http://www.issd.org

 P-1507 **National Alliance for the Mentally Ill (NAMI): Dissociative Disorders Helpline Fact Sheet** Dissociative disorders are discussed at this site, including dissociative amnesia, dissociative fugue, dissociative identity disorder, and depersonalization disorder. Common treatments are also briefly discussed.
http://www.nami.org/helpline/dissoc.htm

 P-1508 **New England Society for the Treatment of Trauma and Dissociation** This society, an affiliate of the nonprofit International Society for the Study of Dissociation (ISSD), serves professional members from Connecticut, Maine, Massachusetts, New Hampshire, Rhode Island, and Vermont. Quarterly meetings offer professional presentations, discussion groups, consultation clinics, and networking opportunities, and the society sponsors educational workshops on the treatment of dissociative disorders and other topics. There are also recent newsletter articles, a bulletin board, and links to related sites.
http://www.nesttd.org/

 P-1509 **Synergy: Institute for Dissociative Disorders** This nonprofit corporation's mission is to provide education and information to interested professionals and consumers. Book reviews are available, as well as a list of articles relat-

ing to dissociative disorders. Information on membership and a long list of links to related sites are included.
http://ourworld.compuserve.com/homepages/Synergy_Institute/

DEPERSONALIZATION DISORDER

Merck Manual of Diagnosis and Therapy: Depersonalization Disorder This common psychiatric disturbance, characterized by distorted self-perception, is presented at this chapter of the online *Merck Manual of Diagnosis and Therapy*. The variable range of impairment; spontaneous resolution of symptoms; and a variety of successful psychotherapies, including psychodynamic, cognitive-behavioral, and hypnosis, are discussed.
http://www.merck.com/pubs/mmanual/section15/chapter188/188e.htm

DISSOCIATIVE AMNESIA

Merck Manual of Diagnosis and Therapy: Dissociative Amnesia Lost information that is normally part of conscious awareness and further characteristics of dissociative amnesia are discussed at this Web address, including trauma-related occurrences and the controversy surrounding accurate, later recollections. Diagnosis, based on physical and psychiatric examination, is provided, and supportive management goals are presented.
http://www.merck.com/pubs/mmanual/section15/chapter188/188b.htm

DISSOCIATIVE FUGUE

Merck Manual of Diagnosis and Therapy: Dissociative Fugue The loss of identity, formation of a new identity, and other characteristics of dissociative fugue are found at this site of the online Merck reference. The disorder's remarkable array of symptoms and its relation to dissociative identity disorder are described. Switching of personalities, amnesic barriers, and physical manifestations are presented. Evaluative and diagnostic procedures are listed, and variability of prognosis is explained. Successful treatment, with the aim of either achieving personality integration or cooperation among the personalities, is explained, and includes three separate phases of psychotherapy.
http://www.merck.com/pubs/mmanual/section15/chapter188/188c.htm

DISSOCIATIVE IDENTITY DISORDER

Alliance for the Treatment of Trauma and Dissociation This site describes the Alliance for the Treatment of Trauma and Dissociation, a professional practice of two psychotherapists offering services to practitioners, patients, and their families in the treatment of dissociative identity disorder. The disorder is discussed, as well as specific treatment services offered by the alliance. http://www.netreach.net/~alliance

 Amongst Ourselves This site contains links to information on dissociative identity disorder, its causes, FAQs, symptoms, and a number of related links. In addition, interested parties can subscribe to the list, view the bulletin board, and join the chat room.
(free registration) http://foxfiremad.com/amongst

 International Society for the Study of Dissociation (ISSD) Directed to professionals, the ISSD site offers treatment guidelines for dissociation identity disorder in adults, information on the ISSD *Journal of Trauma and Dissociation,* conference information, and a bibliography on dissociation disorder. A comprehensive listing of Internet links is categorized as associations, veterans, centers of study, tests, general resources, online journals, and recovered memory. A members-only section offers conference abstracts.
(some features fee-based) http://www.issd.org/

 Network to Explore and Express Dissociative Identity Disorder (NEEDID) Support Network The NEEDID Web page offers a broad array of resources for patients and their families coping with dissociative identity disorder. Their Web page offers an online support group, a discussion board, information on their newsletter, and a comprehensive listing of related Internet links. In addition, there are articles, poems, humor, and art by people with dissociative identity disorder. A "Funland" page offers games, humor, and a variety of animated characters.
http://www.needid.bizland.com/

 Sidran Foundation: Dissociative Identity Disorder The Sidran Foundation offers this report on dissociative identity disorder. Topics include related disorders, definition of dissociation, process of disorder development, behavioral symptoms, incidence, and diagnostic problems. Treatment information and offline support are available.
http://www.sidran.org/didbr.html

9.9 EATING DISORDERS

GENERAL RESOURCES

 Academy for Eating Disorders (AED) Information on the professional organization, the Academy for Eating Disorders, is provided on this site. Visitors to the site will find conference details, online AED newsletters, and related Internet links. In addition, there is information on special interest groups of the AED. Members can access a member directory.
http://www.aedweb.org/

American Anorexia Bulimia Association Eating disorders are the focus of this Web page, with fact sheets on anorexia nervosa, bulimia nervosa, and binge eating disorders. There is information provided specifically for families and friends, as well as the opportunity for professionals to get on the association's referral list. An article on risk factors for eating disorders is found, along with information on therapy and support and a bibliography of recommended reading. http://www.aabainc.org/home.html

Anorexia Nervosa and Related Eating Disorders, Inc. This comprehensive site offers links to fact sheets on eating disorders, statistics, warning signs and medical/psychological problems associated with these disorders, risk factors, causes, and treatment. Also, there are links to information about athletes, men, diabetes and eating disorders, and less common eating disorders, such as bigorexia, night eating, gourmand syndrome, and Pica. In addition, there are support resources and prevention information, a list of FAQs, personal stories, and research projects. http://www.anred.com

Center for Eating Disorders Located within Saint Joseph Medical Center, this center provides complete treatment programs for eating disorders. Links include information about these types of disorders; online discussion forums; faculty and staff information; description of the center; current news on relevant issues, such as body image; an events calendar; and other support information. http://www.eating-disorders.com

Concerned Counseling: Eating Disorders This site contains links to conference transcripts on various related topics, definitions and symptoms, warning signs, complications, treatment and recovery information, relapse issues, prevention, and support group details. Research resources include information on clinical trials, causes, treatment, effects, and other related topics. Visitors can subscribe to the newsletter and access the referral network, an online chat conference, and the Concerned Counseling journal. http://www.concernedcounseling.com/Communities/Eating_Disorders/concernedcounseling/

Eating Disorders Awareness and Prevention (EDAP), Inc. EDAP, a national nonprofit organization, increases awareness and prevention of eating disorders through community-based education and advocacy programs. Site visitors will find general information about the organization, news, notices of upcoming events, details of EDAP programs, eating disorder fact sheets, suggested reading lists, press releases for media use, and links to related sites. http://www.edap.org/

Eating Disorders Site Provided by the Close to You Family Resource Network, this large database provides comprehensive information on eating disorders and their assessment, diagnosis, treatment, self-tests, and medical complications. There are also nutrition-related resources, art therapy, a list of

treatment centers, a reference list, current news in eating disorders, recovery and personal stories, and professional associations.
http://closetoyou.org/eatingdisorders

Harvard Eating Disorders Center   The Harvard Eating Disorders Center, a national nonprofit organization, conducts research and education activities in an effort to improve detection, treatment, and prevention of eating disorders. The site presents facts on eating disorders, suggestions on helping a child with an eating disorder and locating support resources, and program details. Answers are available to common questions, helping visitors determine if they need professional help. Answers are also available concerning different forms of counseling, medication, and other forms of therapy.
http://www.hedc.org

International Association of Eating Disorders Professionals (IAEDP)
The International Association of Eating Disorders Professionals offers a certification process for health professionals seeking specialized credentials in the treatment of patients with eating disorders. The Web site provides information regarding the association, membership and certification information, and registration details for symposium events. In addition, there are online discussion forums.
http://www.iaedp.com

Knowledge Exchange Network: Eating Disorders News   Recent news stories on eating disorders are presented on this Web page. More than 30 news stories are listed from a variety of sources including the *Washington Post, ABC News,* and the *New York Times.*
http://www.mentalhealth.org/newsroom/eatingarchives.htm

Mirror-Mirror: Eating Disorders Shared Awareness   Visitors to this address will find resources on anorexia nervosa, bulimia nervosa, and compulsive overeating, including definitions, signs and symptoms, medical complications, dangerous methods of weight control, relapse prevention and warning signs, addictions, and self-injury. Specific resources are available for children, teenagers, college students, athletes, men, and older women. Additional site features include a chat forum, suggested readings, and links to national organizations and treatment centers. Content is written from a personal, nontechnical point of view.
http://www.mirror-mirror.org/eatdis.htm

New York State Psychiatric Institute: Eating Disorders Unit   The Eating Disorders Unit's Web page provides fundamental information for interested professionals and consumers on eating disorders, diagnostic criteria, treatment available for these disorders at the institute, case examples and discussions, and information about the unit itself.
http://www.columbia.edu/~ea12/

Psychosomatics and Eating Disorders The newsletter of the Psychosomatic Discussion Group is provided at this site. Links to articles on various topics such as anorexia nervosa, and bowel disease as well as links to case studies, abstracts, and related papers are present. Academic course listings and links to discussion lists are also available.
http://www.cyberpsych.org/pdg

Society for the Study of Ingestive Behavior This professional society's site includes links to current news and information on ingestive behavior topics, relevant journals, employment, access to the newsletter, awards and grants, and links to related organizations.
http://www.jhu.edu/~ssib/ssib.html

ANOREXIA NERVOSA

Internet Mental Health: Anorexia Nervosa Information resources on anorexia nervosa at this site include American and European diagnostic criteria, an interactive online diagnostic tool, treatment information from the National Institute of Mental Health, research article citations found through PubMed, patient education booklets, general articles, and links to related sites.
http://www.mentalhealth.com/dis/p20-et01.html

National Association of Anorexia Nervosa and Associated Disorders
This national nonprofit organization helps eating disorder victims and their families through hotline counseling, support groups, and referrals to healthcare professionals. The site offers information about the organization, eating disorder definitions, fact sheets, warning signs, therapy information, statistics and demographics, and suggestions on confronting someone with an eating disorder. Visitors will also find information on insurance discrimination and eating disorders, legislative alerts, and links to related useful sites.
http://www.anad.org

BULIMIA NERVOSA

Internet Mental Health: Bulimia Nervosa Information resources on bulimia nervosa at this site include American and European diagnostic criteria, an interactive online diagnostic tool, treatment information from the National Institute of Mental Health, research article citations found through PubMed, patient education booklets, general articles, and links to related sites.
http://www.mentalhealth.com/dis/p20-et02.html

New York Online Access to Health (NOAH): Bulimia Nervosa A fact sheet on bulimia nervosa, developed by the New York-Presbyterian Hospital, is offered on the Ask NOAH (New York Online Access to Health) Web site. The eating disorder is explained, along with its symptoms, causes, and treatment.

Tips for getting bulimia under control are provided, as well as what to do in the case of relapse.
http://www.noah-health.org/english/illness/mentalhealth/cornell/conditions/bulimia.html

GOURMAND SYNDROME

Anorexia Nervosa and Related Eating Disorders: Gourmand Syndrome A concise description of gourmand syndrome is presented on this site, including a definition, its rarity, symptoms, and its potential relationship to brain injury.
http://www.anred.com/gour.html

HYPERPHAGIA

Hyperphagia For those interested in hyperphagia, an overview of the condition is provided on this personal Web page of Dr. Barton J. Blinder. The condition is defined, along with its associated conditions, such as sleep disorders and psychiatric disorders.
http://www.ltspeed.com/bjblinder/14.htm

NIGHT EATING SYNDROME

Anorexia Nervosa and Related Eating Disorders, Inc.: Night-Eating Syndrome A brief fact sheet on night-eating syndrome is presented on this site, courtesy of Anorexia Nervosa and Related Eating Disorders, Inc. The fact sheet describes signs and symptoms, incidence of the condition, and the need for further research into the problem.
http://www.anred.com/nes.html

PersonalMD.com: Night-Eating Syndrome Examining night-eating syndrome, this news story reports on a study of night eaters and overweight subjects and examines the differences between them, including melatonin and leptin levels.
http://www.personalmd.com/news/a1999081712.shtml

ORTHOREXIA NERVOSA

Orthorexia Nervosa Part of a larger guide to eating disorders, this site describes orthorexia nervosa. A description and typical symptoms of this obsession with a pure diet are discussed. Two links are provided for additional information on the condition.
http://www.something-fishy.org/whatarethey/other.php#ortho

Orthorexia.com: Orthorexia Nervosa   An article on orthorexia nervosa, the health food eating disorder, is featured on this Web page. The article, authored by physician Steven Bratman, describes his personal experiences with alternative dietary medicine. He describes orthorexia nervosa as those individuals who develop an extreme obsession with pure health food.
http://www.orthorexia.com/article.html

Pica

Anorexia Nervosa and Related Eating Disorders, Inc.: Pica Fact Sheet   This fact sheet defines pica and provides general information on symptoms, causes, incidence, and consequences.
http://www.anred.com/pica.html

Prader-Willi Syndrome

Gene Clinics: Prader-Willi Syndrome   A clinical profile of Prader-Willi syndrome is provided on this site. The profile covers disease characteristics, genetic testing, and genetic counseling. Major and minor diagnostic criteria are outlined. Cytogenetic testing and molecular genetic testing are described. Differential diagnosis, management of the condition, and prenatal testing are explained. A bibliography is provided.
http://www.geneclinics.org/profiles/pws/details.html

Prader-Willi Syndrome Association   Information on Prader-Willi syndrome (PWS) for professionals, patients, and their families is presented on this site. Professionals will find clinical facts on PWS, diagnostic criteria, healthcare guidelines, research news, and grant information. There are also FAQs on PWS, along with information on medical considerations prior to treatment, genetics of the condition, and a Prader-Willi food pyramid. The site also contains a chat room, message boards, a bibliography of journal articles, a publications catalog, and a list of related Internet resources. http://www.pwsausa.org/

Screening Programs

National Mental Illness Screening Project: National Eating Disorders Screening Program   This site offers detailed information about the National Eating Disorders Screening Program, which includes an educational presentation on eating disorders, a written screening test, and the opportunity to meet privately with a health professional. The site presents general information and answers to questions about the screening program, a sample screening test, and links to program sponsors.
http://www.nmisp.org/eat.htm

9.10 ELIMINATION DISORDERS

ENCOPRESIS

American Academy of Family Physicians (AAFP): Treatment Guidelines for Primary Nonretentive Encopresis and Stool Toileting Refusal This articles from the *American Family Physician* provides a comprehensive online clinical guide to the treatment of primary encopresis, with the characteristics of the disorder and the necessary medical assessment introduced. A program of appropriate behavior management and an incentive/reward-based system, as well as other guidelines on toilet training and encopresis, are provided. Identification of physical or behavioral pathology, a complete physical examination checklist, and a table outlining differential diagnoses to be considered are found. An illustrative case is provided, as well as a patient information handout. http://www.aafp.org/afp/990415ap/2171.html

Problems with Soiling and Bowel Control Reasons for soiling and the social and psychiatric difficulties that coexist with encopresis in children are discussed at this paper of the American Academy of Child and Adolescent Psychiatry. The importance of a complete physical exam is stressed, and a description of soiling not caused by an illness or disability is found. Combination treatment strategies are reviewed.
http://www.brooklane.org/whitepgs/children/chsoil.html

ENURESIS

American Academy of Family Physicians (AAFP): Primary Nocturnal Enuresis Originally published in the March 1999 issue of *American Family Physician,* this article addresses current concepts in primary nocturnal enuresis. A definition of the condition is offered, along with possible etiologies and diagnostic evaluation. Treatment methods discussed include motivational therapy, behavioral conditioning, bladder training exercises, and pharmacologic therapy. References are provided, along with a patient information handout written by the author of this article.
http://www.aafp.org/afp/990301ap/1205.html

American Enuresis Foundation This site focuses on treatment for children with enuresis at the American Enuresis Foundation's "Stopping Point." There is also a fact sheet on enuresis. http://www.galstar.com/~aef/

9.11 FACTITIOUS DISORDERS

Dr. Marc Feldman's Munchausen Syndrome, Factitious Disorder, and Munchausen by Proxy Page Within this comprehensive site, there are

links to articles, case reports, firsthand accounts, general information, and abstracts about various aspects of these psychiatric disorders.
http://ourworld.compuserve.com/homepages/Marc_Feldman_2/

 Munchausen Syndrome by Proxy   This site contains a slide presentation that provides comprehensive and descriptive information on this syndrome in an organized format, courtesy of Kiet T. Huynh. More than 50 slides offer case study reports, definitions of the condition, epidemiology, causes, risk factors, incidence, diagnosis strategies, tools and assessment, clinical signs and evidence, and prognosis and follow-up information.
http://www.medicine.uiowa.edu/pa/sresrch/Huynh/Huynh/sld001.htm

 mylifepath.com: Factitious Disorders   An overview of factitious disorders, the exaggeration or production of symptoms, is provided on this Web page. Munchausen syndrome, Munchausen by proxy, and Ganser's syndrome are described. General symptoms of factitious disorders are described, as well as diagnosis, treatment, and prognosis. A glossary of key terms and recommendations for further reading are provided.
http://www.mylifepath.com/article/gale/100273143

 WebMD: Munchausen Syndrome   A dictionary definition of Munchausen syndrome is provided on this site. In addition, the history of the term "Munchausen" is also presented.
http://my.webmd.com/content/c4_asset/merriam-webster_medical_dictionary_165330

9.12 FALSE MEMORY SYNDROME

 False Allegations and False Memory Syndrome   A listing of articles related to false allegations and false memory syndrome is featured on this site, courtesy of the National Clearinghouse on Child Abuse and Neglect Information. Nine articles are listed with hyperlinks to the publisher's Web page.
http://www.calib.com/nccanch/pubs/bibs/falsall.cfm

 False Memory Syndrome Facts   This site offers article citations, links, and information resources related to false memory syndrome, presenting information mainly refuting the false memory syndrome theory. Resources are available under the categories of scientific analysis, clinical issues, legal issues, media, organizations, philosophy, and support.
http://www.fmsf.com

 False Memory Syndrome Foundation   The False Memory Syndrome Foundation seeks reasons for the spread of this disorder, works for the prevention of new cases, and aids the primary and secondary victims of the syndrome. Resources at the site include information on the foundation, a bibliography, events, articles about this syndrome, an online newsletter, mailing lists, and links to related sites.
http://www.fmsfonline.org/

Recovered Memory Project   This project's Web site is devoted to issues relating to recovered memory, including case files from legal proceedings, clinical and other scientific cases, and other corroborated recovered memory cases. There is access to articles, abstracts, data files, research summaries, peer-reviewed studies, and other publications relating to recovered memories. A large number of links to other resources is included in the research and scholarly resources section. The project is directed by Professor Ross Cheit of Brown University. http://www.brown.edu/Departments/Taubman_Center/Recovmem/Archive.html

9.13   IMPULSE-CONTROL DISORDERS, OTHER

GENERAL RESOURCES

Psychology Information Online: Impulse Control   An overview of impulse control disorders is provided on this Web page. Brief descriptions are provided of intermittent explosive disorder, domestic violence, kleptomania, pyromania, pathological gambling, and trichotillomania. http://www.psychologyinfo.com/problems/impulse_control.html

INTERMITTENT EXPLOSIVE DISORDER

HealthinMind.com: Intermittent Explosive Disorder   A brief description of intermittent explosive disorder is provided on this Web site. Also available are a short list of links for books on the subject and links to related Web sites. http://healthinmind.com/english/intermitexp.htm

Treating Intermittent Explosive Disorder with Neurofeedback   This site presents a case study of a young male with intermittent explosive disorder and his positive experience with neurofeedback. The article suggests that EEG biofeedback may help in reducing abuse of spouses, partners, and children. http://www.brainwavetx.com/library/explosiv.html

KLEPTOMANIA

Kleptomania: Symptoms   Summarized criteria of kleptomania, taken from the *Diagnostic and Statistical Manual of Mental Disorders,* is presented at this site of the Mentalhealth.net online information source. http://mentalhelp.net/disorders/sx23.htm

Kleptomaniacs and Shoplifters Anonymous   A comparison between kleptomania and addictive-compulsive stealing is offered on this Web page. A table contains the traits of both conditions, including impulse control, and examines the psychological basis of both. http://www.shopliftersanonymous.com/Comparison.htm

PATHOLOGICAL GAMBLING

Illinois Institute for Addiction Recovery: About Pathological Gambling This site describes pathological gambling, including a discussion of differences between casual social gambling and pathological gambling, affected groups, and teen gambling. The site also discusses the Custer Three-Phase Model, including the winning, losing, and desperation phases. A link is available to information on diagnosis, prevention, and treatment of addiction in the workplace. http://www.addictionrecov.org/aboutgam.htm

Mount Sinai: Department of Psychiatry: Compulsive, Impulsive, and Anxiety Disorders Program: Gambling This site provides a short description of pathological gambling and lists the department's research interests. Cognitive-behavioral group therapy is currently offered by the department for this disorder.
http://www.mssm.edu/psychiatry/ciadp.shtml

North American Training Institute (NATI): Compulsive Gambling The North American Training Institute, a division of the Minnesota Council on Gambling, provides products and courses aimed towards the education and prevention of compulsive gambling, especially among senior citizens and teens at risk. A listing of educational books, audiovisual materials, and professional training programs offered by the organization is presented. Current and back issues of *Wanna Bet* magazine are offered online especially for teens concerned about gambling. Also available from NATI are translated materials and information on state and national reports examining compulsive gambling problems and exploring long-term management strategies. Users who take an online survey can receive free informational packets. A brief registration for ordering materials is required. (free registration) http://www.nati.org/

Postgraduate Medicine: Pathological Gambling Originally published in *Postgraduate Medicine* (October 1997), this editorial on pathological gambling examines when a social issue becomes a medical issue. The disease signs and phases of pathological gambling are described. The societal and personal costs of compulsive gambling are also examined. References are provided, along with resources for additional information.
http://www.postgradmed.com/issues/1997/10_97/editorial.htm

PYROMANIA

Mental Health Net: Pyromania The symptoms of pyromania are briefly outlined on this Web page. Several symptoms are listed, including purposeful firesetting, gratification when setting fires, and when firesetting is not done for monetary gain. http://mentalhelp.net/disorders/sx88.htm

Predictors of Violent Adult Behavior   A "predictive triad" of adult violent behavior, including persistent bedwetting, cruelty to animals, and firesetting, is described at this online review article. The classic analysis of a pyromaniac is discussed, and, out of the three triad characteristics, pyromania is described as being most widely associated with adult violent behavior. The distinctions between fire setters and non-fire setters in attempting to seek internal solutions to their problems is explained, with fire setters more apt to seek external objects on which to project their emotions. The possible existence of physical unattractiveness, multiple medical problems, and social isolation often found in these individuals is discussed, and the importance of recognition of the triad in a person's background is emphasized.
http://www.ozemail.com.au/~jsjp/violence.htm

SEXUAL ADDICTION

Sexual Addiction   Created by the Counseling Affiliates Sexual Addiction Treatment Center, this Web page offers information and resources on sexual addiction. A fact sheet describes the history of sexual addiction, along with symptoms, early childhood roots, and different forms of the condition. Sexual addiction and the Internet is also discussed. There is an online self-test, information for partners of sexual addicts, and resources for out-patient and inpatient treatment programs. Contact details for free 12-step programs are also provided. (fee-based) http://www.sexaddictionhelp.com/

American Foundation for Addiction Research (AFAR)   This organization supports research and education on addictive disorders by providing funds for addiction research. In addition to organization information, there is a database on sexual addiction, research project funding priorities, general facts about addiction, and donation information.
http://www.addictionresearch.com

National Council on Sexual Addiction and Compulsivity (NCSAC)
This national nonprofit organization is devoted to the promotion of the awareness of sexual addiction and compulsivity in both public and professional areas. In addition to detailed member information, there are media contact resources, a suggested reading list, NCSAC position papers on sexual addictions, support groups, and general information about sexual addiction and compulsivity.
http://www.ncsac.org/main.html

SexHelp.com   This site provides information about sexual addiction, its causes and treatments, as well as interactive tests, and articles on sexual addiction and other topics. Also available are an online bulletin, a suggested reading list, and links to sexual addiction databases, clinics and clinicians, and other support resources. http://www.sexhelp.com

TRICHOTILLOMANIA

Trichotillomania Learning Center This nonprofit organization provides comprehensive informational resources on this compulsive disorder. The site offers links to support groups, therapists, and other sites of interest, as well as basic information on the disorder.
http://www.trich.org

Trichotillomania Library A library of resources related to trichotillomania is presented on this site, developed by Denise Plourde. Resources include FAQs, a dictionary, and an e-mail discussion list. Information on treatment for the condition focuses on dietary measures. Personal experiences, suggestions for coping, and related Internet resources are provided.
http://www.irishlace.net/trichlibrary/

9.14 INFANCY, CHILDHOOD, OR ADOLESCENCE DISORDERS, OTHER

REACTIVE ATTACHMENT DISORDER

Association for Treatment and Training in the Attachment of Children This coalition of parents and professionals exchanges information on attachment and bonding issues. Information on healthy attachment, events and training notices, a newsletter, recommended reading lists, book reviews, assessment instrument reviews, and clinical notes are found at this address. Details of the organization's structure, research reviews, links to related sites and contact details for non-Internet resources, and lists of suggested professional resources are also available.
http://www.attach.org

Attachment Disorder Network Dedicated to children and families affected by attachment disorder, this Web site offers articles, poems, and personal stories on attachment disorder. A fact sheet on the common symptoms is provided, along with information on the Attachment Disorder Network newsletter. There is also a listing of related links on adoption and attachment disorder, as well as information on support groups and attachment disorder workshops. http://www.radzebra.org/

Attachment Disorder Support Group The Attachment Disorder Support Group provides education and support to parents facing the challenge of raising a child with reactive attachment disorder. A description of attachment disorder, symptoms, potential parenting mistakes in a child with this disorder, support resources, and links to related sites are listed at the address. Also provided are chat forums; articles; personal stories; answers to FAQs; information on choos-

ing a therapist; directories of group homes, centers, and other resources; and lists of suggested books and other publications.
http://www.syix.com/adsg

North Dakota Center for Persons with Disabilities: Reactive Attachment Disorder   Examining reactive attachment disorder, this Web page offers a brief fact sheet, courtesy of the North Dakota Center for Persons with Disabilities. The condition is defined, along with risk factors and symptoms. Two techniques for treatment are described: holding therapy and creating a safe home environment. A short list of links is provided for additional information.
http://ndcd.org/ndcpd/projects/ipcm/reactive.html

Reactive Attachment Disorder   This personal Web page was developed to help others in supporting their children with reactive attachment disorder. A fact sheet describing the disorder is presented, along with the symptoms and potential causes. There are also many links for parenting information, self-help, therapy, and nurturing activities. A list of Internet links for further information, recommended reading, a directory of international adoption counselors, and conference details are also provided.
http://www.attachmentdisorder.net/What_Is_Attachment_Disorder.htm

Reactive Attachment Disorder Slide Presentation   A slide presentation is featured on this site on reactive attachment disorder. It can be viewed online or downloaded. The presentation defines attachment disorder, its causes, and the importance of attachment. First- and second-year child development are examined. In addition, the keys to bonding, effective treatment, and effective parenting are discussed. References are provided, along with speaker's notes.
http://members.tripod.com/~radclass/

SELECTIVE MUTISM

Selective Mutism Foundation   This foundation's site offers considerable information on the description, diagnosis, assessment, treatment, and other issues concerning selective mutism. Also available are current research studies, a bibliography, a healthcare providers referral list, information about the foundation and its members, and a number of links to related sites. Special education information can also be accessed.
http://www.orgsites.com/fl/selectivemutismfoundation/

Selective Mutism Group   Selective mutism in children is the focus of this Web page. A library on the site offers an article on selective mutism, a bibliography for further reading, and a short list of Internet links. In the "Interaction section," there are discussion forums and a list of e-mail pen pals, as well as an article written for teachers and a "kids view" FAQ section. Members have access to an ask-the-doctor column.
(some features fee-based)   http://www.selectivemutism.org/

Selective Mutism Group: Links   More than 15 sites related to selective mutism are provided on this Web page. Resources cover general information, educational Web sites, medical information, psychiatric drugs, and cognitive-behavioral therapy.
http://www.selectivemutism.org/Htm/links500.htm

9.15 LEARNING DISORDERS

GENERAL RESOURCES

Instant Access Treasure Chest: The Foreign Language Teacher's Guide to Learning Disabilities   Handouts on learning disabilities are provided at this site, courtesy of Virginia Commonwealth University and Longwood College. Hyperlinks are provided for each topic and include information on dyslexia, dysgraphia, dyscalculia, language deficits, visual deficits, and auditory deficits. There is also information on ADD/ADHD, legal issues, and teaching strategies.
http://www.fln.vcu.edu/ld/conf.html

LD Online   This interactive site offers a wealth of information on learning disabilities and attention deficit/hyperactivity disorders, including assessment, behavior, legal information, and other related topics. Links to the online newsletter, the online store, various discussion forums and events calendars, and a large listing of resource guides are available. Personal stories and a database are also present.
http://www.ldonline.org

Learning Disabilities Association (LDA)   This national nonprofit organization, composed of individuals with learning disabilities, their families, and professionals, aims to enhance the education and general welfare of children and adults with learning disabilities. Information about LDA includes goals of the organization, a description of services offered, and membership details. Organizations and other sources for information are listed at the site, under topic categories such as audio tapes, culturally diverse national organizations, government agencies, organizations, publications, toll-free resources for adults with learning disabilities, video tapes, and Web search tools. Information alerts and bulletins, fact sheets, links to state chapters, and subscription information for LDA publications are all available at the address.
http://www.ldanatl.org

MEDLINEplus: Learning Disorders   A comprehensive listing of resources related to learning disorders is presented on this site. There is an overview of learning disabilities, clinical trial information for dyslexia, tips for parents on helping their children, and evaluation information. Specific conditions covered include adult learning disabilities, dyslexia, Gerstmann's syndrome, reading and

learning disabilities, and nonverbal learning disorder. Legal rights for children and adults with learning disabilities; organizations; and information specific to children, teenagers, and women are found. Some publications are in Spanish.
http://www.nlm.nih.gov/medlineplus/learningdisorders.html

National Institute of Mental Health (NIMH): Learning Disabilities
This online educational pamphlet describes different types of learning disabilities, the causes of these disabilities, diagnosis, education options, medication, and family coping strategies. The site also provides details on current research, government aid, and sources of information and support.
http://www.nimh.nih.gov/publicat/learndis.htm

Unicorn Children's Foundation This nonprofit foundation supports parents and professionals through research, treatment advocacy, and information exchange. A nationwide directory of professionals and involved parents, fact sheets, presentations, warning signs, chat forums for both parents and professionals, a list of accommodations for students with learning disorders, and an online store are all available at this site. Visitors can also download forms, for both professional and caregiver use, to help in the diagnosis of communication and learning disorders.
http://www.saveachild.com

DISORDERS OF WRITTEN EXPRESSION (DYSGRAPHIA)

Diagnosis and Intervention Strategies for Disorders of Written Language A detailed discussion of written language disorders, written by an Ed.D., is presented at this site. Topics include multiple brain mechanisms, physical and psychological requirements for written language, dysgraphia classification systems, assessment issues, intervention for written language disorders, and a discussion summary.
http://www.margaretkay.com/Dysgraphia.htm

Dyscalculia.org: Dysgraphia An academic paper on the causes and treatment of dysgraphia is posted on this Web page. The paper offers recommendations for creating a supportive classroom, along with information on the physiology of language function. Diagnosis and treatment of dysgraphia are described. In addition, instructional methods for written composition are outlined. A bibliography is included.
http://www.dyscalculia.org/Edu563.html

National Institute of Neurological Disorders and Stroke (NINDS): Dysgraphia Information on dysgraphia is presented in this fact sheet. The condition is described, along with treatment and prognosis. Resources for additional information are provided.
http://www.ninds.nih.gov/health_and_medical/disorders/dysgraphia.htm

MATHEMATICS DISORDER (DYSCALCULIA SYNDROME)

Dyscalculia International Consortium Resources on dyscalculia at this site include links to information related to diagnosis, research, prognosis, assistance, and education law. Educational math books are listed at the site and can be ordered through links to Amazon.com.
http://www.shianet.org/~reneenew/DIC.html

Dyscalculia Syndrome This site allows interested individuals free access to this master's thesis by Renee M. Newman, which is devoted to the study of dyscalculia. Extensive coverage of various topics is present, including describing the disorder, personal accounts, statistical data, testing and diagnostic issues, treatment, and therapeutic strategies, including educational and teaching advice, cognitive assessment, and other information. Tables, references, and related information are all included. http://www.dyscalculia.org/thesis.html

Dyscalculia.org: Dyscalculia A broad array of resources related to dyscalculia is provided on this site, created by Renee M. Newman, M.S. General information on dyscalculia is presented such as symptoms, items to discuss with math teachers, and recommended reading. For institutions, resources include a guide for diagnosing math learning disabilities, classroom techniques, and developmental perspectives on middle and secondary school. There are also home learning aids; an online diagnostic test, which is available for a fee; information on special education; and numerous educational articles.
(some features fee-based) http://www.dyscalculia.org/

International Dyslexia Association: Dyscalculia The International Dyslexia Association provides resources related to the problem of mathematical dyslexia, also known as dyscalculia. Related disorders, the symptoms and educational manifestations, intervention strategies, and references are included.
http://www.ldonline.org/ld_indepth/math_skills/math-skills.html

NONVERBAL LEARNING DISORDERS

NLDline: Nonverbal Learning Disorders Information at this site devoted to nonverbal learning disorders describes this disorder in detail, including specific types, and also offers a discussion of NLDline's purpose and a section devoted to useful information resources. These resources include suggested book and video lists, support resources, hotlines, links to related sites, and sources for audio tapes.
http://www.nldline.com/welcome.htm

Nonverbal Learning Disorders An article on nonverbal learning disorder syndrome is presented on this Web page, maintained by the Learning Disabilities Association of California. The article explains the symptoms, neurological basis, and incidence of the condition. The deviations in development for motoric coordination, visual-spatial organization, and socialization are examined. Recommendations for treatment are made, including accommodations, modifications, and strategies for schools. http://www.ldaca.org/gram/thompson.htm

 What is Nonverbal Learning Disorder Syndrome?   First appearing in *Hydrocephalus Association Newsletter,* this article describes the syndrome and its effects on various aspects of the patients life, including educational symptoms. Biological causes are discussed and therapeutic interventions are presented. http://www.matrixparents.org/faqnonverbal.html

Reading Disorder (Dyslexia)

 Bright Solutions for Dyslexia   Bright Solutions for Dyslexia is an organization offering seminars, in services, training, and coordination of parent programs in techniques related to teaching dyslexics. Definitions of dyslexia from several sources, along with symptoms, research discussions, and testing and assessment tools are discussed at the site. http://www.dys-add.com

 Davis Dyslexia Association International   The Davis Dyslexia Association International offers workshops and training to teachers and professionals on helping individuals with dyslexia and other learning disabilities. A resource library at the site includes articles, questions and answers about dyslexia, book excerpts, and links to other information sources. Educational materials, professional resources, chat forums, a Davis Program provider directory, and workshop calendars are all found at the site. Resources are provided in English, Spanish, German, French, Dutch, and Italian. http://www.dyslexia.com

 Dyslexia—The Gift: Internet Circle of Friends   More than 200 sites related to dyslexia are linked through this address. Sites are indexed by topic, including dyslexia resources, other learning differences, health information, education, families, and international resources. http://www.dyslexia.com/links.htm

 International Dyslexia Association   This nonprofit association is devoted to the study and treatment of dyslexia. Site resources include information about the organization, position papers, conference and seminar calendars, an online bookstore, technology resources, legal and legislative information, research discussions, and a bulletin board. The site also offers a detailed discussion of dyslexia, including information and links to Internet resources for adolescents, college students, parents, adults, and educators and other professionals. http://www.interdys.org

 National Institute of Neurological Disorders and Stroke (NINDS): Dyslexia   A fact sheet on dyslexia is presented on this Web page. The condition is described, along with treatment, prognosis, and ongoing research at the

National Institutes of Health. Resources for additional information include a bibliography, clinical trial information, and a link to PubMed for a literature search. http://www.ninds.nih.gov/health_and_medical/disorders/dyslexia_doc.htm

SENSORY INTEGRATION DYSFUNCTION

Sensory Integration International Sensory Integration International is a nonprofit organization dedicated to helping children with sensory integrative dysfunction. Their site offers information on occupational therapy programs available at the Ayres Clinic, along with FAQs and a publication catalog. Professionals will find information on courses, workshops, and certification. There is also a therapist database, and a recommended reading list.
http://home.earthlink.net/~sensoryint/

9.16 MENTAL RETARDATION

American Association on Mental Retardation (AAMR) The AAMR promotes "progressive policies, sound research, effective practices, and universal human rights for people with intellectual disabilities." Site resources include information about the AAMR, current news, a bookstore, reference materials from the annual meeting, abstracts from the *American Journal on Mental Retardation* and *Mental Retardation,* a list of the divisions of the AAMR, and links to the discussion group and chat rooms.
http://www.aamr.org

Down Syndrome Created in part by members of the Down syndrome LISTSERV, this site provides a number of informative links for professionals and consumers. Included are links to worldwide organizations relevant to Down syndrome, support groups, an events and conferences calendar, education and inclusion information, family essays, healthcare guidelines, and a large number of online medical articles covering all aspects of the syndrome. There is also online access to *Disability Solutions,* a publication providing information on mental disability.
http://www.nas.com/downsyn

Mental Retardation Resources More than 35 Web sites are listed here as mental retardation resources, presented as a service of Hood College. Short descriptions of each site are provided. Topics covered include the Special Olympics, government agencies, developmental disabilities, mental retardation, and Down syndrome.
http://www.hood.edu/seri/mr.htm

National Association for the Dually Diagnosed (NADD) NADD, an association for persons with developmental disabilities and mental health needs, provides this site on dual diagnosis: psychiatric disorders in persons with mental

retardation. Available resources include an online store; articles, including one describing dual diagnosis and mental retardation, reasons for its prevalence, and available treatments; conference details; information on the association; and an assortment of related links. Some features, including an online bulletin, are available only to NADD members.

(fee-based) http://www.thenadd.org/

The Arc of the United States   This nonprofit organization is committed to the welfare of all children and adults with mental retardation and their families. The site offers information on government affairs, services, publications, promotional products, fact sheets, and local and state home pages. A comprehensive list of links offers additional sources for information, including support for community living, employment transition, special education, assistive technology, health promotion, organizations, grant resources, and disability-related products and services.

http://www.thearc.org

9.17 MOOD DISORDERS

GENERAL RESOURCES

Depression and Related Affective Disorders Association (DRADA) This site provides information about DRADA, links to research reports and other reference materials, book reviews, an online store for videos and books, and information about support groups and other related organizations, as well as a link to clinical research studies seeking participants.

http://www.med.jhu.edu/drada

DSM-IV Criteria   This site lists the DSM-IV criteria for major depressive episode, hypomanic episode, bipolar I disorder, bipolar II disorder, manic episode, major depressive disorder, mixed episode, dysthymic disorder, and cyclothymic disorder.

http://members.aol.com/faery116/dsm.html

Mental Health Clinical Research Center   This center, located within the University of North Carolina at Chapel Hill, conducts research that examines the neurobiology and treatment of mood and psychotic disorders, as well as the psychopathology and physiology of stress. At this site, summaries of the major research focus issues, such as mood disorder neurobiology, pathophysiology of stress, neurobiology of psychotic disorders, and psychopharmacology, are presented. Also included are overviews of the center's core services programs, such as the behavioral and cognitive neuroscience core and the clinical assessment and procedures core. A link to clinical trials currently running at the University, news updates from the center, and a faculty directory are located at this site.

http://www.mhcrc.unc.edu

Merck Manual of Diagnosis and Therapy: Mood Disorders   Drawn from the *Merck Manual of Diagnosis and Therapy,* this site offers a clinical discussion of mood disorders. Epidemiology, etiology, primary and secondary mood disorders, risk of suicide, and diagnosis are examined. There are links for specific information on depression, dysthymic disorder, bipolar disorders, and cyclothymic disorder.
http://www.merck.com/pubs/mmanual/section15/chapter189/189a.htm

Mood Disorders Association of British Columbia   This association's Web site has links to general information about certain mood disorders and offers personal stories and links to related sites.
http://www.mdabc.ca

Mood Disorders Clinic   At this site there is information regarding depressive and bipolar disorders for both professionals and consumers. Resources include assessment and diagnosis details, symptoms lists, and information on the Canadian clinic itself. http://www.psychiatry.ubc.ca/mood/

National Depressive and Manic-Depressive Association   The National Depressive and Manic-Depressive Association strives to educate patients, families, professionals, and the public concerning the nature of depressive and bipolar disorders as treatable medical disorders; foster self-help; eliminate discrimination; and improve access to care. The site contains extensive information on the association and links to support groups, patient assistance programs, education, advocacy, clinical trials, and reference materials are listed.
http://www.ndmda.org

BIPOLAR DISORDERS

Bipolar Children and Teens Homepage   Personal stories and links to useful Internet resources are included at this site devoted to bipolar disorder in children. General information for patients and parents, news, chat forums, service providers, professional associations, prevention resources, Internet directories, advocacy and policy information, medication information, support groups, and major organizations are found through this site.
http://hometown.aol.com/DrgnKpr1/BPCAT.html

Bipolar Disorder Diagnosis, Treatment, and Support   This fact sheet from the National Depressive and Manic-Depressive Association discusses major depressive disorder and bipolar disorder, including causes, general statistics, and symptoms of depression and mania.
http://www.ndmda.org/biover.htm

Bipolar Disorder in Children and Adolescents   Visitors to this site will find a brochure on bipolar disorder in children and adolescents, written by a psychiatrist, that includes case studies, prevalence (statistics), causes, diagnosis, comorbidity, and mania in young children. In addition, there is information on

the course and prognosis of bipolar disorder, factors making another episode more or less likely, and how bipolar disorder can adversely affect a person's life.
http://www.klis.com/chandler/pamphlet/bipolar/bipolarpamphlet.htm

Bipolar Disorder in Children and Adolescents: Advice to Parents An article written by a professor of psychiatry at the University of Texas Medical Branch is available at this site. Detailed but nontechnical information about the disorder is available for parents, including symptoms in children and adolescents, evaluation, treatment, and medications. The article also offers specific issues in the education of children and teenagers about their disorder.
http://www.nami.org/youth/bipolar.htm

Bipolar Disorder Patient/Family Handout Resources at this site answer common questions about bipolar disorder, with topics including causes, diagnosis, genetics, symptoms, different patterns of the disease, treatment, medication and side effects, and psychotherapy. Contact information for support groups and suggestions for those diagnosed with the disorder, along with a list of suggested readings, are also found at the site.
http://www.psychguides.com/bphe.html

Bipolar Disorders Portal Included in this Web site are various links to bipolar information, including diagnosis, treatment and medicine, support groups, books and other reference materials, alternative treatments, and a list of comorbid disorders. A number of bipolar-related links are also included.
http://www.pendulum.org

Bipolar Kids Homepage This address serves as an Internet directory for patients, caregivers, doctors, and teachers searching for resources on bipolar disorders in children. General information sources, professional associations, articles, and resources on educational issues are found through the site. Parents will also find a questionnaire assisting physicians in diagnosing bipolar disorder and a mailing list for parents of bipolar children.
http://www.geocities.com/EnchantedForest/1068

Child and Adolescent Bipolar Foundation (CABF) Created to provide information about early-onset bipolar disorder, this Web page offers a "Learning Center" with fact sheets on the disorder, history of the condition, and educational needs of the child. Within the same section, a "Reference Room" offers full-text journal articles, interviews, research findings, and personal stories. Members can access message boards, online support groups, and chat rooms. A list of related Internet resources is also provided.
(some features fee-based) http://www.bpkids.org/

Joy Ikelman's Information on Bipolar Disorder This site provides an examination of the author's own experiences with the disorder, as well as information on treatment, self-education, assessment and classification of bipolar disorder information from professional organizations, suicide advice, news updates, and links to related Web sites. http://www.frii.com/~parrot/bip.html

MEDLINEplus: Bipolar Disorder   Resources from MEDLINEplus on bipolar disorder include links to information from the National Library of Medicine and National Institutes of Health, and other government and general resources. Overviews, research resources, information in Spanish, law and policy resources, news sites, organizations, information for teenagers, and treatment details are found through this address.

http://medlineplus.nlm.nih.gov/medlineplus/bipolardisorder.html

Mental Health InfoSource: Bipolar Disorders Information Center
This site offers a general discussion of bipolar disorder, including diagnosis, treatment, and contact information for sources of help. Visitors can ask questions of experts, read archived questions and answers, and earn continuing medical education credits while reading about current trends in the treatment of bipolar disorder. Chat forums, online support resources, treatment information, directories of support organizations, patient education articles, and links to related sites are all found through this address.

http://www.mhsource.com/bipolar/index.html

Mental Health Sanctuary: Bipolar Disorder   Both professionals and patients will find a wealth of information related to bipolar disorder on this site. Professionals will find a comprehensive listing of related Internet links, as well as articles on bipolar disorder that include treatment guidelines, diagnostic information, and research news. Patients can read personal stories, as well as access a chat room, and discussion boards. Additional resources available at this site include an ask-the-expert column, online counseling (fee-based), an online trauma wellness workshop, and support information that includes suicide intervention, a hotline, and help in locating a therapist.

(some features fee-based) http://www.mhsanctuary.com/bipolar/

National Institute of Mental Health (NIMH): Bipolar Disorder   An online booklet on bipolar disorder, intended for individuals and their families, is provided on this Web page. Bipolar disorder is described, and information is provided on its symptoms, diagnosis, and the tendency towards suicidal feelings. The course of the condition, its causes, and presentation in children are examined. Treatment of the disorder is discussed, including medications and psychosocial therapies. Clinical research is also described. Resources for help with bipolar disorder are provided, along with links for additional information and a bibliography.

http://www.nimh.nih.gov/publicat/bipolar.cfm

PsyCom.net: Bipolar Disorder   This site provides links to many resources on bipolar disorder, offering news of research advances, general information for patients, answers to FAQs, suggested reading lists, practice guidelines, consensus statements, and support resources. Professionals can find links to sites offering specific discussions of diagnosis and treatment issues.

http://www.psycom.net/depression.central.bipolar.html

Resources for Parents of Kids with Bipolar Disorder The mother of a child diagnosed with bipolar disorder offers a list of suggested resources at this site. Materials include suggested books for children, books for parents, general books, articles from professional journals, books on therapy, organizations, Internet resources, audio tapes for children, videotapes, articles from popular media, and psychiatric hospitals for children. Links to online resources are provided when available.

http://www.bpso.org/BPKids.htm

Stanley Center for the Innovative Treatment of Bipolar Disorder As part of the Stanley Foundation Bipolar Network, this research center's Web site includes informative links to current clinical trials, access to the center's newsletter, affective disorders literature, information on genetics and bipolar disorder study, conference details, and an overview of the center's background and goals.

http://www.wpic.pitt.edu/stanley

World Wide Handbook on Child and Youth Psychiatry and Allied Disciplines: Bipolar Disorder An organizational and occupational psychiatrist has developed this handbook, which provides information on bipolar disorder in children at this site. Information includes an introduction to the disorder, symptoms, assessment, differential diagnosis, epidemiology, etiology, treatment, prevention, and prognosis. Reference citations and information about the author are available.

http://Web.inter.nl.net/hcc/T.Compernolle/bipol.htm

Co-occurrence of Depression

Co-occurrence Of Depression with Medical and Psychiatric Disorders A fact sheet, developed by the National Mental Health Association, on co-occurrence of depression with medical, psychiatric, and substance abuse disorders is provided on this site. The fact sheet addresses the impact of depression in primary care settings, why depression and medical illnesses often occur together, and the prevalence of depression with a variety of other illnesses, including heart disease, stroke, cancer, diabetes, eating disorders, and alcohol/drugs. Common symptoms and the importance of treatment are discussed. Resources for help are provided, along with a bibliography.

http://www.nmha.org/infoctr/factsheets/28.cfm

National Institute of Mental Health (NIMH): Co-occurrence of Depression Fact sheets on co-occurrence of depression with other diseases and disorders are provided on this site. Topics include the occurrence of depression with general medical disorders, as well as with psychiatric disorders and substance abuse, cancer, heart disease, stroke, and HIV. In addition, there is a fact sheet on the link between depression and heart disease. A news story on depression and bone loss is also found.

http://www.nimh.nih.gov/publicat/cooccurmenu.cfm

CYCLOTHYMIC DISORDER

Internet Mental Health: Cyclothymic Disorder   The resources on cyclothymic disorder can be accessed by the disorder in the list of mental health disorders on the left side of the page. Resources include a description of the condition, online diagnostic tests, treatment information, and research findings. General links related to mood disorders offer booklets, magazine articles, and related Internet resources.
http://www.mentalhealth.com/fr20.html

Mental Health Net: Cyclothymic Disorder   A fact sheet on cyclothymic disorder is offered on this Web page. Common symptoms are listed, and hyperlinks are provided for additional information on treatment and online resources. The "Treatment" section describes psychotherapy, medications, and self-help. Comprehensive online resources are offered, with descriptions of the sites.
http://mentalhelp.net/disorders/sx38.htm

DEPRESSIVE DISORDERS

Andrew's Depression Page   This site contains links to numerous online fact sheets and sites on various issues regarding depression. Topics included are treatment, suicide, online support resources, mood scales, general mental health, children and adolescents, general psychiatry links, a depression FAQ, and a collection of papers written by people with depression.
http://www.blarg.net/~charlatn/depression/Depression.html

Asher Center for the Study and Treatment of Depressive Disorders
As part of Northwestern University, this multidisciplinary center combines basic and applied research to address depressive disorders. Brief summaries of clinical research projects, as well as links to collaborating centers and departments, are included. Faculty and staff information, training opportunities, seminar information, and other links of interest are also provided.
http://www.ashercenter.nwu.edu

Depression: What You Need to Know   This report summarizes the types of depressive disorders, supplying definitions for each. Symptoms of depression and mania, causes, treatments, warnings about side effects, and offers information about behavioral therapy and research findings are also provided.
http://www.vh.org/Patients/IHB/Psych/PatientEdMaterials/Depression/DepressionTOC.html

Dr. Ivan's Depression Central   This comprehensive site provides information on the numerous types of depressive disorders and treatments for those suffering from depression and other mood disorders. It contains a large number of links to articles, papers, and other informative resources, including support groups, research centers, and psychiatrists specializing in mood disorders. In addition, there arc links to the diagnosis, classification, and treatment of de-

pression and mood disorders, as well as to other important Web sites and newsgroups devoted to depression and other mental illnesses.
http://www.psycom.net/depression.central.html

Internet Mental Health: Major Depressive Disorder Resources related to major depressive disorder are provided on this Web page. There are descriptions of depression, an online diagnostic test, and several links to treatment information from the U.S. Surgeon General, American Psychological Association, and the Agency for Health Care Policy and Research. Other resources include research findings, a discussion board, personal stories, and booklets. Magazine articles covering general depression, causation, epidemiology, diagnosis, and treatment are also featured.
http://www.mentalhealth.com/dis/p20-md01.html

Knowledge Exchange Network: Depression The latest news stories related to depression are featured on this Web site. More than 50 stories are listed, dating back to 1999.
http://www.mentalhealth.org/newsroom/depressionarchives.htm

Mental Help Net: All About Depression Depression information for consumers at this site includes details of symptoms, treatment, research information through PubMed, and links to information resources, organizations, and online support. Visitors can also take an online quiz for a personal assessment of depression. http://depression.mentalhelp.net

National Foundation for Depressive Illness (NAFDI), Inc. Within this Web site there are descriptions of the symptoms, treatment, and diagnosis of depressive illness. Information on the foundation's goals, a list of the national board of directors and advisors, and online access to the NAFDI newsletter are also available.
http://www.depression.org

National Institute of Mental Health (NIMH): Depression A guide to depression is provided on this Web page, of interest to patients and professionals. The 27-page booklet explains the types of depression, symptoms of depression and mania, and causes of depression. Diagnostic evaluation and treatment options such as medication, herbal therapies, and psychotherapies are discussed. Tips and resources for getting help are provided. There is also a bibliography.
http://www.nimh.nih.gov/publicat/depressionmenu.cfm

Wing of Madness Described as one of the oldest depression pages available, this site offers informative pages on all aspects of depression. A number of questions about depression are answered, providing information about symptoms, treatments, online and offline support, reference materials, online articles and booklets, related newsgroups, and support organizations. Other resources available include a fact sheet on antidepressant advice, a book list, and a number of depression-related links.
http://www.wingofmadness.com/index.htm

DYSTHYMIC DISORDER

Dysthymic Disorder   This fact sheet describes dysthymic disorder, psychotherapy choices, drug treatment, and support issues.
http://mentalhelp.net/disorders/sx14t.htm

Internet Mental Health: Dysthymic Disorder   Dedicated to dysthymic
disorder, this Web page offers both American and European descriptions of the
condition, an online diagnostic test, and a connection to comprehensive information on medical and psychosocial interventions. An algorithm for the pharmacotherapy of depression, important research details, mood disorder booklets,
and a variety of articles on the subject are available, as well as a presentation of
the Surgeon General regarding the etiology, assessment, and treatment of mood
disorders. http://www.mentalhealth.com/dis/p20-md04.html

Psychology Information Online: Dysthymic Disorder   Intended for
patients, this site offers a fact sheet on dysthymic disorder. The disorder is described, along with identifying factors such as changes in thinking, feelings, behavior, and physical well-being. Psychotherapy is discussed as the treatment of
choice, along with medications.
http://www.psychologyinfo.com/depression/dysthymic.htm

POSTPARTUM DEPRESSION

BehaveNet: Postpartum Depression   Examining postpartum depression,
this fact sheet offers mothers an explanation of the condition, its incidence, and
symptoms. Postpartum obsessive- compulsive disorder and postpartum psychosis are also described. Treatment options are briefly covered. Resources for help
and support are provided.
http://www.behavenet.com/dadinc/

Postpartum Depression   In addition to describing the symptoms and
frequency of occurrence, this article outlines the time course of onset, causes,
especially endocrine factors, treatment options, related mental problems, prognosis, prevention information, and supportive organizations and literature.
http://www.rcpsych.ac.uk/info/help/pndep/index.htm

Pregnancy and Depression   Resources on depression and pregnancy at this
site include full-text professional journal articles, news stories, answers to readers' questions, discussion forums, and links to related sites. Similar resources are
available on the treatment of depression during breastfeeding, pregnancy, child-
birth, and mothering. Visitors will also find MEDLINE-based reference lists on
pregnancy and breastfeeding; access to PubMed, MEDLINE, and MedExplorer
for individual services; relevant sites listed by drug; and suggested reading lists.
http://www.angelfire.com/de2/depressionpregnancy/index.html

Your Emotional Well-Being: Understanding the Blues   The distinction between the baby blues and postpartum depression is explained at this online brochure, with facts about each and an easily scored quiz for gauging the severity of postpartum symptoms offered. Reassuring information on adjusting to motherhood and making the most of a sometimes trying period is presented.
http://www.duke.edu/~bkc/html/webdoc7.htm

PREMENSTRUAL DYSPHORIC DISORDER (PMDD)

Premenstrual Dysphoric Disorder   Originally published in the *Journal of Gender-Specific Medicine* (1999), this full-text article examines the medical management of premenstrual dysphoric disorder. A definition is provided, along with a discussion of the incidence, symptoms, and diagnostic criteria for the illness. Hormonal treatments are identified. In addition, studies on the effectiveness of antidepressants are discussed. Proper administration of medication and length of treatment are also examined. A bibliography is included.
http://www.mmhc.com/jgsm/articles/JGSM9906/Yonkers.html

Sentinel Healthcare: Premenstrual Dysphoric Disorder   A fact sheet on premenstrual dysphoric disorder is provided on this Web page. The disorder is defined, along with its incidence, theories on the causes, and risk factors. A detailed table of symptoms lists psychological symptoms, gastrointestinal symptoms, skin problems, fluid retention, neurologic and vascular symptoms, respiratory problems, eye complaints, and general complaints. Diagnosis of the disorder is explained, along with treatment options.
http://www.sentinelhealthcare.org/clinical/gyneonc/pmdd.htm

SEASONAL AFFECTIVE DISORDER (SAD)

Internet Mental Health: Seasonal Affective Disorder   An article on seasonal affective disorder is provided on this Web site. The article discusses symptoms, diagnosis, and epidemiology. Treatment studies with light therapy are examined. In addition, the psychobiology of SAD is discussed. References are found. There is also information on manufacturers of light therapy devices.
http://www.mentalhealth.com/book/p40-sad.html

Seasonal Affective Disorder Information Sheet   This Web site, created by Outside In, Ltd., provides information about seasonal affective disorder, including symptoms, treatment, products, mechanism of action, a symptom scoring table, and research abstracts.
http://www.outsidein.co.uk/sadinfo.htm

Seasonal Affective Disorder: About Light, Depression, and Melatonin   A psychologist presents information at this site about seasonal affective disorder. Topics include light therapy, sadness, anxiety, irritability, violence, other symptoms, causes of the disorder, the history of light therapy, and the significance of winter holidays in coping with seasonal changes. The site also contains discussions of light of light and melatonin, bright light therapy, and suggestions for avoiding seasonal depression.

http://www.newtechpub.com/phantom/contrib/sad.htm

9.18 PARANOIA

Hopkins Technology: Paranoia   This site provides a patient education booklet on paranoia from the National Institute of Mental Health. The text defines paranoia and discusses specific mental conditions involving paranoia, including paranoid personality disorder, delusional disorder, and paranoid schizophrenia. Genetic contributions, biochemistry, and stress are discussed as possible causes of these disorders. Current treatments, including medications and psychotherapy, and outlook for paranoid patients are also discussed. The site lists references for additional information.

http://www.hoptechno.com/paranoia.htm

9.19 PARAPHILIAS

GENERAL RESOURCES

Sexual Deviancy   A large number of resources related to sexual deviancy are provided on this Web page, written and developed by psychologists Dr. Julie Medlin and Steven Knauts. There are fact sheets on sexually deviant behaviors, including child molestation, peeping, exposing, sadism, cross dressing, rape, frotteurism, fetishism, masochism, and addiction. In addition, there is a multimedia presentation on deviancy. Information is also provided on adolescent offenders, sexualized children, and treatment methods. There is a report on sex in America, personal stories, and a list of related links.

http://www.sexualdeviancy.com/

FETISHISM

Sinclair Intimacy Institute: Fetishism   A fact sheet on fetishism, a fixation on an inanimate object or body part, is featured on this site. The types of inanimate object fetishes are described, along with sexual response, and the distinction between fetishism and sexual preferences. Possible causes of the condition are examined.

http://www.intimacyinstitute.com/sex_data/topics/fetishism.html

SADISM

Sexual Sadism This site has lecture notes on sexual sadism from a criminal justice course at North Carolina Wesleyan College. A clinical definition of a sadist is provided, as well as symptoms. The pattern of a sadist is described in terms of the examination of criminal scene behavior. The difference between a psychopath and a sadist is discussed, as well as routine criminal behaviors that are not sadism. Examples of routine criminal behaviors are given. A bibliography is provided.
http://faculty.ncwc.edu/toconnor/401/401lect13.htm

9.20 PERSONALITY DISORDERS

GENERAL RESOURCES

Aggression and Transference in Severe Personality Disorders This scientific article summarizes the association between aggressive behavior expression and personality disorders. Theories of aggression and how it relates to personality disorder, therapeutic procedures in dealing with the patients, symptoms, treatment assessment, and reviews on recent literature dealing with this subject are included. References are listed.
http://www.mhsource.com/pt/p950216.html

Borderline Personality Disorder and More Links are available at this address to sites offering information and other resources related to antisocial, avoidant, borderline, conduct, and narcissistic personality disorders. Short descriptions are provided with each site link, and links are also available to book descriptions from Amazon.com, therapist and doctor directories, and hotlines.
http://www.mental-health-matters.com/borderline.html

Mental Help Net: Personality Disorders An overview of personality disorders is presented on the home page of this Web site. Links for more specific information on 10 personality disorders, including antisocial, avoidant, borderline, dependent, histrionic, and schizoid, are provided. Symptoms for each of the 10 personality disorders are described, and a treatment section explains psychotherapy, medications, and self-help methods for each disorder. Online support groups can be found in the organizations section. There is also a link to MEDLINE for research, a link to a chapter on personality and development from the online book *Psychological Self-Help,* book reviews, and a therapist database. http://personalitydisorders.mentalhelp.net/

National Mental Health Association: Personality Disorders A general information sheet on personality disorders is presented on this site. Personality disorders are defined, along with their causes. Specific types are described such as schizoid, paranoid, antisocial, borderline, narcissistic, avoidant, dependent,

and compulsive. Treatment is briefly discussed. Resources for further information are provided.
http://www.nmha.org/infoctr/factsheets/91.cfm

ANTISOCIAL PERSONALITY DISORDER

Internet Mental Health: Antisocial Personality Disorder American and European diagnostic criteria, online interactive diagnostic tools, extensive treatment resources, research article searches through PubMed, and patient education booklets are offered at this site. Links are also available to several additional sources for information. This site serves as a suitable source for general professional information on the disorder.
http://www.mentalhealth.com/dis/p20-pe04.html

Psychopathology and Antisocial Personality Disorder: A Journey into the Abyss This site discusses antisocial personality disorder, classification systems of psychopaths, and testing and assessment. Definitions of the primary psychopath, the secondary or neurotic psychopath, and the dyssocial psychopath are accompanied by discussions of comparative differences and the effects of studying a non institutionalized population. Information is technical and is presented for professional use.
http://www.flash.net/~sculwell/psychopathology.htm

WebMD: Antisocial Personality Disorder Antisocial personality disorder is explained in this patient fact sheet. A definition is provided, along with incidence, risk factors, and symptoms. Signs and tests are briefly covered. Treatment, prognosis, and potential complications are also explained. Hyperlinks are provided for additional information on certain terms.
http://my.webmd.com/content/asset/adam_disease_sociopathic_personality

AVOIDANT PERSONALITY DISORDER

Avoidant Personality Disorder This site is devoted to providing information on avoidant personality disorder. Included are a number of links to clinical descriptions, along with diagnostic criteria for this and related disorders. Also included are several personal experience articles, a book list, and a list of relevant links.
http://www.geocities.com/HotSprings/3764

Internet Mental Health: Avoidant Personality Disorder For those interested in avoidant personality disorder, this site offers a description, an online diagnostic test, treatment, and research information. There are also links to general information on personality disorders.
http://www.mentalhealth.com/dis/p20-pe08.html

PSYweb.com: Avoidant Personality Disorder   A definition and DSM-IV criteria for avoidant personality disorder are available at this site, as well as links to descriptions of psychiatric therapies, including Adlerian, behavioral, existential, Gestalt, person-centered, psychoanalytic, rational-emotive, reality, and transactional analysis therapies.
http://www.psyweb.com/Mdisord/avpd.html

BORDERLINE PERSONALITY DISORDER

Borderline Personality Disorder   This address offers a professional overview of several schools of thought concerning borderline personality disorder. Topics include Kernberg's Borderline Personality Organization, Gunderson's theories, the Diagnostic Interview for Borderlines, and the DSM-IV definition. The site also discusses possible causes of the disorder.
http://www.palace.net/~llama/psych/bpd.html

Borderline Personality Disorder (BPD) Central   This comprehensive Web site is devoted to providing informative resources on BPD. Included are links to information and Web sites on the fundamentals of BPD, a list of professionals and therapists, BPD FAQs, a list of relevant books, self-help, abuse, and online resources, including support groups, mailing lists, and other related Web sites. http://www.bpdcentral.com

Borderline Personality Disorder Sanctuary   This site provides resources related to borderline personality disorder, including diagnosis and medication information, a forum for asking questions of professionals, articles, personal stories, suicide resources, a bulletin board, chat forums, and suggested reading lists. Profiles of site hosts are also found at the site. Visitors can also search MEDLINE and find information on non-Internet resources, professional directories, toll-free resources, contact details for mental health clinics, and listings of borderline personality disorder advocates at the site.
http://mhsanctuary.com/borderline/

Internet Mental Health: Borderline Personality Disorder   Information on borderline personality disorder at this site includes American and European diagnostic criteria, an online interactive diagnostic tool, treatment details, patient education booklets, and links to related sites. Visitors can also conduct searches for research articles on borderline personality disorder and specific subtopics through PubMed.
http://www.mentalhealth.com/dis/p20-pe05.html

Mental Health Sanctuary: Borderline Personality Disorder   Visitors to this site will find a broad array of resources related to borderline personality disorder, including articles, diagnostic information, news, and an ask-the-expert column. Patients will find chat rooms, discussion boards, book reviews, and support information.
http://www.mhsanctuary.com/borderline/

DEPENDENT PERSONALITY DISORDER

Dependent Personality Disorder: Treatment   Users can click on "Dependent Personality" on the left side of the site to view an article on the treatment of dependent personality disorder, including fundamental guidelines, psychosocial treatment, drug treatment, clinical signs of the disorder, behavior therapies, and hospitalization.
http://www.mentalhealth.com/fr20.html

PSYweb.com: Dependent Personality Disorder   A brief overview of dependent personality disorder is provided on this site. A definition and diagnostic criteria are featured. General psychotherapy treatment is provided for several types of therapy, such as Adlerian, behavioral, existential, Gestalt, and psychoanalysis.   http://www.psyweb.com/Mdisord/depd.html

HISTRIONIC PERSONALITY DISORDER

Dual Diagnosis: Histrionic Personality Disorder   An article on histrionic personality disorder, primarily for professionals, is found on this site. The essential features of the disorder are described, along with their self-image, view of others, and approach to relationships. Additional topics covered include issues with authority, behavior, affective issues, and defensive structure. Treatment provider guidelines, techniques, and goals are discussed. In addition, treatment for those who also have a substance abuse problem is examined.
http://www.toad.net/~arcturus/dd/histrion.htm

Internet Mental Health: Histrionic Personality Disorder   The pervasive pattern of emotionality and attention-seeking typical of histrionic personality disorder is outlined, with characteristic behaviors noted. General information on personality disorders, numerous diagnostic differentials, and guidelines for diagnosis are found. Long-term psychotherapy and a flexible psychotherapeutic approach, emphasizing compassion and appropriate confrontation, are summarized. Online questions, to be answered by either professionals or patients, may assist with making an accurate psychiatric diagnosis.
http://www.mentalhealth.com/dis/p20-pe06.html

NARCISSISTIC PERSONALITY DISORDER

Health Center.com: Narcissistic Behavior   A short discussion of narcissistic personality disorder is available at this address, including a description of major traits and suggested treatments.
http://www4.health-center.com/mentalhealth/personality/narcissistic.htm

Internet Mental Health: Narcissistic Personality Disorder   Links to information on narcissistic personality disorder are found on this Web page.

Topics include an overview, treatment, and research. There is also an online diagnostic test, as well as general Internet links to sites related to personality disorders. http://www.mentalhealth.com/dis/p20-pe07.html

 Malignant Self-Love: Frequently Asked Questions   Information on narcissistic personality disorder is presented at this site in the form of answers to FAQs related to narcissism and violence, parenting, personal relationships, exploitation, and many other topics. The site also offers book excerpts and information on publications authored by the host.
http://www.geocities.com/Athens/Forum/6297/faq1.html

PARANOID PERSONALITY DISORDER

 Internet Mental Health: Paranoid Personality Disorder   Internet Mental Health provides the American and European descriptions of paranoid personality disorder, with links to an online diagnostic tool and an information booklet from the National Institute of Mental Health. Several characteristics and principal diagnostic criteria are explained, including a pervasive distrust of others and the existence of the symptoms independent of any psychotic disorder. A treatment link offers information on the basic principles of both medical and psychosocial interventions, in addition to summaries of antianxiety medications, antipsychotic medications, and individual psychotherapy.
http://www.mentalhealth.com/dis/p20-pe01.html

 Mental Health Net: Paranoid Personality Disorder   DSM-IV criteria for paranoid personality disorder are presented at this site, accompanied by links to symptoms and treatment information. Links are also available to related Internet resources, online support sources, organizations, and a directory of therapists. Book reviews and excerpts are also found at this address.
http://mentalhelp.net/disorders/sx37.htm

SCHIZOID PERSONALITY DISORDER

 Dual Diagnosis: Schizoid Personality Disorder   Professionals will find an article on schizoid personality disorder on this site. Common signs and diagnostic criteria are examined. The individual's perception of self, others, and authority figures is discussed. A treatment section covers medication, provider guidelines, countertransference, techniques, and goals. Dual diagnosis treatment for the addicted schizoid personality patient is also described.
http://www.toad.net/~arcturus/dd/schizoid.htm

 Internet Mental Health: Schizoid Personality Disorder   Schizoid personality disorder, a pervasive pattern of detachment from social relationships, is presented at this Internet Mental Health Web location. Characteristics of the disorder, as outlined in the American description, are listed, in addition to symptoms and diagnostic guidelines found at the European description link.

An online diagnostic tool may assist practitioners in making an accurate assessment. The basic principles of long-term psychosocial intervention and the advantages of group therapy are discussed.
http://www.mentalhealth.com/dis/p20-pe02.html

9.21 PERVASIVE DEVELOPMENTAL DISORDERS

GENERAL RESOURCES

Autism, Asperger's Syndrome, and Other Pervasive Developmental Disorders A Long Island parent group developed this Web page as a resource for the unique needs of people with high- functioning autism, Asperger's syndrome, and other pervasive developmental disorders. While there is mostly local information on the site, there are also Internet resources on autism, including a very comprehensive suggested reading list, with parent reviews.
http://www.lightlink.com/schissel/aap/index.html

National Information Center for Children and Youth (NICHCY) with Disabilities: Pervasive Developmental Disorders A briefing paper (January 1998) on pervasive development disorders, by the National Information Center for Children and Youth with Disabilities, is provided on this site. Descriptions and diagnostic criteria for autism, Rett's disorder, childhood disintegrative disorder, Asperger's syndrome, and pervasive developmental disorder not otherwise specified (PDDNOS) are provided. PDDNOS is emphasized, with information on its causes and symptoms, including impairments to social behavior, nonverbal communication, understanding speech, and speech development. In addition, several forms of unusual behavior patterns are described, such as compulsive behaviors. Diagnostic assessment is described. Treatment options, along with educational services, are discussed. A bibliography is provided, as well as resources for additional information.
http://www.nichcy.org/pubs/factshe/fs20txt.htm

National Institute of Neurological Disorders and Stroke (NINDS): Pervasive Developmental Disorders Information on pervasive developmental disorders is featured on this Web page, courtesy of the National Institute of Neurological Disorders and Stroke. A fact sheet is offered that describes this general category, treatment, and prognosis. Related organizations are listed. Additionally, there are links for clinical trials and to the MEDLINE bibliographic database.
http://www.ninds.nih.gov/health_and_medical/disorders/pdd.htm

Pervasive Developmental Disorder (PDD) Support Designed to give the user as much information as possible concerning pervasive developmental disorder, this text-only site provides descriptions and connections to nearly 20 links related to all aspects of pervasive developmental disorders. Selected links include "User to User," a correspondence site for communication with those in similar situations; "Dear Jim," a user-to-user advice page; a conferences/meetings link; publications list; and "Words of Wisdom.

http://www.geocities.com/HotSprings/9647

Pervasive Developmental Disorders   The diagnostic criteria (DSM-IV) for pervasive developmental disorders, including autism, Rett's disorder, childhood disintegrative disorder, Asperger's syndrome, and pervasive developmental disorder not otherwise specified, are presented on this personal Web page. Diagnostic features, associated disorders, associated medical findings, age and gender features, prevalence, course, and differential diagnosis are examined for each condition.

http://www.thelaughtongroup.com/pddsupport/dsm-iv.htm

Angelman Syndrome (AS)

Angelman Syndrome Association   The Australian Angelman Association provides general information at its Web site pertaining to the diagnosis, research, and treatment of the rare, neuro-genetic disorder. The Angelman syndrome LISTSERV is provided for communication via e-mail. Past issues of the association's newsletter are also available.

http://www.angelmansyndrome.org/

Angelman Syndrome Foundation, USA   This foundation was created to provide information and education, promote research, and serve as advocates for those interested in Angelman syndrome. At this site, there are links to documents providing basic and specific information about the syndrome; diagnostic criteria and testing files; detailed information on the genetics of the syndrome, including clinical descriptions, differential diagnosis, and molecular genetics; foundation-based conferences, electronic forums, and other support; and advocacy links. Included are links to information and organizations in other countries, as well as other AS-related sites.

http://www.angelman.org/

Angelman Syndrome Information for Families and Professionals
This comprehensive site provides information and support resources for professionals and families interested in Angelman syndrome. Included are links to informative documents describing the symptoms of the syndrome, including physical and mental problems; issues regarding development, education; testing, and genetic counseling; article references; a detailed fact file on the genetics of the disorder; and photographs of patients. Also included are links to mailing lists and conference information, as well as to a detailed summary of previous conference presentations and publications.

http://www.asclepius.com/angel

International Angelman Syndrome Association (IASO)   The organization's mission and member countries are enumerated at this site along with information on joining the IASO electronic mailing list. The Web site's conference announcements are also available and may be viewed in English, French, Spanish, or German.

http://www.asclepius.com/iaso

ASPERGER'S DISORDER

Asperger Syndrome Coalition of the United States   This nonprofit organization promotes education and provides current information on social and communication disorders, such as Asperger's and nonverbal learning disorder. At this site, links to detailed fact sheets on Asperger's and nonverbal learning syndrome are available, as well as resources on related conditions. These fact sheets include links to FAQs, scientific articles, personal stories, research reports, and organizations. Conference calendars and a reference list of books, videos, and other materials are present, in addition to membership information and the ASPEN newsletter.

http://www.asperger.org

Asperger's Disorder   This Web site provides information on Asperger's disorder, including its epidemiology, biology, diagnostic criteria, Asperger's treatment; a bibliography; a list of clinicians that evaluate patients with the disorder; and the difference between this disorder and high-functioning autism. Links to other Asperger's disorder - related Web sites are included.

http://www.aspergers.com

Asperger's Syndrome   Hosted by the Autism Society of America, this Web site provides general information concerning the recognition and treatment of this pervasive developmental disorder as well as effective strategies for working with individuals with the disorder. Educational packages, cassettes, videos, books, and links to related organizations are included. Adobe Acrobat Reader is needed to view this site.

http://www.autism-society.org/packages/aspergers_disorder.pdf

DisabilityResources.org: Asperger's Syndrome   Many resources related to Asperger's syndrome are provided on this site. There are links for full-text articles, FAQs, and a personal home page from the mother of a child with Asperger's syndrome. There are lists of Internet links, and support information is available.   http://www.disabilityresources.org/ASPERGERS.html

Families of Adults Afflicted with Asperger's Syndrome (FAAAS)
This informative and comprehensive site of the FAAAS strives to give support to family members of adults afflicted with Asperger's syndrome by promoting education and awareness of the neurological disorder and all its ramifications. Recommended educational materials, Asperger's syndrome specialists, adult evaluation centers, articles, and personal thoughts written by family members of affected individuals are included.

http://www.faaas.org

Online Asperger Syndrome Information and Support This Web site has an extensive amount of information on Asperger's and related syndromes. There are links to fact sheets on the description of Asperger's, related research papers and research projects, diagnostic criteria, information about socialization and education, related disorders, support groups, clinicians, medical centers, and newsletters, as well as to a number of related sites.
http://www.udel.edu/bkirby/asperger

Autistic Disorders

Applied Behavior Analysis (ABA) Resources This personal Web page, created by the father of an autistic child, has a large number of links to organizations, articles, fact sheets, FAQs, and support resources. An informative section is presented on ABA research, including personal success stories, lists of support groups, specialized therapists and schools, treatment centers, legal and government resources, online discussion groups, and a great deal of information on ABA programs and how to start one. International autism resources and links to more detailed fact sheets on various aspects of ABA and autism are included. http://members.tripod.com/RSaffran/aba.html

Autism Continuum Connections, Education, and Support Site (ACCESS): Verbal Dyspraxia/Apraxia Newsgroups, suggested book lists, information resources, and sites from therapists are available through links at this address.
http://access.autistics.org/information/ld/dvd.html

Autism Independent UK This nonprofit organization exists to bring an increased awareness of autism and expand patients exposure to well-established and newly developed approaches in the diagnosis, assessment, education, and treatment of the disease. This comprehensive site has many links describing autism, its treatment, and diagnosis, including updated news on the latest research and treatment approaches. There are large news and fact files, as well as informative links to topics such as sexuality, the culture and treatment of autism, and a list of worldwide conferences, workshops, and seminars relating to autism. There is also access to Europe's largest autism library, a message board, and related links.
http://www.autismuk.com

Autism Network International (ANI) This self-help and advocacy organization for autistic people describes its philosophies and goals as well as the services provided for all ANI members. Provided are an Internet discussion list, a pen-pal directory for autistic people, a reference library, and a speaker referral service for organizations wishing to engage autistic speakers. Autism as experienced by some individuals and as defined by some professionals is described. Articles and links to other autism Web sites are available.
http://ani.autistics.org/

Autism Research Foundation This organization promotes research of the neurobiological causes of autism and other childhood developmental disorders. At this site, the mission statement can be accessed, as well as an overview of current research projects at the foundation, information on secretin, conference and employment resources, and brain donation information.
http://www.ladders.org/tarf

Autism Research Institute (ARI) The Autism Research Institute is devoted primarily to conducting research on the causes, prevention, and treatment of autism and to disseminating the results of such research. ARI's Web site provides its information request form for subscription to its newsletter, *Autism Research Review International,* as well as ordering information for diagnostic checklists, and a parent/professional packet. Newsletter excerpts and editorials are viewable from the Web site, providing many answers to autism controversies.
http://www.autism.com/ari

Autism Resources Visitors to this address will find links to autism resources on the Internet, answers to FAQs on autism, advice to parents, book recommendations, a larger bibliography of autism publications, and information about the site creator, who is the parent of an autistic child.
http://www.autism-resources.com/

Autism Society of America (ASA) The mission of the Autism Society of America is to promote lifelong access and opportunities for persons within the autism spectrum and their families, to be fully included, participating members of their communities through advocacy, public awareness, education, and research related to autism. This site contains a large amount of information and links pertaining to all aspects of autism. There are links to advocacy and government action alerts, the ASA and membership information, legislative action news, and conference information. Other links provide access to research in autism, including articles from autism research professionals; reference materials; glossary; information on treatment and diagnosis; medical and insurance information; other related organizations and sites.
http://www.autism-society.org

Autism/Pervasive Developmental Disorder The purpose of this site is to guide the visitor to the key issues associated with autism spectrum disorders. A growing awareness of the nature of autism and the multiple approaches to diagnosis, treatment, and care that are likely to be effective in meeting the needs of autistic individuals and their families are presented. The site is packed with information on such topics as job accommodation, college admissions, and respite care. Online children's workbooks and a parent's special guide to parents' rights and responsibilities regarding special education and related services are provided. Books for children with autism and a large assortment of titles for parents and caregivers may be ordered.
http://www.autism-pdd.net/autism.htm

Autistic Continuum Connections, Education, and Support Site (ACCESS) At this site, both general and support information related to autism is provided. An abundant amount of detailed information about autism and related disorders, language and communication disorders, and other related conditions is present, as well as summaries and articles of research on the causes, treatment, and psychology of autism. Support and research organizations links are offered, along with resources for families and caregivers of autistic individuals. Resources on educating and mainstreaming affected children are available, in addition to message boards, personal Web pages, and other online activities for autistic individuals and their families. Each topic includes links to related Web sites and support information.
http://sr7.xoom.com/viah/

Autistics.org: Autism Autistics.org describes itself as "resources by and for persons on the autistic spectrum." Their Web page offers an Institute for Autistic Action section with information on activism, disability rights, influence and persuasion, and publicity. The library offers numerous fact sheets on autism, "curing" autism, and the autistic perspective. There are also more than 100 Internet links on advocacy, autistic culture, general information, products, and services. Several discussion boards are available.
http://www.autistics.org/

Cambridge Center for Behavioral Studies: Links to Other Autism Sites Autism resources found through this site include support groups, information sources, professional associations, a directory of services, National Institute of Neurological Disorders and Stroke fact sheets, and clinical practice guidelines. http://www.behavior.org/autism/autism_links.cfm

Center for the Study of Autism (CSA) The Center for the Study of Autism provides information about autism to parents and professionals, and conducts research on the efficacy of various therapeutic interventions. The Web site includes an overview of autism in six different languages, subgroups and related disorders of autism, discussions of issues specific to autism, and interventions, such as music therapy and auditory integration training. Over 80 autism-related resource links can be accessed.
http://www.autism.org

Cure Autism Now (CAN) Cure Autism Now is a large private funder of autism research. Their Web site offers information on research awards, workshops, and the Autism Genetic Resource Exchange, a registry of families who have more than one autistic relative. The "Resources" section offers Web sites specifically for parents and researchers. A "Science Watch" section offers epidemiology citations, clinical studies, and abstracts. Other resources include conference information, a photo gallery of autistic children, and policy and advocacy information.
http://www.canfoundation.org/

Future Horizons Future Horizons is a major distributor of autism/PDD books and videos, as well as publications and audiovisual materials that are available for online ordering. The online library offers such titles as *Behavioral Interventions, Asperger's Syndrome, Little Rain Man,* and *Creating a "Win-Win" Individualized Education Program (IEP).* A listing of upcoming conferences relating to autism and a number of related links are also available.
http://www.futurehorizons-autism.com

On the Same Page: Asperger/Autism Informational Index A wide variety of interesting links are found in this large index of areas of interest to both professionals and lay people concerned with autism/Asperger's syndrome. Included are the "Asperger/Autism Rights," section; the "Asperger/Autism Bill of Rights" with position statements, self-advocacy, and behavioral supports; and a complete listing of links to relevant online journals. E-mail lists, bulletin boards, and support groups are also available at this comprehensive resource.
http://www.amug.org/~a203/table_contents.html

Syndrome of Hyperlexia versus High-Functioning Autism and Asperger's Syndrome This fact sheet, written by professionals from the Center for Speech and Language Disorders, presents information on the symptoms of these disorders and the differences between them in order to aid in differential diagnosis.
http://www.hyperlexia.org/gordy001.html

University Students with Autism and Asperger's Syndrome This site offers enlightening first-person accounts from individuals with Asperger's and autism. FAQs, books, and the University Students with Autism and Asperger's Syndrome mailing list are available.
http://www.users.dircon.co.uk/~cns/index.html

Childhood Disintegrative Disorder

Childhood Disintegrative Disorder A synopsis of childhood disintegrative disorder is offered at this page of the ThirdAge Web reference. Alternative names for the disorder; causes, incidence, and risk factors; and links to symptoms and treatment information are provided.
http://thirdage.adam.com/ency/article/001535.htm

Rett's Disorder

International Rett Syndrome Association The International Rett Syndrome Association home page, available for translation into multiple languages, offers information on breakthrough research, related news, patient education, and professional gatherings. Pages from the "Rettnet Digest" contain interesting posts and useful suggestions regarding communication and language, therapy, and special equipment, in addition to several other relevant topics. Per-

sonal stories of those afflicted with the disorder are found, and clinical information on Rett syndrome diagnosis, stages, and genetics is reviewed. A listing of upcoming scientific meetings, support groups and regional representatives, and a comprehensive listing of related resources can be found.
http://www.rettsyndrome.org

Rett Syndrome   A fact sheet on Rett Syndrome is presented on this site by the National Institute of Neurological Disorders and Stroke. An overview of the disorder is provided, along with its incidence, treatment options, and prognosis. References, as well as resources for further information, are provided.
http://www.ninds.nih.gov/health_and_medical/disorders/rett_doc.htm

9.22 SCHIZOPHRENIA AND OTHER PSYCHOTIC DISORDERS

GENERAL RESOURCES

Futurcom in Psychiatry   At this Web site, dedicated solely to schizophrenia and other psychoses, both professionals and the public can access articles on schizophrenia and psychoses from a variety of scientific journals, gather information on major international conferences, learn about the treatment products available, and get online educational information on schizophrenia.
(free registration) http://www.futur.com

BRIEF PSYCHOTIC DISORDER

Internet Mental Health: Brief Psychotic Disorder   Brief psychotic disorder, formerly known as brief reactive psychosis, is detailed at this site of the Internet Mental Health database. An American description of the illness includes diagnostic symptoms, episode duration, and other disorder comparisons, as well as specifications regarding onset of symptoms in relation to marked life stressors. Associated features and differential diagnoses are included. The European version, termed "acute and transient psychotic disorder," emphasizes acute stress, the absence of organic causes, and a rapidly changing and variable state. Internet links to psychotic disorder sites, psychotic disorder booklet connections, and instructions for accessing indexed literature on related, chosen subjects are available.
http://www.mentalhealth.com/dis/p20-ps03.html

DELUSIONAL DISORDER

Internet Mental Health: Delusional Disorder   Coverage of delusional disorder is found at this page of the Internet Mental Health database, where both American and European descriptions of the disorder may be accessed. Di-

agnostic criteria are outlined and subtypes to be assigned, based on predominant delusional theme, are recognized. Associated features and an extensive listing of differential diagnoses are included.
http://www.mentalhealth.com/dis/p20-ps02.html

Internet Mental Health: Delusional Disorder Research Topics
Articles related to delusional disorder research can be ordered through the Loansome Doc system at the National Library of Medicine. Users can search for articles categorized by topic. Some topics include classification, chemically induced delusion, complications, diagnosis, history, metabolism, prevention and control, rehabilitation, and many therapy topics.
http://www.mentalhealth.com/dis-rs/frs-ps02.html

PSYCHOTIC DISORDER NOT OTHERWISE SPECIFIED (NOS)

Psych Central: Psychotic Disorder Not Otherwise Specified This Mental Health page of Psych Central summarizes the category of psychotic symptomatology for which no specific diagnostic criteria are met. Example disorders are listed, such as postpartum psychosis and persistent auditory hallucinations in the absence of any other features. A link to the criteria for brief psychotic disorder is accessible for differential diagnosis information.
http://www.psychcentral.com/disorders/sx83.htm

SCHIZOAFFECTIVE DISORDER

Schizoaffective Disorder and Related Behaviors A registered nurse in the field of psychiatric nursing hosts this site, offering discussions of schizoaffective disorder, schizophrenia, mania, depression, and available treatments. A mental health resource directory, links to mental health sites, and links to mental health Internet reference sources, including general and professional articles, offer many valuable sources for additional information.
http://www.geocities.com/CollegePark/Classroom/6237

SCHIZOPHRENIA

Doctor's Guide: Schizophrenia Intended for patients and their families, this site offers resources on schizophrenia. There are news and alert items, along with general information on schizophrenia such as a definition, causes, symptoms, and treatment. There is also a discussion group, as well as a list of related sites.
http://www.docguide.com/news/content.nsf/
PatientResAllCateg/Schizophrenia?OpenDocument

Expert Consensus Guidelines: Treatment of Schizophrenia Full reprints of this expert consensus guidelines document, "Schizophrenia," from the *Journal of Clinical Psychiatry,* can be downloaded in Adobe Acrobat PDF format from this site. A companion guide for patients and families is also available to download. Both guides offer a wealth of useful information on schizophrenia and its treatment.
http://www.psychguides.com

Knowledge Exchange Network: Schizophrenia The most recent news stories related to schizophrenia are featured on this Web page. Dating back to December 1999, the stories are drawn from sources such as the *New York Times, CBS Healthwatch,* and the *BBC News.*
http://www.mentalhealth.org/newsroom/schizophreniaarchives.htm

Meador-Woodruff Laboratory Located in the Department of Psychiatry at the University of Michigan Medical Center, this laboratory's primary research focus is on brain communication via chemical signaling and its pathology in mental illness, such as in schizophrenia. Specific information on the pathophysiology of schizophrenia experiments is provided, as well as summaries of recent experimental information and findings on various aspects of brain research and schizophrenia. A comprehensive description of schizophrenia is also present. http://www.umich.edu/~jmwlab

National Alliance for Research on Schizophrenia and Depression This organization appropriates funds for research into the causes, cures, treatments, and prevention of schizophrenia, depression, and bipolar disorders. Information on the organization, access to its newsletter, and media news updates are included. Links to current events and announcements, educational materials, an information hotline, and a mailing list are provided. In addition, reading list, study participation, grant guidelines, and staff directory links are present.
http://www.mhsource.com/narsad.html

National Institute of Mental Health (NIMH): Schizophrenia A 28-page booklet on schizophrenia is provided on this Web page. Visitors can view it online or print it in PDF format. The booklet provides detailed information on the disease, including its causes, treatment options, how to help, and prognosis. Additional information available on the site includes fact sheets on schizophrenia, clinical trial information, conference proceedings, news releases, and a link to MEDLINE. http://www.nimh.nih.gov/publicat/schizmenu.cfm

Open the Doors: World Psychiatric Association Programme to Fight Stigma Due to Schizophrenia This international organization's Web site contains sections with resources for teens, families, and friends, as well as for professionals and scientists. In addition to details about the program itself, information is presented on the symptoms, physiological causes, societal problems related to schizophrenia, treatment, and the consequences of stigmatization. A large amount of information on support resources and links to related sites are provided. http://www.openthedoors.com/eng_home.html

Schizophrenia Provided by Magpie Publishing, this Web site has links to information on schizophrenia and the problem of suicide, symptoms, medication, alternative treatment, rehabilitation, research, and legal issues. A list of seminars and events, as well as companies and other contacts of interest, is included. A database of schizophrenia information, provided by Janssen Pharmaceuticals, is accessible through the site. Links to *Schizophrenia Digest,* a magazine devoted to the disorder; news updates; conference and meeting information; and success stories are provided.
http://www.vaxxine.com/schizophrenia

Schizophrenia Research Clinic As part of Yale University's Department of Psychiatry, this center promotes progress in schizophrenia and other psychotic disorder treatment. The *Schizophrenia Newsletter* is available online, as well as faculty directories, clinical sites, and other related links within Yale and on the Internet. http://www.med.yale.edu/psych/clinics/schizophrenia.html

Schizophrenia Therapy Online Resource Center The Anne Sippi Clinic offers a combination of medication and individual psychotherapy, in a residential setting, for the treatment of schizophrenia. This site offers a description of treatment facilities at the clinic, articles from program directors, personal stories, and an informative online brochure for consumers.
http://www.schizophreniatherapy.com

Schizophrenia-Help: Online Resource Center This resource center, provided by the Association for the Psychotherapy of Schizophrenia and the Anne Sippi Foundation, offers a discussion of the organization's philosophy, a newsletter of professional articles and archives, personal stories, and suggested reading. Links are available to the Anne Sippi Clinic and other related resources.
http://www.schizophrenia-help.com

Schizophrenia.com This not-for-profit Web site contains an extensive number of links to articles and fact files on schizophrenia information, such as causes, diagnosis, treatment, support groups, success stories, and assisted/involuntary treatment. There are links to more comprehensive information for professionals, such as funding organizations, related journals, discussion forums, and current research. For consumers, there are a number of links to basic information about schizophrenia, as well as support groups, treatment, academic and pharmaceutical research, health insurance, and many other topics. A site search engine allows users to search the database of sites by keyword.
http://www.schizophrenia.com

Schizophrenia.com: Information for People Who Have Schizophrenia
Information resources at this site devoted to schizophrenia include an introduction to neurobiologic disorders, personal stories, links to support resources and social centers, links to information on illegal drugs, and discussions and links to further information on causes, diagnosis, treatment, and medications. Links are also available to online education programs, employment resources for schizophrenics, clinical trials information for those wishing to participate, recom-

mended reading lists, and additional information resources for consumers and patients.   http://www.schizophrenia.com/newsletter/newpages/consumer.html

 P-1755 **World Psychiatric Association (WPA): Schizophrenia**   The World Psychiatric Association has launched a global anti-stigma campaign on schizophrenia. Visitors to the site will find a description of the program's activities, along with participants, under the "Global Programme" section. A section for healthcare professionals offers a guide to schizophrenia with a definition, symptoms, causes, detailed treatment information, and related Internet resources. Patients and families will find a section with facts on schizophrenia and information on misconceptions, stereotypes, and coping. Under the "Programme Participants" section, there are personal stories.
http://www.openthedoors.com/index_2.htm

Schizophreniform Disorder

 P-1756 **Internet Mental Health: Schizophreniform Disorder**   Internet Mental Health's chapter on schizophreniform disorder offers both the complete American and European descriptions of the disorder, in addition to current research, online booklets, and accessible magazine articles. The diagnostic criteria; associated features of the disorder; and differential diagnosis, including schizophrenia and brief psychotic disorder, are found. By clicking on a chosen subject at the research page, visitors will gain access to ready-made MEDLINE literature searches. http://www.mentalhealth.com/dis/p20-ps04.html

Shared Psychotic Disorder

 P-1757 **Shared Psychotic Disorder**   This Internet site offers visitors an overview of shared psychotic disorder, formerly known as induced psychotic disorder, with both American and European descriptions found. The "folie a deux," shared by two or more people with close emotional links, is explained, and the likely schizophrenic illness of the dominant person is explained. The American reference of the disorder contains three diagnostic criteria, associated features, and a listing of five differential diagnoses. Internet links to psychotic disorder sites may be found. http://www.mentalhealth.com/dis/p20-ps06.html

9.23 Self-Injurious Behavior

 P-1758 **Befrienders International: Self Harm**   Resources on self harm are featured on this Web page, including fact sheets directed specifically to young people and to women. Other resources available include a personal Web page, related Internet resources, and a help section. The "I Need Help!" section offers hotlines and services around the world, as well as e-mail support.
http://www.befrienders.org/directory/selfharm/

Links to Self-Injury Sites   Several sites related to self-injury can be accessed through this address. Support resources, personal stories, and organizations are included. Suggested books related to self-injury are also listed at the site. http://www.geocities.com/HotSprings/6446/selfinjury.html

Self-Injurious Behavior and Prader-Willi Syndrome   An abstract on self-injurious behavior and Prader-Willi syndrome is featured on this Web page, maintained by the Prader-Willi Syndrome Association. Specific forms and body locations of self-injury were studied among individuals with PWS and non PWS mental retardation. The results are described. http://www.pwsausa.org/Scnceday/13_SD_09.htm

Self-Injury Information and Support   Created by Deb Martinson, this Web page offers a broad array of resources for individuals who self-injure (SI) and their families. There are fact sheets on SI that cover what it is, why people do it, psychological profile of a self-injurer, and causes. There are brief descriptions of disorders often associated with SI. Treatment, coping, help for families and friends, and personal stories are provided. A list of support resources, an e-mail discussion list, a chat room, and a discussion board for friends and families are also available. A comprehensive listing of related Internet resources is provided. http://www.palace.net/~llama/psych/injury.html

Self-Injury Resources   A comprehensive listing of Internet resources on self-injury is provided here by NotVictims. There are more than 40 links to articles, organizations, personal stories, and Web pages. http://www.smalltime.com/notvictims/cutting.html

Self-Injury: Information and Resources   This United Kingdom - based site includes links to informative pages about different aspects of self-injury; a comprehensive introduction to the disorder, including a personal experience story; methods to cope with the disorder; lessening the damage; myths; support groups; online resources; links to other self-injury sites; and an online forum. http://www.selfinjury.freeserve.co.uk/

9.24 SEXUAL AND GENDER IDENTITY DISORDERS

GENDER IDENTITY DISORDERS

Gender Education and Advocacy: Gender Programs   More than 20 clinics offering structured sex reassignment programs are listed at this site. The listing indicates clinics with resident surgeons and provides detailed contact information. http://www.gender.org/resources/programs.html

Gender Web Project   In addition to providing links to forums and mailing lists related to gender identity issues, this site offers access to lists of scientific article abstracts, personal experiences, support groups, legal issues, and medical

information, including fact sheets and links to sites on psychiatric information on gender identity topics. A list of related links is included.
http://www.genderweb.org

Harry Benjamin International Gender Dysphoria Association, Inc.
This professional association is committed to the understanding and treatment of gender identity disorders, with members from the fields of psychiatry, endocrinology, surgery, psychology, sociology, and counseling. Site resources include general information about the association, details of the association's biennial conference, membership information, the full text of the *Benjamin Standards of Care for Gender Identity Disorders,* and links to related sites.
http://www.hbigda.org/

Ingersoll Gender Centre: Gender Dysphoria—A Sensitive Approach
The Ingersoll Gender Centre hosts this site devoted to patient information about gender dysphoria. The *Benjamin Standards of Care* text with definitions is available at the site. Topical discussions include suggestions on seeking help, self-esteem and self-doubt, family and other relationships, employment, name changes and other documents, insurance, and dealing with emotional crisis after a sex change. Detailed information is available on hormones, surgical procedures, and the effects of these therapies on the body. Suggested reading and sources for support and products are also available.
http://www.genderweb.org/medical/psych/dysphor.html

International Foundation for Gender Education (IFGE)
The IFGE promotes "the self-definition and free expression of individual gender identity," providing information and referrals to the public. The site offers news, information for support groups and other organizations, links to related sites, commentary, and an online bookstore. Information resources at this site include general definitions and discussions of cross-dressing and transgenderism, legal and medical information, and links to activist groups and friendly businesses. Tables of contents for current and archived issues of the organization's magazine, *Tapestry,* are also available at the site. http://www.ifge.org

Intersex Society of North America (ISNA)
The ISNA advocates and educates on behalf of individuals born with anatomy or physiology that differs from male and female cultural ideals. Their site offers a wealth of information including recommended books, the ISNA newsletter, online articles, FAQs, and treatment information. There are also fact sheets on the incidence of the condition, history, and legal rights. A comprehensive listing of related links is provided. http://www.isna.org/

PSYweb.com: Sexual and Gender Identity Disorders
Information on sexual and gender identity disorders at this site includes a general definition and list of subtypes. General descriptions of Adlerian, behavioral, existential, Gestalt, person-centered, psychoanalytic, rational-emotive, reality, and transactional analysis therapies are also available.
http://www.psyweb.com/Mdisord/sexd.html

Transgender Resources Visitors to this address will find a list of suggested books with links to Amazon.com for purchasing, as well as links to treatment centers and support groups.
http://www.drbanks.com/serious/transgender.html

KLINEFELTER'S SYNDROME

Understanding Klinefelter Syndrome: A Guide for XXY Males and Their Families A description of the syndrome, including the genetic causes, as well as the physical and cognitive problems, is presented in this report from the National Institutes of Health. Issues such as diagnosis, social and personal problems, detection of the syndrome, education, legal advice, and treatment and consequences are discussed. Overviews of topics related to this syndrome and its effects in different stages of life are present, as well as support information. http://www.nih.gov/health/chip/nichd/klinefelter

WebMD: Klinefelter's Syndrome A patient's guide to Klinefelter's syndrome is provided on this site. A definition of the condition is offered, along with its cause, symptoms, and diagnostic tests. Treatment options are discussed. Prognosis and the complications associated with the syndrome are examined.
http://webmd.lycos.com/content/asset/adam_disease_klinefelters_syndrome

SEXUAL DYSFUNCTIONS

Impotence Information Center Medic Drug's site on impotence offers links to fact sheets on the erectile process, impotence causes, treatment choices, implant types, premature ejaculation treatments, and related product information. http://www.medicdrug.com/impotence/impotence.html

Mental Health Net: Orgasmic Disorders The symptoms of both male and female orgasmic disorders are presented here, drawn from an American Psychiatric Association publication. Diagnostic criteria for each are described.
http://mentalhelp.net/disorders/sx58.htm

Merck Manual of Diagnosis and Therapy: Dyspareunia Painful coitus or attempted coitus is explained at this site of the online Merck publication, in addition to potential psychological factors involved. Inadequate stimulation, psychological inhibition of arousal, and other etiological features are discussed. Treatment of possible medical causes, such as cysts or abscesses, is summarized, and the prophylaxis of problems through patient education is emphasized.
http://www.merck.com/pubs/mmanual/section18/chapter243/243d.htm

Merck Manual of Diagnosis and Therapy: Female Orgasmic Disorder Orgasmic disorder, characterized as lifelong, acquired, general, or situational, is reviewed in this chapter of the online Merck reference. The etiological roles of

relationship conflict, traumatic experiences, and fear of losing control are introduced. Counseling measures to remove obstacles to orgasm are discussed.
http://www.merck.com/pubs/mmanual/section18/chapter243/243c.htm

Merck Manual of Diagnosis and Therapy: Sexual Arousal Disorder
Diminished capacity for sexual arousal, its etiology, and the distinction between decreased arousal and lessened desire is made at the site. Psychological and physical causes are reviewed, and an explanation of the importance of the history and physical exam is presented.
http://www.merck.com/pubs/mmanual/section18/chapter243/243b.htm

Merck Manual of Diagnosis and Therapy: Sexual Dysfunctions   This
general chapter on sexual dysfunctions presents information on proper sexual functioning, the sexual response cycle, and psychological factors involved in the etiology of lifelong and acquired dysfunction. Specific information regarding hypoactive sexual desire disorder, sexual aversion disorder, substance-induced disorder, male orgasmic dysfunction, and sexual dysfunction due to a physical disorder are differentiated.
http://www.merck.com/pubs/mmanual/section15/chapter192/192b.htm

Psych Central: Hypoactive Sexual Desire Disorder   A brief description
of the symptoms and diagnostic criteria for hypoactive sexual desire disorder is provided on this site. General Internet resources for a variety of disorders are also found.
http://psychcentral.com/disorders/sx56.htm

University of Sydney: Aversion Disorder   A fact sheet is provided on this
Web page that describes both hypoactive sexual desire and sexual aversion disorder. A definition and the causes of each disorder are described.
http://www.cchs.usyd.edu.au/bio/sex2000/desire_disorders.html

9.25 SLEEP DISORDERS

GENERAL RESOURCES

About.com: Sleep Disorders   Links available at this site are listed by
category, including chronic fatigue syndrome, circadian rhythm, dreams and nightmares, enuresis, herbal remedies, medication, restless legs syndrome, snoring, and treatment centers. News, articles, chat rooms, an online bookstore, and links to related About.com guides are also available from the site.
http://sleepdisorders.miningco.com/health/sleepdisorders

American Academy of Sleep Medicine (AASM)   Professionals will find
resources related to sleep medicine on this Web page. There are CME opportunities; an online catalog of educational products that includes slides, reference materials, and patient educational materials; and a legislative action center.

There are also fellowship training program details, fact sheets on sleep disorders, a directory of accredited sleep centers, and a short list of related links. http://www.aasmnet.org/

American Board of Sleep Medicine Information on certification by the American Board of Sleep Medicine, for physicians and Ph.D. applicants, is provided on this site. Eligibility requirements, maintaining certification, and exam dates are found. There is also a directory of diplomats, along with a link to the American Academy of Sleep Medicine.
http://www.absm.org/

AtHealth: Sleep Disorders A patient's guide to sleep disorders is featured on this site. Two major kinds of sleep disorders are covered: dyssomnias and parasomnias. Descriptions of dyssomnias include primary insomnia, primary hypersomnia, narcolepsy, breathing-related sleep disorders, and circadian rhythm sleep disorders. Parasomnias such as nightmare disorder, sleep terror disorder, and sleep-walking disorder are also described.
http://www.athealth.com/Consumer/disorders/Sleep.html

Basics of Sleep Behavior This online textbook, supported by the University of California Los Angeles Medical School, provides psychology students, clinicians, and other interested persons with a comprehensive overview of sleep behavior. Descriptive and detailed chapters, with related images and tables, include the basic characteristics and physiology of sleep, types of sleep, brain processes in sleep and waking, chemical and neuronal mechanisms, pharmacology of sleep, dreams, regulation of and functions of sleep, and alertness. Links to definitions used within the textbook and a reference guide are also present.
http://bisleep.medsch.ucla.edu/sleepsyllabus/sleephome.html

MEDLINEplus: Sleep Disorders Resources related to sleep disorders are provided on this site. There are news releases, overviews of the sleep process, alternative therapy information, and clinical trials. Information on getting a good night's sleep, current research, and fact sheets on specific conditions such as daytime sleepiness, narcolepsy, and sleep apnea are provided. Treatment information, a directory of sleep centers, statistics, and specific information for children, teenagers, and women are also found. Some publications are available in Spanish. http://www.nlm.nih.gov/medlineplus/sleepdisorders.html

National Center on Sleep Disorders Research Part of the National Institutes of Health, the National Center on Sleep Disorders Research offers information on sleep disorders for professionals and consumers. Professionals will find the center's research plan, funding opportunities, and publications on sleep disorders. There is also a short list of related sites. Patients will find an online interactive quiz, as well as fact sheets.
http://www.nhlbi.nih.gov/about/ncsdr/

National Center on Sleep Disorders Research: Patient Education
Part of the National Center on Sleep Disorders Research Web page, this site of-

fers patient information on sleep disorders. There is an interactive sleep quiz; online publications on disorders such as insomnia, narcolepsy, and sleep apnea; and a short list of related organizations.
http://www.nhlbisupport.com/sleep/patpub/patpub-a.htm

National Sleep Foundation (NSF)   The NSF, a nonprofit organization, offers a wide range of information for professionals and consumers on sleep. Their site offers brochures on such topics as the nature of sleep, sleep and shift work, sleep and aging, women and sleep, and sleep and the traveler. There are also newsletters, as well as fact sheets on sleep disorders. Information on NSF activities, advocacy information, an online marketplace, and a directory of sleep centers are provided. There is also a comprehensive listing of related Internet resources covering general information, support groups, professional societies, and international organizations.
http://www.sleepfoundation.org/

Northside Hospital Sleep Medicine Institute   This institute is dedicated to the assessment and treatment of sleep disorders. A summary of various sleep disorders symptoms is provided, in addition to information on pediatric sleep disorders, the facilities, a staff directory, an online sleep disorders test, and links to related sites.
http://nshsleep.com

Sleep Home Pages   Bibliographic article lists, publications, funding opportunities, training information, research chat forums, and other resources are available at this site. The site offers direct links to features of use to researchers, clinical professionals, and the public, including professional, scientific, and support organizations. Excessive daytime sleepiness, adolescent sleep, sleep and cognitive function, sleep and health, and the management of insomnia are discussed. Most resources are designed for use by investigators and clinicians. http://bisleep.medsch.ucla.edu

Sleep Medicine   This site contains a large number of links to online resources related to sleep disorders. Included are links to information about sleep discussion groups and FAQs, abstracts, sleep disorder sites, clinical practice text files from the National Institutes of Health, professional associations, organizations, journals, medications, research sites, conferences, federal and state information, related products, and other mental health sites.
http://www.users.cloud9.net/~thorpy

SleepNet   Resources at this address include a general site description, historical and background information on sleep disorders, trends in current research, public and professional chat forums, a weekly column, and disorder fact sheets. Links are provided to support groups, professional organizations, information on dreams, sleep deprivation information, research resources, news, and sleep laboratories. http://www.sleepnet.com

DYSSOMNIAS

About.com: Circadian Rhythm Abnormalities Circadian rhythm disorder is described on this site. Brief articles are provided on the biological clock, circadian rhythm sleep disorder, worker safety, and a historical background on the condition.
http://sleepdisorders.about.com/health/sleepdisorders/msubcircadian.htm

American Sleep Apnea Association This organization is dedicated to reducing injury, disability, and death from sleep apnea, as well as to enhancing the well-being of those affected by this common disorder. General information and personal stories, publications, support groups, membership details, and links to related sleep medicine sites are found at this address. Visitors can e-mail questions to a doctor or lawyer or request a general information packet from the organization.
http://www.sleepapnea.org

Center for Narcolepsy The Stamford University School of Medicine includes this center, whose Web site has information on symptoms, treatment options, drug information, and a comprehensive overview of the Center's research on the disorder. A publications list, a staff list, and a list of relevant links are included.
http://www.med.stanford.edu/school/Psychiatry/narcolepsy/

Evaluation and Management of Insomnia This issue of *Hospital Practice* provides an online version of an article relaying the diverse causes of insomnia and its proper evaluation and treatment. Authored by a physician from the University of Colorado Health Sciences Center, the article provides information on the circadian rhythm of sleep; sleep cycles and associated brain wave patterns; and age-related changes in sleep patterns. The structure of sleep, depending on age, is illustrated via online graphs, and recommendations are made addressing the complaints of insomnia in older patients. The etiology of insomnia and guidelines for evaluation and referral are presented. Management strategies described include behavior modification practices, exercise, and drug treatments. A table outlining the pharmacokinetic properties of these therapies is found, and differentiation is made between short/intermediate-acting and long-acting benzodiazepines.
http://www.hosppract.com/issues/1998/12/meyer.htm

HealthinMind.com: Primary Insomnia Visitors will find a fact sheet on primary insomnia on this site. A description of the condition, its symptoms, diagnostic criteria, and treatment are provided. Recommended books and Web sites are found.
http://healthinmind.com/english/primary_insomnia.htm

HealthinMind.com: Sleep Apnea A short description of sleep apnea is provided on this site. Symptoms, the causes, and similar sleep disorders are described. There is a link to another site on sleep apnea that includes personal stories and facts on the condition.   http://healthinmind.com/english/sleepapnea.htm

 Psych Central: Circadian Rhythm Sleep Disorder   The symptoms of circadian rhythm sleep disorder are presented on this site, including a pattern of sleep disruption and impairment in important areas of function.
http://psychcentral.com/disorders/sx92.htm

PARASOMNIAS

 Parasomnias   Disruptive sleep events, such as sleepwalking, sleep terrors, and nocturnal bruxism, are summarized at this site of the About.com online resource. http://sleepdisorders.about.com/health/sleepdisorders

 Parasomnias: Sleepwalking, Sleeptalking, Nightmares, Sleep Terrors, Sleep Eating   The information at the site, provided by the National Sleep Foundation, describes several sleep disorders of arousal and sleep-stage transition. Summaries of sleepwalking, sleeptalking, nightmares, sleep terrors, and sleep eating are found, along with each synopsis discussing possible causes and common concerns related to the disorder.
http://www.healthtouch.com/bin/EContent_HT/hdShowLfts.asp?lftname=SLEEP006&cid=H THLTH&print=yes

9.26 SOMATOFORM DISORDERS

GENERAL RESOURCES

 BehaveNet: DSM-IV Somatoform Disorders   This site provides definitions of body dysmorphic disorder, conversion disorder, hypochondriasis, pain disorder, somatization disorder, undifferentiated somatoform disorder, and factitious disorder. Ordering information is available for the American Psychiatric Association DSM-IV, related publications, and books and other media through Amazon.com.
http://www.behavenet.com/capsules/disorders/somatoformdis.htm

 International Society of Psychosomatic Obstetrics and Gynecology   The International Society of Psychosomatic Obstetrics and Gynecology promotes the study of the psychobiological, psychosocial, ethical, and cross-cultural problems in the fields of obstetrics and gynecology. This site presents the objectives of the society, as well as a newsletter and links to local chapters. Free online access to the abstracts of the *Journal of Psychosomatic Obstetrics and Gynecology* is available, as well as links to information on international meetings and congresses. Additional related links are also available.
http://ispog.org/

Merck Manual of Diagnosis and Therapy: Somatoform Disorders An overview of somatoform disorders—psychiatric disorders with physical symptoms—is featured on this Web page, courtesy of Merck. Written in clinical terms, the overview presents the causes, symptoms, diagnosis, treatment, and prognosis for somatization disorder, conversion disorder, and hypochondria. Although it isn't a somatoform disorder, there is also a discussion of Munchausen syndrome. http://www.merck.com/pubs/mmanual_home/sec7/82.htm

Somatoform Disorders This descriptive article provides an overview of the different somatoform disorders, including conversion, pain, hypochondriac behavior, and body dysmorphic disorders. Diagnostic criteria, symptoms, overviews of the specific disorders, and epidemiology and differential diagnosis are included in the discussion.
http://www.uams.edu/department_of_psychiatry/syllabus/somatoform/somatoform.htm

Somatoform Disorders Outline This site contains a concise outline of the characteristics and specific types of somatoform disorders, adapted from the American Psychiatric Association DSM-IV, 1994.
http://clem.mscd.edu/~hsp/syllabi/4320/somatoform.html

BODY DYSMORPHIC DISORDER

Body Dysmorphic Disorder A thorough explanation of body dysmorphic disorder is available at this site. DSM-IV diagnostic criteria for the disorder are available, and links to several related sites are provided. Visitors can also find information on many eating disorders and related topics through this address.
http://www.sfwed.org/whatarethey/other.php#bdd

Body Dysmorphic Disorder (BDD): A Common but Underdiagnosed Clinical Entity First appearing in *Psychiatric Times,* this article describes BDD, its psychiatric history, symptoms, behavioral and social consequences, incidence, and behavior therapies, with references provided.
http://www.mhsource.com/pt/p980111.html

Discovery Channel Canada: A news story on the condition, bigorexia, is presented on this site. The article explains how individuals with bigorexia see themselves as too small and often become weight-lifters to make themselves bigger. The physiological and psychological components of the condition are explored. Treatment is also examined. http://exn.ca/Stories/2000/01/11/57.cfm

HomeArts: Body Image - Body Dysmorphic Disorder Quiz Body dysmorphic disorder is discussed at this consumer site. A description of the disorder and general discussion of prevalence is followed by a short questionnaire, designed to assess concerns about physical appearance. Users can complete the questionnaire and receive immediate results. Questionnaire results are accompanied by links to several related pages within the site.
http://www.homearts.com/depts/health/12bodqz1.htm

Merck Manual of Diagnosis and Therapy: Body Dysmorphic Disorder This address offers a short discussion of body dysmorphic disorder, including a definition and overview of symptoms, diagnosis, and treatment. Links are available to information on related disorders within the manual.
http://www.merck.com/pubs/mmanual/section15/chapter186/186f.htm

Muscle Dysmorphia Basic information on muscle dysmorphia at this site includes a definition of this disorder, its symptoms, its effects, and treatment.
http://anred.com/musdys.html

CONVERSION DISORDER

Merck Manual of Diagnosis and Therapy: Conversion Disorder A short discussion of conversion disorder at this address includes a definition and information on symptoms, diagnosis, and possible treatments. Links are available to information on related disorders within the manual.
http://www.merck.com/pubs/mmanual/section15/chapter186/186c.htm

Psych Central: Conversion Disorder The symptoms and diagnostic criteria associated with conversion disorder are outlined on this site. These criteria are derived from standards outlined by the American Psychiatric Association. http://psychcentral.com/disorders/sx43.htm

HYPOCHONDRIASIS

Hypochondria A fact sheet on hypochondria is provided on this Web page, maintained by the University of Bergen, Norway. The disorder is described, along with diagnosis, typical symptoms, and treatment. Current research, along with a self-test, is provided on the site.
http://www.uib.no/med/avd/med_a/gastro/wilhelms/hypochon.html

Hypochondria Self-Test Part of a larger hypochondria Web page, hosted by the University of Bergen, Norway, this site offers a self-test for hypochondria. A list of questions is provided, along with what the results mean. Advice on when to see one's doctor is provided.
http://www.uib.no/med/avd/med_a/gastro/wilhelms/whiteley.html

Merck Manual of Diagnosis and Therapy: Hypochondriasis Hypochondriasis is described briefly at this site, offering an overview of symptoms, diagnosis, prognosis, and treatment. Links are available to information on related disorders within the manual.
http://www.merck.com/pubs/mmanual/section15/chapter186/186d.htm

PAIN DISORDER

Merck Manual of Diagnosis and Therapy: Pain Disorder   This site offers information on pain disorder, including a definition and descriptions of symptoms, signs, diagnosis, and suggested treatment. Links are available to information on related disorders within the manual.
http://www.merck.com/pubs/mmanual/section15/chapter186/186e.htm

Psych Central: Pain Disorder   Examining pain disorder, this site presents its symptoms and diagnostic criteria. Information is drawn from the American Psychiatric Association's diagnostic manual.
http://psychcentral.com/disorders/sx61.htm

SOMATIZATION DISORDER

Postgraduate Medicine: Somatization Disorder   A full-text article on somatization disorder is provided on this Web page from the November 2000 issue of *Postgraduate Medicine*. The article examines a simplified approach to patients with somatization disorder. Characteristics of the patient are outlined, along with a strategy of listening more than treating. The unlikelihood of effective treatment is emphasized. Physicians are advised on the importance of regular brief visits and reassurance, as well as on the high incidence of depression and anxiety in this group. Psychotherapy and antidepressant medications are discussed. A bibliography and a list of related online articles are provided.
http://www.postgradmed.com/issues/2000/11_00/holloway.htm

Somatization Disorder   Pain, gastrointestinal, sexual, and pseudoneurological symptoms characteristic of somatization disorder are listed at the Web site, as well as additional criteria for making an appropriate diagnosis.
http://bipolar.cmhc.com/disorders/sx94.htm

9.27 SUBSTANCE-RELATED DISORDERS

GENERAL RESOURCES

Addiction Technology Transfer Center of New England (ATTC)   In an effort to exchange resources, promote culturally competent treatment services, and translate and disseminate research-based substance abuse information, the ATTC Web site provides online patient and professional education and resources. Useful links include upcoming conferences and training opportunities, multicultural and special population resources, an academia resource list, and the national ATTC product catalog. Connections to tobacco-related Web sites and prominent mental health organizations such as the Centers for Mental

Health Services and the Center for Disease Control and Prevention can be found.   http://center.butler.brown.edu/ATTC-NE

Addiction Treatment Forum   Devoted to issues surrounding addictions and their treatments, the Addiction Treatment Forum provides professionals and consumers with online articles, updates on treatment and medication news, references to written information on addiction, and current conference and events schedules. There are also a number of links to addiction-related sites.
http://www.atforum.com

American Academy of Addiction Psychiatry   Informational links on the academy and membership, as well as the different committees and policy statements, are provided. Links to details concerning previous, present, and future annual meetings; Accreditation Council for Graduate Medical Education (ACGME) information; and an online store for reference tapes and other materials are present.
http://www.aaap.org

American Council for Drug Education   Information on substance abuse is available on this site for health professionals, parents, college students, educators, youth, and employers. Professionals will find a physician's guide to youth substance abuse, tools for mental health professionals, and fact sheets on drugs. For parents, resources include advice on talking to children about drugs, information on drugs and pregnancy, symptoms of drug use, and youth drug use statistics. College students can link to the "Facts on Tap" Web site for information on alcohol and student life. For educators, there are lesson plans, a newsletter, and tips for talking to students about drugs. Children will find an interactive quiz, along with an art gallery. In addition, there are resources for employers that include model workplace programs, along with information on drug and alcohol in the workplace.   http://www.acde.org/

American Society of Addiction Medicine (ASAM)   The American Society of Addiction Medicine aims to educate physicians and improve the "treatment of individuals suffering from alcoholism and other addictions." Medical news items related to addiction treatment, clinical trials, practice guidelines, and other topics are available at the site. Publications offered at the site include practice guidelines, Chapter One of ASAM's *Principles of Addiction Medicine,* newsletters, patient placement criteria, and the table of contents and abstracts for the *Journal of Addictive Diseases.* General information about ASAM, activities of the AIDS and HIV Committee of ASAM, a physician directory, certification resources, discussion forums, resources on nicotine addiction, pain management information, and links to related sites are all found at this address. http://www.asam.org

Association for Medical Education and Research in Substance Abuse
The Web site for this multidisciplinary organization of professionals interested in substance abuse has links to the mission statement, organization and mem-

bership information, conference information, an online discussion group, and a link to the table of contents for the journal, *Substance Abuse*.
http://www.amersa.org

Center for Education and Drug Abuse Research Funded by the National Institute on Drug Abuse, the center is a collaborative effort of the University of Pittsburgh and St. Francis Medical Center. The Web site provides information on the mission, goals, experimental designs, research findings and faculty, research modules overviews, training, and an education faculty list.
http://cedar.pharmacy.pitt.edu/main.html

Center for Online Addiction The Center For Online Addiction provides resources on the psychology of cyberspace addiction. Risk factors involved, an online Internet addiction test, and treatment options for those addicted are available. A series of nationwide conferences and events as well as helpful links to online booklets, research, and resources on what makes certain Internet applications so time-consuming are offered. Additionally, a "Virtual Clinic" provides online e-mail, chat room, or telephone counseling as necessary.
http://www.netaddiction.com/

Center for Substance Abuse Prevention Funded by the federal government, this training service offers technical assistance to communities and professionals on program development, fundraising, coalition building, and multicultural communication. A basic overview of the center, as well as criteria for technical assistance services applications evaluations is provided.
http://www.covesoft.com/csap.html

Centre for Addiction and Mental Health The Web site for the Ontario-based Centre for Addiction and Mental Health offers drug and alcohol fact sheets and brochures, statistics, FAQs, public education materials, a list of staff publications, and links to sites providing additional information. Users can also access information on materials available at their library, including a searchable library catalog, audiovisual subject lists, and a bibliography of library materials listed by subject. Professionals can access information on training courses and materials, and order publications from an online catalog. All resources are available in French and English.
http://www.camh.net

Columbia University: National Center on Addiction and Substance Abuse This national center provides the public with information on substance abuse and its impact on peoples' lives, prevention, treatment, and law enforcement. Full-text articles from the center are available at the site, as well as information on research activities and training programs, links to federal resources, grants and funding resources, resources for children and teens, and answers to FAQs. http://www.casacolumbia.org/information1455/information.htm

Drug Abuse Research Center As part of the University of California Los Angeles, this research center is part of a larger drug abuse research consortium.

A list of summaries for the over 30 current drug abuse research projects, as well as past projects, is provided at this site. In addition, a list of the many publications, which can be ordered online, is available. Fellowship and other educational opportunities, ethnic issues projects, and research training information is obtainable. Links to other appropriate sites are present.
http://www.medsch.ucla.edu/som/npi/DARC

Higher Education Center for Alcohol and Other Drug Prevention
Part of the U.S. Department of Education and supported by the Robert Wood Johnson Foundation, the center's primary mission is to provide support to higher education institutions in their attempt to resolve alcohol and other drug abuse problems. Free online access to many related publications, links to information on learning opportunities, consultation services, and staff presentations are available. A number of links to other useful resources, as well as related databases, mailing lists, and other services, are present.
http://www.edc.org/hec

Knowledge Exchange Network: Substance Abuse/Addiction
A variety of links to those in need of information and support for alcohol and drug abuse is provided at this Web page. Links include Mental Health Net and the National Clearinghouse for Alcohol and Drug Information (NCADI). Of particular interest is information on Web sites offering therapeutic options for addicts. Included are SMART Recovery, an abstinence-based alternative to Alcoholics Anonymous (AA), and the World Wide Web Rational Recovery Center, which presents an Internet Course on Rational Recovery, another 12-step alternative.   http://www.mentalhealth.org/links/substanceabuse.htm

Mid-Atlantic Addiction Technology Transfer Center
This Web site offers current research on treatment for addiction. Links include addiction education programs, related conferences, access to technical publications, a newsletter, and a list of other addiction technology transfer centers. There are a large number of links, divided into categories such as substance abuse, drug and alcohol information, government and professional organizations, research and addiction, and treatment and prevention.
http://www.mid-attc.org

National Clearinghouse for Alcohol and Drug Information (NCADI): Prevention Online
This comprehensive site, a service of the Substance Abuse and Mental Health Services Administration, offers valuable resources on drug use and abuse prevention for professionals and the general public. Links are provided to databases offering directories of prevention services, research summaries, conference reports, journal articles, and public education documents. Professional resources include monthly research briefs, a conference calendar, information on the latest research, funding and grants information, and links to important online forums. Publications on workplace issues are available for professionals and employers. Other resources include links to treatment organizations, information on funding opportunities, drug testing guidelines, a

list of laboratories meeting minimum standards for urine drug testing, resources for runaways, and information on Addiction Technology Transfer Centers. The catalog section lists available online publications from NCADI, presented by subject and audience. The online publications offer an abundance of resources for educators, family, and friends; health professionals and clinicians; scientists and researchers; teens/youth; and women. Spanish publications are also listed. Alcohol and drug fact sheets, media resources, and resources for children are also available.
http://www.health.org

National Institute on Drug Abuse (NIDA) As part of the National Institutes of Health (NIH), this organization supports international research, advocacy, and education on drug abuse and related issues. The site provides information on the mission and goals of the organization; a list of descriptive fact sheets on commonly abused drugs and their treatment; and links to publications, monographs, teaching materials, and reports on various aspects of substance abuse and addiction. Information on conferences, including summaries of previous meetings; relevant news articles; funding and training opportunities; advocacy items; a clinical trial network; employment listings; and related links are also available at this site.
http://www.nida.nih.gov/NIDAHome1.html

National Institute on Drug Abuse (NIDA): Trends and Statistics More than 25 articles on trends in drug abuse are presented on this site. There are fact sheets addressing costs to society, adolescent drug abuse, hospital visits and deaths, national trends, and drug abuse during pregnancy. There are also articles on drug abuse trends from the NIDA newsletter, news releases, and links to other sources for information.
http://www.nida.nih.gov/DrugPages/Stats.html

Recovery Resources Online More than 2,100 Internet links in more than 50 categories related to recovery from substance abuse, mental disorders, eating disorders, and anxiety are provided on this site. Categories include Alcoholics Anonymous meetings, anxiety disorders, online counseling, residential treatment facilities, mental health recovery, eating disorder treatment, grief and loss, and narcotics anonymous. There are also discussion boards for a variety of topics under "Support Forums.
http://www.soberrecovery.com/

Research Institute on Addictions Part of the University of Buffalo, this institute's Web page offers a list of current and past research projects, as well as online access to full-length articles and presentations from the institute's faculty and staff. In addition, abstracts and summaries of related research studies performed at the institute are available. A list of online documents at this site is given, as well as investigator and scientist directories. http://www.ria.org

Substance Abuse and Mental Health Services Administration (SAMHSA) The official Web site for the substance abuse and mental health

agency for the U.S. Department of Health and Human Services, this page offers program information databases, information on substance abuse and mental health issues, and statistics. Links to other related centers are provided, as well as links to general information on substance abuse and mental health problems. http://www.samhsa.gov

Web of Addictions This award-winning site provides information on drug and alcohol addictions. The drug information database has an extensive number of fact sheets on the different drug issues, as well as technical information on the drugs themselves. Also included are links to meetings and conferences, support groups, and associations related to substance abuse. http://www.well.com/user/woa

ALCOHOL-RELATED DISORDERS

Al-Anon/Alateen Organization Al-Anon and Alateen are part of a worldwide organization providing a self-help recovery program for families and friends of alcoholics. Resources available at this official site include meeting information; the 12 steps, traditions, and concepts of the programs; information on Alateen; pamphlets; suggested readings and videotapes; and an online newsletter. Professional resources include information on the organization, reasons people are referred to Al-Anon/Alateen, a description of group activities and how they help, and details of how Al-Anon/Alateen cooperates with professionals. http://www.al-anon.org

Alcoholism Index This comprehensive Web site has links to information under a number of topics regarding alcoholism, such as related organizations, drunk driving, relationships, health, information, support groups, treatment, and personal pages. Mental health information includes links to alcoholism and psychiatry, as well as to related disorders, such as depression, suicide, denial, and bipolar disorder.
http://www.alcoholismhelp.com/index

Alcoholism/Treatment For individuals exploring the possibility of alcoholism in themselves or loved ones, the site offers general but in-depth information on the signs and symptoms of alcoholism. After a brief self-diagnosis, the user can gain access to treatment-oriented Web sites, including the Betty Ford Center, the Hazleden Center, and a 12-step overview Web site. Alcoholism experts can be directly e-mailed with questions.
http://www.alcoholismtreatment.org

Center for Alcohol and Addiction Studies Devoted to the study of addiction and alcohol and located in Brown University, the Center for Alcohol and Addiction Studies provides at this address information on training, research news, an online forum, a number of links to medical resources and other related sites. The annual report is available online; topics include new grants and pro-

jects, research activities, medical education and clinical training, research training, a faculty directory and publications list.
http://center.butler.brown.edu/98report/activities.html

Children of Alcoholics Foundation Dedicated to breaking the cycle of substance abuse between generations, the Children of Alcoholics Foundation offers a broad array of resources to consumers and professionals. For children of alcoholics (COAs) and children of substance abusers (COSAs), there is a guide to help the children cope with their families; information for adult COAs/COSAs; and personal coping stories. A section of the site is dedicated to professionals, including health professionals, teachers, and social workers, and contains facts on COA/COSAs, training information, research findings, and publications on communication. In addition, there are resources specific to caregivers and to college students. The site also contains information on the foundation's programs, training courses, and publications. Research information, support, and related Internet links are provided.
http://www.coaf.org/

Internet Alcohol Recovery Center Provided by the University of Pennsylvania Health System, this online center provides information for both consumers and professionals. Consumer resources include treatment information, a reference list to substance abuse topics, help directories, and online forums. Professional resources include treatment information, a substance abuse reference list, alcohol-related news, and a comprehensive fact file on naltrexone for alcohol dependence treatment. http://www.med.upenn.edu/~recovery

National Association for Children of Alcoholics (NACoA) Created by the National Association for Children of Alcoholics, this Web page offers resources related to surviving alcoholic families. There are articles covering topics such as the facts about alcoholism and the importance of support groups, teachers, and physicians. In addition, a "Just for Kids" section offers children of alcoholics facts, coping information, inspirational messages, and online resources. There is also an online catalog of publications and videos. Research information, a recommended reading list, and a list of Internet links are provided.
http://www.nacoa.net/

National Institute on Alcohol Abuse and Alcoholism (NIAAA) The National Institute on Alcohol Abuse and Alcoholism supports and conducts biomedical and behavioral research on the causes, consequences, treatment, and prevention of alcoholism and alcohol-related problems. Legislative activities, scientific review groups, and other activities of the institute are described at the site, and users can also access a staff directory and employment announcements. The site provides professional online publications, conference and events calendars, research program information, links to other sites of interest, and answers to FAQs. Users can also access fact sheets, MEDLINE, and ETOH, a database of alcohol-related research findings, through this site.
http://www.niaaa.nih.gov

Pittsburgh Adolescent Alcohol Research Center (PAARC) This site dedicates itself to the accomplishments of the center, including the generation of more than 150 publications, and over 170 presentations and the sponsorship of two scientific conferences. Also outlined is an overview of the center's research training and major projects and studies conducted.
http://www.pitt.edu/~paarc/paarc.html

Psychoanalytic Perspective on the Problematic Use of Alcohol This Web site's goal is the promotion of awareness of the psychoanalytic contributions to issues related to alcohol misuse. The psychoanalytic view of alcoholism is presented explaining many of the contributing factors leading to compulsive drinking. http://www.cyberpsych.org/alcohol/main.htm

Wernicke-Korsakoff Syndrome (Alcohol-Related Dementia) In this fact sheet, the syndrome is defined and the biological causes are discussed. Also, an overview of the related symptoms, diagnostic procedures, treatment options, and familial issues is presented. Caregiver information and references are provided. This site is offered by the Family Caregiver Alliance.
http://www.caregiver.org/factsheets/wks.html

Amphetamine-Related Disorders

Internet Mental Health: Amphetamine Dependence Amphetamine dependence leading to significant social and medical impairment is explained at the Internet Mental Health database, with connections to both American and European descriptions of the disorder. Withdrawal symptoms, greater use of the drug than intended, and other signs and diagnostic criteria are outlined. Several criteria are described at the European diagnostic page, and an online diagnostic quiz assists the practitioner in diagnosis. An introduction to management of amphetamine dependence outlines the basic principles of hospitalization, medications, and psychosocial intervention.
http://www.mentalhealth.com/dis/p20-sb02.html

MEDLINEplus: Amphetamine Abuse Resources on amphetamine abuse are provided on this Web page. There are overviews, news, clinical trials, and information on specific aspects of methamphetamine abuse. Statistics, teenagers and drugs, and related organizations are also topics of interest. Some publications are available in Spanish.
http://www.nlm.nih.gov/medlineplus/amphetamineabuse.html

National Institute on Drug Abuse (NIDA): Methamphetamine A broad array of information on methamphetamine is presented on this site, by the National Institute on Drug Abuse. There is a NIDA research report on methamphetamine abuse, a fact sheet, brochures, and information on a youth program to prevent drug abuse. In addition, NIDA newsletter articles are provided. There are also news releases and a link to MEDLINEplus for additional information. http://www.nida.nih.gov/DrugPages/Methamphetamine.html

Anabolic Steroid Abuse

National Institute on Drug Abuse (NIDA): Anabolic Steroids The National Institute on Drug Abuse offers resources related to anabolic steroid abuse on this site. There are fact sheets, a research report, and articles on steroid abuse. In addition, links to related Internet sources, as well as news stories, are provided. http://www.nida.nih.gov/DrugPages/Steroids.html

Caffeine-Related Disorders

Caffeine Dependence A news review of a 1994 study from JAMA identifies "caffeine dependence syndrome" and reviews the criteria for this substance-abuse diagnosis. Questions are raised regarding the regulation of caffeine products. http://ndsn.org/SEPOCT94/CAFFEINE.html

Cannabis-Related Disorders

Internet Mental Health: Cannabis Dependence Internet Mental Health provides visitors with an American and European description of cannabis dependence, its causes, typical patterns of behavior, and associated features. An online diagnosis may assist the therapist or patient in assessment, and a treatment introduction, including medical and psychosocial principles, is found. Fact sheets on marijuana use are available, and a magazine article describing the long-term brain impairment associated with cannabis dependence is accessible. http://www.mentalhealth.com/dis/p20-sb03.html

MEDLINEplus: Marijuana Abuse Information on marijuana abuse is provided on this site under categories such as overviews, research, and treatment. Articles on specific conditions cover the adverse effects of marijuana, the brain's response, and medical myths. Statistics, related organizations, and information on teenagers and children are also found. Some publications are available in Spanish. http://www.nlm.nih.gov/medlineplus/marijuanaabuse.html

Cocaine-Related Disorders

Internet Mental Health: Cocaine Dependence Characteristics of cocaine abuse and the American criteria for dependence may be accessed from this page of the Internet Mental Health database. Cocaine tolerance, withdrawal symptoms, and continued usage despite recurrent related physical and psychological problems are explained, and recognized associated features are listed. The European description of "cocaine dependence syndrome" is outlined, and an online diagnostic quiz is provided, which may be answered by ei-

ther the patient or the therapist. An external link to treatment guidelines for patients with substance-abuse disorders may be accessed.
http://www.mentalhealth.com/dis/p20-sb04.html

MEDLINEplus: Cocaine Abuse   The purpose of this site is to provide resources for information on cocaine abuse. Of interest to consumers and professionals, the site offers news, general information on cocaine, clinical trials, and several articles on research findings. Specific aspects of cocaine abuse are addressed such as use during pregnancy and the gradual addiction of the drug. Treatment information is provided, as well as statistics, teen information, and related organizations.
http://www.nlm.nih.gov/medlineplus/cocaineabuse.html

DUAL DIAGNOSIS

Dual Diagnosis   This site is designed to provide information and resources for service providers, consumers, and family members seeking assistance and/or education in the field of dual diagnosis, which is the co-occurrence of mental illness with drug/alcohol addiction. Features include a glossary of terms, clinical profiles of dual diagnosis, an education and upcoming training event section, and dual diagnosis literature. A bulletin board provides information on resources for dual diagnosis services, such as those pertaining to grants and legislation, and other pertinent resources. A 24-hour chat room and LISTSERV are available, as is the Dual Diagnosis Directory of Programs and Services.
http://users.erols.com/ksciacca

GAINS National Center for People with Co-occurring Disorders in the Justice System   At the GAINS Center Web site, the organization's role as a national center for the collection and dissemination of information regarding mental health and substance abuse in those who come in contact with the justice system is described. The center's primary goals, agenda, and functions are outlined, including information on technical services offered, publications produced, and the organization's sponsoring agencies and approaches. Programs to break the cycle of those who repeatedly enter the criminal justice system, such as the Jail Diversion Knowledge Development and Application Program, are discussed.
http://www.prainc.com/gains/index.html

Parallel Paths of Recovery Support Group   The Parallel Paths of Recovery site describes itself as a resource center and support group for those with a mental illness and an addictive disorder. The "Resource Library" contains fact sheets on a variety of disorders including anxiety, depression, and obsessive-compulsive disorder. In the same section, there are links to several drug databases, and a medical dictionary. Web links on the site offer 12-step programs, as well as information on advocacy, mental health, dual diagnosis, and

support groups. The site also has its own online support group, with message boards and a chat area.
http://www.parallel-paths.org/

ECSTACY

National Institute on Drug Abuse (NIDA): MDMA (Ecstasy)   Site contents, focused on MDMA, also known as Ecstacy, include a fact sheet on Ecstacy, general publications on drug abuse, National Institute on Drug Abuse articles on Ecstacy, and news releases. There is also a link for further information from MEDLINEplus.
http://www.nida.nih.gov/DrugPages/MDMA.html

HALLUCINOGEN-RELATED DISORDERS

Internet Mental Health: Hallucinogen Dependence   At this Internet Mental Health site is an online diagnostic tool provided to assist the therapist with assessment or to give the patient a better self-understanding of this condition. The American description of hallucinogen abuse and several associated features of dependence are reviewed. The European description, termed "hallucinogen dependence syndrome" and derived from the ICD-10 Classification of Mental and Behavioral Disorders, is also found. Treatment recommendations may include antianxiety, antipsychotic, and antidepressant agents, as well as psychosocial interventions described at the site. A concise introduction to the Narcotics Anonymous program is offered.
http://www.mentalhealth.com/dis/p20-sb05.html

National Institute on Drug Abuse (NIDA): Acid/LSD   Visitors to this site will find information on acid/LSD. There is a fact sheet, along with publications on community drug awareness programs and teen drug abuse prevention. In addition, there is a link to MEDLINEplus for additional information.
http://www.nida.nih.gov/DrugPages/ACIDLSD.html

INHALANT-RELATED DISORDERS

Inhalant Dependence   An online diagnosis, for use by either therapist or patient; introductions to both medical and psychosocial interventions; and complete descriptions of both the American and European diagnostic criteria for inhalant dependence are found, outlining the destructive patterns commonly occurring with abuse of this substance. Internet Mental Health's "Booklets" links contain further information on substance abuse, and connections to substance-related disorder sites are accessible.
http://www.mentalhealth.com/dis/p20-sb06.html

Inhalant Disorders Lecture notes from a University of Tennessee College of Pharmacy course on substance disorders are posted on this site. The notes primarily focus on inhalant-induced disorders. The DSM IV criteria for intoxication are listed, along with medical complications. Inhalants covered include nitrous oxide and volatile nitrates. Additional information on the site includes opioid-related disorders and abuse of phencyclidine (PCP), marijuana, and steroids. http://pharmacy.utmem.edu/classof2001/notes/Ther4Exam1/021500B.htm

 National Institute on Drug Abuse (NIDA): Inhalants For those concerned about inhalant abuse, the National Institute on Drug Abuse Web site offers a NIDA research report, fact sheet, and articles on the topic. There is also a link for more information, along with a publication on preventing drug abuse in teenagers.
http://www.nida.nih.gov/DrugPages/Inhalants.html

NICOTINE-RELATED DISORDERS

 Internet Mental Health: Nicotine Dependence The destructive pattern of nicotine use and symptoms of dependence are reviewed at this site of the Internet Mental Health Web pages. An online diagnostic test, for use by either practitioners or patients, offers an aid to diagnosis. Practice guidelines for the treatment of nicotine dependence are accessible, and articles linking nicotine abuse with depression, as well as a higher mortality rate, are found.
http://www.mentalhealth.com/dis/p20-sb07.html

 Practice Guideline for the Treatment of Patients with Nicotine Dependence The American Psychiatric Association (APA) presents a complete practice guideline for the treatment of nicotine dependence at this Internet location. These parameters of practice, developed by psychiatrists who are active in the clinical field, offer DSM-IV information on nicotine use disorders, specific features of diagnosis, and complete treatment principles and alternatives. Formulations and implementation of treatment strategies, clinical features influencing treatment, and future research directions are reviewed.
http://www.psych.org/clin_res/pg_nicotine.cfm

OPIOID-RELATED DISORDERS

 Internet Mental Health: Opioid Dependence The Internet Mental Health database provides this comprehensive resource for general information and treatment guidance for opioid abuse. Visitors will find two clinical descriptions of opioid dependence, with diagnostic criteria completely outlined, in addition to external links on effective addiction management and practice guidelines for patients with substance-abuse disorders. Users may access topic-specific MEDLINE searches under the "Research" section, as well as substance-related disorder booklets.   http://www.mentalhealth.com/dis/p20-sb08.html

National Institute on Drug Abuse (NIDA): Heroin   Intended for consumers and professionals, this site offers resources related to heroin. There is a National Institute on Drug Abuse research report, fact sheet, news releases, and several NIDA articles on heroin addiction. Additional information includes a teen drug abuse prevention program, as well as a link for additional information. http://www.nida.nih.gov/DrugPages/Heroin.html

PHENCYCLIDINE (PCP)

eMedicine: Toxicity, Phencyclidine   The background, pathophysiology, and incidence of phencyclidine toxicity are discussed at this eMedicine review, which includes the physical presentation and access to several differential links within the eMedicine database. Laboratory workups, treatment in various settings, and profiles of pharmacologic agents used in therapy are offered. http://www.emedicine.com/EMERG/topic420.htm

Internet Mental Health: Phencyclidine Dependence   Phencyclidine dependence is the focus of this Web page. There are definitions of the condition, an online diagnostic test, and treatment information. Current research, along with general information on substance abuse in booklets, articles, and Internet links, is provided. http://www.mentalhealth.com/dis/p20-sb09.html

National Institute on Drug Abuse (NIDA): Phencyclidine   Hosted by the National Institute on Drug Abuse, this site offers a fact sheet on PCP that explains its properties and the health hazards associated with its use. Information on preventing drug abuse in teens is presented. There is also a link for additional information from MEDLINEplus. http://www.nida.nih.gov/DrugPages/PCP.html

RECOVERY ORGANIZATIONS

Online Recovery   Recovery Online provides a comprehensive range of links to over 50 anonymous self-help organizations ranging from the well-known Alcoholics Anonymous and Al-Anon Family Groups to the less frequently encountered Depressed Anonymous, Phobics Anonymous, and Recovering Couples Anonymous. Nearly a dozen religious and secular anonymous group listings are included for help with alcoholism, homosexuality, survival of sexual abuse, and trauma. The listing also includes Schizophrenics Anonymous, Kleptomaniacs and Shoplifters, and Parents Anonymous. In addition to organizational listings, a listing of FAQs and a "Recovery Message Board" are available. http://www.onlinerecovery.org/index.html

SEDATIVE-RELATED DISORDERS

Internet Mental Health: Sedative Dependence The specifics of sedative abuse, with common withdrawal symptoms and other diagnostic features, are outlined at the American description page, accessible from the site. Associated problems, such as antisocial personality and learning disorders, are listed, and a separate European description of "sedative or hypnotic dependence syndrome" is found. Information on barbiturate and benzodiazepine withdrawal, therapeutic communities and halfway houses, and psychosocial treatment principles is provided. http://www.mentalhealth.com/dis/p20-sb10.html

9.28 SUICIDE

GENERAL RESOURCES

American Association of Suicidology This nonprofit organization is dedicated to the understanding and prevention of suicide. The Web site includes information regarding the association, conference information, links to other relevant sites, internship information, and a directory for support groups and crisis centers. In addition, there are links to sources for books and other printed resources, links to legal and ethical issues, treatment, assessment and prediction, and certification and accreditation manuals.
http://www.suicidology.org

American Foundation for Suicide Prevention This foundation provides funds for research, education, and treatment programs for suicide prevention. The site has links to research updates, treatment news, suicide facts, and survivor support. Other topics include assisted suicide, depression and suicide, neurobiology of suicide, and youth suicide. Foundation information, as well as current funding opportunities, is provided.
http://www.afsp.org

Befrienders International This international charity, dedicated to preventing suicide worldwide, offers information for depressed persons, their family, and loved ones, as well as access to an online directory of crisis helplines. Statistics, details about self-harm, an online newsletter, and a fact sheet that details the warning signs of suicide are provided. The site can be viewed in a variety of languages, including Chinese, Spanish, Arabic, and French.
http://www.befrienders.org/

Living with Suicide A number of personal stories of experiences with suicide, a discussion group and links to suicide support groups, hotlines, associations, national directories of groups, and other related information are available at this site.
http://www.pbs.org/weblab/living/lws_0.html

Suicide   This Web site is a support page for those considering suicide, offering information on hotlines and links to additional Internet resources for aid and support. Suggested literature can be ordered from Amazon.com through the site. In addition, there is information on how to handle a person who is suicidal.
http://www.metanoia.org/suicide

Suicide Awareness/Voices of Education: (SA/VE)   This support organization's site provides answers to common questions on suicide, a list of symptoms and warning signs, personal stories, depression and suicide fact sheets, hospitalization information, resources on students and elderly depression, a book list, and a fact sheet on depression. Contact information and related links are included.
http://www.save.org

Training Institute for Suicide Assessment   Intended for professionals, this Web page offers information on courses in suicide assessment and clinical interviewing. Detailed information on the Training Institute for Suicide Assessment's training workshops and methodology is provided. In addition, there is information on books on this subject, as well as related links.
http://www.suicideassessment.com/

DOCTOR-ASSISTED SUICIDE

Doctor-Assisted Suicide: A Guide to WEB Sites and the Literature   Presented at this site are the multiple vantage points of the medical, legal, and religious communities, as well as current coverage of the topic via recent publications, Web sites, and United States Supreme Court decisions. State statutes and proposed legislation are explored and provoke further discussion regarding the "right to die" debates.
http://Web.lwc.edu/administrative/library/suic.htm

National Council on Disability: Assisted Suicide: A Disability Perspective   A review of the issues surrounding doctor-assisted suicide is presented at this position paper, authored by Robert L. Burgdorf, Jr., of the University of the District of Columbia School of Law. The stance of the National Council on Disability is described, taking into consideration Supreme Court cases, the perspectives of those with disabilities, and other viewpoints that weigh the dangers and benefits of physician-assisted suicide.
http://www.ncd.gov/newsroom/publications/suicide.html

9.29 TIC DISORDERS

GENERAL RESOURCES

Rush-Presbyterian—St. Luke's Medical Center: Section of Movement Disorders   This center conducts research into the causes and treatment of

movement disorders, treating patients with Parkinson's disease, Huntington disease, Tourette's disorder, other tic-related illnesses, dystonia, tremor, and myoclonus. Clinical features, causes, treatment, and current research projects associated with each disorder are described at the site.
http://www.rush.edu/patients/neuroscience/movement.html

Tics and Tourette's   This site presents a valuable patient and caregiver pamphlet on motor tics, vocal tics, complex tics, tic-related phenomena, and specific types of tic disorders. Discussions on the course, comorbidity, prevalence, diagnosis, causes, and strategies, including nonmedical and pharmacological interventions, are available.
http://www.klis.com/chandler/pamphlet/tic/ticpamphlet.htm

CHRONIC MOTOR OR VOCAL TIC DISORDER

BehaveNet: Clinical Capsule: DSM-IV—Chronic Motor or Vocal Tic Disorder   This BehaveNet Clinical Capsule, concisely defines the DSM-IV diagnosis of chronic motor or vocal tic disorder, in order to provide the reader with a rapid, basic understanding of the term and its relationship to other disorders. Provided are links to information on Tourette's disorder.
http://behavenet.com/capsules/disorders/chrontic.htm

HealthCentral.com: Chronic Motor Tic Disorder   HealthCentral's online encyclopedia presents an information sheet at the Web site relating to chronic motor tic disorder, with its definition, causes, symptoms, and treatments briefly reviewed. Links to fact sheets on transient tic disorder, facial tics, and other definitions and differential diagnoses are found.
http://www.healthcentral.com/mhc/top/000745.cfm

TOURETTE'S DISORDER

Internet Mental Health: Tourette's Syndrome   This site presents an education booklet, providing physicians, psychologists, nurses, and other professionals with important information on Tourette's disorder. Topics include tic disorders, differential diagnosis, symptomatology, associated behaviors and cognitive difficulties, etiology, stimulant medications, epidemiology and genetics, nongenetic contributions, clinical assessment, and treatment. References, authors, and a link to the Tourette's Syndrome Association are listed at the site.
http://www.mentalhealth.com/book/p40-gtor.html

Tourette's Syndrome Association (TSA), Incorporated   Described as the only national organization dedicated to providing information on Tourette's syndrome (TS), the Tourette's Syndrome Association offers a variety of resources at its Web site, including links to public service announcements and a chat room. The site contains numerous general facts about TS, as well as scientific links, such as a publications list, research grant awards, and information on

TS diagnosis and treatment. Interested persons will find links to national chapters of the association and to international contacts. There are links to order TSA publications, as well as online access to selected relevant articles. http://www.tsa-usa.org/

Tourette's Syndrome Resources   More than 35 Internet resources related to Tourette's disorder are listed at this address. Specific site topics include disability, attention deficit/hyperactivity disorder, neurology, patient advocacy, movement disorders, nervous system diseases, obsessive-compulsive disorder, psychology self-help, stuttering, and Ritalin. Resources specific to Tourette's disorder are provided through organizations and other Tourette's information sites. http://members.tripod.com/~tourette13/links.html

Virtual Hospital: Medical Treatment of Tourette's Syndrome   This site offers an outline of medical treatments for Tourette's disorder, including suggested dose, side effects, and other notes. The medications information is accompanied by a list of sensory symptoms of Tourette's syndrome, biochemistry of the condition, environmental factors, and a list of possible reasons for poor attention in school. http://www.vh.org/Patients/IHB/Psych/Tourette/TSMed.html

TRANSIENT TIC DISORDER

Transient Tic Disorder   A simple definition and information on the causes, incidence, and risk factors associated with transient single or multiple motor tics are presented at this site of the adam.com online health information database. A symptom link stresses ruling out any physical causes of transient tics, and a treatment connection provides a list of actions to be taken if tics are recognized. http://medlineplus.adam.com/ency/article/000747.htm

GENERAL MEDICAL
WEB RESOURCES

10

REFERENCE INFORMATION
AND NEWS SOURCES

10.1 GENERAL MEDICAL SUPERSITES

Visitors interested in medical supersites may also find similar information under the medical search engine section.

American Medical Association (AMA) The AMA develops and promotes standards in medical practice, research, and education; acts as advocate on behalf of patients and physicians; and provides discourse on matters important to public health in America. General information is available at the site about the organization; journals and newsletters; policy, advocacy, activities, and ethics; education; and accreditation services. AMA news and consumer health information are also found at the site. Resources for physicians include membership details; information on the AMA's current procedural terminology (CPT)information services, the resource-based relative value scale (RBVS), and electronic medical systems; information on the AMA Alliance (a national organization of physicians' spouses); descriptions of additional AMA products and services; a discussion of legal issues for physicians; and information on AMA's global activities. Information for consumers includes medical news; detailed information on a wide range of conditions; family health resources for children, adolescents, men, and women; interactive health calculators; healthy recipes; and general safety tips. Specific pages are devoted to comprehensive resources related to HIV/AIDS, asthma, migraines, and women's health.
http://www.ama-assn.org

BioSites BioSites is a comprehensive catalog of selected Internet resources in the medical and biomedical sciences. The sites were selected as part of a project by staff members of Resource Libraries within the Pacific Southwest Region of the National Network of Libraries of Medicine. Sites are organized by medical topic or specialty field, and users can also search the site by keyword. Featured Web sites are listed by title, but detailed descriptions are not provided.
http://www.library.ucsf.edu/biosites

Doctor's Guide The Doctor's Guide to the Internet is provided by PSL Consulting Group, Inc. and its purpose is to provide a comfortable environment for physicians to search the Internet and World Wide Web. The site contains a professional edition for healthcare professionals and a section directed at pa-

tients. Information of medical and professional interest includes medical news and alerts, new drugs or indications, medical conferences, a Congress Resource Center, a medical bookstore, and Internet medical resources. Patient resources are organized by specific diseases or condition. Users can search the World Wide Web through Excite, InfoSeek, McKinley, and Alta Vista search engines or can search the Doctor's Guide medical news and conference database.
http://www.docguide.com

Emory University: MedWeb   Maintained by the library staff of Emory University, MedWeb offers more than 100 subjects encompassing a comprehensive catalog of thousands of biomedical and health-related sites. Visitors can perform a keyword search or browse through categories such as biological and physical sciences, clinical practice, consumer health, diseases and conditions, drugs, healthcare, institutions, mental health, publications, and specialties. A subject index is available to browse the entire catalog.
http://www.medweb.emory.edu/Medweb/

Galaxy: Medicine   Intended primarily for consumer reference, the Galaxy Health directory of online resources can be searched by keyword or browsed by category. Categories include diseases and disorders, family health, fitness, health news, medical testing, procedures, and therapeutics. Each topic contains links to online articles, discussion groups, periodicals, and organizations.
http://health.galaxy.com

Hardin Meta Directory   Hosted by the Hardin Library for the Health Sciences at the University of Iowa, this site features a meta-directory of Internet health sites. More than 40 subjects are listed in the directory such as AIDS, cancer, dermatology, neurology, pregnancy, and pediatrics. The directory contains thousands of sites. By clicking on a subject, visitors will find several lists of Internet sites that have been compiled from other Web pages. Each list is ranked according to the size of the list. In addition to the meta-directory, links are provided to an array of news sources, medical libraries, and consumer organized sites. http://www.lib.uiowa.edu/hardin/md/

Health On the Net (HON) Foundation   The Health On the Net Foundation site offers an engine that searches the Internet as well as the foundation's database for medical sites, hospitals, and support communities. A media gallery contains a searchable database of medical images and videos from various sources. The site also features a list of online journals, articles and abstracts, and papers from conferences and various other medical sources. The HON MeSH tool allows users to browse Medical Subject Headings (MeSH), a hierarchical structure of medical concepts from the National Library of Medicine (NLM). Users can also select a target group, such as healthcare providers, medical professionals, or patients and other individuals, to receive more tailored search results. http://www.hon.ch

HealthGate   HealthGate's consumer resource offers information and health-related articles for the general public, including patient education materials, ar-

ticles on current health issues and advances, information on symptoms and medical tests, and several articles devoted to specific topics, including alternative medicine, fitness, nutrition, mental well-being, parenting, travel health, and sexuality. A drugs and medications database is searchable by letter, and in-depth information on over 30 common conditions is found. Additional channels are devoted specifically to men, women, children, and seniors.
http://www.healthgate.com

HealthWeb   With support from a National Library of Medicine grant, this collaborative effort of over 20 health sciences libraries, offers a meta-directory of health-related, non-commercial Web sites. The sites are categorized into approximately 70 different subjects such as AIDS, anatomy, dermatology, hematology, and toxicology. Within each subject, sites are further classified by clinical resources, academic institutes, statistics, conferences, consumer health resources, online publications, and organizations. For each site listed, there is a brief description of its contents.
http://healthweb.org/index.cfm

Karolinska Institutet: Diseases, Disorders and Related Topics
Karolinska Institutet, a medical university, offers ample resources for both professionals and the general public at this collection. Covering every major field of medicine, the site provides a searchable database of fact sheets on individual diseases, pathology databases, clinical guidelines, research, and anatomy and other medical tutorials. Visitors can easily locate information via an alphabetical list of diseases or can visit any one of more than 20 directories in a particular field of medicine. Other resources of the Karolinska Institutet include Medline access, electronic journals, and a Medical Subject Headings (MeSH) tree tool for finding references and links to other resources.
http://www.micf.mic.ki.se

MedExplorer   Created by a Canadian paramedic, resources at this comprehensive site cover a wide array of health topics for health professionals and the public. Links to an enormous number of sites are found, along with brief descriptions of site contents, categorized into 28 topics such as allied health, alternative medicine, education, employment, government, laboratory, medical imaging, research, and specialty medicine. There are also discussion forums, an employment center, and health news headlines. Resources are categorized into sections that include a diet and nutrition center, as well as health centers for women, men, children, and seniors. Also available are a searchable nutrition database, an online health exam, access to MEDLINE, and more than 250 health newsgroups.   http://www.medexplorer.com/

Medical Matrix   Medical Matrix offers a list of directories categorized into specialties, diseases, clinical practice resources, literature, education, healthcare and professional resources, medical computing, Internet and technology, and marketplace resources containing classifieds and employment opportunities. Additional features include a site search engine, access to MEDLINE, clinical

searches, and links to symposia on the Web, medical textbook resources, patient education materials, continuing medical education information, news, and online journals. Free registration is necessary to access the site.
(free registration) http://www.medmatrix.org

 Medicine Online Offering a broad range of medical information, this site offers resources of interest to both physicians and patients. The reference section contains a medical dictionary, fact sheets on diseases and treatments, and a drug index. Visitors will also find comprehensive listings of Internet resources in categories such as diseases and conditions, medicine, public health, women's health, and allied health. Unique to the site is a "Bid for Surgery" center where consumers enter their requirements for cosmetic procedures and physicians respond with their qualifications, location, and price. Searchable directories of physicians, hospitals, and vendors are provided, and a link to MOL.net takes one to a portal offering a customizable home page for professionals with access to bid for surgery, reference information, message boards, and information on laboratory management. By accessing the "Health Topics" menu viewers are taken to large selections of general resources for the chosen topic and are able to connect further to individual disorder Web sites.
(free registration) http://www.medicineonline.net/

 MedicineNet.com Described as "100% doctor-produced healthcare information," this Web page offers fact sheets—written in laymen's terms—on a variety of health-related topics. By clicking on the subject at the top of the page, visitors can access fact sheets on diseases and conditions, procedures and tests, medications, and healthy living (nutrition and fitness). There is also a medical dictionary, as well as an online drug store. The home page features news, updates, and information on commonly requested conditions such as acne, asthma, cancer, and diabetes. Also on the home page is quick reference information such as first aid, poison control, and product recalls.
http://www.medicinenet.com/Script/Main/hp.asp

 MEDLINEplus Sponsored by the world's largest medical library, the National Library of Medicine, and the National Institutes of health, this site provides up-to-date, high quality healthcare information. Resources on this Web page cover an array of health information for professionals and consumers. The "Health Topics" section offers more than 30 broad topics, each with several subsections, leading to a page with links to information such as overviews, clinical trials, diagnosis and symptoms, specific conditions, policy, organizations, statistics, and Spanish publications. The site also features drug information with a guide to more than 9,000 prescription and over-the-counter medications, from the United States Pharmacopeia (SUP) and the USPDI and Advice for the Patient. There are several medical dictionaries, along with directories of physicians and hospitals. Information found under the "Other Resources" section includes organizations, libraries, publications, databases, and access to MEDLINE.
http://www.medlineplus.gov/

MedMark: Medical Bookmarks   Designed by a physician, this Web page is a comprehensive directory of thousands of health-related sites with information for both the professional and consumer. Sites are categorized under more than 30 specialties such as endocrinology, immunology, and pediatrics. Clicking on a specialty brings up a list of Internet sites organized in categories such as associations, centers, departments, education and training, for consumer, guidelines, journals, and programs. There are also links for free access to MEDLINE (registration required), as well as a list of related sites that also contain large directories of resources. At the top of the site, there is a link for sites in Korea.
http://members.kr.inter.net/medmark/

MedNets   This site houses a collection of proprietary search engines, searching only medical databases. Users can access search engines by medical specialty or disease topic. Other resources include links to the home pages of associations, journals, hospitals, companies, research, government sites, clinical practice guidelines, medical news, and consumer and patient information. The site also includes a set of medical databases and links to search engines provided on the Internet by medical schools.
http://www.internets.com/mednets

Medscape   Medscape offers a searchable directory of Web sites that provide information on a wide range of medical specialties. Registration is free, and users can customize the site's home page from a particular computer by choosing a medical specialty. Information in a personalized home page includes news items, conference summaries and schedules, treatment updates, practice guidelines, and patient resources, all pertaining to the chosen field of specialization. The site also includes clinical feature articles and links to special clinical resources.
(free registration) http://www.medscape.com

Medscout   The Medscout Web page offers a directory of health-related Web sites. More than 50 broad topics are listed such as clinical alerts, CME, diseases, employment, guidelines, hospitals, informatics, journals, medical supplies, and telemedicine. Each topic is broken down into further subtopics with hyperlinks leading directly to appropriate sites. The site also includes extensive information on HIPAA (Health Insurance Portability and Accountability Act), and several fee-based tools for securely connecting healthcare professionals to payers, pharmacies, and each other.
(some features fee-based) http://www.medscout.com/

Megasite Project: A Metasite Comparing Health Information Megasites and Search Engines   The Megasite Project, created by librarians at Northwestern University, the University of Michigan, and Pennsylvania State University, evaluates and provides direct links to 26 of the largest health information Internet sites. Criteria for evaluation and comparison include administration and quality control, content, and design. Users can access results of site evaluations, tips for successful site searches, lists of the best general and health information search engines reviewed, and site comparisons listed by evaluation criteria. A bibliography of articles on Web design and Internet resource evaluation is found at the address, as well as descriptions of other aspects of the project. http://www.lib.umich.edu/megasite/toc.html

National Library of Medicine (NLM)   The National Library of Medicine, the world's largest medical library, collects materials in all areas of biomedicine and healthcare and focuses on biomedical aspects of technology, the humanities, and the physical, life, and social sciences. This site contains links to government medical databases, including MEDLINE and MEDLINEplus, information on funding opportunities at the National Library of Medicine and other federal agencies, and details of services, training, and outreach programs offered by NLM. Users can access NLM's catalog of resources (LocatorPlus), as well as NLM publications, including fact sheets, published reports, and staff publications. NLM research programs discussed at the site include topics in computational molecular biology, medical informatics, and other related subjects. The Web site features 15 searchable databases, covering journal searches via MEDLINE; AIDS information via AIDSLINE, AIDSDRUGS, and AIDSTRIALS; bioethics via BIOETHICSLINE; and numerous other important topics. The NLM Gateway—a master search engine—searches MEDLINE using the retrieval engine called PubMed. It is very user-friendly. There are over 9 million citations in MEDLINE and PreMEDLINE and the other related databases. Additionally, the NLM provides sources of health statistics, serials programs, and services maintained through a system called SERHOLD.
http://www.nlm.nih.gov

New York Online Access to Health (NOAH): Health Topics and Resources   The entire NOAH Web page is available in English and Spanish and offers a broad array of health information. Visitors can browse by subject or alphabetically. The home page features more than 30 health topics such as AIDS, arthritis, cancer, kidney diseases, and nutrition. By clicking on a topic, a long list of links appears for in-depth information such as a description of the disease or condition along with diagnosis, symptoms, and treatment. There is also a resource section for more information including patient rights, medications, support groups, and New York City and county healthcare and community services resources.
http://www.noah-health.org/english/qksearch.html

University of Iowa: Virtual Hospital   A service of the University of Iowa Health Care system, this Web page features the Virtual Hospital—a digital library with more than 350 peer-reviewed books and booklets. Separate sections are available for healthcare providers and patients. The provider section is organized by categories such as specialty, problem, department, organ system, and by type of information, including multimedia, textbooks, journals, and guidelines. The patient section contains categories such as problem, department, organ system, FAQs, and staff articles. By clicking on the "Common Problems" link, a comprehensive list of the site's contents is found, organized by problem,

with separate professional and patient links. The home page also features a link to the Virtual Children's Hospital, as well as CME online courses.
http://www.vh.org

Virtual Medical Center: Martindale's Health Science Guide   The Virtual Medical Center claims to have more than 61,500 teaching files, 129,800 medical cases, 1,155 courses/textbooks, 1,580 tutorials, 4,100 databases, and 10,700 movies. The information is listed in categories on the home page such as a physician finder, clinical trials, CME, medical codes, laboratory diagnostics, blood-related information, hospitals worldwide, medical auctions, and medical dictionaries in eight languages. There is also a table with more than 25 specialties such as biochemistry, gynecology, and hematology with further clinical and consumer information. In addition, a considerable section is found for environmental health.
http://www-sci.lib.uci.edu/~martindale/Medical.html

WebMD   High-quality consumer health information and resources for healthcare professionals are available at this address. Consumer resources include information on conditions, treatments, and drugs; medical news and articles on specific topics; a medical encyclopedia; drug reference resources; a forum for asking health questions; online chat events with medical experts; transcripts of past chat events; message boards; and articles and expert advice on general health topics. Consumers can also join a "community" for more personalized information and forums. Physicians services, available for a fee of US$29.95 monthly (in a 12-month contract), include access to medical news, online journals, and reference databases; online insurance verification and referrals; e-mail, voice mail, fax, and conference call capabilities; practice management tools; online trading; financial services; and other resources. The site includes a preview tour of the service for interested professionals.
(some features fee-based) http://www.webmd.com

10.2 ABBREVIATIONS

Acronym and Abbreviation List   This site offers a database of acronyms and abbreviations. Visitors can search for an acronym and see what it means, or search for a word and its related acronym.
http://www.ucc.ie/info/net/acronyms/index.html

Common Medical Abbreviations   Several hundred major medical abbreviations are defined in an alphabetical listing at this educational information site.
http://courses.smsu.edu/jas188f/690/medslpterm.html

How to Read a Prescription   A guide to interpreting a prescription is offered on this Web page, directed to healthcare professionals. More than 20 common abbreviations are listed along with their interpretation.
http://www.dallas.net/~stonemik/sigs.html

National Council for Emergency Medicine Informatics (NCEMI) The National Council for Emergency Medicine Informatics provides a searchable database for medical abbreviations and acronyms. By clicking on "Abbreviation Translator" and entering the letters to be identified, single or multiple definitions will be returned.
http://www.ncemi.org

10.3 ABSTRACT, CITATION, AND FULL-TEXT SEARCH TOOLS

EMBASE: Medical Abstracts Database Produced by Elsevier Science, the EMBASE database contains more than 13 million citations from the biomedical and pharmacological literature. Entries from 1974 to the present also contain abstracts. A distinction noted from the site asserts that EMBASE is "renowned for its comprehensive international coverage." The database is updated daily, and a free demo is available from this site.
(fee-based) http://www.embase.com/

Infomine: Scholarly Internet Resources Infomine offers searchable biological, agricultural, and medical Internet Web site collections, primarily consisting of university- level research and education. There are close to 20,000 links, covering databases, electronic journals, textbooks, conference proceedings, and more. Web sites can be browsed by title of resource, subject and title, subject, or keyword. Recently added sites are stored in a separate section. The site also offers links to additional Internet medical resources.
http://infomine.ucr.edu/search/bioagsearch.phtml

InfoTrieve: Article Finder A database of more than 20 million citations drawn from over 30,000 scientific, technical, and medical journals can be searched on this site, dating back to 1966. Users can order reprints of articles through the site for a fee.
(some features fee-based) http://www4.infotrieve.com/search/databases/newsearch.asp

National Cancer Institute (NCI): Literature and Bibliographic Database of Cancer Information The National Cancer Institute offers this Web page with links to a broad array of cancer literature. Visitors can search Cancer Lit, the NCI's bibliographic database with more than 1.5 million citations and abstracts. NCI publications for professionals and the public are available online; categories include types of cancer, treatment options, clinical trials, genetics, coping with cancer, testing for cancer, and risk factors. A general category encompasses clinical research and statistics. Peer-reviewed summaries on treatment, screening, prevention, genetics, and supportive care are available through a link to PDQ, NCI's cancer database. There are separate sections for professionals and patient information in PDQ, as well as directories of physicians and cancer care organizations. The *Journal of the National Cancer Institute* is available online to subscribers. In addition, there are links to other cancer literature Internet sites. (some features fee-based) http://cnetdb.nci.nih.gov/cancerlit.html

National Library of Medicine (NLM): Online Databases This site offers links to and descriptions of the databases and electronic information sources provided by the National Library of Medicine. Topics covered include bioethics, biotechnology, cancer information, clinical trials, consumer information, HIV/AIDS resources, history of medicine, population information, and toxicology and environmental health information. Links provided include MEDLINE via PubMed; MCA/MR; a multiple congenital anomaly/mental retardation database, and MEDLINEplus; information for consumers. Hyperlinks on each topic offer further information on the resources available and how to access them.
http://www.nlm.nih.gov/databases/databases.html

National Library of Medicine (NLM): PubMed PubMed is a free MEDLINE search service, from the National Library of Medicine, providing access to over 11 million citations with links to the full text of articles from more than 4,000 biomedical journals. Probably the most heavily used and reputable free MEDLINE site, PubMed permits advanced searching by subject, author, journal title, and many other fields. It includes an easy-to-use "citation matcher" for completing and identifying references, and its PreMEDLINE database provides journal citations before they are indexed, making this version of MEDLINE more up-to-date than most.
http://www.ncbi.nlm.nih.gov/PubMed

National Library of Medicine Gateway Designed as a "one-stop shopping" portal for Internet users seeking information in the extensive National Library of Medicine collections, the NLM Gateway offers an extremely convenient and powerful search tool to simultaneously search multiple retrieval systems at NLM. Information for both professionals and consumers is drawn from MEDLINE; a bibliographic database containing more than 11 million journal citations from 1966 to the present, OLDMEDLINE; journal citations from 1958 to 1965, MEDLINEplus; consumer health information on more than 400 topics, and MEDLINEplus drug information covering more than 9,000 drugs. Additional resources at NLM include LOCATORplus; a catalog of records for books, serials, and audiovisual materials, DIRLINE; a directory of health organizations, research resources, projects, and databases; meeting abstracts from AIDS meetings and health services research (HSR) meetings; as well as information on HSR projects in progress. Links on the site direct visitors to information on ordering documents; clinical trials; clinical alerts; TOXNET; a toxicology database, and the health services/technology assessment text (HSTAT) database. http://gateway.nlm.nih.gov/gw/Cmd

10.4 FEDERAL HEALTH AGENCIES

GENERAL RESOURCES

Federal Web Locator   This is a useful search engine for links to federal government sites and information on the World Wide Web. Users can search agency names and access a table of contents.
http://www.infoctr.edu/fwl

HEALTH AND HUMAN SERVICES

Department of Health and Human Services (HHS)   This site lists HHS agencies and provides links to the individual agency sites. It offers news, press releases, and information on accessing HHS records and contacting HHS officials. It also provides a search engine for all federal HHS agencies and access to HealthFinder.
http://www.os.dhhs.gov

Administration for Children and Families (ACF)   This site provides descriptions of, resources for, and links to ACF programs and services. These sites detail programs and services that relate to areas such as welfare and family assistance, child support, foster care and adoption, Head Start, and support for Native Americans, refugees, and the developmentally disabled. Updated news and information is provided as well.
http://www.acf.dhhs.gov

Administration on Aging (AOA)   This site provides resources for seniors, practitioners, and caregivers. Resources include news on aging, links to Web sites on aging, statistics about older people, consumer fact sheets, retirement and financial planning information, and help finding community assistance for seniors.   http://www.aoa.dhhs.gov

Agency for Healthcare Research and Quality (AHRQ)   The Agency for Healthcare Research and Quality site offers healthcare professionals clinical information, research findings, quality assessment, and more. In the clinical information section there are evidence-based practice reports, outcomes research findings, technology assessments, preventive services, and clinical practice guidelines. There are funding opportunities, as well as data and surveys such as the medical expenditure panel survey and an interactive tool for hospital statistics. A publications catalog and an electronic reading room are also available. A section of the site is dedicated to consumers and offers fact sheets on health conditions, health plans, prescriptions, prevention, quality of care, smoking cessation, and surgery. Some fact sheets are available in Spanish.
http://www.ahrq.gov/

Agency for Toxic Substances and Disease Registry (ATSDR) The mission of this agency is "to prevent exposure and adverse human health effects and diminished quality of life associated with exposure to hazardous substances from waste sites, unplanned releases, and other sources of pollution present in the environment." Toward this goal, the site posts national alerts and health advisories. It provides answers to frequently asked questions about hazardous substances and lists the minimal risk levels for each of them. The site has a HazDat database developed to provide access to information on the release of hazardous substances from Superfund sites or from emergency events and on the effects of hazardous substances on the health of human populations. A quarterly *Hazardous Substances and Public Health Newsletter* is available for viewing on the site, as are additional resources for children, parents, and teachers.
http://www.atsdr.cdc.gov/atsdrhome.html

Food and Drug Administration (FDA) The FDA is one of the oldest consumer protection agencies in the United States, monitoring the manufacture, import, transport, storage, and sale of about $1 trillion worth of products each year. This comprehensive site provides information on the safety of foods, human and animal drugs, blood products, cosmetics, and medical devices. The site also contains details of field operations, current regulations, toxicology research, medical products reporting procedures, and answers to frequently asked questions. Users can search the site by keyword and find specific information targeted to consumers, industry, health professionals, patients, state and local officials, women, and children.
http://www.fda.gov

Healthcare Financing Administration Information on Medicare, Medicaid, and child health insurance programs is provided here. Statistical data on enrollment in the various programs as well as analysis of recent trends in healthcare spending, employment, and pricing is also provided. The site offers consumer publications and program forms, which are available for download.
http://www.hcfa.gov

Indian Health Service (IHS) The Indian Health Service provides federal health services to American Indians and Alaskan Natives. Information of interest to physicians is primarily contained in the "About the IHS" section. This section offers access to the Native Health Research bibliographic database; some entries have full-text articles. There is also a Native Health History database that covers the years 1652-1970. Clinical practice guideline information is provided, including IHS patient education protocols. Also within this section is an IHS facility locator. The site also describes their programs under the "Medical Programs" section, relating to such topics as AIDS, child health, diabetes, and elder care. In addition, there is information on health professional jobs, scholarships, and office locations.
http://www.ihs.gov

National Center for Toxicological Research (NCTR)   Charged with supporting the U.S. Food and Drug Administration's regulatory needs by researching the effects of toxicity and improving human exposure and risk assessment methods, the National Center for Toxicological Research describes their activities on this site. Under the "Science" section, there are descriptions of NCTR research projects, a bibliography of related NCTR publications, and the full text of the report on each year's activities.
http://www.fda.gov/nctr/index.html

National Guideline Clearinghouse (NGC)   The National Guideline Clearinghouse is a database of evidence-based clinical practice guidelines and related documents produced by the Agency for Healthcare Research and Quality (AHRQ), in partnership with the American Medical Association (AMA) and the American Association of Health Plans (AAHP). Users can search the database by keyword or browse by disease category.
http://www.guidelines.gov/index.asp

Public Health Service (PHS)   The Public Health Service is an umbrella organization consisting of many health service agencies and programs. Their site offers links to public health service agencies such as the National Institutes of Health, the Centers for Disease Control and Prevention, and the U.S. Food and Drug Administration. Links to offices dedicated to public health include the Office of Minority Health and the Office of Women's Health. In addition, Health and Human Services vacancy announcements are available at the site. The site is linked directly to the Office of the surgeon general, providing transcripts of speeches and reports, a biography of the current Surgeon General, and a history and summary of duties associated with the position.
http://www.hhs.gov/phs/

Substance Abuse and Mental Health Services Administration (SAMHSA)   Examining substance abuse and mental illness, the Substance Abuse and Mental Health Services Administration site offers resources dedicated to the prevention, treatment, and rehabilitation of these conditions. The site features SAMHSA programs and centers, namely the Center for Mental Health Services, the Center for Substance Abuse Prevention, and the Center for Substance Abuse Treatment. Information clearinghouses on the site feature online booklets, fact sheets, and conference proceedings from these three centers. There is also information on their managed care initiative, including reports on quality improvement, policy studies, and technical assistance and training. Grant opportunities, along with data and statistics on substance abuse and mental illness, are included. A public information section offers publications written in an easy-to- understand way, as well as directories of service providers.
http://www.samhsa.gov

NATIONAL INSTITUTES OF HEALTH

G-0050

National Institutes of Health (NIH) NIH is one of eight health agencies of the Public Health Service which, in turn, is part of the U.S. Department of Health and Human Services. The NIH mission is to uncover new knowledge that will lead to better health for everyone. NIH works toward that mission by conducting research in its own laboratories; supporting the research of non-federal scientists in universities, medical schools, hospitals, and research institutions throughout the country and abroad; helping in the training of research investigators; and fostering communication of biomedical information. The site provides a Director's message about the agency, e-mail and telephone directories, visitor information, employment and summer internship program information, science education program details, and a history of NIH. A site search engine and links to the home pages of all NIH institutes and centers are available.
http://www.nih.gov

G-0051

Center for Information Technology (CIT) The Center for Information Technology incorporates the power of modern computers into the biomedical programs and administrative procedures of the NIH by conducting computational biosciences research, developing computer systems, and providing computer facilities. The site provides information on activities and the organization of the center, contact information, resources for Macintosh users, and links to many useful information technology sites. Users can search the site or the CIT Help Desk Knowledgebase for specific information.
http://www.cit.nih.gov/home.asp

G-0052

Center for Scientific Review (CSR) The Center for Scientific Review is the focal point at NIH for the conduct of initial peer review, which is the foundation of the NIH grant and award process. The center carries out a peer review of the majority of research and research training applications submitted to the NIH. The center also serves as the central receipt point for all such Public Health Service applications and makes referrals to scientific review groups for scientific and technical merit review of applications and to funding components for potential award. To this end, the center develops and implements innovative, flexible ways to conduct referral and review for all aspects of science. The site contains contact information, transcripts of public commentary panel discussions, news and events listings, grant applications, peer review notes, and links to additional biomedical and government sites.
http://www.drg.nih.gov

G-0053

Fogarty International Center (FIC) The Fogarty International Center for Advanced Study in the Health Sciences leads NIH efforts to advance the health of the American public, and citizens of all nations, through international cooperation on global health threats. Resources at the site include the centers publications, regional information on programs and contacts, research and training opportunities, a description of the center's Multilateral Initiative on Malaria

(MIM), details of the NIH Visiting Program for Foreign Scientists, and news and vacancy announcements.
http://www.nih.gov/fic

National Cancer Institute (NCI) The National Cancer Institute leads a national effort to reduce the burden of cancer morbidity and mortality, and ultimately to prevent the disease. Through basic and clinical biomedical research and training, the NCI conducts and supports programs to understand the causes of cancer; prevent, detect, diagnose, treat, and control cancer; and disseminate information to the practitioner, patient, and public. The site provides visitors with many informational resources related to cancer, including CancerTrials for clinical trials resources and CancerNet for information on cancer tailored to the needs of health professionals, patients, and the general public. Additional resources relate to funding opportunities as well as to events and research at NCI.
http://www.nci.nih.gov

National Center for Biotechnology Information (NCBI) A comprehensive site that provides a wide array of biotechnology resources to the user, the NCBI includes sources such as a genetic sequence database (GenBank); links to related sites, a newsletter, site and genetic sequence search engines; information on programs, activities, and research projects; seminar and exhibit schedules; and database services. Databases available through this site include PubMed (for free MEDLINE searching) and OMIM (Online Mendelian Inheritance in Man) for an extensive catalog of human genes and genetic disorders.
http://www.ncbi.nlm.nih.gov

National Center for Complementary and Alternative Medicine (NCCAM) The National Center for Complementary and Alternative Medicine identifies and evaluates unconventional healthcare practices; supports, coordinates, and conducts research and research training on these practices; and disseminates information. The site describes specific program areas; answers common questions about alternative therapies; and offers news, research grants information, and a calendar of events. Information resources at the site include a citation index related to alternative medicine obtained from MEDLINE, a bibliography of publications; the NCCAM clearinghouse of information for the public, media, and healthcare professionals; and a link to the National Women's Health Information Center (NWHIC).
http://nccam.nih.gov

National Center for Research Resources (NCRR) The National Center for Research Resources creates, develops, and provides a comprehensive range of human, animal, technological, and other resources to support biomedical research advances. The center's areas of concentration are biomedical technology, clinical research, comparative medicine, and research infrastructure. The site offers more specific information on each of these research areas, grants informa-

tion, news, current events, press releases, publications, research resources, and a search engine for locating information at the site.
http://www.ncrr.nih.gov

National Eye Institute (NEI) The National Eye Institute conducts and supports research, training, health information dissemination, and other programs with respect to blinding eye diseases, visual disorders, mechanisms of visual function, preservation of sight, and the special health problems and requirements of the visually impaired. Information at the site is tailored to the needs of researchers, health professionals, the general public and patients, educators, and the media. Resources include a clinical trials database, intramural research information, funding, grants, contract information, a news and events calendar, publications, visitor information, a site search engine, and an overview of the NEI offices, divisions, branches, and laboratories.
http://www.nei.nih.gov:80

National Heart, Lung, and Blood Institute (NHLBI) The National Heart, Lung, and Blood Institute provides leadership for a national research program in diseases of the heart, blood vessels, lungs, and blood, and in transfusion medicine through support of innovative basic, clinical, and population-based and health education research. The site provides health information; scientific resources; research funding information; news and press releases; details of committees, meetings, and events; clinical guidelines; notices of studies seeking patient participation; links to laboratories at the NHLBI; and technology transfer resources. Highlights of the site include cholesterol, weight, and asthma management resources.
http://www.nhlbi.nih.gov

National Human Genome Research Institute (NHGRI) The National Human Genome Research Institute supports the NIH component of the Human Genome Project, a worldwide research effort designed to analyze the structure of human DNA and determine the location of the estimated 50,000-100,000 human genes. The NHGRI Intramural Research Program develops and implements technology for understanding, diagnosing, and treating genetic diseases. The site provides information about NHGRI, the Human Genome Project, grants, intramural research, policy and public affairs, workshops and conferences, and news items. Resources include links to the institute's Ethical, Legal, and Social Implications Program and the Center for Inherited Disease Research, genomic and genetic resources for investigators, a glossary of genetic terms, and a site search engine.
http://www.nhgri.nih.gov

National Institute of Allergy and Infectious Diseases (NIAID) NIAID provides the major support for scientists conducting research aimed at developing better ways to diagnose, treat, and prevent the many infectious, immunologic, and allergic diseases that afflict people worldwide. This site provides NIAID news releases, contact information, a calendar of events, links to related

sites, a clinical trials database, grants and technology transfer information, and current research information (including meetings, publications, and research resources). Fact sheets for public use are available for different immunological disorders, allergies, asthma, and infectious diseases.
http://www.niaid.nih.gov

National Institute of Arthritis and Musculoskeletal and Skin Diseases (NIAMS) NIAMS conducts and supports a broad spectrum of research on normal structure and function of bones, muscles, and skin, as well as the numerous and disparate diseases that affect these tissues. NIAMS also conducts research training and epidemiologic studies in addition to disseminating information. The site provides details of research programs at the institute and offers personnel and employment listings, news, and an events calendar. Health information at the site is provided in the form of fact sheets, brochures, health statistics, and other resources, and contact details are available for ordering materials. Scientific resources include bibliographies of publications, consensus conference reports, grants and contracts applications, grant program announcements, and links to scientific research databases. Information on current clinical studies and transcripts of NIAMS advisory council, congressional, and conference reports are also available at the site.
http://www.nih.gov/niams

National Institute of Child Health and Human Development (NICHD) The NICHD conducts and supports laboratory, clinical, and epidemiological research on the reproductive, neurobiological, developmental, and behavioral processes that determine and maintain the health of children, adults, families, and populations. Research in the areas of fertility, pregnancy, growth, development, and medical rehabilitation strives to ensure that every child is born healthy and wanted and grows up free from disease and disability. The site provides general information about the institute; funding and intramural research details; information about the Division of Epidemiology, Statistics, and Prevention Research; a publications bibliography; fact sheets; reports; employment and fellowship listings; and research resources.
http://www.nichd.nih.gov

National Institute of Dental and Craniofacial Research (NIDCR) The National Institute of Dental and Craniofacial Research provides leadership for a national research program designed to understand, treat, and ultimately prevent the infectious and inherited craniofacial-oral-dental diseases and disorders that compromise millions of human lives. General information about the institute, news and health information, details of research activities, and NIDCR employment opportunities are all found at the site. A site search engine and staff directory are also available.
http://www.nidr.nih.gov

National Institute of Diabetes and Digestive and Kidney Diseases (NIDDK) The National Institute of Diabetes and Digestive and Kidney Dis-

eases conducts and supports basic and applied research and also provides leadership for a national program in diabetes, endocrinology, and metabolic diseases; in digestive diseases and nutrition; and in kidney, urologic, and hematologic diseases. NIDDK information at the site includes a mission statement, history, organization description, staff directory, and employment listing. Additional resources include news; a database for health information; clinical trials information, including a patient recruitment section; and information on extramural funding and intramural research at the institute.
http://www.niddk.nih.gov

National Institute of Environmental Health Sciences (NIEHS) The National Institute of Environmental Health Sciences reduces the burden of human illness and dysfunction from environmental causes by defining how environmental exposures, genetic susceptibility, and age interact to affect an individual's health. News and institute events, research information, grant and contract details, fact sheets, an institute personnel directory, employment and training notices, teacher support, and an online resource for kids are all found at this site. Library resources include a book catalog, electronic journals, database searching, NIEHS publications, and reference resources. Visitors can use search engines at the site to find environmental health information and news, publications, available grants and contracts, and library resources.
http://www.niehs.nih.gov

National Institute of General Medical Sciences (NIGMS) The National Institute of General Medical Sciences supports basic biomedical research that is not targeted to specific diseases but that increases the understanding of life processes and lays the foundation for advances in disease diagnosis, treatment, and prevention. Among the most significant results of this research has been the development of recombinant DNA technology, which forms the basis for the biotechnology industry. The site provides information about NIGMS research and funding programs, information for visitors, news, a publications list, reports, grant databases, a personnel and employment listing, and links to additional biomedical resources. http://www.nih.gov/nigms

National Institute of Mental Health (NIMH) The National Institute of Mental Health provides national leadership dedicated to understanding, treating, and preventing mental illnesses through basic research on the brain and behavior as well as through clinical, epidemiological, and services research. Resources available at the site include staff directories, information for visitors to the campus, employment opportunities, NIMH history, and publications from activities of the National Advisory Mental Health Council and Peer Review Committees. News, a calendar of events, information on clinical trials, funding opportunities, and intramural research are also provided. Pages tailored specifically for the public, health practitioners, or researchers contain mental disorder information, research fact sheets, statistics, science education materials, news, links to NIMH research sites, and patient education materials.
http://www.nimh.nih.gov

National Institute of Neurological Disorders and Stroke (NINDS)

The National Institute of Neurological Disorders and Stroke supports and conducts research and research training on the normal structure and function of the nervous system and on the causes, prevention, diagnosis, and treatment of more than 600 nervous system disorders including stroke, epilepsy, multiple sclerosis, Parkinson's disease, head and spinal cord injury, Alzheimer's disease, and brain tumors. The site provides visitors with an organizational diagram, an e-mail directory, links to advisory groups, the mission and history of NINDS, a site search engine, employment and training opportunities, and information on research at NINDS. Information is available for patients, clinicians, and scientists, including publications, details of current clinical trials, links to other health organizations, and research funding information.
http://www.ninds.nih.gov

National Institute of Nursing Research (NINR)

The National Institute of Nursing Research supports clinical and basic research to establish a scientific basis for the care of individuals across the life span, from management of patients during illness and recovery to the reduction of risks for disease and disability and the promotion of healthy lifestyles. NINR accomplishes its mission by supporting grants to universities and other research organizations as well as by conducting research intramurally at laboratories in Bethesda, Maryland. Visitors to this site can find the NINR mission statement and history, employment listings, news, conference details, publications, speech transcripts, answers to frequently asked questions, information concerning legislative activities, research program and funding details, health information, highlights and outcomes of current nursing research, and links to additional Web resources.
http://www.nih.gov/ninr

National Institute on Aging (NIA)

The National Institute on Aging leads a national program of research on the biomedical, social, and behavioral aspects of the aging process; the prevention of age-related diseases and disabilities; and the promotion of a better quality of life for all older Americans. The site presents recent announcements and upcoming events, employment opportunities, press releases, and media advisories of significant findings. Research resources include news from the National Advisory Council on Aging, links to extramural aging research conducted throughout the United States, and funding and training information. Health professionals and the general public can access publications on health and aging topics or order materials online.
http://www.nih.gov/nia

National Institute on Alcohol Abuse and Alcoholism (NIAAA)

The National Institute on Alcohol Abuse and Alcoholism conducts research focused on improving the treatment and prevention of alcoholism and alcohol-related problems to reduce the enormous health, social, and economic consequences of this disease. General resources at the site include an introduction to the institute, extramural and intramural research information, an organizational flowchart, details of legislative activities, Advisory Council roster and minutes, information on scientific review groups associated with the institute, a staff directory, and employment announcements. Institute publications, data tables, press releases, conferences and events calendars, answers to frequently asked questions on the subject of alcohol abuse and dependence, and links to related sites are also found at the site. The ETOH Database, an online bibliographic database containing over 100,000 records on alcohol abuse and alcoholism, can be accessed from the site, as well as the National Library of Medicine's MEDLINE database. http://www.niaaa.nih.gov:80

National Institute on Deafness and Other Communication Disorders (NIDCD)
The National Institute on Deafness and Other Communication Disorders conducts and supports biomedical research and research training in the normal and disordered processes of hearing, balance, smell, taste, voice, speech, and language. The institute also conducts and supports research and research training related to disease prevention and health promotion; addresses special biomedical and behavioral problems associated with people who have communication impairments or disorders; and supports efforts to create devices that substitute for lost and impaired sensory and communication function. The site provides visitors with many fact sheets and other information resources on hearing and balance; smell and taste; voice, speech, and language; hearing aids; otosclerosis; vocal abuse and misuse; and vocal cord paralysis. Other resources include a directory of organizations related to hearing, balance, smell, taste, voice, speech, and language; a glossary of terms; an online newsletter; information for children and teachers; clinical trials details; and a site search engine. Information on research funding and intramural research activities, a news and events calendar, and general information about NIDCD are also available at this site. http://www.nih.gov/nidcd

National Institute on Drug Abuse (NIDA)
Part of the National Institutes of Health, the National Institute on Drug Abuse site offers resources for healthcare professionals. The home page features news, events, research updates, and special NIDA Web sites covering common drugs of abuse, such as steroids and club drugs. There are also sections on drug abuse research and prevention, grant funding, international opportunities, and legislative issues. The publications section offers some online publications as well as items for purchase. Research training at NIDA, as well as the proceedings from their scientific meetings, can also be found. A comprehensive list of related resources is provided. http://www.nida.nih.gov/

National Library of Medicine (NLM)
The National Library of Medicine, the world's largest medical library, collects materials in all areas of biomedicine and healthcare and focuses on biomedical aspects of technology, the humanities, and the physical, life, and social sciences. This site contains links to government medical databases, including MEDLINE and MEDLINEplus, information on funding opportunities at the National Library of Medicine and other federal agencies, and details of services, training, and outreach programs offered by NLM. Users can access NLM's catalog of resources (LocatorPlus), as well as

NLM publications, including fact sheets, published reports, and staff publications. NLM research programs discussed at the site include topics in computational molecular biology, medical informatics, and other related subjects. The Web site features 15 searchable databases, covering journal searches via MEDLINE; AIDS information via AIDSLINE, AIDSDRUGS, and AIDSTRIALS; bioethics via BIOETHICSLINE; and numerous other important topics. The NLM Gateway—a master search engine—searches MEDLINE using the retrieval engine called PubMed. It is very user-friendly. There are 9 million citations in MEDLINE and PreMEDLINE and the other related databases. Additionally, the NLM provides sources of health statistics, serials programs, and services maintained through a system called SERHOLD.
http://www.nlm.nih.gov

Warren Grant Magnuson Clinical Center   The Warren Grant Magnuson Clinical Center is the clinical research facility of the National Institutes of Health, supporting clinical investigations conducted by the NIH. The clinical center was designed to bring patient-care facilities close to research laboratories, allowing findings of basic and clinical scientists to move quickly from the laboratory to the treatment of patients. The site provides visitors with news, events, details of current clinical research studies, patient recruitment resources, links to departmental Web sites, and information resources for NIH staff, patients, physicians, and scientists. Topics discussed in the center's Medicine for the Public Lecture Series and resources in medical and scientific education offered by the center are included at the site.
http://www.cc.nih.gov:80

CENTERS FOR DISEASE CONTROL AND PREVENTION

Centers for Disease Control and Prevention (CDC)   The mission of the Centers for Disease Control and Prevention is to promote health and quality of life by preventing and controlling disease, injury, and disability. The site provides users with links to 11 associated centers, institutes, and offices; a Web page devoted to travelers' health; publications, software, and other products, data, and statistics; training and employment opportunities; and subscription registration forms for online CDC publications. Highlighted publications include the *Emerging Infectious Disease Journal* and the *Morbidity and Mortality Weekly Report,* both of which can be e-mailed on a regular basis by registering on this site. Links are available to additional CDC resources as well as to state and local agencies concerned with public health issues. The CDC offers a comprehensive, alphabetical list of general and specific health topics at the site. Visitors can also search the site by keyword and read spotlights on current research and information presented by the Web site.
http://www.cdc.gov

Epidemiology Program Office   Information and resources on public health surveillance are available here. Publications and software related to epidemiol-

ogy are available for download. Updated news, events, and international bulletins are also featured at the site.
http://www.cdc.gov/epo/index.htm

National Center for Chronic Disease Prevention and Health Promotion (NCCDPHP) Maintained by the Centers for Disease Control and Prevention, this site focuses on many different aspects of chronic disease prevention. Intended for healthcare professionals, resources on the site include facts on the economic burden of chronic disease, risk prevention, and comprehensive approaches to prevention. Under the chronic diseases section, there is information on NCCDPHP's programs, reports, and fact sheets for arthritis, cancer, cardiovascular disease, diabetes, epilepsy, and oral diseases. Additional links on the site provide information on specific populations such as pregnant women and minorities. http://www.cdc.gov/nccdphp/index.htm

National Center for Environmental Health (NCEH) The NCEH Web page offers information on their programs and activities related to the prevention of health problems from environmental hazards. The health topics section offers an A-to-Z listing of topics covered on the site. Descriptions of their programs and activities can also be found, such as the prevention of birth defects by the use of folic acid. Their publications section offers fact sheets, brochures, and scientific publications on such topics as lead poisoning and the indoor use of pesticide. There is also a searchable index of articles from their *Morbidity and Mortality Weekly Report*. In addition, the site offers current employment opportunities and information on training programs. Spanish and child-oriented versions of the NCEH site are also available.
http://www.cdc.gov/nceh/ncehhome.htm

National Center for Health Statistics (NCHS) The National Center for Health Statistics Web page features health data and statistics on a broad array of topics, including AIDS, chicken pox, divorce, and obstetrical procedures. Visitors can read descriptions of the NCHS survey and data collection systems; healthcare professionals can learn how to include their patients in the surveys. A "Data Warehouse" section offers tabulated data on the national and state level, as well as an international classification of diseases. A link to FASTATS A to Z provides national statistics, along with links for more comprehensive data. There is also information on NCHS research and development.
http://www.cdc.gov/nchs/default.htm

National Center for HIV, STD, and TB Prevention Part of the Centers for Disease Control and Prevention, the National Center for HIV, STD, and TB Prevention offers general information for professionals and the public on the control and prevention of HIV/AIDS, sexually transmitted diseases and tuberculosis. The home page highlights news and CDC updates. Information of interest to professionals is easily accessed by clicking on the link for "Site Highlights" in the sidebar menu. Among the highlights is a link to the National Prevention Information Network, which offers information on HIV/AIDS, STD, and TB and the connections between them. By clicking on the disease, visitors will find resources, related links, a bulletin board, distance learning, publications, and FAQs. Another site highlight is a searchable database of organizations that provide HIV/AIDS, STD and TB prevention, education, healthcare, and social services. CDC laboratory research is accessible including disease information and reports. In addition, the top of the home page has a link for funding opportunities. http://www.cdc.gov/nchstp/od/nchstp.html

National Center for Infectious Diseases (NCID)   Dedicated to the study of infectious diseases, the National Center for Infectious Diseases Web page provides an A-to-Z listing of disease information with links to fact sheets, laboratory assistance information, and related articles. Visitors can access the NCID online journal, *Emerging Infectious Diseases,* with full-text articles. There are also articles, booklets, and a video on preventing emerging infectious diseases. Data and reports on diseases can also be found under "Surveillance Resources." A link to "DPDx" features reviews on parasites and parasitic diseases, diagnostic procedures, diagnostic assistance, and an image library. A travel section covers, by region, diseases, recommended vaccinations, and tips. In addition, the publications section offers many free online brochures. A short list of related links is provided. http://www.cdc.gov/ncidod/index.htm

National Center for Injury Prevention and Control   Healthcare professionals and the public will find a broad array of information on injury prevention on this Web page. The site offers fact sheets on injuries and safety such as child passenger safety, fireworks injury prevention, suicide and fall prevention programs for seniors. The data section features WISQARS, an interactive database of injury-related mortality data. There is also a list of publications, viewable online, and information on research funding. On the left side of the page are facts and data in categories such as injury care, violence, and unintentional injury. Consumers can click on the SafeUSA link to access safety tips. http://www.cdc.gov/ncipc/ncipchm.htm

National Immunization Program   The National Immunization Program of the Centers for Disease Control and Prevention offers a wide range of immunization information resources directed to healthcare professionals and consumers. The home page features clinical information in categories such as vaccine recommendations, advances in immunization, educational resources (including training for professionals), and vaccine safety. Information on grants and funding, as well as data and statistics, is available through links on the left side of the page. Under the category of "Subsites," visitors can find information on the development of immunization registries, and downloadable clinical assessment software (CASA) to track immunization practices within an office. Publications for both the professional and consumers can be accessed through a link at the top of the page. Also at the top of each page is a link to the Web site's Dictionary of Immunization Terms.
http://www.cdc.gov/nip/

National Institute for Occupational Safety and Health (NIOSH)

Created to conduct research on work-related illnesses and injuries, the National Insititute for Occupational Safety and Health (NIOSH) describes their activities and recommendations on this site. A topic index provides articles and guidelines on topics such as chemical safety, indoor air quality, and latex. The publications section features fact sheets, brochures, and bulletins, some available online. In addition, there is information on NIOSH research activities, funding opportunities, and training information.

http://www.cdc.gov/niosh/homepage.html

National Prevention Information Network

Designed to provide information on HIV/AIDS, STDs, and TB, the CDC's National Prevention Information Network site offers useful resources for the healthcare professional and consumer. Categorized by disease; namely HIV/AIDS, STD, TB, there are a bulletin board, distance learning, FAQs, mortality/morbidity reports, and related links. A large list of publications is found, along with a database of organizations. Information on the CDC's prevention research is also available with links to numerous reports and journal articles.

http://www.cdcnpin.org/

OTHER HEALTH AGENCIES

Center for Nutrition Policy and Promotion (CNPP)

The Center for Nutrition Policy and Promotion, within the U.S. Department of Agriculture, conducts research on the nutritional needs of Americans and disseminates their findings. Their site provides statistical information and resources for educators, contains dietary guidelines for Americans, and offers official USDA food plans. A database on the nutrient content of the U.S. food supply (on a per capita basis) is provided. In addition, there is a 76-page booklet available that offers recipes and tips for healthy meals.

http://www.usda.gov/cnpp

Food and Nutrition Service (FNS)

The Food and Nutrition Service "reduces hunger and food insecurity in partnership with cooperating organizations by providing children and needy families access to food, a healthful diet and nutrition education in a manner that supports American agriculture and inspires public confidence." The site provides details of FNS nutrition assistance programs such as Food Stamps, WIC, and Child Nutrition. Research, in the form of published studies and reports, is also made available at the site.

http://www.fns.usda.gov/fns

Food Safety and Inspection Service (FSIS)

The Food Safety and Inspection Service, part of the U.S. Department of Agriculture, is dedicated to food safety. Its site offers news, recall notification on meat and poultry products, a newsletter, and related links. A consumer education section offers fact sheets on the safe handling and cooking of meat, poultry, and eggs. Technical publications and a video library can be accessed under the publications section. Also of interest to professionals is a fellowship program related to food safety, which can be found in the drop-down menu under "Featured Topics." In addition, information on distance learning at the Food Safety Virtual University is provided and can be accessed through a drop-down menu.

http://www.fsis.usda.gov

National Bioethics Advisory Commission (NBAC) The NBAC studies bioethical issues related to genetics and the protection of humans as research subjects. Their reports are directed to the National Science and Technology Council. The NBAC also advises on the applications, including the clinical applications, of their research. This site lists meeting dates, full-text transcripts of meetings, and news. Reports they have produced can be read on the site for such topics as ethical issues in human stem cell research, research involving persons with mental disorders, and cloning human beings. A list of relevant links to related sites is provided.

http://bioethics.gov/cgi-bin/bioeth_counter.pl

National Science Foundation (NSF): Directorate for Biological Sciences The Division of Integrative Biology and Neuroscience (IBN), part of the National Science Foundation, supports research aimed at understanding the living organism—plant, animal, microbe—as a unit of biological organization. Current scientific emphases include biotechnology, biomolecular materials, environmental biology, global change, biodiversity, molecular evolution, plant science, microbial biology, and computational biology (including modeling). Research projects generally include support for the education and training of future scientists. IBN also supports doctoral dissertation research, research conferences, workshops, symposia, Undergraduate Mentoring in Environmental Biology (UMEB), and a variety of NSF-wide activities. This site describes in detail the activities and divisions of IBN and offers a staff directory, award listings, and deadline dates for funding applications.

http://www.nsf.gov/bio/ibn/start.htm

Office of National Drug Control Policy (ONDCP) This site states the missions and goals of the ONDCP. It has a clearinghouse of drug policy information with a staff that will respond to the needs of the general public, providing statistical data, topical fact sheets, information packets, and more. There is information on related science, medicine, and technology. There are also resources on prevention, education, and treatment programs. Information on the enforcement of the policies is provided for the national, state, and local levels.

http://www.whitehousedrugpolicy.gov

10.5 FULL-TEXT ARTICLES

Amedeo Amedeo is a free medical literature service, allowing users to select topics and journals of interest. The service sends a weekly e-mail with an overview of new articles reflecting the specifications indicated by the user and also creates a personal home page with abstracts of relevant articles. The site allows registered users to access a network center, which facilitates literature exchange among users with similar interests. This service is supported through educational grants by numerous pharmaceutical companies.

(free registration) http://www.amedeo.com

BioMed Central: Online Journals Produced by the commercial publisher, Current Science Group, BioMed Central (BMC) makes full-text peer-reviewed articles available on this Web page. The site's content is grouped by subject into journals published by BMC including BMC Cancer, BMC Infectious Diseases, BMC Surgery, and BMC Pediatrics. Each journal's articles are available for download in PDF format.

http://www.biomedcentral.com/browse/medicine/

CatchWord There are more than 1,100 journals on a variety of subjects available on this Web page. Visitors can view the journal's table of contents and abstracts, then purchase the full-text articles online. Institutions can utilize the services of CatchWord to provide a single interface to their online journal collections. Twenty specialties of medicine are found, including cardiology, oncology, and psychiatry.

(some features fee-based) http://www.catchword.co.uk/

EurekAlert This site allows professionals and consumers to search the archives for the latest articles, news items, events, awards, and grants in science and medicine, including psychiatry. The peer-reviewed journals link connects visitors to full-text articles, and current news can be obtained from the Howard Hughes Medical Institute and the National Institutes of Health.

http://www.eurekalert.org

FreeMedicalJournals.com: Full-Text Articles Healthcare professionals will find more than 550 free medical journals on this site with access to full-text articles. The home page lists journals by categories such as: free one to six months after publication, free one year after publication, and free two years after publication. However, the home page only shows a fraction of what is available; visitors should click on "Journals Sorted by Specialty" on the left side of the page to view all of the journals. Specialties include AIDS, cardiology, dermatology, hematology, oncology, infectious diseases, psychiatry, rheumatology, and pediatrics. Some journals are available in other languages. Visitors can register for a free alerting service which will e-mail information on new free online journals as they become available.

http://www.freemedicaljournals.com/

HighWire Press: Full-Text Articles Stanford University's Highwire Press, developer of the Web versions of many important biomedical journals, maintains this extensive listing of links to full-text journal archives. A list of journals offering free access is provided at this site, with a notation indicating whether a title is free, free for a trial period, or free for back issues. More than 100 journals

are listed, and a link on the left side of the page brings up a list of full-text science archives on the Web.
http://highwire.stanford.edu/lists/freeart.dtl

Journal Watch Online   Subscribers to the Journal Watch service can access summaries of the most recent clinical research literature, summarized by physicians, for their specialty at this Web site. Produced by the Massachusetts Medical Society, publishers of the *New England Journal of Medicine,* Journal Watch updates its summaries four times a week in the specialties of dermatology, cardiology, psychiatry, women's health, infectious diseases, neurology, and gastroenterology. Research summaries and commentary are drawn from 50 journals.
(fee-based) http://www.jwatch.org/

MD Consult   Physicians can access the full-text of nearly 40 major medical textbooks and 48 core medical journals on this Web site. Journals available on the site include *Arthritis and Rheumatism, The Cancer Journal, Chest,* and the *Journal of the American Academy of Dermatology.* The site also offers the ability to search MEDLINE and other key databases simultaneously n order to locate full-text articles. Other features include clinical practice guidelines, CME modules, patient education handouts, and prescription information. A 10-day free trial of full site access is available for physicians.
(fee-based) http://www.mdconsult.com/

MedBioWorld: Medical Journals Main Index   Visitors to this address will find comprehensive listings of online journals, categorized by specialty topic. Major broad-coverage medical journals, nursing journals, science journals, and books on medical writing are also listed through the site, as well as links to many publishers' Web sites.
http://www.medbioworld.com/journals/medicine/med-bio.html

MEDLINE Journal Links to Publishers   Through the National Library of Medicine, the MEDLINE service provides direct access to hundreds of medical journals in all fields, listed alphabetically by name, with direct links to their respective publishers. Upon accessing an individual publication, the reader can normally view the current issue table of contents and abstracts for the articles. In certain cases, the complete article texts are available without charge, but in other cases it is necessary to pay a fee and obtain an access password. Each page explains the available information and the conditions for access, since policies vary by publisher and journal.
http://www.ncbi.nlm.nih.gov/entrez/journals/loftext_noprov.html

Medscape   Visitors to this site can access more than 25,000 full-text articles from more than 40 journals and medical news periodicals. Medical journals include *Chest, American Heart Journal,* and *Southern Medical Journal.* The site also features "Journal Scan;" clinical summaries of the latest literature for specialties such as cardiology, dermatology, infectious diseases, psychiatry, and

respiratory care. There are also several online textbooks available.
(free registration) http://www.medscape.com/
Home/Topics/multispecialty/directories/dir-MULT.JournalRoom.html

PubList: Health and Medical Sciences This site contains an extensive list of links to thousands of medical journals, divided by subject areas. Useful information, such as frequency, publisher, and format, is included for each publication, and a search engine can be used to identify titles of interest.
http://www.publist.com/indexes/health.html

PubMed Central: Full-Text Article Archive PubMed Central aims to be a digital library with archives for all the biomedical literature. It is still in the process of development by the National Center for Biotechnology Information and the National Library of Medicine. Currently, eight journals with full-text articles and archives are found on the site with 10 more slated for addition in the future. Available journals include all BioMedCentral journals (see separate write-up of this site), *Arthritis Research, Breast Cancer Research,* and the *British Medical Journal.* Many of these journals delay release of their full-text content to this site, with the most current content available at their own sites on a subscription basis.
http://www.pubmedcentral.nih.gov/

UnCover Web This enormous database of medical and nonscientific journals' tables of contents permits searching by keyword, journal title, or author. Full articles can be faxed or e-mailed for a fee. For a modest price, the "Reveal" service provides e-mailed tables of contents for specific journals as they are published and added to the database.
(some features fee-based) http://uncweb.carl.org

University of Georgia: Science Library An A-to-Z listing of free full-text science journals available on the Internet is provided on this site. The list can be navigated by clicking on the appropriate letter at the bottom of the site. Some journals can only be accessed by faculty and students at the University of Georgia. http://www.libs.uga.edu/science/fullalph.html

WebMedLit WebMedLit provides access to the latest medical literature on the Web by indexing medical Web sites daily and presenting articles from each site organized by subject categories. All WebMedLit article links are from the original source document at the publisher's Web site, and most articles are available in full text.
http://webmedlit.silverplatter.com/index.html

10.6 GOVERNMENT INFORMATION DATABASES

Agency for Healthcare Research and Quality (AHRQ): Search Tool This site offers a search tool to find information located on the Agency for

Healthcare Research and Quality Web page. There is information appropriate to professionals and the public.

http://www.ahcpr.gov/query/query.htm

Centers for Disease Control and Prevention (CDC): Web Search

Both healthcare professionals and consumers can find useful information using the search tool provided on the CDC site. Visitors have the opportunity to search all CDC Web sites by keyword and to search state health departments. By checking the box next to the state health department of interest, one can search one or more of them or all of them at once.

http://www.cdc.gov/search.htm

Combined Health Information Database

Designed as a bibliographic database, the Combined Health Information Database draws upon health information from health-related Federal government agencies. The database is categorized under 16 health topics such as Alzheimer's, cancer, diabetes, and weight control. Searches can be limited to individual subtopics, or the database can be searched in its entirety. Access to information is only available through a keyword search, which can be done with a simple or detailed search. Results include health promotion and educational materials aimed at consumers and not indexed elsewhere.

http://chid.nih.gov/

CRISP: Computer Retrieval of Information on Scientific Projects

CRISP is a searchable database of federally funded biomedical research projects conducted at universities, hospitals, and other research institutions. Users, including the public, can use CRISP to search for scientific concepts, emerging trends, and techniques or to identify specific projects and/or investigators. This site provides a direct gateway into the searchable database. The NIH funds the operation of CRISP.

http://www-commons.cit.nih.gov/crisp

Department of Energy (DOE): Comprehensive Epidemiologic Data Resource

Compiled by the U.S. Department of Energy, this site features a collection of resources on health and radiation exposure data related to DOE installations. Included are data from epidemiologic studies performed by DOE-funded investigators on health and mortality, classic radiation, and dose reconstruction. The site also covers studies of populations living near DOE installations and other studies on radiation effects, such as the classic ones on atomic bomb survivors.

http://cedr.lbl.gov/

FedWorld Information Network

Information from many federal agencies can be accessed through this Web page. By clicking on the database section at the top of the page, visitors will find links to 20 searchable databases encompassing a variety of information such as Supreme Court decisions, EPA Clean Air Act data, and U.S. Customs Headquarters' rulings. The home page also allows browsing the entire FedWorld network, searching Web pages on the network by keyword, and searching U.S. government reports by keyword. There is also a link to search all government Web sites.

(some features fee-based) http://www.fedworld.gov/

Government Databases: Health   Maintained by St. Mary's University of San Antonio, Texas, this site features a list of more than 25 selected government sites dealing with health and medicine. Each site listed has a description of its contents. Sites covered include those on clinical trials, Congressional Research Service reports, food composition data, and MEDLINE.

(free registration) http://library.stmarytx.edu/acadlib/doc/electronic/dbhealth.htm

Government Information Locator Service   Intended to pool access to government information through one search engine, this federal locator service enables a search by topic in which the search word or phrase is placed in quotation marks. Instructions for searching are located at the site.

http://www.access.gpo.gov/su_docs/gils/index.html

Healthfinder   Healthfinder provides links to national medical libraries, such as the National Library of Medicine and the National Institutes of Health Library, and other medical or health sciences libraries on the Internet. Directories of libraries are also available to find local facilities. Visitors can also use a site search engine to find specific health Web resources or an A-to-Z directory of topics.   http://healthfinder.gov/moretools/libraries.htm

MEDLINEplus: Health Information Database   A comprehensive database of health and medical information, MEDLINEplus serves a different purpose from its sister service, MEDLINE, which is a bibliographic search engine to locate citations and abstracts in medical journals and reports. MEDLINEplus offers the ability to search by topic and obtain full information rather than citations. The search engine brings up extensive resources on every possible topic, giving complete information on all aspects of the topic. One can search body systems, disorders and diseases, treatments and therapies, diagnostic procedures, side effects, and numerous other important topics related to personal health and the field of medicine in general.

http://www.nlm.nih.gov/medlineplus/medlineplus.html

10.7   HEALTH AND MEDICAL HOTLINES

Toll-Free Numbers for Health Information   A categorized list of hundreds of toll-free health information hotlines is provided by this site. Each hotline provides educational materials for patients.

http://nhic-nt.health.org/Scripts/Tollfree.cfm

10.8 HEALTH INSURANCE PLANS

HealthPlanDirectory.com Produced by a commercial marketing company, DoctorDirectory.com, this site contains a directory of health insurance plans, listed by state. Contact information for each plan is provided.
http://www.doctordirectory.com/healthplans/directory/default.asp

10.9 HEALTHCARE LEGISLATION AND ADVOCACY

American Medical Association (AMA): AMA in Washington The purpose of this site is to encourage physicians around the country to get involved in the AMA's grassroots lobbying efforts. It covers information on legislation relevant to the medical profession, the AMA's congressional agenda, and educational programs available through the AMA on political activism for physicians. The Web site is updated regularly with the latest news on medical issues in the government.
http://www.ama-assn.org/ama/pub/category/4015.html

American Medical Group Association (AMGA): Public Policy and Political Affairs The AMGA provides legislative advocacy to medical groups, addressing current political debates in the medical community. Updated legislative and media alerts, an electronic newsletter for members, and comments and testimony on several subjects affecting healthcare providers are offered. Relevant Web sites of interest are accessible.
(some features fee-based)
http://www.amga.org/AMGA2000/PublicPolicy/index_publicPolicy.htm

American Medical Student Association (AMSA): Health Policy The AMSA is an organization that attempts to improve healthcare and medical education. Its "Health Policy" department contains news of legislation that affects medical education; educational information on how to be a health policy activist; and a listing of printable documents concerning relevant health policy issues, such as gene patents and prescription drug coverage.
http://www.amsa.org/hp/hpindex.cfm

American Medical Women's Association (AMWA) The AMWA promotes issues related to women's health and professional development for female physicians. The site's advocacy and actions sections contain articles on news and legislation that is relevant to these issues and also give advice on how to get involved.
http://www.amwa-doc.org/index.html

THOMAS: U.S. Congress on the Internet Within THOMAS, one can find information on bills, laws, reports, or any current U.S. federal legislation. The site's engine can be used to find current congressional bills by keyword or bill number. http://thomas.loc.gov

10.10 HOSPITAL RESOURCES

American Hospital Association   Everything pertaining to hospitals is either available at this site or at a link from this site, including advocacy, health insurance, extensive hospital information, research and education, health statistics, and valuable links to the National Information Center for Health Services Administration as well as other organizations and resources.
http://www.aha.org

HospitalDirectory.com   This useful site provides a listing of states and territories, each of which is a hot link to a further listing of cities in the state or territory. By clicking on a city, the database provides a listing of hospitals in that area, including name, address, and telephone numbers. The site also offers other links pertaining to health plans, doctors, health news, insurance, and medical products for physicians.
http://www.doctordirectory.com/hospitals/directory

HospitalWeb   This site is a guide to global hospitals on the World Wide Web (not including the United States). It lists over 50 countries. Under each country, the names of a number of hospitals in that country are listed. By clicking on the hospital name, the user is taken to the hospital's Web site which provides further information.   http://neuro-www2.mgh.harvard.edu/hospitalwebworld.html

10.11 INTERNET MEDICAL NEWSGROUPS

General Medical Topic Newsgroups
Internet newsgroups are places where individuals can post messages on a common site for others to read. Many newsgroups are devoted to medical topics, and these groups are listed below. To access these groups you can either use a newsreader program (often part of an e-mail program) or search and browse using a popular Web site, groups.google.com

On the Google site, visitors can look for one of the newsgroup names listed below, such as sci.med, by either browsing the list of newsgroups or searching by the group name. Once there, the forum appears as a bulletin board with a posting on a particular topic, followed by responses to it. One can navigate the discussion by clicking on the postings of interest or post a reply.

Since newsgroups are mostly unmoderated, there is no editorial process or restrictions on postings. The information at these groups is therefore neither authoritative nor based on any set of standards.

alt.image.medical	alt.med.equipment	alt.med.veterinary
alt.med	alt.med.fibromyalgia	alt.med.vision.improve
alt.med.allergy	alt.med.outpat.clinic	sci.engr.biomed
alt.med.cfs	alt.med.phys-assts	sci.med
alt.med.ems	alt.med.urum-outcomes	sci.med.aids

sci.med.cardiology	sci.med.laboratory	sci.med.prostate.bph
sci.med.dentistry	sci.med.nursing	sci.med.prostate.cancer
sci.med.diseases.cancer	sci.med.nutrition	sci.med.prostate.prostatitis
sci.med.diseases.hepatitis	sci.med.occupational	sci.med.psychobiology
sci.med.diseases.lyme	sci.med.orthopedics	sci.med.radiology
sci.med.diseases.viral	sci.med.pathology	sci.med.telemedicine
sci.med.immunology	sci.med.pharmacy	sci.med.transcription
sci.med.informatics	sci.med.physics	sci.med.vision

10.12 LOCATING A PHYSICIAN

American Medical Association (AMA): Physician Select Online Doctor Finder   The AMA is the primary "umbrella" professional association of physicians and medical students in the United States. The AMA Physician Select system provides information on virtually every licensed physician, including more than 650,000 physicians and doctors of osteopathy. According to the site, physician credentials have been certified for accuracy and authenticated by accrediting agencies, medical schools, residency programs, licensing and certifying boards, and other data sources. The user can search for physicians by name or by medical specialty.
http://www.ama-assn.org/aps/amahg.htm

DoctorDirectory.com   Produced by a commercial marketing company, DoctorDirectory.com, this site contains a directory of physicians, organized by specialty. Within the specialties, visitors can click on the state and city of interest. Results include the physician's name, gender, graduation year, specialties, and address.
http://www.doctordirectory.com/doctors/directory/default.asp?newSession=true

HealthPages   This search tool allows visitors to locate doctors in their area by specialty and location. Over 500,000 physicians and 120,000 dentists are listed. Doctors may update their profiles free-of-charge. Local provider choices are displayed to consumers in a comparative format. They can access charts that compare the training, office services, and fees of local physicians; the provider networks and quality measures of area managed care plans; and the size, services, and fees of local hospitals. Patients can post ratings and comments about their doctors.
http://www.thehealthpages.com

Physicians' Practice   This site allows the user to search for doctors in many specialty areas. Searches are performed by specialty and zip code. Physicians must pay a fee to be listed but enjoy other benefits such as referrals, Internet presence, and a newsletter.
http://www.physicianpractice.com

10.13   MEDICAL AND HEALTH SCIENCES LIBRARIES

Medical Libraries at Universities, Hospitals, Foundations, and Research Centers   This site includes an up-to-date listing of libraries that can be accessed through links produced by staff members of the Hardin Library at the University of Iowa. Libraries are listed state by state, enabling easy access to hundreds of library Web sites. Numerous foreign medical library links are also provided.
http://www.lib.uiowa.edu/hardin-www/hslibs.html

National Institutes of Health (NIH): Library Online   Information on the NIH Library is presented on this site, including a staff listing, current exhibits, hours, materials available to NIH personnel and the general public, current job vacancies, maps for visitors, and answers to frequently asked questions about the library. Users can search the library's catalog of books, journals, and other periodicals; access public and academic medical databases; and find seminar and tutorial information as well as links to related sites.
http://nihlibrary.nih.gov

National Library of Medicine (NLM)   The National Library of Medicine, the world's largest medical library, collects materials in all areas of biomedicine and healthcare and works on biomedical aspects of technology, the humanities, and the physical, life, and social sciences. This site contains links to government medical databases, including MEDLINE and MEDLINEplus; information on funding opportunities at the National Library of Medicine and other federal agencies; and details of services, training, and outreach programs offered by NLM. Users can access NLM's catalog of resources (LocatorPlus), as well as NLM publications, including fact sheets, published reports, and staff publications. NLM research programs discussed at the site include topics in computational molecular biology, medical informatics, and other related subjects. The Web site features 15 searchable databases, covering journal searches via MEDLINE; AIDS information via AIDSLINE, AIDSDRUGS, and AIDSTRIALS; bioethics via BIOETHICSLINE; and numerous other important topics. The NLM Gateway—a master search engine—searches MEDLINE using the retrieval engine called PubMed. It is very user-friendly. There are over 9 million citations in MEDLINE and PreMEDLINE and the other related databases. Additionally, the NLM provides sources of health statistics, serials programs, and services maintained through a system called SERHOLD.
http://www.nlm.nih.gov

National Network of Libraries of Medicine (NN/LM)   Composed of eight regional libraries, the NN/LM also provides access to numerous health science libraries in each region, located at universities, hospitals, and institutes. The Web site enables the user to link directly to each of the libraries in any region of the United States. These libraries have access to the NLM's SERHOLD system database of machine-readable holdings for biomedical serial titles. There

are approximately 89,000 serial titles that are accessible through SERHOLD-participating libraries.
http://www.nnlm.nlm.nih.gov

10.14 Medical Conferences and Meetings

Doctor's Guide: Medical Conferences and Meetings   This address lists several hundred conferences and meetings, including continuing medical education programs worldwide, organized by date, meeting site, and subject. Location and other details are provided.
http://www.docguide.com/crc.nsf/web-byspec

EventOnline.org   Sponsored by Excerpta Medica, this site offers a comprehensive database of medical, biotechnical, and scientific events. Search results yield contact information, as well as a basic description of the event. Some events have links to the sponsor's Web page. In addition, there are links for weather, hotels, and maps to assist in planning a visit.
http://www.eventonline.org/

Medical Conferences.com   A broad range of medical conference listings are covered on this site, including meetings related to many different areas of healthcare including pharmaceuticals and hospital supplies, as well as the clinical medical specialties. An easy-to-use search mechanism provides access to the numerous listings, each of which links to details concerning each conference. The site claims to be updated daily, providing details on over 7,000 forthcoming conferences.   http://www.medicalconferences.com

MediConf Online   This well-organized site lists conferences by medical subject, chronology, and geographic location, mostly covering meetings to be held in the next month or two. The listings include research conferences, seminars, annual meetings of professional societies, medical technology trade shows, and opportunities for CME credits. What is provided free on the Internet is only a small percentage of the complete fee-based database, which includes more than 60,000 listings of meetings to be held through 2014 and is available through the information vendors, Ovid or Dialog.
(some features fee-based) http://www.mediconf.com/online.html

Medscape: Multispecialty Conference Schedules   Medical conference schedules are posted on this Web page, courtesy of Medscape. The schedules are listed chronologically and categorized by specialties such as family medicine, pediatrics, nursing, and radiology. Conference dates, addresses, Web site links and contact information are provided.
http://www.medscape.com/Home/Topics/multispecialty/directories/dir-MULT.ConfSchedules.html

Physician's Guide to the Internet Dates and locations for major national medical meetings are listed alphabetically by association at this site. There are also some hyperlinks to association pages and contact persons.
http://www.physiciansguide.com/meetings.html

 Princeton Medicon: The Medical Conference Resource Details regarding worldwide major medical conferences of interest to medical specialists and primary care professionals are featured on this site. It is also periodically published in printed form. Access to lists of meetings is provided through a useful search engine that permits searching by specialty, year, and geographic region. http://www.medicon.com.au

10.15 MEDICAL DATABASE SERVICES

 American Chemical Society: SciFinder This site provides information on the SciFinder research database, designed for scientists to use for searching Chemical Abstracts and Medline. The database system contains more than 16 million abstracts, with links to full-text articles. Users can search by company name, chemical reactions, substructure, or keyword. Subscription information for research organizations is provided.
(fee-based) http://www.cas.org/SCIFINDER/

 Cambridge Scientific Abstracts: Internet Database Service More than 50 bibliographic databases and electronic journals can be searched through this site. Databases include MEDLINE, TOXLINE and other sci-tech databases such as Biotechnology & Bioengineering. CSA-published electronic collections of abstracts, called "journals" such as *Genetics Abstracts, Medical & Pharmaceutical Biotechnology Abstracts,* and *Virology and AIDS Abstracts* are also included. (fee-based) http://www.csa.com/csa/ids/ids-main.shtml

 Cochrane Library An international working group of experts has developed the Cochrane Library database with evidence-based medicine reviews, by specialty, and a controlled trials register. Searching, browsing and displaying of abstracts is available free-of-charge; full access is available only to subscribers.
(fee-based) http://www.cochranelibrary.com/enter/

Database of Abstracts of Reviews of Effectiveness (DARE) Quality assessed reviews of the literature are compiled in the DARE database of evidence-based medicine, courtesy of the University of York. Reviews included have been assessed and selected for their high methodological value. Searches return structured abstracts that state the author's objective, intervention, participants included, and outcomes assessed. Additional information includes the sources searched, methods by which data was extracted, and results. A complete guide to searching the DARE database is provided.
http://agatha.york.ac.uk/darehp.htm

EBSCO Information Services EBSCO information services provides subscription services for biomedical libraries plus access to numerous electronic journals and databases (some with full-text) such as Alternative Medicine, CancerLit, International Pharmaceutical Abstracts, and MEDLINE. (fee-based) http://www.epnet.com/database.html

Electric Library The Electric Library is an online database containing full-text articles from more than 150 newspapers; hundreds of magazines; national and international news wires; 2,000 books; photos; maps; television, radio, and government transcripts; and a free, complete encyclopedia. There is a 10-day free trial period. (fee-based) http://wwws.elibrary.com

Information Quest A description of the Information Quest service is provided on this Web site. The database is divided into libraries. A medicine library offers access to hundreds of journals and their abstracts. Some have full-text articles. (fee-based) http://www.informationquest.com/

Institute for Scientific Information (ISI) A list of the searchable bibliographic databases and research information available to ISI subscribers is provided on this site. Database topics include biotechnology, clinical medicine, and neuroscience. In addition, many of these databases provide citation searching capabilities through the ISI search tool, Web of Science, the unique search feature for which ISI is known. Users can find all of the published materials that have cited a particular work, regardless of discipline. (fee-based) http://www.isinet.com/isi/products/index.html

International Digital Electronic Access Library (IDEAL) IDEAL offers users access to the full-text of journals published by Academic Press, Churchill Livingstone, W.B. Saunders, Bailliere Tindall, and Mosby. There are also full-text reference encyclopedias related to immunology, human nutrition, virology, and food microbiology. Subscriptions are available for libraries; individuals can access articles on a pay per view basis. (fee-based) http://www.idealibrary.com

LINK: Online Library: Medicine The LINK online library, dedicated to medicine, is described on this site. More than 100 journals are listed, many containing full-text articles. The site can be searched and abstracts viewed free-of-charge; access to full-text articles requires a subscription. (some features fee-based) http://link.springer.de/ol/medol/index.htm

Manual, Alternative, and Natural Therapy (MANTIS) Database The MANTIS database contains citations and abstracts for healthcare disciplines such as acupuncture, alternative medicine, chiropractic, herbal medicine, homeopathy, naturopathy, osteopathic medicine, physical therapy, and traditional Chinese medicine. The database covers domestic and international sources, covering more than 1,000 journals. (fee-based) http://www.healthindex.com/MANTIS.asp

Ovid Medical Databases Bibliographic databases available through Ovid include MEDLINE and EMBASE for medicine and allied health, CINAHL for nursing, and BIOSIS for bioscience. Additional databases cover topics such as evidence-based medicine, drug information, and substance abuse. In total, there are more than 80 commercial bibliographic databases available. The Ovid interface includes many advanced search features, including links to full-text, and for most databases, it incorporates database-specific thesauri to promote retrieval of relevant results.
(fee-based) http://www.ovid.com/products/databases/index.cfm

ScienceDirect Described as the "largest online full-text platform for scientific, technical, and medical information," the ScienceDirect database offers more than one million full-text articles from more than 1,100 journals, most published by Elsevier Science. Subject areas include biochemistry, clinical medicine, microbiology and immunology, pharmacology and toxicology, and neurosciences. Subscriptions are available only to libraries. (fee-based)
http://www.sciencedirect.com/science/page/static/scidir/static_scidir_splash_about.html

SilverLinker A new service from SilverPlatter.com, SilverLinker offers more than 2.5 million Internet links to over 6,500 journals and 2 million articles from more than 90 SilverPlatter databases. The SilverLinker database Internet links take visitors directly from citations to full-text articles.
(fee-based) http://www.silverplatter.com/silverlinker/index.htm

SilverPlatter: Medical and Pharmaceutical Collection Full-text access to research, clinical findings, policy issues, and practice is available through this collection of databases. The databases include MEDLINE, EMBASE, International Pharmaceutical Abstracts, Patient Education Library, Biological Abstracts, and Drug Information Fulltext.
(fee-based) http://www.silverplatter.com/hlthsci.htm

STNEasy This site provides subscribers with a "user friendly" interface for searching Chemical Abstracts Service databases, plus a variety of databases covering bioscience, health, medicine, and pharmacology. More than 30 databases are listed under "Medicine." A new feature called eScience provides relevant Web content by automatically entering ones search terms into the Google or Chemindustry.com search engines. Users are charged by the length of time spent searching for information.
(fee-based) http://stneasy.fiz-karlsruhe.de/html/english/login1.html

SwetsnetNavigator More than 5,000 journals related to medicine are found in the SwetsnetNavigator database, some with access to full-text articles. This tool is designed to help institutions organize access to the tables of contents and full-text for the titles to which they subscribe. Journals published by major biomedical publishers, such as Academic Press, Elsevier, and Kluwer are included.
(fee-based) http://www.swetsnet.nl/cgi-bin/SB_main

10.16 MEDICAL EQUIPMENT AND MANUFACTURERS

Medical Equipment and Pharmaceutical Companies An A-to-Z listing of medical equipment and pharmaceutical manufacturers is provided on this site, courtesy of the Andrews School of Medical Transcription. The list is comprehensive with hyperlinks to hundreds of companies.
http://www.mtdesk.com/mfg.shtml

10.17 MEDICAL GLOSSARIES

Boston University: Pharmacology Glossary Provided by the Boston University School of Medicine, this Web page features a glossary of terms and symbols used in pharmacology. Each word has a definition and related terms.
http://www.bumc.bu.edu/www/busm/pharmacology/Programmed/framedGlossary.html

CancerWEB: Online Medical Dictionary This site offers an extremely comprehensive medical dictionary online for clinical, medical student, and patient audiences. It is a convenient source for a quick definition of an unfamiliar term. http://www.graylab.ac.uk/omd/index.html

drkoop.com: Insurance-Related Terms This site provides descriptions of both terms and phrases relating to health insurance. Terms are listed alphabetically. http://www.drkoop.com/hcr/insurance/glossary.asp

Healthanswers.com: Disease Finder A wide range of diseases are listed in this alphabetical directory of information for patients and consumers. Visitors can search by keyword or browse the directory for information. Details include alternative names, definitions, causes, incidences, risk factors, prevention, symptoms, signs and tests, treatment, prognosis, and complications. Many helpful diagrams or representative photographs related to the condition are also provided. http://www.healthanswers.com/Centers/Disease/default.asp

Healthanswers.com: Injury Finder Patients can access an alphabetical directory of common injuries at this address. Information available includes a definition and important considerations about the injury, causes, symptoms, prevention, and suggested first aid.
http://www.healthanswers.com/medenc/index.asp?topic=Injury

Immunology Glossary A glossary of immunology is featured on this Web page, courtesy of the University of Leicester, Department of Microbiology and Immunology, in the United Kingdom. The entire glossary can be browsed at once, since it is all located on this one page.
http://www-micro.msb.le.ac.uk/MBChB/ImmGloss.html

InteliHealth: Vitamin and Nutrition Resource Center InteliHealth offers this comprehensive glossary of vitamins and minerals, listed under fat-

soluble vitamins, water-soluble vitamins, and minerals. Information provided under each entry includes important facts about the vitamin or mineral, daily intake recommendations for men and women, benefits, food sources, amounts of the substance present in various food sources, and cautions in terms of health consequences of the overuse or deficiency of the substance.
http://www.intelihealth.com/IH/ihtIH/WSIHW000/325/20932.html

MedicineNet.com: Medications An index of medications is featured on this Web page, produced by MedicineNet. Of interest to both professionals and consumers, the index consists of an A-to-Z listing of prescription and over-the-counter drugs. Each drug has information such as its generic name, brand names, drug class and mechanism, storage, reasons for use, dosing, drug interaction, and side effects. In addition, each drug has links to further information such as related diseases, medications, and health facts.
http://www.medicinenet.com/Script/Main/AlphaIdx.asp?li=MNI&p=A_PHARM

MedicineNet.com: Procedures and Tests Index By clicking on "Procedures and Tests" at the top of the MedicineNet.com Web page, visitors will find a comprehensive, user-friendly index to common and not- so-common diagnostic tests and treatment procedures. Each diagnostic and treatment mini-forum contains a main article for general information, outlining the purpose and safety of the procedure, related diseases and treatments, articles written by physicians on related topics of interest, and interesting related consumer health facts.   http://www.medicinenet.com

National Human Genome Research Institute (NHGRI): Genetics Glossary The National Human Genome Research Institute has developed this online glossary of genetic terms. The glossary can be browsed alphabetically or searched by keyword. Each term comes with a definition, an audio clip explaining the term, and a list of related terms.
http://www.nhgri.nih.gov/DIR/VIP/Glossary/

Spellex Development: Medical Spell-Check Spellex Medical and Spellex Pharmaceutical online spelling verification allows visitors to check the spelling of medical terms. The search returns possible correct spellings if the word entered was not found.
http://www.spellex.com/speller.htm

Stedman's Shorter Medical Dictionary (1943): Poisons and Antidotes Posted as an item of historical interest only, this site features poisons and their antidotes from Stedman's Shorter Medical Dictionary (1943). An alphabetical listing of poisons is provided; each has a description of symptoms and appropriate treatment.
http://www.botanical.com/botanical/steapois/poisonix.html

University of Texas: Life Science Dictionary This free online dictionary designed for the public and professionals contains terms that deal with biochemistry, biotechnology, botany, cell biology, and genetics. The dictionary also

contains some terms relating to ecology, limnology, pharmacology, toxicology, and medicine. The search engine allows the user to search by a specific term or by a term contained within a definition.
http://biotech.icmb.utexas.edu/search/dict-search.html

10.18 MEDICAL JOURNAL PUBLISHERS

Academic Press This site lists a variety of journals published by Academic Press, a Harcourt Science and Technology Company. By clicking on "Biomedical Sciences" in the "Subject Categories" drop-down box, a listing of journals is presented including *Epilepsy and Behavior, Experimental Neurology, Seminars in Cancer Biology,* and *Virology.* A table of contents, along with abstracts, is available at no charge. Full-text articles can be purchased individually online or viewed by subscribers. (some features fee-based) http://www.academicpress.com/journals/

Annual Reviews: Biomedical Sciences Volumes of the *Annual Reviews,* for biomedical sciences are listed on this site. The "reviews" are critical reviews of the scientific literature. Subjects include genomic and human genetics, immunology, and medicine. Visitors can access abstracts of articles from the current and past volumes. Full-text articles are available online to subscribers.
(some features fee-based) http://arjournals.annualreviews.org/biomedicalhome.dtl

Ashley Publications Ltd. The Ashley publishing group offers journals related to pharmacology, including *Expert Opinion on Pharmacotherapy, Emerging Drugs,* and *Pharmacogenomics.* In addition to free sample issues, visitors can access tables of contents and abstracts from back issues of each journal. Subscribers can access full-text articles.
(some features fee-based) http://www.ashley-pub.com/html/journals.asp

Blackwell Science This site offers online access to information regarding well over 200 Blackwell Science publications. Journals are sorted alphabetically by title and are available in all major fields of science and medicine. Blackwell Science provides a good general overview regarding the content and aim of each of its journals. Tables of contents are available for current and back issues of each title. Access to abstracts and articles requires a fee.
http://www.blackwell-science.com/uk/journals.htm

Brookwood Medical Publications of PJB Publications Five journals related to clinical research are described on this site, including the *Journal of Drug Assessment,* the *Journal of Clinical Research,* and the *Journal of Outcomes Research.* Abstracts of selected articles are available on the site. There is also a link to PharmaProjects, a leading pharmaceutical intelligence database available only on a subscription basis.
http://www.pjbpubs.co.uk/pjb5a.htm

Cambridge University Press Journal titles available from Cambridge University Press are listed at this address. Topics encompass all subject areas,

but many are devoted to medical specialties. The journals can be browsed alphabetically, by subject, and by online availability. Tables of contents are provided once a user chooses the publication and issue of interest. Visitors can browse both current and archived issues. Journals can be ordered online.
http://us.cambridge.org/journal/default.htm

Carden Jennings Publishing Co, Ltd.   The Carden Jennings medical multimedia publishing division offers journals, online publications, CD-ROMs, and books. Abstracts and free full-text articles (in Adobe Acrobat PDF format) are available online for selected journals, including the *Biology of Blood and Marrow Transplantation, Laboratory Hematology,* and *Medicine & Psychiatry.*
http://www.cjp.com/stories/storyReader$6

Elsevier Science   Covering all Reed-Elsevier publications related to medicine, this site includes a subject index for access to individual journals in a variety of specialties including cardiology, obstetrics and gynecology, and psychiatry. Free sample copies of the journals are available online. Information is also included on Elsevier's books, CD-ROMs, and related products. http://www.elsevier.com

Gordon and Breach Publishing Group   This section of the Gordon and Breach Web page offers books, journals, and magazines related to medical and life sciences. Journals are available in general medicine, hematology, oncology, pediatrics, and surgery. Tables of contents are available for current and past issues. Some journals have a link to online full-text articles for subscribers.
(some features fee-based) http://www.gbhap-us.com/medical.htm

Guilford Press   Primarily a publisher of psychology, public health, and social criticism publications, Guilford Press offers PDF samples on this page of each of its journals. Information is also provided such as ordering information and which titles are available online.
http://www.guilford.com/cartscript.cgi?page=home.html&cart_id=202303.24572

Hanley & Belfus   A list of over 10 medical journals published by Hanley & Belfus is provided on this site. Titles include *Academic Medicine, Journal of Cancer Education,* and *Medical Decision Making.* Tables of contents, along with article abstracts, are available online. Subscribers can read full-text articles.
(some features fee-based)
http://www.hanleyandbelfus.com/CATALOG/default.html#Anchor-Journals

Harcourt Health Sciences   Information on journals published by the Harcourt Health Sciences group, which includes Churchill Livingstone, JEMS Communications, Mosby, and W.B. Saunders, is presented on this site. By clicking on "Find a Journal by Specialty," visitors can access journals related to cardiology, endocrinology, oncology, and more. Table of contents and subscription information are provided.
http://www.harcourthealth.com/scripts/om.dll/serve?action=home

Harcourt International International medical journals published by Harcourt are provided on this site, sorted by specialty. Topics covered include clinical cancer, gastroenterology, midwifery, and surgery. Visitors can access the table of contents and abstracts to current and back issues of the journals. Full-text articles are available for a fee.

(some features fee-based) http://www.harcourt-international.com/journals/jsbrowse.cfm

 Haworth Medical Press Information on the Haworth Medical Press, an imprint of the Haworth Press, is provided at this site including a listing of its more than 20 medical journals and related books. The Online Catalog provides additional information on the journals, including a section for reader reviews.

http://www.haworthpressinc.com/Imprints/abtthmp.htm

 HighWire Press HighWire Press presents a list of its biomedical journals, organized alphabetically or by subject, including detailed information regarding what is available at no charge for each title. For each journal, there is a link to its home page, where tables of contents and abstracts are available. Full text of entire journals or back issues are available for a good number of titles.

http://highwire.stanford.edu

 Karger Medical journals published by Karger are listed alphabetically on this site. The tables of contents, along with abstracts, of current and back issues are available online. Subscribers can access full-text articles. A free sample copy of each journal is available online.

(some features fee-based) http://www.karger.com/journals/index.htm

 Kluwer Academic Publishers Journals of interest in medicine and related subjects are listed on this page. Journal categories include cardiology, internal medicine, neurology, oncology, and urology. Visitors can browse through the table of contents of each publication, for current and archived issues, or conduct searches by keyword for returns of specific articles.

http://kapis.www.wkap.nl/jrnlsubject.htm/E+0+0+0

 Lippincott Williams & Wilkins Medical and scientific journals published by Lippincott Williams & Wilkins can be browsed by specialty on this site. There are more than 80 specialties and subspecialties represented. A table of contents, abstracts, and subscription information are provided for each journal, including full-text access options and links.

http://www.lww.com/periodicals.htm

 Marcel Dekker Scientific, technical, and medical journals published by Marcel Dekker are listed on this site. By clicking on the subject of "Medicine," journals, and other types of publications, can be searched. There are more than a dozen journals related to medicine, including the *Journal of Toxicology, Immunopharmacology and Immunotoxicology,* and the *Journal of Asthma.* The tables of contents and abstracts are free. Many full-text articles are available online to subscribers.

(some features fee-based) http://www.dekker.com/index.jsp

Mary Ann Liebert, Inc. This site offers more than 50 journals published by Mary Ann Liebert, Inc. Journal titles include *AIDS Patient Care and STDs, Microbial Drug Resistance,* and *Thyroid.* General information on each journal is provided, as well as the table of contents for current and archived issues, and a free sample copy.
http://www.liebertpub.com/journals/default1.asp

Medical Economics Company The Medical Economics Company site offers healthcare professionals journals and newsletters related to the diagnosis and treatment of disease. Journals include *Contemporary OB/GYN, Contemporary Urology, Contemporary Pediatrics,* and the *Journal of the American Academy of Physician Assistants.* By clicking on "More Information" for each publication, links to the publication's Web site are provided. Some include full-text articles. In addition, there are clinical newsletters.
(some features fee-based) http://www.medec.com/

Munksgaard New titles—along with an alphabetical index—of scientific, technical, and medical journals are provided on this site, which also allows visitors to view journals by subject. The journals are international in scope. General information on each journal is provided, along with a sample issue. Subscribers can access some of the journals online.
(some features fee-based) http://journals.munksgaard.dk/

Nature Publishing Group of Macmillan Publishers, Ltd. An alphabetical list of specialist medical journals is provided on this Web site. Titles include the *European Journal of Human Genetics, Leukemia,* and the *Hematology Journal.* Tables of contents and abstracts are available online. There is also an online sample copy. Full-text articles are only available to subscribers.
(some features fee-based) http://www.stockton-press.co.uk/journals/

Oxford University Press Medical journals from Oxford University Press are listed on this site. There are over 20 journals listed; each publication offers tables of contents and abstracts. Subscribers can access full-text articles. A free e-mail table of contents alert service is available.
(some features fee-based) http://www.oup.co.uk/medicine/journals/

Parthenon Publishing Group Links to more than a dozen journals published by Parthenon are featured on this Web page. Titles include *Gynecological Endocrinology, The Aging Male, The Journal of Drug Evaluation,* and *The Journal of Maternal-Fetal Medicine.* The table of contents from the most recent issue of each journal is posted. In addition, a catalog of the Group's books, slides, videos, and CD-ROMs is provided.
http://www.parthpub.com/journal.html

Pulsus Group The Pulsus Group offers information at this site on journals published by the group for specialties such as plastic surgery, cardiology, gastroenterology, infectious diseases, and pediatrics. Visitors can access abstracts and full-text articles in some of the journals. http://www.pulsus.com/

SLACK Inc.   In addition to journals, this site lists books, Internet resources, and symposia on the Web for a variety of medical specialties, allied health, and nursing subspecialties. A sample table of contents, along with general information about each journal, is provided. Visitors must scroll down the page to view the entire index of publications.
http://www.slackinc.com/areas.asp

Springer-Verlag   Covering the large list of journals published by Springer-Verlag, this site primarily contains abstracts rather than full-text articles. Full-text articles are available for those titles for which individuals or institutions maintain print subscriptions. The site covers a broad range of biomedical titles, all of which provide tables of contents from the most recent years.
(some features fee-based) http://link.springer.de/ol/medol/index.htm

Swets & Zeitlinger   The journal catalog of Swets & Zeitlinger is featured on this Web site. Journals related to health can be found under life sciences, neuroscience, ophthalmology, and psychology. The list of journals includes *Pharmaceutical Biology, Neuro-Ophthalmology,* and *The Clinical Neuropsychologist.* Tables of contents and abstracts for the current issue, as well as back issues, of each journal are available.
http://www.swets.nl/sps/journals/jhome.html

Taylor & Francis Group   Journals are listed by subject on this site and include the behavioral sciences, biomedical sciences, and biosciences. The journals are international in nature. Although the table of contents is free, access to the articles is by subscription only.
(some features fee-based) http://www.tandf.co.uk/journals/sublist.html

Thieme   There are over 30 medical journals listed on this Web page, published by the German publisher, Thieme. Topics covered include pediatric surgery, reproductive medicine, liver disease, and perinatology. Selected article citations are provided.
http://www.thieme.com/onGJMIIAEMMLHFF/prodlist/journ

VSP: International Science Publishers   A listing of more than 40 VSP journals is offered on this site. The journals cover a broad array of sciences; titles of interest to healthcare professionals include *Gene Therapy and Regulation, Haematologia, Inflammopharmacology,* and *Trauma Quarterly.* The tables of contents from previous issues are online. A free sample issue can be requested through the Web site.
http://www.vsppub.com/journals/index.html

Wiley Interscience   This site is maintained by John Wiley and Sons, Inc., and provides a subject index to all Wiley journals. Journals are available in business, law, and all areas of science, including life and medical sciences. More than 90 journals are listed under the "Life and Medical Sciences" section. Free registration allows access to tables of contents and abstracts published within the last

12 months. Full-text access is available via registration to both individual and institutional subscribers of the print counterparts of the Wiley online journals. (some features fee-based) http://www3.interscience.wiley.com/journalfinder.html

10.19 MEDICAL NEWS

1st Headlines: Health The Health section of this news information site offers a keyword search engine for access to nationwide health news derived from more than 70 daily publications and reputable broadcast and online networks, including *USA Today's* Health section, Reuters Health, MSNBC, and drkoop.com. News coverage includes treatment discoveries, pharmacological updates, the latest in managed care, product recalls, and hundreds of other breaking news bulletins.
http://www.1sthealthnews.com/index.htm

American Medical Association (AMA): American Medical News Published by the American Medical Association, *American Medical News* offers free access to the latest issue online, with each electronic publication providing coverage of top stories, legislative updates, professional issues. Business information and the ability to read a mobile edition on any handheld device are provided, as well as archived issues and e-mail headline alerts.
http://www.ama-assn.org/public/journals/amnews/amnews.htm

CNN: Health News Health News from CNN is produced in association with WebMD. Specific articles are available in featured topics, ethics matters, research, and home remedies, and an allergy report is also provided. National and international health news is presented, and users can access specific articles on AIDS, aging, alternative medicine, cancer, children's health, diet and fitness, men's health, and women's health. Visitors can also access patient questions and answers from doctors, chat forums, and special community resources available through WebMD. Information and articles are also offered by Mayo Clinic and AccentHealth.com.
http://www.cnn.com/HEALTH

Doctor's Guide: Medical and Other News This site provides very current medical news and information for health professionals. Visitors can search the Doctor's Guide Medical News Database and access medical news broadcast within the past week or the past month. News items organized by subject, firsthand conference communiques, and journal club reviews are also available at this informative news site.
http://www.pslgroup.com/MEDNEWS.HTM

MDLinx MDLinx offers daily medical journal articles organized by subspecialty. There are twenty-four medical fields represented in the menu at this home page. Article selections are updated daily to reflect the release of new monthly journals.
http://www.mdlinx.com

Medical Breakthroughs Daily news updates are delivered to individual e-mail addresses from this site, accessible after a free registration. Visitors can also search archived articles by keyword, read weekly general interest articles, find links to related sites, and watch videos related to current health issues. The site is sponsored by Ivanhoe Broadcast News, Inc., a medical news gathering organization providing stories to television stations nationwide.
(free registration) http://www.ivanhoe.com/#reports

Reuters Health The Reuters Health Web page provides breaking medical news, updated daily, as well as a subscription-based searchable database of the News Archives of Reuters News Service. Visitors can access MEDLINE from the site. Group subscribers have access to a database of drug information.
(some features fee-based) http://www.reutershealth.com

UniSci: Daily University Science News This site offers current articles related to all branches of science, including medicine. Many medical articles are available, and special archives offer additional medical resources. Users can access news from the past 10 days and perform searches for archived material.
http://unisci.com

USA Today: Health *USA Today's* feature stories and headline archives are directly accessible at this Web site where visitors can view some of the best in nationwide medical news coverage. Articles are listed by topic, including addiction, AIDS, allergies, alternative medicine, arthritis, cancer, diabetes, genetics, hepatitis, mental health, surgery, and vision. Visitors will also find the latest in medical and pharmacotherapeutic research.
http://www.usatoday.com/life/health/archive.htm

Yahoo!: Health Headlines Updated several times throughout the day, Health Headlines at Yahoo! offers full news coverage and Reuters News with health headlines from around the globe. Earlier daily and archived stories may be accessed, and the site's search engine allows viewers to browse, with full color, the latest in photographic coverage of news and events.
http://dailynews.yahoo.com/headlines/hl

10.20 MEDICAL SEARCH ENGINES

Similar information can be found under the medical supersites section.

Achoo Healthcare Online A directory of Web sites in three main categories—human health and disease, business of health, and organizations and sources—is featured on this Web page. Extensive subcategories and short descriptions are provided for each site. Daily health news of interest to patients, the public, or medical professionals is available at the site, as well as links to journals, databases, employment directories, and discussion groups.
http://www.achoo.com

All the Web This comprehensive site provides a variety of search engines including Fast Search. Fast Search allows users to search the Internet in 25 language catalogs and covers over 200 million high-quality Web pages in very high speed. Visitors can copy the code needed to add Fast Search to their Web sites. Additionally at this site are search engines to search pictures and sounds.
http://www.alltheweb.com

Biocrawler: The Life Science Search Engine Described as a life science search engine, this Web page contains a large directory with thousands of Internet sites. The directory can be searched by keyword or by clicking on a particular topic such as anthropology, biotechnology, genetics, bioinformatics, and biomedicine. There is also a directory of biology-related jobs that have been posted on the Internet.
http://www.biocrawler.com/

Citeline.com Search Tool The search tool on this Web page allows visitors to search the Web by keyword and, if desired, to limit that search to any or all of the following categories: disease and treatment, organizations, news and journals, and research and trials.
http://www.citeline.com/C1SE/search

CliniWeb International CliniWeb, a service of Oregon Health Sciences University, is a searchable index and table of contents to clinical resources available on the World Wide Web. Information found at the site is of particular interest to healthcare professional students and practitioners. Search terms can be entered in five different languages: English, German, French, Spanish, and Portuguese. The site offers links to additional search resources and is linked directly to MEDLINE.
http://www.ohsu.edu/cliniweb

Galen II: The Digital Library of the University of California, San Francisco (UCSF) This online library directory includes UCSF and UC resources and services, links to the AMA Directory, Drug Info Fulltext, Harrison's Online (requires a password), the *Merck Manual,* Consumer Health, and a searchable database of additional resources and publications including electronic journals. Visitors can search the Galen II database or the World Wide Web using a variety of search engines.
http://galen.library.ucsf.edu

Google Google offers a comprehensive search tool, integrating resources from several smaller search engines. Several subject areas are available for more specific queries, including health and related subtopics. Visitors can enter a search term, view Google results, and try the same query through AltaVista, Excite, HotBot, Infoseek, Lycos, and Yahoo through the site.
http://www.google.com

Health On the Net (HON) Foundation: MedHunt The Health On the Net Foundation provides several widely used medical search engines including

MedHunt, Honselect, and MEDLINE. Users can access databases containing information on newsgroups, LISTSERVs, medical images and movies, upcoming and past healthcare-related conferences, and daily news stories on health-related topics. Topical searches yield brief site descriptions, which are ranked by relevance. http://www.hon.ch/MedHunt

InfoMedical.com: Medical Search Engine   This site features a directory with hundreds of medical sites categorized as companies, distributors, products, organizations, services, and Web resources. The directory can be searched or browsed by category. Of interest to physicians, the Web resources section contains clinical trial postings, job postings, online libraries, online medical discussions, and online medical multimedia. Each site has a company profile and a list of their products and services.
http://www.infomedical.com/

MDchoice.com   MDchoice.com is a privately held company founded by academic physicians with the goal of making access to health and medical information on the Internet as efficient and reliable as possible. The site features an UltraWeb search with all content selected by board-certified physicians. In addition, users have access to MEDLINE, drug information, health news, and a variety of clinical calculators. Also offered are several interactive educational exercises, online journals and text books, and employment opportunities.
http://www.mdchoice.com

Med411.com: Medical Research Portal   This site offers access to a variety of comprehensive search tools, allowing users to search medical libraries, professional associations, online health manuals, the National Library of Medicine, peer-reviewed journals, health services, images, clinical trials, the Combined Health Information Database (CHID), CancerNet, the National Institute of Diabetes and Digestive and Kidney Diseases, HealthFinder, and WebPath directly from the site.
http://www.med411.com/resources.html

MedExplorer   MedExplorer is a comprehensive, searchable medical and health directory. Short descriptions of each site are provided. The site also lists related newsgroups and has information on conferences and employment.
http://www.medexplorer.com

Medscape   Medscape provides several databases from which users can search the Web. Resources that can be accessed include articles, news, information for patients, MEDLINE, AIDSLINE, TOXLINE, drug information, a dictionary, a bookstore, the Dow Jones Library, and medical images. There is a wealth of additional information provided including articles, case reports, conference schedules and summaries, continuing medical education resources, job listings, journals, news, patient information, practice guidelines, treatment updates, and links to medical specialty sites. Requires free online registration.
(free registration) http://www.medscape.com

Metacrawler   At the Metacrawler site users can search for Web resources through a directory or search engine. This search engine offers extensive coverage in the field of medicine.
http://www.metacrawler.com

Search Taxi.com: Health   A directory dedicated to health is featured on this site. There are thousands of sites listed under categories such as alternative, conditions and diseases, medicine, and mental health. These categories are broken down further into topics such as employment, health insurance, men's health, and substance abuse.
http://www.searchtaxi.com/dir/Health/

Stanford University: MedBot   Offered by Stanford University, this site allows users to search medical and health resources on the Web using major general and medical search engines. More specific searches can be performed within topics such as education and learning, news and information, and medical images, as well as multimedia resources.
http://www-med.stanford.edu/medworld/medbot

Yahoo!   Yahoo offers visitors the opportunity to search the Web and browse sites listed in multiple categories including health and science. Within each category are more specific subcategories that indicate the number of entries available. Most sites are suggested by users. Additionally, Yahoo offers a wealth of services such as free e-mail, shopping, people search, news, travel, weather, and stock reports.
http://www.yahoo.com/health

10.21 MEDICAL STATISTICS

Centers for Disease Control and Prevention (CDC): Biostatistics/Statistics   This address provides visitors with links to sources of national statistics. Resources include federal, county, and city data, as well as statistics related to labor, current population, public health, economics, trade, and business. Sources for mathematics and software information are also found through this site.
http://www.cdc.gov/niosh/biostat.html

Health Sciences Library System (HSLS): Health Statistics   The University of Pittsburgh's Falk Library of the Health Sciences developed this site to provide information on obtaining statistical health data from Internet and library sources. Resources include details on obtaining statistical data from United States population databases, government agencies collecting statistics, organizations and associations collecting statistics, and other Web sites providing statistical information. The site explains specific Internet and library tools for locating health statistics and offers a glossary of terms used in statistics.
http://www.hsls.pitt.edu/intres/guides/statcbw.html

National Center for Health Statistics (NCHS)   The NCHS, located within the Centers for Disease Control and Prevention of the U.S. Department of Health and Human Services, provides an extensive array of health and medical statistics for the medical, research, and consumer communities. This site provides express links to numerous surveys and statistical sources at the NCHS. http://www.cdc.gov/nchs/default.htm

University of Michigan: Statistical Resources on the Web: Health
Online sources for health statistics are cataloged at this site, including comprehensive health statistics resources and sources for statistics by topic. Topics include abortion, accidents, births, deaths, disability, disease experimentation, hazardous substances, healthcare, health insurance, HMOs, hospitals, life tables, mental health, noise, nursing homes, nutrition, pregnancy, prescription drugs, risk behaviors, substance abuse, surgery, transplants, and vital statistics. Users can also access an alphabetical directory of sites in the database and a search engine for locating more specific resources.
http://www.lib.umich.edu/libhome/Documents.center/sthealth.html

World Health Organization (WHO): Statistical Information System
The Statistical Information System of WHO (WHOSIS) is intended to provide access to both statistical and epidemiological data and information from this international agency in electronic form. The site provides health statistics, disease information, mortality statistics, AIDS/HIV data, immunization coverage and incidence of communicable diseases, and links to statistics from other countries as well as links to the Centers for Disease Control and Prevention in the United States. This site is the premier resource for statistics on diseases worldwide. The WHO main site, http://www.who.int, provides additional disease-related statistics. http://www.who.int/whosis

10.22 ONLINE TEXTS AND TUTORIALS

eMedicine: World Medical Library   A medical library is featured on this Web page with online textbooks for professionals and consumers, courtesy of eMedicine. The books are accessed through a window of folders; each folder represents a book. Professionals can read *Emergency Medicine,* and they have access to Gold Standard Multimedia online books. The Gold Standard books focus on basic science such as clinical pharmacology, human anatomy, and immunology. Clicking on the Gold Standard link brings one to their Web site, where the desired book can be selected from a drop-down menu. Books for consumers include *Consumer Treatment Guidelines* and *Wilderness Emergencies.*
(free registration) http://www.emedicine.com/

Harrison's Online   Directed to physicians, this Web page features the online text of *Harrison's Principles of Medicine.* Each chapter includes information such as diagnosis, prevalence, pathogenesis, clinical features, treatment, complications, and a bibliography. Links are also provided on each topic for related sites, updates, clinical trial information, and self-assessment quizzes. (fee-based) http://www.harrisonsonline.com/

Medical Textbooks Online   Professionals will find a directory of medical textbooks available online on this Web page, maintained by medic.com. Twenty-seven specialties are represented, including geriatric medicine, neurosurgery, microbiology, and pediatrics.
http://www.medic8.com/MedicalTextbooksOnline.htm

Medical Texts on the Internet   This list of medical texts, arranged by specialty, includes access to a variety of medical papers and articles in over 25 areas. Links to documents in cardiology, dermatology, oncology, and urology are included, with each listing a series of related tutorials and texts.
http://members.tripod.com/gustavo_01/textmed.html

Merck Manual of Diagnosis and Therapy   Hosted by Merck, this site features the *Merck Manual of Diagnosis and Therapy*. Primarily of interest to healthcare professionals, the site offers a table of contents with links to a broad range of disorders categorized in sections such as nutritional disorders, gastrointestinal disorders, pulmonary disorders, and pediatrics. In total, there are 23 sections with 308 chapters. Typical chapters provide a detailed clinical discussion of the disorder including an overview, etiology, symptoms and signs, and treatment information. Within the chapter, links are provided to related topics.
http://www.merck.com/pubs/mmanual/sections.htm

University of Illinois: Atlases and Other Medical Texts   Maintained by the University of Illinois at Urbana-Champaign, this Web page features more than 50 links for atlases and online medical textbooks. At the bottom of the page, there are hyperlinks for a list of general medical links, and medical education links.
http://alexia.lis.uiuc.edu/~buenker/atlases.html

University of Iowa: Family Practice Handbook   The University of Iowa Family Practice Handbook is featured on this Web page, primarily of interest to physicians. This searchable textbook has 20 chapters covering the range of family medicine such as cardiology, pulmonary medicine, gynecology, pediatrics, and dermatology. Chapters typically cover diseases and conditions by providing an overview, along with causes, diagnosis, and treatment information. In addition to disorders, office and hospital procedures, as well as drug doses of commonly prescribed medications, are covered.
http://www.vh.org/Providers/ClinRef/FPHandbook/FPContents.html

Virtual Hospital: Multimedia Textbooks   Intended for healthcare providers, a list of multimedia textbooks is featured on this Web page, hosted by the University of Iowa Virtual Hospital. All textbooks listed are drawn from the Virtual Hospital and include more than 40 topics such as anatomy, derma-

tology, pediatrics, the human brain, and pathology. Along with text, there are also video clips, microphotographs, photographs, and radiographic images.
http://www.vh.org/Providers/Textbooks/MultimediaTextbooks.html

10.23 PHARMACEUTICAL INFORMATION

CenterWatch: Newly Approved Drug Therapies   For many researchers and physicians, information about FDA drug approvals is of central concern. A concise summary of such approvals by medical specialty and condition for each year up to the present is featured on this Web page.
http://www.centerwatch.com/patient/drugs/druglist.html

Doctor's Guide: New Drugs and Indications   Doctor's Guide provides an ongoing source of new drug information, including FDA approvals and drug indications. Drug articles are presented in order of article datelines, with the most current stories listed first. Information for drug releases for the past 12 months is provided.
http://www.pslgroup.com/NEWDRUGS.HTM

drkoop.com: Drug Interactions Search   Users can enter several drug names into a search tool, checking for drug interactions.
http://www.drkoop.com/drugstore/pharmacy/interactions.asp

Drug InfoNet   Information and links to areas on the Web concerning healthcare and pharmaceutical-related topics are available. The drug information is available by brand name, generic name, manufacturer, and therapeutic class. Visitors can ask questions of experts or access disease information, pharmaceutical manufacturer information, healthcare news, and other resources.
http://www.druginfonet.com/phrminfo.htm

DrugFacts.com Library   Described as the "most comprehensive source of free and premium drug, interaction, and herbal information on the Internet," this site offers information drawn from *Drug Facts,* courtesy of the Wolters Kluwer International Health & Science companies. An "A to Z Drug Facts" section offers more than 4,500 drugs, along with information such as action, indication/contraindication, dosage, interactions, adverse reactions, precautions, and patient education tips. An abridged version for professionals is available after a free registration process. Other highlights of the site include information drawn from *Drug Interaction Facts,* and a guide to 125 herbal products. Patients can access "Med Facts" for easy-to-read information on more than 4,000 drugs.
http://www.drugfacts.com/DrugFacts/tabs/library.jhtml?pf=&ps=&cr=&si=#druginfo

Food and Drug Administration (FDA)   The FDA site provides extensive information on all aspects of drug research, regulations, approvals, trials, adverse reactions, enforcement, conferences, clinical alerts, reports, and drug news. The FDA Web Site Index is the first place to go to research a topic. There are several hundred subjects listed. One of these many sections covers FDA-

related acronyms and abbreviations, which itself is a very useful tool in understanding much of the material at this site.
http://www.fda.gov

Food and Drug Administration (FDA): Approved Drug Products

The U.S. Food and Drug Administration's *Electronic Orange Book* for approved drug products is posted on this Web site. The book can be searched by active ingredient, proprietary name, applicant holder, or application number. The results for a search provide the application number, active ingredient, dosage form and route, strength, proprietary name, and applicant.
http://www.fda.gov/cder/ob/default.htm

Food and Drug Administration (FDA): Center for Drug Evaluation and Research

The Center for Drug Evaluation and Research broadcasts valuable information on prescription, consumer, and over-the-counter drugs at this address. Resources include alphabetical lists of new and generic drug approvals, new drugs approved for cancer indications, a searchable Orange Book listing all FDA-approved prescription drugs, a National Drug Code directory, new over-the-counter labeling notices, patient information on over-the-counter drugs, and alerts of new over-the-counter indications. Links are available to many resources related to drug safety and side effects, public health alerts and warnings, and pages offering information on major drugs. Reports and publications, special projects and programs, and cancer clinical trials information are also found through this address.
http://www.fda.gov/cder/drug/default.htm

MedicineNet.com: Medications Index

This all-inclusive pharmacological database from MedicineNet.com provides a mini-forum for each prescription and nonprescription medication, including a brief main article pertaining to the medication, related medications, related news and updates, diseases associated with the medication, and a listing of articles pertinent to the pharmacological agent's usage.
http://www.medicinenet.com/Script/Main/AlphaIdx.asp?li=MNI&d=51&p=A_PHARM

MedWatch: The FDA Medical Products Reporting Program

The FDA Medical Products Reporting Program, MedWatch, is designed to educate health professionals about the importance of being aware of, monitoring for, and reporting adverse events and problems to the FDA and/or the manufacturer. The program is also intended to disseminate new safety information rapidly within the medical community, thereby improving patient care. To these ends, the site includes an adverse event reporting form and instructions as well as safety information for health professionals, including "Dear Health Professional" letters and notifications related to drug safety. It also includes relevant full-text continuing education articles and reports regarding drug and medical device safety issues. http://www.fda.gov/medwatch

PDR.net

Visitors to PDR.net will find health-related articles geared towards them, whether they are physicians, pharmacists, physician assistants, oncologists, nurse practitioners, nurses, or consumers. Sections dedicated to each type of audience are presented with articles from sources that include CenterWatch, MEDLINE, Cancerfacts.com, the Centers for Disease Control and Prevention, the Government Clinical Trial Website, and the Mayo Health Clinic Oasis. Physicians can access "PDR Online" and obtain extensive information on drugs, herbal medicine, multi-drug interactions, and drug pricing. Online continuing medical education materials are provided for physicians, nurses, pharmacists, and veterinarians at this site as well.

(free registration) http://www.pdr.net

Pharmaceutical Information Network (PharmInfoNet) PharmInfoNet is a source of information on diseases, disorders, drug treatments, and research. In addition, there are links to more than 100 pharmaceutical companies, both domestic and international. Organized by specialty areas, the site is a well-organized compilation of resources for physicians, researchers, medical students, and the public. The site is organized into information on disorders, archived articles, drugs used in the treatment of disorders, and other information sources, including newsgroups, e-mail lists, and related Web sites. An extensive medical sciences bulletin section and pharmacotherapy department provide articles on dozens of developments in research and drug therapies. Finally, the site provides a lengthy listing of drugs for treating disorders, with links to more extensive information sources. Resources are found easily at this address through the "Site Contents" link.

http://pharminfo.com

Pharmaceutical Research and Manufacturers of America This association Web site includes a "New Medicines in Development" database; a publications section containing reports relating to the pharmaceutical industry; various links for facts and figures on pharmaceutical research and innovation; and an issues and policies section covering many current topics of interest to pharmaceutical companies, such as genetics research and healthcare liability reform. http://www.phrma.org

RxList: The Internet Drug Index This site allows users to search for drug information by name, imprint code, or keyword (action, interaction, etc.) The top 200 prescribed drugs for the previous year are listed alphabetically or by rank. Patient monographs are available for a wide range of drugs, and one section is devoted to alternative medicine information and answers to frequently asked questions. The site also provides a forum for drug-specific discussions. http://www.rxlist.com

Virtual Library Pharmacy This is truly a library of pharmacy information for professionals in all medical areas. The site provides information on pharmacy schools, companies, journals and books, Internet databases relating to pharmaceutical topics, conferences, hospital sites, government sites, pharmacy LISTSERVs, and news groups. Hundreds of site links are provided for the above areas. http://www.pharmacy.org

World Standard Drug Database   Information on pharmaceutical products at this address includes ingredients, dosage, routes of administration, indications, contraindications, prescription cautions, patient cautions, toxicity, side effects, liver disease cautions, renal failure procedures, pregnancy and lactation warnings, pharmacological actions, and diagnostic procedures. Visitors can search for relevant information by drug, ingredient, indications, contraindications, or side effects.
http://209.235.64.5:8888

10.24 PHYSICIAN BACKGROUND

American Board of Medical Specialties (ABMS)   This verification service contains the names of all physicians certified by an ABMS member board. It permits the public to verify the credentials and certification status of any physician free-of-charge, searching by name, city, state, and specialty within the 24 member board specialty areas. The user enters the name of the physician and information is immediately available.
http://www.abms.org

Healthgrades.com   This resource specializes in healthcare ratings, providing hospital ratings by procedure or diagnosis, physician ratings by specialty and geographic area, and ratings of health plans. Directories of hospitals, physicians, health plans, mammography facilities, fertility clinics, assisted-living facilities, dentists, and chiropractors are also available. Visitors can access tips on choosing a hospital, physician, or health plan, as well as a glossary of terms and health news articles. Online health stores offer books, videos, magazines, greeting cards, flowers and gifts, pharmaceutical products, nutritional products, and insurance quotes. http://www.healthgrades.com

Physician Background Information Service   Searchpointe.com offers background information on doctors and chiropractors licensed in the United States, such as name of medical school and year of graduation, residency training record, ABMS certifications, states where certified, and records of sanctions or disciplinary actions. There is a fee for license and sanction reports.
(some features fee-based) http://www.searchpointe.com

10.25 STATE HEALTH DEPARTMENTS

State Health Departments   A list of links to U.S. state health departments is featured on this site, maintained on the Centers for Disease Control and Prevention Web page. The site has a search tool that enables one to search one or more state health departments for certain information. In addition, links to related international resources can be found on the left side of the page, such as the Pan American Health Organization and the World Health Organization.
http://www.cdc.gov/mmwr/international/relres.html

11

PROFESSIONAL TOPICS AND CLINICAL PRACTICE

11.1 ANATOMY AND PHYSIOLOGY

American Medical Association (AMA): Atlas of the Body The Atlas of the Body is a site offered by the American Medical Association that provides detailed information and labeled illustrations of the various systems and organs of the human body. The site also provides descriptions of disorders that affect these systems and organs.

http://www.ama-assn.org/insight/gen_hlth/atlas/atlas.htm

Health On the Net (HON) Foundation: Medical Images Part of a larger Health On the Net Foundation Web page, this site features a medical image and video library on anatomy. There are more than 750 images related to body regions such as the cardiovascular system, digestive system, musculoskeletal system, and nervous system. In addition to body regions, other categories include organisms, diseases, chemicals and drugs, techniques, and biological sciences. Each image has a hyperlink to its source for additional information.

http://www.hon.ch/Media/anatomy.html

Karolinska Institutet: Anatomy and Histology Resources available on this site, directed to physicians, include more than 40 links on anatomy and 14 on histology. Many of the sites contain numerous illustrations and photographs, and some have video. The sites are drawn primarily from universities all around the world.

http://www.mic.ki.se/Anatomy.html

Martindale's Health Science Guide: Virtual Medical Center: Anatomy and Histology Center This site offers links to examinations, tutorials, and associations. It lists numerous atlases and sites with anatomical images, including some on embryology and developmental anatomy. Anatomy is just one of the many medical areas covered by the Virtual Medical Center, which also provides links to general medical dictionaries, glossaries, and encyclopedias, plus sites containing information on metabolic pathways and genetic maps.

http://www-sci.lib.uci.edu/HSG/MedicalAnatomy.html

MedBioWorld: Anatomy and Physiology Journals More than 65 journals related to anatomy and physiology are listed on this Web page. Hyper-

links are provided to go to the online version of the journal; some are for subscribers only.
http://www.medbioworld.com/journals/medicine/anatomy.html

MedNets: Anatomy   Dedicated to anatomy, this site features links for information such as associations, databases, and journals. Some journals are for subscribers only. General resources include information on specific parts of the anatomy, as well as 3-D anatomy for students.
(some features fee-based) http://www.mednets.com/anatomy.htm

Purdue University: Anatomy Links   A list of links on human anatomy and resources for medical students are featured on this Web page, courtesy of Purdue University. The links are accessed in a sidebar menu where there are more than 50 human anatomy links listed under categories such as cardiology, clinical information, neuroscience, and surgery. Medical students will find a section dedicated to them with links for general resources.
http://www.vet.purdue.edu/bms/ai/frames/intlink_00.htm

University of Arkansas for Medical Sciences: Anatomy Tables
Maintained at the University of Arkansas for Medical Sciences, this site features anatomy tables. The tables are organized by system such as arteries or bones and by region of the body. Each table includes the proper name of the anatomical part and a description.
http://anatomy.uams.edu/HTMLpages/anatomyhtml/medcharts.html

Whole Brain Atlas   Administered by the Harvard Medical School, this site shows imaging of the brain using magnetic resonance imaging (MRI), roentgenray computed tomography (CT), and nuclear medicine technologies. Structures within the images are labeled. Normal brain images are provided, as well as images of brains subjected to cerebrovascular disease, neoplastic disease, degenerative disease, and inflammatory or infectious disease. The entire atlas is available free-of-charge online or can be ordered on CD-ROM for a fee.
http://www.med.harvard.edu/AANLIB/home.html

11.2 BIOMEDICAL ETHICS

American Society of Bioethics and Humanities (ASBH)   The American Society of Bioethics and Humanities is an organization that promotes scholarship, research, teaching, policy development, and professional development in the field of bioethics. The site offers information on the society, the annual meeting, position papers, and awards. There is also a large list of related resources covering academic centers, education, ethics and philosophy, law, medicine and the humanities, online texts, organizations, and science and technology.
http://www.asbh.org

American Society of Law, Medicine, and Ethics (ASLME)   This site offers information on the American Society of Law, Medicine, and Ethics; the

Journal of Law, Medicine, and Ethics; and the *American Journal of Law and Medicine.* Also provided are details on research projects; a news section that gives updates on recent developments in law, medicine, and ethics; and information on future and past conferences held by the society. A comprehensive listing of related resources is also provided in categories such as bioethics, cancer, genetics, geriatrics, health law, managed care, and nursing.
http://www.aslme.org

Bioethics Discussion Pages   This page is a forum for people to discuss and share their views on selected topics in the field of biomedical ethics. There are also polls and articles on ethical issues.
http://www-hsc.usc.edu/~mbernste/#Welcome

Bioethics.net   Produced by the Center for Bioethics of the University of Pennsylvania, Bioethics.net contains a host of resources relating to biomedical ethics. Included are sections on cloning and genetics, emergency room bioethics, surveys for pay, and assisted suicide. There is also a virtual library with links to Internet resources. "Bioethics for Beginners" contains material that is meant to educate the general public and people interested in the field about bioethics, its meaning, and its applications. At this beginner's site, there are resources for students and educators, including a list of different biomedical ethics associations.
http://www.med.upenn.edu/bioethics/index.shtml

Human Genome Project: Ethical, Legal, and Social Issues (ELSI)
With funding from the U.S. Department of Energy and the National Institutes of Health, the ethical, legal, and social issues surrounding availability of genetic information are being explored. This site describes the issues and offers links for additional information. A link to "Privacy and Legislation" gives more detail on who should have access to genetic information and how it can be used. Gene testing and gene therapy links feature the risks and limits of genetic technology, as well as the implementation of standards. A section on behavioral genetics examines conceptual and philosophical implications. In addition, a section on patenting covers who owns genes and other pieces of DNA. There are also links on the site for more information on the Human Genome Project.
http://www.ornl.gov/TechResources/Human_Genome/resource/elsi.html

Medical Ethics: Where Do You Draw the Line?   Interactive scenarios on ethical decisions are featured on this site. Visitors can answer multiple choice questions about living with cancer, understanding cloning, or handling headaches. A summary of how other people responded to the questions gives a comparison between one's choices and others. Links at the end of each section lead to an ethics forum, for a bulletin board discussion, and to related sites on cancer, cloning, and headaches.
http://www.learner.org/exhibits/medicalethics

National Bioethics Advisory Commission (NBAC)   In addition to providing information on current research trends in the biotechnology industry, NBAC explores the ethical implications of technological advances. The site acts

as a forum for the ethical concerns of the public regarding rapidly advancing technology. Transcripts from its meetings are available on the site, as well as NBAC reports on topics such as ethical issues in human stem cell research and cloning human beings. A short list of bioethics-related links is provided.
http://bioethics.gov/cgi-bin/bioeth_counter.pl

National Reference Center for Bioethics Literature   Linked to the Kennedy Institute of Ethics of Georgetown University, this center holds a large collection of literature on biomedical ethics. Serving as a resource for both the public and scholarly researchers, the library lists its resources on this Web site. The site also provides access to free searching of the world's literature in this area using BIOETHICSLINE or the Ethics and Human Genetics Database. Other relevant links are provided in the areas of educational and teaching resources, bibliographies, and Internet resources for bioethics.
http://www.georgetown.edu/research/nrcbl

The Hastings Center   The Hastings Center is a major center for the study of biomedical ethics. Its Web site provides information about the center as well as detailed explanations of current research activities. Information on educational opportunities at the center is provided. There are also a catalog of publications and a list of related links.
http://www.thehastingscenter.org

UNESCO: International Bioethics Committee (IBC)   The International Bioethics Committee of the United Nations Educational, Scientific, and Cultural Organization (UNESCO) has created this Web site to inform the public of their work on human rights in relation to advances made in genetics and molecular biology. The site outlines their activities, along with proceedings from their meetings. The Universal Declaration on the Human Genome and Human Rights resolution is available on the site. Under the "Ethical Issues" section, visitors can read IBC reports on subjects such as the teaching of bioethics, neuroscience, the human genome, bioethics and human rights, and genetics.
http://www.unesco.org/ibc

University of Buffalo Center for Clinical Ethics and Humanities in Health Care   Information about the center, news and events notices, a library of bioethics and medical humanities documents, and the Ethics Committee Core Curriculum are available at this address. Links are presented to Internet resources on featured topics, including bioethics education, hospice and palliative care, advance directives, philosophy of mind, medical record privacy, genetics and ethics, and other relevant sites.
http://wings.buffalo.edu/faculty/research/bioethics/nav.html

11.3 BIOTECHNOLOGY

Bio Online   Bio Online is a comprehensive Web site for the life sciences and the biotechnology industry. This site provides general information, current

news, an industry guide, academic and government links, and an extensive career center. It is an informative resource for seeking information on the biotechnology industry and related sciences.
http://www.bio.com

Biofind.com   Biofind.com provides insight into the biotechnology industry and is a resource for general information, news, and developments in emerging technologies. The site also contains a job search database, chat room, the "Biotech Rumor Mill" for anonymous public discussion of current events in the field, and links to other biotech Web sites. A subscription service is also available for a fee, which provides daily e-mail updates on jobs, candidates, business opportunities, innovations, and press releases.
http://www.biofind.com

BioPortfolio.com   A database of biotechnology companies, technology, and products worldwide is featured on this Web site. More than 11,000 companies are included in the database. Some have detailed profiles, as well as hyperlinks for investor information and news. Subscribers can search the database by key word, category, organization name, or region. The site allows a limited search on a free trial basis.
(fee-based) http://www.bioportfolio.com/bio/

Bioresearch Online   Bioresearch Online is a virtual community, forum, and marketplace for biotechnology professionals. Users have access to the latest headlines, product information, new and industry analyses, as well as career information. There are also specific pages devoted to pharmaceutical research and laboratory science.
http://www.bioresearchonline.com/content/homepage

Biotechnology Industry Organization   This industry-sponsored Web site provides weekly news updates on developing technology and world news. The site also offers general information, links to corporate Web sites, an online library, and a number of other educational resources.
http://www.bio.org/welcome.html

Biotechnology: An Information Resource   Dedicated to providing current information in all areas of biotechnology, this site is a subsidiary of the National Agricultural Library and the U.S. Department of Agriculture. The site catalogs press releases and offers an exhaustive listing of links to other Web-based resources from around the world, providing a wealth of information, especially in the area of agricultural biotechnology.
http://www.nal.usda.gov/bic

BioWorld Online   BioWorld Online tracks the growth of the biotechnology market. In addition to providing stock and financial information, the site provides access to current industry headlines, job search resources, forums, and news worldwide.
http://www.bioworld.com

CorpTech Database   This comprehensive database provides details on companies involved in high-tech industries, including biotechnology and pharmaceutical companies. Basic information such as each company's description, address, annual sales, and CEO name is available free; however, more in-depth financial and business data is only accessible to fee-paying subscribers. Searches for products or names of company officers are also available, again with some amount of information provided at no cost.

(some features fee-based) http://www.corptech.com

Enzyme Nomenclature Database   Enzyme information of a very specific nature is available at this site. The database at this Web site provides access to enzyme information by Enzyme Commission (EC) number, enzyme class, description, chemical compound, and cofactor. There is an accompanying user manual for the enzyme database as well.

http://www.expasy.ch/enzyme

Infobiotech   Infobiotech is a collaboration of government, academic, and private sector resources. This Canadian-based site provides general information, resources, and links to both Canadian and non-Canadian sites. In addition, it offers a large list of related sites providing current information on advances in the biotechnology industry.

http://www.cisti.nrc.ca/ibc/home.html

International Food Information Council   The International Food Information Council collects and disseminates scientific information on food safety, nutrition, and health by working with experts to help translate research findings into understandable and useful language for opinion leaders and consumers. This site provides information and news on emerging technologies in the food industry. Resources available through this site include publications, recent news articles, government guidelines and regulations, and links to other resources on the Internet.

http://ificinfo.health.org

MedWebPlus: Biotechnology   MedWebPlus contains an extensive guide to online resources in biotechnology and a wide variety of other fields. The site catalogs hundreds of Internet resources containing many forms of information on the biotechnology industry. In addition, links are provided to journals, online publications, and recent articles of interest. Vast amounts of information are provided at this site, and links are kept current.

http://www.medwebplus.com/subject/Biotechnology.html

National Center for Biotechnology Information (NCBI)   A collaborative effort produced by the National Library of Medicine and the National Institutes of Health, NCBI is a national resource for molecular biology information. The center creates public databases, conducts research in computational biology, develops software tools for analyzing genome data, and disseminates biomedical information in an effort to improve the understanding of molecular processes affecting human health and disease. In addition to conducting and cataloging its own research, NCBI tracks the progress of important research projects worldwide. The site provides access to public molecular databases containing genetic sequences, structures, and taxonomy; literature databases; catalogs of whole genomes; tools for mining genetic data; teaching resources and online tutorials; and data and software available to download. Research performed at NCBI is also discussed at the site.

http://www.ncbi.nlm.nih.gov

Recombinant Capital   This online magazine provides analysis of the biotechnology industry. This resource is particularly appropriate for those seeking to invest in companies on the forefront of this rapidly growing industry. Although much of the information presented here is from a financial perspective, the site gives an overview of the entire industry and provides daily news updates. The progress of developing technology can be closely monitored via this site.

http://www.recap.com

World Wide Web Virtual Library: Biotechnology   A directory of sites in the field of biotechnology is featured on this Web page. This site catalogs hundreds of reviewed links, including publications, educational resources, general information, and government links. There is also a rating system used by the editor of the site to point out links of specific importance.

http://www.cato.com/biotech

11.4 CLINICAL PRACTICE MANAGEMENT

GENERAL RESOURCES

Cut to the Chase   Healthcare management information for physicians is available at this site, including articles about practice management issues, career development resources, publications and software sources, information about other products and services related to healthcare management, and links to sites offering additional healthcare management resources. Free site registration is required for access to these resources.

(free registration) http://www.cuttothechase.com

Guide to Clinical Preventive Services   This guide is a comprehensive online reference source covering recommendations for clinical practice on more than 150 preventive interventions, including screening tests, counseling interventions, immunizations, chemoprophylactic regimens, and other preventive medical tools. Sixty target conditions are discussed in the report.

http://cpmcnet.columbia.edu/texts/gcps/gcps0000.html

Health Services/Technology Assessment Text (HSTAT)   This electronic resource for physicians provides access to consumer brochures, evidence reports, reference guides for clinicians, clinical practice guidelines, and other full-text documents useful in making healthcare decisions. Users can download documents from the site, access general information about the system, and browse links to additional sources for information. Searches can be comprehensive or limited to specific databases within the HSTAT system, and users can also search by keyword.

http://text.nlm.nih.gov

Medsite.com   Described as an e-services portal for the medical community, this site offers books, medical software, and supplies at discounted prices; financial resources; a scheduling tool geared for medical professionals; and free e-mail accounts. The service requires free registration.

(free registration) http://www.medsite.com

PDR.net   PDR.net is a medical and healthcare Web site created by the Medical Economics Company, publisher of healthcare magazines and directories including the Physicians' Desk Reference. The site has specific areas and content for physicians, pharmacists, physician assistants, nurses, and consumers. Access to the full-text reference book is free for U.S.-based M.D.s, D.O.s and P.A.s in full-time practice. There is a fee for other users of this service, but most of the site's features are free.

(some features fee-based) http://www.PDR.net

Physician's Guide to the Internet   A directory of Web sites for physicians is offered on this site. Features include physician lifestyle resources, such as sites offering suggestions on stress relief; news items; clinical practice resources, including access to medical databases and patient education resources; and post-graduate education and new physician resources. Other resources include links to sites selling medical books, products, and services for physicians; links to Internet search tools; and Internet tutorials.

http://www.physiciansguide.com

State Medical Boards Directory   This directory provides the names, addresses, telephone numbers, and e-mail or Web site information for each of the state medical boards. Physicians can contact a board for information on licensing in that state or for other information regarding medical regulation or standards. http://www.fsmb.org/members.htm

CLINICAL CALCULATORS

MedCalc 3000 Medical Calculator   MedCalc 3000, offering several hundred online medical calculator tools, can be utilized at this site. It combines various equations, clinical criteria scores, and decision trees used in healthcare. In addition, there is a quick converter, to convert value units easily, and a math calculator. Alphabetical lists of the medical equations and clinical criteria topics are presented, with links to the actual calculators.

http://calc.med.edu/

Medical Tools and Clinical Calculators   Medic.com provides clinicians with 60 medical calculators to measure blood oxygen content, body mass, opioid drug dosage, and numerous other factors. Scores such as coronary disease probability, the geriatric depression scale, the Glasgow coma scale, and the TWEAK alcoholism score are also included. A sidebar menu offers links to reference information on medical subjects, specialties, medical news, books, software, and services.
http://www.medic8.com/MedicalTools.htm

Online Clinical Calculators: Medstudents   Medstudents.com hosts this site providing visitors with 24 online clinical calculators for various measurements, including arterial oxygen content, oxygen consumption, water deficit, and pulmonary shunt. By filling in spaces for critical measurements, then clicking on the result box, the desired results are produced.
http://www.medstudents.com.br/calculat/index2.htm

EVIDENCE-BASED MEDICINE

Cochrane Collaboration   The Cochrane Collaboration is an international working group of experts who catalog and maintain evidence-based medicine by specialty. The site explains the history of the collaboration, along with descriptions of the Cochrane library site, which contains a database of systematic reviews and a controlled trials register. Abstracts are available on the library site free-of-charge; full access is available only to subscribers.
(some features fee-based) http://www.cochrane.org/default.html

Evidence-Based Medicine Resource Center   Resources offered on the New York Academy of Medicine's evidence-based medicine site may be useful to both teaching and practicing physicians. There are links to databases, publications, teaching tools, education resources, and tips on searching for evidence-based medicine. The "Practicing" section includes clinical guidelines, clinical trials, and systematic reviews. There are also organizations, glossaries, journals, LISTSERV discussion groups, and related links.
(some features fee-based) http://www.ebmny.org/thecentr2.html

Medscout: Evidence-Based Medicine Guidelines   Targeted to physicians, this site offers a comprehensive list of evidence-based medicine guidelines available on the Internet. There are more than 30 sites drawn mostly from universities and journals around the world.
http://www.medscout.com/guidelines/evidence_based/

New York Online Access to Health (NOAH): Evidence-Based Medicine   Patients seeking information on evidence-based medicine (EBM) will find this site by the New York Online Access to Health project (NOAH) very useful. There are more than 55 sites listed offering information on types of evidence, research methods, statistical terms in EBM, and a basic overview of EBM.
http://www.noah-health.org/english/ebhc/ebhc.html

MEDICAL ETHICS

American Medical Association (AMA): Ethics Standards Reports of the Council on Ethical and Judicial Affairs, an organization that sets ethics policy for the AMA, are accessible from this site. Visitors will discover an online policy finder, which can be browsed alphabetically, or get answers to frequently asked questions about the role of the Council, the Code of Medical Ethics, and the End-of-Life Care (EPEC) project. The Institute for Ethics at the AMA, functioning as an independent research organization, provides news from its task force and information about the E-Force program. Other AMA Ethics Web sites and pages of professional standards are available.
http://www.ama-assn.org/ama/pub/category/2416.html#ethics

American Society of Law, Medicine, and Ethics (ASLME) The search engine at this site allows visitors to access a variety of educational information related to the law, medicine, and ethics. Details about the organization's peer-reviewed journals, access to research projects on pain undertreatment, and a news section offering up-to-date information on recent developments in the field are offered. A multimedia educational link connects visitors to more than 50 streaming audio presentations in the fields of genetics, health law, and end-of-life decision making.
http://www.aslme.org/

Medical Ethics A comprehensive listing of more than 100 links related to ethics are offered on this Web page. The links are categorized as bioethics, professional ethics, institutional ethics, scientific misconduct, humanism, and morals. The sites are drawn from Internet sources around the world.
http://www.mic.ki.se/Diseases/k1.316.html

Medscout: Medical Ethics Over 100 medical ethics resources are presented at this site from Medscout. Examples of resources are the American Society of Bioethics and Humanities, the Center for Ethics and Professionalism, the Center for Clinical Ethics and Humanities in Health Care, and the National Human Genome Research Institute. Visitors to this site will also find topical links to resources in areas such as diseases, government, immunizations, journals, and health policy.
http://www.medscout.com/ethics/

The Hastings Center This independent, interdisciplinary research and education center explores the ethical issues surrounding health, medicine, and the environment. Examination of the moral issues arising from advances in medicine can be found at the site's project pages on medicine and biomedical research, values and biotechnology, and health policy. Several relevant online resources for bioethics-related information are offered.
http://www.thehastingscenter.org/

MEDICAL INFORMATICS

Agency for Healthcare Research and Quality (AHRQ): Healthcare Informatics Healthcare informatics is featured on this Web site, courtesy of the Agency for Healthcare Research and Quality. The site provides data and survey reports covering public health, standard activities for federal agencies, medical informatics and health services research data, and the use of computers to advance healthcare. In addition, there are links to research findings, funding opportunities, consumer health, clinical information, and medical news.
http://www.ahcpr.gov/data/infoix.htm

American Health Information Management Association Directed to health information managers, the American Health Information Management Association Web page offers details about their association and the field. There is information on careers in information management, as well as certification. Their publications catalog is found. An interactive campus allows visitors to complete online courses. In addition, members have access to a job bank.
(some features fee-based) http://www.ahima.org/

American Medical Informatics Association (AMIA) With the proliferation of medical information, the growth of medical research, the development of medical information systems, and the creation of management systems for computerized patient data, the medical informatics field has grown substantially. Major themes of the AMIA are privacy and confidentiality of medical records, public policy development for legislation in the field, conferences of medical informatics professionals, and the issuance of papers and publications covering various aspects of the medical information field. The site features publications, including the *Journal of the American Medical Informatics Association,* and related reports and videos. There is also information on the various AMIA working and special interest groups, a job bank, and related resources.
http://www.amia.org

American Telemedicine Association Dedicated to promoting access to medical care for consumers and professionals through the use of telecommunications technology, the American Telemedicine Association promotes education, research, and advocacy in the field. Visitors to the site can learn more about the association, its member groups, and meetings. Information under the "News and Resources" section includes bulletin boards, a comprehensive list of related links, and a job bank. In the same section is a library containing a member directory, telemedicine news updates, and proceedings from their annual meetings. (some features fee-based) http://www.atmeda.org

Duke University: Medical Informatics Links Maintained by the Division of Clinical Informatics of Duke University Medical Center, this Web page offers more than 50 links related to medical informatics. The Web pages listed are drawn from associations and universities around the world.
http://dmi-www.mc.duke.edu/dukemi/misc/links.html

Galaxy Health Directory: Medical Informatics Resources A dozen U.S. and international centers and medical departments dealing with medical informatics can be accessed from this central listing by clicking on "Professional Medicine, Medical Informatics." Included in this list are centers at Oregon Health Sciences University, Stanford University, Columbia University, and European institutions. There are also articles, directories, and discussion group links for further resources on medical informatics.
http://www.healthwave.com/healthwave/
Professional-Medicine/Medical-Informatics?id=49524&v=healthwave

International Medical Informatics Association (IMIA) The International Medical Informatics Association's Web site features their newsletter, along with information on their working groups and member societies. A report on the recommendations of the IMIA on education in health and medical informatics is provided. There is also an extensive list of related resources that includes institutions and organizations, medical resources, and health informatics resources. http://www.imia.org

Medscout: Medical Informatics For those interested in medical informatics, this Web page contains a comprehensive list of Internet resources. The sites are categorized as national information associations, newsletters and journals, and medical informatics on the Internet. In total, there are more than 85 sites from both domestic and international sources.
http://www.medscout.com/informatics/index.htm

Telemedicine More than 20 telemedicine resources are provided at this site from Galaxy, a medical portal. Featured resources include the Armed Forces Institute of Pathology, the Center for Telemedicine Law, Cyberspace Telemedicine Law, MediaStation 5000, and the Telemedicine Research Center. Links are provided to access remote consultation, telepathology, and teleradiology resources.
http://www.galaxy.com/galaxy/Medicine/Medical-Informatics/Telemedicine.html

MEDICAL LAW

American Medical Association (AMA): Legal Issues for Physicians
Healthcare providers can access information regarding legal issues in the areas of business and management, patient-physician relationships, and compliance at this Web site, maintained by the American Medical Association. Various medical case summaries are provided, as well as a Compliance Interactive Tutorial System offering online assistance with fraud and abuse regulations for members of the American Medical Association.
(some features fee-based) http://www.ama-assn.org/ama/pub/category/4541.html

MedNets: Medical Law Links to more than 30 medical law resources, including the American Bar Association Health Law Section, AMA Statements on Advanced Directives, Expert Witness Net, the Health Care Liability Alliance, Medical Care Law, the U.S. States Abortion Laws, and the Law and Legislative

Center are offered at this site from MedNets. Visitors can also access medical law databases, health law journals, news, and resources related to medical ethics through this site.
http://www.mednets.com/medlaw.htm

MEDICAL LICENSURE

Administrators in Medicine: Association of State Medical Board Executive Directors A list of participating state licensing authorities is compiled at this page, maintained by DocFinder. The list is not exhaustive but contains many connections to state medical examiners home pages and tools that allow visitors to search for physicians by name or license number.
http://www.docboard.org/

Federation of State Medical Boards (FSMB) The Federation of State Medical Boards site provides visitors with policy documents, details on post-licensure assessment, a credentials verification service, and state medical board information. A publications catalog is provided, which includes the *Journal of Medical Licensure and Discipline* and the FSMB Handbook. The FSMB library is accessible to members of the organization. There is also information on their database of board actions taken against physicians.
(some features fee-based) http://www.fsmb.org/

PRACTICE GUIDELINES AND CONSENSUS STATEMENTS

Medscout: Medical Specialty Guidelines Sponsored by Medscout, this Web page offers a comprehensive listing of more than 50 clinical guidelines plus links to other guidelines sites available on the Internet. The guidelines are drawn primarily from American and Canadian sources.
http://www.medscout.com/guidelines/medical_specialty/

National Guideline Clearinghouse (NGC) The National Guideline Clearinghouse is a comprehensive database of evidence-based clinical practice guidelines and related documents produced by the Agency for Healthcare Research and Quality, in partnership with the American Medical Association and the American Association of Health Plans. The guidelines can be searched by keyword or browsed by category such as disease/condition, treatment/intervention, and issuing organization. Each guideline has a brief summary and information for obtaining the full text. A useful tool on the site is the ability to "Compare Guidelines;" this feature allows users to add guidelines on a specific topic to their collection and then select a comparison button to produce a report that compares them. In addition, there are guideline syntheses on certain topics such as asthma treatment and childhood immunizations in which all the guidelines written on the topic are combined into one report.
http://www.guideline.gov/index.asp

Primary Care Clinical Practice Guidelines   Clinical practice guidelines for primary care providers are offered on this Web page, courtesy of the University of California, San Francisco. The guidelines can be searched by keyword, browsed alphabetically, or selected through clinical content categories such as mental disorders, cardiovascular system, and pregnancy. Each category has many subtopics listed, along with hyperlinks to the appropriate guideline. Also of interest is the resources section, which offers an enormous list of online textbooks, journals, superlists of links, and other related resources.
(some features fee-based) http://medicine.ucsf.edu/resources/guidelines/

PRACTICE MANAGEMENT TOOLS

Medical Group Management Association   Primarily targeted to healthcare administrators, the Medical Group Management Association focuses on practice management solutions and tools. The site contains information on their research activities, as well as policy issues. A job bank and career services are also provided. Interactive tools include a risk assessment calculator and a compliance-assessment calculator. A catalog of survey reports features medical group practice performance data.
(some features fee-based) http://www.mgma.com/

Medscape: The Journal of Medical Practice Management   Abstracts and full-text articles are available to registered users at this online journal site of Medscape. Available content includes current feature articles and archived issues that address software systems, managed care, economic trends in healthcare delivery, and billing and coding topics.
(free registration) http://managedcare.medscape.com/JMPM/public/JMPM-journal.html

11.5 CLINICAL TRIALS

CenterWatch   This clinical trials listing service offers patient resources, including a listing of clinical trials by disease category, links to current NIH trials, listings of new FDA drug therapy approvals, and current research headlines. Background information on clinical research is also available to patients unfamiliar with the clinical trials process. Industry professional resources include research center profiles, industry provider profiles, industry news, and career and educational opportunities. Links to related sites of interest to patients and professionals are also available.
http://www.centerwatch.com/main.htm

ClinicalTrials.gov   The National Institutes of Health and the National Library of Medicine provide access to information about clinical trials through ClinicalTrials.gov. Visitors can search the database by entering keywords or phrases into the search engine; by using a focused search by disease, location, treatment, or sponsor; or by browsing alphabetical listings of thousands of

conditions and sponsors. Links to information on studies recruiting offer additional details on study purpose, protocol, and researcher contact.
http://clinicaltrials.gov/ct/gui/c/b

11.6 DISSERTATION ABSTRACTS

Dissertation Abstracts Database A database of more than 1.6 million citations and abstracts from doctoral dissertations and master's theses is provided on this site. Visitors are offered free access to the most current two years of citations, which includes an abstract and a 24-page preview. Subscriber institutions are able to download the entire dissertation in PDF format for the years 1997 to the present. Subscribers can also search for citations dating back to 1861. (some features fee-based) http://wwwlib.umi.com/dissertations/about_pqdd

11.7 ENVIRONMENTAL HEALTH

Agency for Toxic Substances and Disease Registry (ATSDR) Environmental and occupational public health hazards and risks are the focus of this division of the U.S. Department of Health and Human Services. A variety of resources can be accessed, including national alerts, health advisories, answers to frequently asked questions about hazardous substances, and relevant legislation. Databases available from the site provide information on specific hazardous waste sites, as well as information on those exposed to such substances. Scientific papers published by the Agency, site addressing issues specific to children, and a calendar of events are included.
http://www.atsdr.cdc.gov/atsdrhome.html

New York Online Access to Health (NOAH): Environmental Health
The New York Online Access to Health (NOAH) site features a directory of environmental health links available on the Internet. There are more than 55 links categorized under environmental health topics such as air quality, chemical sensitivities, toxins and pesticides, and water quality. More than 45 sites are found under a resources section that includes advocacy, governmental agencies, and legal resources. By clicking on the icon at the top of the page titled "Espanol," the same site appears in Spanish.
http://www.noah-health.org/english/illness/environment/environ.html

11.8 GENETICS AND GENOMICS

GeneClinics Funded by NIH and developed by the University of Washington, GeneClinics is a knowledge base of expert-authored, up-to-date information relating genetic testing to the diagnosis, management, and counseling of individuals and families with inherited disorders. Directed at healthcare professionals, the site contains textbook-type genetic testing and counseling information on a

large number of diseases. The disease profiles are peer-reviewed and continuously updated.
http://www.geneclinics.org

Genetics Virtual Library   A comprehensive listing of links to major Web sites on specific topics in genetics is featured on this site. Links are subdivided by organism, providing genetics information on many animals, from transgenic mice to humans. Brief descriptions are provided for many links.
http://www.ornl.gov/TechResources/Human_Genome/genetics.html

Genomics: A Global Resource   Presented by the Pharmaceutical Research and Manufacturers of America, this Web page offers a broad array of resources related to genomics and bioinformatics. Drawn from around the world, and updated daily, the most recent news stories can be found in the "News & Tools" section. Also within this section are links to journals from around the world, as well as education resources such as online textbooks, organizations, academic programs, and grants. The section titled "Lexicon" offers a searchable glossary of terms. There are also links for legislative issues, controversial issues such as cloning, and biodiversity. A therapeutics section covers medical testing and bioethics. In addition, the bioinformatics home page can be accessed, as well as bioinformatic databases for microbial, plant, invertebrate, vertebrate, and humans. (some features fee-based) http://genomics.phrma.org/

Kyoto Encyclopedia of Genomes and Genetics (KEGG)   The Kyoto Encyclopedia of Genes and Genomes attempts to computerize current knowledge of molecular and cellular biology in terms of information pathways consisting of interacting molecules or genes. The site also provides links to gene catalogs produced by genome sequencing projects. Information indexed at this site ranges from basic genetic information to extremely technical descriptions of molecular pathways. Also provided is a listing of links to other major Internet sites containing information relevant to genetic research.
http://www.genome.ad.jp/kegg

MedBioWorld: Genetics, Genomics, and Biotechnology Journals
This site offers a comprehensive list of genetics, genomics, and biotechnology journals. There are more than 100 links to journals from the United States and abroad. http://www.medbioworld.com/journals/genetics.html

Molecular Genetics Jump Station   This site provides a comprehensive listing of Web-based resources for geneticists. Sites indexed here are technical in nature and intended for investigators. Resources include links to molecular biology, microbiology, and genetics jump sites, which contain catalogs of links; sites containing protocols on laboratory techniques; journals and other online publications, news groups, and mail lists; institutes and organizations; conferences and meetings announcements; commercial sites; and sources for ordering technical books. The site is sponsored by Beckman, Horizon Scientific Press, the *Journal of Molecular Microbiology and Biotechnology*, and MWG-Biotech.
http://www.horizonpress.com/gateway/genetics.html

National Center for Biotechnology Information (NCBI): Online Mendelian Inheritance in Man (OMIM) Dr. Victor A. McKusick, a researcher at Johns Hopkins University, and his colleagues have authored this database of human genes and genetic disorders. The database was developed for the World Wide Web by the National Center for Biotechnology Information. Reference information, texts, and images are found through the site, as well as links to the Entrez database of MEDLINE articles and sequence information. Visitors can search the OMIM Database, OMIM Gene Map, and OMIM Morbid Map (a catalog of cytogenetic map locations organized by disease) from the site. Information on the OMIM numbering system, details on creating links to OMIM, site updates, OMIM statistics, information on citing OMIM in literature, and the OMIM gene list are all found at the site. Links are available to allied resources, and the complete text of OMIM and gene maps can be downloaded from the site.
http://www.ncbi.nlm.nih.gov/Omim

National Human Genome Research Institute (NHGRI) The National Human Genome Research Institute supports the NIH component of the Human Genome Project, a worldwide research effort designed to analyze the structure of human DNA and determine the location of the estimated 50,000 to 100,000 human genes. The NHGRI Intramural Research Program develops and implements technology for understanding, diagnosing, and treating genetic diseases. The site provides information about NHGRI, the Human Genome Project, grants, intramural research, policy and public affairs, workshops and conferences, and news items. Resources include links to the institute's Ethical, Legal, and Social Implications Program and to the Center for Inherited Disease Research. The site also provides genetic resources for investigators, a glossary of genetic terms, and a site search engine.
http://www.nhgri.nih.gov

Office of Genetics and Disease Prevention Created by the Centers for Disease Control and Prevention, this site offers access to current information on the impact of human genetic research and the Human Genome Project on public health and disease prevention. The site provides general information, indexes recent articles, lists events and training opportunities, and offers an extensive listing of links to other resources. Users can search the site by keyword and access the Human Genome Epidemiology Network (HuGENet), a global collaboration of individuals and organizations committed to the development and dissemination of population-based epidemiologic information on the human genome. http://www.cdc.gov/genetics

Primer on Molecular Genetics The United States Department of Energy presents a comprehensive resource for those seeking basic background information on genetics and genetic research at this site. Discussions at the site include an introduction to genetics, DNA, genes, chromosomes, and the process of mapping the human genome. Mapping strategies, genetic linkage maps, and various physical maps are available, as well as links to mapping and sequence

databases and a glossary of terms. The site also summarizes the predicted impact of the Human Genome Project on medical practice and biological research.
http://www.ornl.gov/hgmis/publicat/primer/intro.html

The Genomics Lexicon Part of a larger genomics site produced by the Pharmaceutical Research and Manufacturers of America and the Foundation for Genetic Medicine, Inc., this site features "Lexicon," a glossary of genomic terms. The glossary can be browsed alphabetically or by an index. Reference sources for the glossary are listed along with hyperlinks to the original source.
http://209.52.56.28/lexicon/index.html

The Institute for Genomic Research (TIGR) The Institute for Genomic Research is a not-for-profit research institute with interests in structural, functional, and comparative analysis of genomes and gene products in viruses, eubacteria, archaea, and eukaryotes. Information on recent advances in genetics and continuing research projects in the area of human genomics, an extensive searchable database of previous research, and links to other genome centers worldwide are available at this site.
http://www.tigr.org

University of Kansas Medical Center: Genetics Education Center
Links are available at this address to Internet resources for educators interested in human genetics and the Human Genome Project. Sites are listed by topic, including the Human Genome Project, education resources, networking, genetic conditions, booklets and brochures, genetics programs and other resources, and glossaries. Lesson plans are offered both by the University of Kansas and other sources at the site. A description of different careers in genetics is also available. This site provides access to useful genetics Internet resources for nonprofessionals and educators.
http://www.kumc.edu/gec

11.9 GERIATRIC MEDICINE

American Geriatrics Society (AGS) A national nonprofit association of geriatrics health professionals, research scientists, and other concerned individuals, the American Geriatrics Society is dedicated to "improving the health, independence, and quality of life for all older people." The site offers a description of the society, adult immunization information, AGS news, conference and other events notices, legislation news, career opportunities, directories of geriatrics healthcare services in managed care, position statements, practice guidelines, awards information, and other professional education resources. Patient education resources, a selected bibliography in geriatrics, links to related organizations and government sites, surveys, and a site search tool are also found at this address.
(some features fee-based) http://www.americangeriatrics.org

ElderWeb   Designed as a research source for consumers and professionals, this Web page offers a broad array of resources related to the care of the elderly. In the "Finance and Law" section, more than 20 topics are listed such as drug costs, elder law, and Medicaid. Each topic lists resources that can be found on the site, in their newsletter, and on the Internet. Resources are listed in the same way under sections such as living arrangements and body and soul. There are also a regional directory of sites related to living arrangements, finance, and law; a list of associations, and an eldercare locator that covers domestic and international sites. Visitors can access news on the home page, or register for a free newsletter.
(free registration) http://www.elderweb.com/

Hardin Meta Directory: Geriatrics and Senior Health   The Hardin Meta Directory on this site features geriatrics and senior health. Categorized as large and medium lists, there are links to Web pages that contain lists of relevant Internet resources. The lists are drawn from both domestic and international sources and cover hundreds of sites. There are also links to additional directories of lists on Alzheimer's and Parkinson's.
http://www.lib.uiowa.edu/hardin/md/ger.html

MedBioWorld: Geriatrics and Gerontology Journals   A listing of geriatrics and gerontology journals available on the Internet is found on this site. There are more than 75 journals listed, some with full-text articles.
http://www.medbioworld.com/journals/medicine/geriatrics.html

Medscout: Geriatric Medicine   Resources on geriatric medicine can be found on this Web site, maintained by Medscout. More than 60 sites are listed and categorized as geriatric news, associations, geriatric education, hospitals and medical centers, and geriatrics on the Internet.
http://www.medscout.com/specialties/geriatrics/

Merck Manual of Diagnosis and Therapy: Geriatrics   The full-text of the *Merck Manual of Geriatrics* is featured on this Web page. Sixteen chapters are provided for topics such as the basics of geriatric care; falls, fractures, and injury; surgery and rehabilitation; psychiatric disorders; neurologic disorders; and musculoskeletal disorders. In addition, disorders related to endocrinology, hematology/oncology, pulmonology, cardiology, urology/nephrology, infectious disease, dermatology, and gastroenterology are found. Each chapter contains numerous diseases and disorders with information on etiology, pathophysiology, symptoms, diagnosis, and treatment.
http://www.merck.com/pubs/mm_geriatrics/contents.htm

Resource Directory for Older People   The National Institute on Aging and the Administration on Aging have compiled this directory of resources, serving older people and their families, health and legal professionals, social service providers, librarians, researchers, and others interested in the field of aging. The directory includes names of organizations, addresses, telephone numbers (including toll-free numbers), and links to Internet sites, when available.

Visitors can search the directory by keyword or view the entire table of contents from this address.

http://www.aoa.dhhs.gov/aoa/dir/intro.html

11.10   GRANTS AND FUNDING SOURCES

Foundation Center   The Foundation Center provides direct, hot links to thousands of grant-making organizations, including foundations, corporations, and public charities, along with a search engine to enable the user to locate sources of funding in specific fields. In addition, the site provides listings of the largest private foundations, corporate grant makers, and community foundations. There is also information on funding trends, a newsletter, and grant-seeker orientation material. More than 900 grant-making organizations are accessible through this site.

http://fdncenter.org

GrantSelect   More than 10,000 funding opportunities are contained in the GrantSelect database for a variety of disciplines including biomedical and health care. The database is available to subscribers only, a free 30-day trial period is offered on the site. Subscribers can also receive an e-mail alert service for new additions to the database.

(fee-based)   http://www.grantselect.com

Mental Health Net: Grants and Funding Opportunities   Part of a larger Mental Health Net Web page, this site features grant funding opportunities, related to mental health and biomedicine in general, that are available online. There are 19 sites listed with descriptions and ratings. The sites are categorized as Web resources, mailing lists, an article, professional organizations, and other resources.

http://mentalhelp.net/guide/pro28.htm

National Institutes of Health (NIH): Funding Opportunities   Funding opportunities for research, scholarship, and training are extensive within the federal government. At this site for the National Institutes of Health, there is a grants page with information about NIH grants and fellowship programs, information on research contracts containing information on requests for proposals (RFPs), research training opportunities in biomedical areas, and an NIH guide for grants and contracts. The latter is the official document for announcing the availability of NIH funds for biomedical and behavioral research and research training policies. Links are provided to major divisions of NIH that have additional information on specialized grant opportunities.

http://grants.nih.gov/grants

National Science Foundation (NSF): Grants and Awards   Because approximately 20 percent of the federal support to academic institutions for basic research comes from the National Science Foundation, this site is an important source of information for award opportunities, programs, application procedures, and other vital information. Forms and agreements may be downloaded as well, and regulations and policy guidelines are set forth clearly. http://www.nsf.gov/home/grants.htm

Society of Research Administrators (SRA): GrantsWeb   The Society of Research Administrators has created an extremely useful grant information site, with extensive links to government resources, general resources, private funding, and policy/regulation sites. The site section devoted to U.S., Canadian, and other international resources provides links to government agency funding sources, the *Commerce Business Daily,* the Catalog of Federal Domestic Assistance, scientific agencies, research councils, and resources in individual fields, such as health, education, and business. Grant application procedures, regulations, and guidelines are provided throughout the site, and extensive legal information is provided through links to patent, intellectual property, and copyright offices. Associations providing funding and grant information are also listed, with direct links.
http://sra.rams.com/cws/sra/resource.htm

11.11 MEDICAL IMAGING AND RADIOLOGY

CT Is Us   The CT (computed tomography) site offers information on medical imaging with a specific focus on spiral CT and 3D imaging. Images of the body and various medical conditions are organized by region, and information on continuing medical education courses, teaching files, medical illustrations, and a 3D vascular atlas are all available at the site.
http://www.ctisus.org

Dr. Morimoto's Image Library of Radiology   This site provides users with access to images and videos collected by Dr. Morimoto, Department of Radiology, Osaka National Hospital. Images were scanned and stored with JPEG, GIF format, and movies with QuickTime format. Ultrasonographic anatomy images related to the liver, pancreas, and bile duct include an illustration of portal anatomy, normal bile duct, tumor of liver hilum, bile duct cancer, pancreatic cancer, esophageal varix, and obstructive jaundice. Heart and major vessels images include a normal heart, major vessels of the body, and abdominal aortic aneurysm. Head images include a surface image of a human head and an image of an arachnoid cyst. Images related to the kidney and urinary tract include that of a renal cell carcinoma.
http://www.osaka-med.ac.jp/omc-lib/noh.html

Health On the Net (HON) Foundation   This site provides links to radiological and surgical images on the Internet. Images are available of the abdomen, ankle, arm, full body, brain, elbow, eye, foot, hand, head, heart, hilum, hip, kidney, knee, leg, liver, lung, muscle, neck, pancreas, pelvis, shoulder, skin, skull, teeth, thorax, trachea, blood vessels, and wrist.
http://www.hon.ch/Media/anatomy.html

Medical Imaging Resources on the Internet Supported by the University of Leeds School of Computing in the United Kingdom, this Web page offers comprehensive resource lists for medical imaging. Visitors can view the list by geographic location, namely Europe, North America, Asia, and Australasia. Within the region are subcategories such as universities, hospitals, research organizations, and the commercial sector. The list can also be viewed by content such as exhibits and publications, teaching aids, software, and general resources. There are also links for newsgroups, funding sources by region, and links to search engines.

http://www.comp.leeds.ac.uk/comir/resources/links.html

MedMark: Radiology The professional resources provided on this site focus on the field of radiology. Hundreds of sites are listed in categories such as associations, centers, departments, education, for consumers, general, imaging, information sources, journals, lists of resources, MRI/NMR, nuclear medicine, other organizations, PET, programs, research, and ultrasound. The sites are drawn from sources around the world and can be browsed in order or by using a drop-down menu to access the topic of interest.

(some features fee-based) http://medmark.org/rad/rad2.html

MultiDimensional-MultiSensor/MultiModality Biomedical Imaging and Processing The MultiDimensional-MultiSensor/MultiModality Biomedical Imaging and Processing Web site provides examples and applications of different techniques used in biomedical imaging. Multidimensional, multimodality, and multi-sensor applications are described in detail with specific examples of medical applications, along with discussions of new developments in this growing field.

http://www.expasy.ch/LFMI

Neurosciences on the Internet: Images Hundreds of Internet sites are found through this address offering resources relating to human neuroanatomy and neuropathology, neuroscience images and methods, medical imaging centers, medical illustration, medical imaging indexes, and neuroanatomy atlases of animals.

http://www.neuroguide.com/neuroimg.html

Pediatric Radiology and Pediatric Imaging Developed by Michael P. D'Alessandro, M.D., this Web page features a pediatric radiology digital library. The library contains common pediatric clinical problems with over 400 diseases represented by over 1,800 cases. There is a section on imaging approaches to common problems, as well as a section on performing common pediatric radiology procedures. Nearly 30 procedures are covered in a patient education section. There is also a link to pediatric radiology normal measurements and to musculoskeletal radiology of fractures. In addition to the library, the site lists hundreds of related links in categories such as textbooks, anatomy atlases, embryology, lectures, and patient education.

http://pediatricradiology.com/

University of Nebraska: Medical Images on the Web A list of 14 links is available at this address to Internet sources for medical images, maintained by the University of Nebraska Medical Center. Web pages listed include *Anatomy of the Human Body* by Henry Gray, a dermatology image library, a digital atlas of ophthalmology, the public health image library, the visible human project from the National Library of Medicine, and the whole brain atlas. All links are accompanied by short descriptions of resources at the site.
http://www.unmc.edu/library/medimag.html

11.12 MEDICAL SOFTWARE

Medical Software Reviews The monthly newsletter found at this site publishes evaluations of medical software products for use by physicians and other health professionals. The contents of each issue is described, and information on Internet access for subscribers is provided. Categories of software include coding, databases, diagnosis, drug interactions, medical records, patient education, practice management, scheduling, and statistics. The table of contents for current and previous months can be viewed from the site's links. However, full reviews require a subscription. Subscriber information can be accessed by clicking on "Medical Software Reviews" at the bottom of the page.
(fee-based) http://www.crihealthcarepubs.com/msrmain.html

11.13 PAIN MANAGEMENT

American Academy of Pain Management (AAPM) This site provides information about AAPM and its activities, resources for finding a professional program in pain management, accreditation and continuing medical education (CME) resources, and a membership directory for locating a pain management professional. It also provides good general information on pain management and a listing of relevant links. Access to the National Pain Data Bank is available at the site, containing statistics on various pain management therapies based on an outcomes measurement system. The site is divided into two sections with information tailored to the needs of both patients and healthcare professionals. http://www.aapainmanage.org

American Academy of Pain Medicine This site contains information about the academy's annual meeting, a member directory, FAQs, and related resources. Visitors can access an online newsletter, as well as a catalog of publications such as their journal, *Pain Medicine,* pocket guides, and position papers.
http://www.painmed.org/

American Pain Foundation The American Pain Foundation is dedicated to education and advocacy for patients and their families coping with pain. A patient information section features fact sheets on a variety of conditions such as arthritis and digestive diseases, as well as information in general on pain man-

agement and medication. There is also a section on policy and legislative issues, with links provided to related sites. On the home page, icons at the bottom lead visitors to the "Pain Care Bill of Rights" which outlines patient rights. The "You are Not Alone" section provides information on support groups, and personal stories can be read under the "Voices of People in Pain" section. In addition, there is a pain action guide and a section on finding help that contains both emotional and financial resources.
http://www.painfoundation.org/

American Pain Society   The American Pain Society is a multidisciplinary, scientific organization that offers information on publications, advocacy, career opportunities, and upcoming events. A pain facility database allows the user to search for facilities by classifications, and additional resources for both patients and professionals provide contact information for related organizations. The American Pain Society site provides an abstract search engine to their database of internal documentation on pain-related topics.
http://www.ampainsoc.org/

New York Online Access to Health (NOAH): Pain   Information on pain can be found through this large consumer health directory of Internet sites, maintained by the New York Online Access to Health (NOAH) project. The directory contains more than 100 sites categorized as the basics, types of pain, basic care, body-specific therapies, types of therapy, pain in children, and information resources.
http://www.noah-health.org/english/illness/pain/pain.html

Pain.com   This site is a comprehensive resource for seeking information on pain and pain management, with separate sections available for health professionals and consumers. For clinicians, information on meetings, free online CME courses, pain management standards, and full-text articles from pain journals are provided. Pages specifically addressing perioperative pain, cancer pain, interventional pain management, migraine and headache pain, and regional anesthesia are found and include information on related CME and discussion forums. Consumers can locate both a list of support groups and a directory of pain clinics.
http://www.pain.com/index.cfm

11.14 Patent Searches

The following sites provide easy access to patent information for medical researchers and healthcare professionals interested in learning about the latest techniques, therapies, products, and drugs.

Intellectual Property Network   A spin-off of IBM, Delphion, Inc. provides this patent site which is ideal for physicians and researchers with an interest in patents, this service offers a searchable database of patent information, titles and abstracts, and inventors and companies. The database brings up patents on

any topic by typing in the subject, along with inventor information, dates of filing, application numbers, and an abstract of the patent.
http://www.delphion.com

U.S. Patent and Trademark Office   Access to the database of the U.S. Patent and Trademark Office is available through this site for detailed searching of patents by number, inventor, and topic. There are both a full-text database and a bibliographic database.
http://www.uspto.gov/patft/index.html

11.15 PATHOLOGY AND LABORATORY MEDICINE

Hardin Meta Directory: Pathology and Laboratory Medicine Resources   Part of the Hardin Meta Directory from the University of Iowa, this site provides more than 20 links to sites that each contain a list of other sites related to pathology and laboratory medicine. The sites are categorized as large, medium, or small lists.
http://www.lib.uiowa.edu/hardin/md/path.html

Indiana University: Pathology Image Library   An image library for pathology is featured on this Web page, maintained by Indiana University. The library is categorized by region such as bone and soft tissue, cardiovascular system, gastrointestinal system, and renal system. There is also a section for gross pathology observations. The library can be browsed by system or searched by keyword.
http://erl.pathology.iupui.edu/c604/Default.htm

MedBioWorld: Laboratory Science, Forensic Science, and Pathology Journals   Visitors to this Web page will find a listing of laboratory science, forensic science, and pathology journals available on the Internet. There are over 75 journals listed alphabetically.
http://www.medbioworld.com/journals/medicine/pathology.html

Pathology Images   Developed by a group of physicians, this site features "The Lightning Hypertext of Disease," which is a searchable database of pathology images with captions. The database is free to nonmembers but query results are limited to 30 images. Membership provides access to an alternate site where queries are returned with unlimited results. The results can be viewed in English, German, or Spanish. There is also a section to help professionals study for their anatomic pathology and pathology specialty boards with a pop quiz. The quiz randomly selects questions from 6,000 multiple choice questions.
(some features fee-based) http://www.pathinfo.com/

Tulane University: Pathology Educational Resources   Primarily for healthcare professionals, this site offers a listing of links related to pathology. More than 30 sites are listed under topics such as catalogs of pathology links,

laboratory resources and images, and other Web resources. The sites are drawn mostly from American universities.
http://www.tmc.tulane.edu/classware/
pathology/medical_pathology/New_for_98/Resources.html

University of Illinois: The Urbana Atlas of Pathology   The site provides a comprehensive collection of pathology images sectioned into general, cardiovascular, endocrine, pulmonary, and renal pathology. The general pathology section includes images of the kidney, heart, spleen, thyroid, testis, cervix, small intestine, lung, artery, pancreas, liver, lymph nodes, brain, colon, skin, mesentery, joints, uterus, and peritoneal cavity. Each image has an explanatory caption. http://www.med.uiuc.edu/PathAtlasf/titlepage.html

University of Michigan: Pathology and Laboratory Medicine Resources   Hundreds of sites related to pathology and laboratory medicine are listed on this Web page, hosted by the University of Michigan Medical School Department of Pathology. The sites are listed in categories such as pathology departments (domestic and international), LISTSERVs, e-mail resources, databases, regulatory agencies, job banks, organizations, and journals. There are also anatomic pathology and laboratory medicine resources. The entire list can be browsed or accessed quickly through a table of contents that lists the categories as well as subspecialty resources.
http://www.pathology.med.umich.edu/pathresourceak/path_resources.html

University of Utah: Pathology Image Library   Intended for students and healthcare professionals, this site offers a pathology image library with more than 1,900 images. Maintained by the Department of Pathology at the University of Utah, the library is organized as general pathology and organ system pathology. There are also special sections, with images and tutorials, dedicated to AIDS pathology and anatomy/histology. A section on laboratory exercises offers case studies with images and questions. In addition, examination questions drawn from more than 1,600 questions are found. Mini-tutorials on a variety of conditions such as breast cancer, inflammatory bowel diseases, and tuberculosis are also provided.
http://medstat.med.utah.edu/WebPath/webpath.html

11.16 PREVENTIVE MEDICINE

MedMark: Preventive Medicine   Dedicated to preventive medicine, this site features a comprehensive listing of Internet resources. Hundreds of sites are found in categories such as associations, centers, departments, education, for consumers, general, government, and guidelines. There are also journals, lists of resources, and programs. The site can be browsed in order or through hyperlinks found in the table of contents presented in a sidebar menu.
http://members.kr.inter.net/medmark/prevent/

11.17 PUBLIC HEALTH

American Public Health Association   Health professionals may find the American Public Health Association site to be of interest. The site offers public health reports, abstracts from the *American Journal of Public Health,* as well as access to full-text articles published on the Web from their newspaper, "The Nation's Health." The site also has information on continuing education, legislative issues, and a publications catalog. Members will find funding opportunities under the programs and projects section. In addition, there are links for state public health associations, the World Federation of Public Health, and related public health resources.
(some features fee-based) http://www.apha.org/

National Health Service Corps   After accessing the introductory page, visitors are automatically taken to the table of contents for the National Health Service Corps Web site. General information about the organization's public health mission in assisting underserved populations, details on opportunities available to health professionals, and a site on community assistance services are provided. Upcoming events and important dates, as well as other news items of the organization are found.
http://www.bphc.hrsa.dhhs.gov/nhsc/

World Health Organization (WHO)   A site index and search tool assist in navigation of this site, which is available for viewing in English, Spanish, or French. World Health Organization press releases are displayed at the main page, and connections to information resources, a press media centre, and disease outbreak information are provided. Information on current emergencies by country is addressed, and a traveler's health advisory is found.
http://www.who.int/home-page/

MEDICAL STUDENT RESOURCES

12.1 GENERAL RESOURCES

American Medical Association (AMA): Medical Student Section The Medical Student Section of the American Medical Association (AMA) is dedicated to representing medical students, improving medical education, developing leadership, and promoting activism for the health of America. The site offers information about the section, current issues and advocacy activities, business issues of the section, chapter information, and leadership news. Special interest groups within the section include those for residents, young physicians, organized staff, students, international medical graduates, and senior physicians. http://www.ama-assn.org/ama/pub/category/14.html

American Medical Student Association (AMSA) Containing many useful resources for medical students, this home page features daily health and medical news, legislative and policy issues, and LISTSERVs for certain populations (under the advocacy section). A student involvement section lists issues such as community and public health, global health issues, health policy, and medical education that students can learn more about, along with resources to get involved. In that same section, there are also resources for positions, internships, and fellowships; leadership training information; and a list of related Internet sites. Under the local chapter resource section, there is an AMSA resource center/catalog that offers many free online publications related to international health; medical education; residency selection, including a residency directory; and training opportunities. Members can register for the career development program online and apply for financial resources such as loans and grants. (some features fee-based) http://www.amsa.org/

American Medical Women's Association (AMWA) A national association, the AMWA provides information and services to women physicians and women medical students, as well as promoting women's health and the professional development of women physicians. Resources include news, discussions of current issues, events, conferences, online publications, fellowship and residency information accessed through the Fellowship and Residency Electronic Interactive Database Access system (FRIEDA), general information and developments from AMA staff members, advocacy activities, a listing of AMWA con-

tinuing education programs, and links to sites of interest. A variety of topics related to women's health are discussed at the site.
http://www.amwa-doc.org

Association of American Medical Colleges (AAMC)   This nonprofit association committed to the advancement of academic medicine consists of American and Canadian medical schools, teaching hospitals and health systems, academic and professional societies, and medical students and residents. News, membership details, publications and other information resources, meeting and conference calendars, medical education Internet resources, research findings, and discussions related to healthcare are all found at the site. Employment opportunities at the AAMC are also listed.
http://www.aamc.org

Integrated Medical Curriculum   The integration of major medical school courses, especially the first two years, is attempted at this Web page with basic science and clinical program departments containing explanatory text, images, and cross-referenced hyperlinks. Anatomy is stressed, as well as basic clinical skills, clinical musculoskeletal pathology, and ethics. In addition, there is a virtual student lounge and related message boards.
(free registration) http://www.imc.gsm.com

Internet Resources for Medical Students   A comprehensive listing of links is offered on this Web page, courtesy of Lviv State Medical University, Ukraine. More than 150 links are found in categories such as associations, general sites, education, study help, multimedia, grants and funding, humor, and other resources. The sites are drawn from around the world; some are in Russian. http://www.meduniv.lviv.ua/inform/studlinks.html

MedicalStudent.com   This site contains an extensive medical textbook section organized by discipline. Also included are patient simulations, consumer health information, access to MEDLINE and medical journals online, continuing education sources, board exam information, medical organizations, and Internet medical directories.
http://www.medicalstudent.com

Stanford University: MedWorld   MedWorld, sponsored by the Stanford Medical Alumni Association, offers information for students, patients, physicians, and the healthcare community. Resources include case reports and global rounds, links to quality medical sites and MEDLINE, doctor diaries and medical news, and newsgroups and discussion forums. Visitors can access Stanford's medical search engine, MEDBOT, to simultaneously utilize many Internet medical search engines.
http://medworld.stanford.edu/home

Student Doctor Network (SDN)   Hosted by the Student Doctor Network, this Web page offers medical students a broad array of resources. The SDN student forums offer discussion boards for medical and premedical students. There

are also medical student diaries, where four medical students post their thoughts and experiences as they go through medical school. "The Links Resource" features more than 740 links to information such as academic success, career choices, finance, dental resources, osteopathic resources, and medical resources. In addition, there is information on getting in and getting through medical school, osteopathic medicine, and getting into dental school.

(free registration) http://www.studentdoctor.net/

12.2 FELLOWSHIPS AND RESIDENCIES

Accreditation Council for Graduate Medical Education (ACGME)

The ACGME reviews and accredits residency programs, establishes standards of performance, and provides a process to consider complaints and possible investigations by the council. The site offers information about ACGME, meetings, workshops, institutional reviews, contact details, links to residency review committees, and a listing of accredited programs.

http://www.acgme.org

American Medical Association (AMA): Fellowship and Residency Electronic Interactive Database Access (FREIDA) Online System

Operated as a service of the AMA, the FREIDA system provides online access to a comprehensive database of information on approximately 7,500 graduate medical educational programs accredited by the Accreditation Council for Graduate Medical Education (ACGME). FREIDA enables the user to search this comprehensive database and offers other services, including label printing for mailing purposes.

http://www.ama-assn.org/cgi-bin/freida/freida.cgi

Educational Commission for Foreign Medical Graduates (ECFMG)

The Educational Commission for Foreign Medical Graduates, through its certification program, "assesses the readiness of graduates of foreign medical schools to enter residency or fellowship programs in the United States that are accredited by the Accreditation Council for Graduate Medical Education (ACGME)." The site provides useful information for foreign students to learn about testing and examination dates, clinical skills required, and available publications to review requirements for applications.

http://www.ecfmg.org

Electronic Residency Application Service

The Association of American Medical Colleges (AAMC) provides this application service for students. It transmits residency applications, recommendation letters, dean's letters, transcripts, and other supporting credentials from medical schools to residency program directors via the Internet. At present, the service covers obstetrics and gynecology, pediatrics, surgery, and psychiatry. The system allows tracking of an application 24 hours a day via a special document tracking system.

http://www.aamc.org

National Residency Matching Program (NRMP)   The NRMP is a mechanism for the matching of applicants to programs according to the preferences expressed by both parties. Last year this service placed over 20,000 applicants for postgraduate medical training positions into 3,500 residency programs at 700 teaching hospitals in the United States. The applicants and residency programs evaluate and rank each other, producing a computerized pairing of applicants to programs, in ranked order. This process provides applicants and program directors with a uniform date of appointment to positions in March, eliminating decision pressure when options are unknown. The site offers information about the service, contact details, publications, and forms for registration. Prospective residents can register with the service for a fee and access the directory of programs.
http://nrmp.aamc.org/nrmp

ResidencySite.com   ResidencySite.com provides an online listing of medical residencies organized by specialty. Program directors can access resumes of residency applicants, and prospective residents can review documents related to residency matching programs and publications offering advice on obtaining a position. http://www.residencysite.com

12.3 MEDICAL SCHOOL WEB SITES

American Universities   All American university home pages are listed at this site.   http://www.clas.ufl.edu/CLAS/american-universities.html

Gradschools.com   Sponsored by several universities and other teaching institutions, Gradschools.com offers a listing of graduate programs nationwide. Programs are found by indicating a specific area of study. A directory of distance learning programs is also available.
http://www.gradschools.com/noformsearch.html

Medical Education   Accredited medical schools are listed, with links, at this site.   http://www.meducation.com/schools.html

Medical Schools   This medical site provides direct links to all of the medical schools in the United States and Canada accredited by the AAMC. These include hundreds of medical school Web sites in the United States and elsewhere.
http://www.scomm.net/~greg/med-ed/schools.html

MedicalSchoolDirectory.com   A directory of medical schools, organized by state, is provided on this site. Contact information, and a hyperlink to each school's Web site, is offered.
http://www.doctordirectory.com/medicalschools/directory/default.asp

13

PATIENT EDUCATION
AND PLANNING

13.1 EXERCISE AND PHYSICAL FITNESS

G-0422

MEDLINEplus: Exercise/Physical Fitness Resources on exercise and physical fitness are provided on this Web page, maintained by the National Library of Medicine. The site provides links for overviews on exercise, nutrition for workouts, preventing injuries, organizations, and statistics. A lot of information comes from government agencies or scientific associations, like the American Heart Association or the American Academy of Family Physicians. Specific aspects of fitness such as tips on buying exercise equipment, stretching, and walking are also covered. Information for specific populations is also included with sections for men, women, teenagers, seniors, and children. Some publications are available in Spanish.
http://www.nlm.nih.gov/medlineplus/exercisephysicalfitness.html

MedNets.com: Fitness A comprehensive listing of links on fitness are presented on this Web page, sponsored by MedNets.com. More than 45 sites are listed in categories including news, fitness tables, associations, and exercise guides. http://www.mednets.com/fitness.htm

Medscout: Physical Fitness This Web page features a listing of links related to physical fitness for both patients and professionals. More than 100 sites are listed covering associations, nutrition guidelines, exercise guides, and a variety of sports and activities.
http://www.medscout.com/physical_fitness/

President's Council on Physical Fitness and Sports (PCPFS) Resources included at this site include a fitness guide, which details the benefits of physical activity and outlines solutions to common problems interfering with physical fitness. News about physical fitness, an online reading room, scientific research reports on physical activity topics, and resources for coaches and fitness professionals are offered. Details about the national President's Challenge and other programs for physical fitness are presented.
http://www.fitness.gov/

Prevention.com: Weight Loss and Fitness Targeted to consumers, this site from *Prevention* magazine offers information and support for losing weight

and exercising. A fitness assessment section offers quizzes on topics such as heart health, hiking, and weight. There are also fitness tools including a calorie calculator, which analyzes calories lost from activities, a meal planner; and a workout planner. Visitors can read expert advice from a fitness expert and a walking expert. A fitness features section offers a variety of articles, some with video clips and message boards. Under the weight loss section, there are articles and recipes. In addition, an online walking club offers information and support. http://www.healthyideas.com/weight/

13.2 FOOD AND NUTRITION

G-0425

American Dietetic Association The American Dietetic Association presents this informative site for consumers, students, and dietetic professionals. This site has information on nutrition resources, government affairs, current issues and publications, and job opportunities, as well as a public relations team to answer media questions. Users can contact other dietitians through the site. A search engine and a site map are provided to ease in the searching process. There are also links to consumer education and public policy sites; dietetic associations and networking groups; dietetic practice groups; food service and culinary organizations; and medical, health, and other professional organizations. http://www.eatright.org

G-0426

Arbor Nutrition Guide The Arbor Nutrition Guide covers all areas of nutrition including applied and clinical nutrition. The site provides links to information on dietary guidelines, special diets, sports nutrition, individual vitamins and minerals, and cultural nutrition. There are also links relating to food science, such as food labeling in other countries, food regulation, food additives, science journals, phytochemistry, and other related topics. http://www.netspace.net.au/%7Ehelmant/search.htm

G-0427

Department of Agriculture: Nutrient Values Visitors can utilize the search engine housed at this site to find the recommended daily allowance (RDA) nutrient values of over 5,000 food items for three different serving sizes for men averaging 174 pounds and for women averaging 138 pounds, between the ages of 25 and 50. http://www.rahul.net/cgi-bin/fatfree/usda/usda.cgi

G-0428

Food and Drug Administration (FDA): Selected Non-FDA Sources of Food and Nutrition Information A list of non-FDA sources of food and nutrition information is featured on this Web page, part of a larger Food and Drug Administration's Center for Food Safety and Applied Nutrition site. The comprehensive list contains more than 75 sites categorized as U.S. government sources, non-U.S. government sources, and nutrition journals. There are also links for related LISTSERVs and commercial sites.
(some features fee-based) http://vm.cfsan.fda.gov/~dms/nutrlist.html

G-0429

Food and Nutrition Information Center (FNIC) Links to hundreds of Web sites are provided through the A-to-Z food and nutrition listing on this site, maintained by the USDA's Food and Nutrition Information Center. Topics in the A-to-Z listing include food allergies, breastfeeding, child nutrition, eating disorders, and food labeling. Additional sections include resource lists and information on dietary supplements, food composition, dietary guidelines, the food guide pyramid, and FNIC databases. Commonly requested topics are listed in the "Consumer Corner.

http://www.nal.usda.gov/fnic/etext/fnic.html

Food Science and Nutrition Journals   Visitors to this site will find an alphabetical listing of over 100 food science and nutrition journals. Some provide full-text articles.

(some features fee-based) http://www.sciencekomm.at/journals/food.html

International Food Information Council   The International Food Information Council presents resources at this site including current issues, up-to-date information for the media, food safety and nutrition facts, and extensive links to government affairs and agencies. The site also serves as a reference tool for educators and provides users with a site search engine for locating specific information.   http://ificinfo.health.org

National Institutes of Health (NIH): Office of Dietary Supplements
The International Bibliographic Information on Dietary Supplements (IBIDS) database is featured on this Web site, courtesy of the National Institutes of Health. Of interest to consumers and professionals, the IBIDS database contains more than 419,000 citations and abstracts on dietary supplements. When searching the database, one can specify to search the consumer version, full version, or peer-reviewed citations only. A journal list is provided to order full-text articles directly from the publisher. In addition, the home page contains links for grant information, a list of publications, and related resources.

http://ods.od.nih.gov/databases/ibids.html

Nutrition and Healthy Eating Advice   A broad array of nutrition resources are presented on this Web page. Hundreds of links are offered in categories such as healthy recipes, aging, child nutrition, cultural foods, diet analysis, diseases and conditions, and eating advice. Fad diets, food products including fast food nutrition, food safety, food science, guidelines, and organic foods are also covered. Links to related directories of sites are found.

http://nutrition.about.com/health/nutrition/

Science Reference Internet Guide to Food Science and Nutrition
Healthcare professionals and consumers may find the listing of food science and nutrition Internet sites on this Web page useful. Maintained by Michigan State University Libraries, the listing covers more than 100 resources. Categories include associations, comprehensive food and nutrition sites, business and industry resources, composition and nutrient analysis databases, safety and handling, human nutrition and health, and online journal abstracts and publications.

(some features fee-based) http://www.lib.msu.edu/science/food.htm

Tufts University: Nutrition Navigator Presented by the Center on Nutrition Communication, School of Nutrition Science and Policy at Tufts University, this site offers an up-to-date, rated guide to other nutrition sites. It provides information on general nutrition and special dietary needs. There are also sections with sites specifically targeted to parents, children, women, health professionals, educators, and journalists. A search engine is provided at the site for more specific resources.
http://navigator.tufts.edu

13.3 GRIEF AND BEREAVEMENT

American College of Physicians: Grieving Part of a larger *Home Care Guide to Advanced Cancer,* this site features the chapter on grieving. The chapter provides an overview of the grieving process and covers when to get help, what you can do to help yourself, common obstacles, and carrying out and adjusting your grieving plan. There are also links to related information.
http://www.acponline.org/public/h_care/10-griev.htm

CancerNet: Loss, Grief, and Bereavement Designed for healthcare professionals, this Physician Data Query (PDQ) from the National Cancer Institute offers guidelines for helping patients to cope with loss, grief, and bereavement. A model of life-threatening illness is provided to aid in understanding of the patient's psychological needs. Other topics covered include end-of-life decisions, patterns of dying, anticipatory grief, and phases of grief. General aspects of grief therapy are described, as well as complicated grief, children and grief, and cross-cultural responses to grief. A bibliography is included, and a link is provided to a patient version of this PDQ.
http://cancernet.nci.nih.gov/cgi-bin/srchcgi.exe?
DBID=pdq&TYPE=search&SFMT=pdq_statement/1/0/0&Z208=208_06750H

MEDLINEplus: Bereavement Bereavement is the focus of this Web page, produced by the National Library of Medicine. The site includes overviews on bereavement and grief as well as specific information for dealing with loss to AIDS, loss from sudden infant death syndrome, stillbirth, and suicide. Tips on helping children, teenagers, and seniors in the grieving process are also included. Some publications are available in Spanish.
http://www.nlm.nih.gov/medlineplus/bereavement.html

13.4 MEDICAL PLANNING

BLOOD BANK INFORMATION

America's Blood Centers America's Blood Centers are found in 46 states and collect approximately 47% of the U.S. blood supply. This site provides contact information for each of this organization's centers.
http://www.americasblood.org

American Association of Blood Banks (AABB) This site provides a contact list for each state on locating and arranging blood donation, including information on storing blood for an anticipated surgery or emergency (autologous blood transfusion). It also answers general questions about blood and blood transfusion.
http://www.aabb.org

CAREGIVER RESOURCES

Family Caregiver Alliance Information on long-term care is featured on the Family Caregiver Alliance Web page. The "Resource Center" section of the site offers an online support group, FAQs, and fact sheets regarding long-term care issues as well as work and eldercare issues. There is also a "Clearinghouse" section with fact sheets on diseases and disorders, caregiving issues, and reading lists. Within that same section are a catalog of publications and an online version of their newsletter. In addition, the home page has information on policy issues and a list of related resources.
http://www.caregiver.org/

National Family Caregivers Association (NFCA) The NFCA is a national organization offering education, information, support, public awareness campaigns, and advocacy to American caregivers. The address discusses caregiving and provides statistics, a survey report, news, an informational pamphlet, a reading list, caregiving tips, and contact details. Caregivers will find this site a source of support, encouragement, and information.
http://www.nfcacares.org

CHRONIC AND TERMINAL CARE PLANNING

Organ Donation This government site answers frequently asked questions, dispels myths, and presents facts about organ donation. Visitors can download and print a donor card or search for additional information via links to related organizations on the Internet.
http://www.organdonor.gov

U.S. Living Will Registry   This free service electronically stores advance directives and makes them available directly to hospitals by telephone. Registration materials are available to download online or by calling 1-800-LIV-WILL.
http://www.uslivingwillregistry.com

USAhomecare.com   USAhomecare.com is a consumer-oriented home care (home health and hospice) site. The site provides answers to common questions, a bookstore, links to related sites, news, contact information, and a directory of agencies offering home care or hospice services, organized state by state.
http://www.USAhomecare.com

DIRECTING HEALTHCARE CONCERNS AND COMPLAINTS

Congress.org   This site offers a Capital directory, including members of Congress, the Supreme Court, state governors, and the White House. Users can also find comments on members of Congress by associations and advocacy groups, determine a bill's status through the site's search engine, send messages to Congress members, and find local congressional representatives.
http://congress.org/main.html

Families USA   Families USA is a national, nonprofit, nonpartisan organization dedicated to the achievement of high-quality, affordable healthcare, and long-term care for all Americans. The site offers a clearinghouse of information on Medicaid, Medicare, and General Managed Healthcare. Assistance and advice is provided on choosing an HMO, how to tell if a health policy or plan is good, and who to address if you have a healthcare complaint. Within the site, at www.familiesusa.org/medicaid/state.htm, a state-specific healthcare information guide is provided. This directory includes phone numbers to every state's department of insurance, which allows users to obtain reports on plans and information on complaint ratios.
http://www.familiesusa.org

Joint Commission of Accreditation of Healthcare Organizations (JCAHO)   The JCAHO site lists a toll-free complaint hotline for patients, their families, and caregivers to express concerns about the quality of care at accredited healthcare organizations at this site. (The toll-free U.S. telephone number is 1-800-994-6610. The hotline is staffed between 8:30 a.m. and 5 p.m., central time, during weekdays.) The site also describes a mechanism for transmitting complaints via e-mail.
http://www.jcaho.org/news/nb189.html

Medicare Rights Center (MRC)   The Medicare Rights Center is a national, nonprofit organization focused to ensure that seniors and people with disabilities on Medicare have access to quality, affordable healthcare. The site offers information on specific MRC programs, news, consumer publications, information on professional membership, and details on the Initiative for the Terminally

Ill on Medicare. Visitors can also subscribe for a fee to a biweekly newsletter delivered by fax.

http://www.medicarerights.org/Index.html

Quality Improvement Organizations This site contains a directory of Peer Review Organizations (PRO) listed by state. These organizations monitor the care given to Medicare patients. Each state has a PRO that can decide whether care given to Medicare patients is reasonable, necessary, provided in the most appropriate setting, and meets standards of quality generally accepted by the medical profession. Peer Review Organizations can also be contacted to investigate beneficiary complaints.

http://www.qio.org

State Insurance Commissioners Deloitte and Touche Financial Counseling Services offers the addresses and phone numbers of each state's insurance commissioner at this site.

http://www.dtonline.com/insur/inlistng.htm

Elder and Extended Care

Administration on Aging (AOA) Dedicated to providing information on older persons and services for the elderly, the Administration on Aging offers a broad array of resources. Information on the site is divided into sections for older persons and their families, healthcare professionals, the Aging Network, and researchers and students. The older persons section offers a comprehensive listing of Internet resources including an AOA guide for caregivers, an eldercare locator, booklets on health topics, and fact sheets on issues such as age discrimination, longevity, and pensions. Professional resources include information on legal issues, general resources, statistics, and specific program resources such as managed care. The Aging Network offers a list of general resources, while the research section emphasizes statistics.

http://www.aoa.dhhs.gov

American Association for Retired Persons (AARP) This nonprofit group is dedicated to the needs and rights of elderly Americans. Topics discussed at the site include caregiver support, community and volunteer organizations, Medicare, Medicaid, help with home care, finances, health and wellness, independent living, computers and the Internet, and housing options. Benefits and discounts provided to members are described, reference and research materials are available, and users can search the site by keyword.

http://www.aarp.org

American Association of Homes and Services for the Aging (AA-HSA) This association represents nonprofit organizations providing healthcare, housing, and services to the elderly. The site offers tips for consumers and family caregivers on choosing facilities and services, notices of upcoming events,

press releases, fact sheets, an online bookstore, and links to sponsors, business partners, an international program, and other relevant sites.
http://www.aahsa.org

Eldercare Locator   The Eldercare Locator is a nationwide directory assistance service designed to help older persons and caregivers locate local support resources for aging Americans. This site helps senior citizens find community assistance and Medicaid information. Interested parties can also contact the Eldercare Locator toll free at 1-800-677-1116.
http://www.aoa.dhhs.gov/aoa/pages/loctrnew.html

Extendedcare.com   This address offers information on choosing an extended care provider, a "Geriatric Library" of information resources, a glossary of terms related to extended care, a forum for asking questions of a participating physician, and information on over 60,000 care providers. Visitors can search for care providers by type of care and zip code, subscribe to an e-mail newsletter, and read archived newsletters and press releases. A tool for assessing an individual's care needs is also available. A professional section is available to users associated with registered hospitals.
(some features fee-based) http://www.elderconnect.com/asp/default.asp

Insure.com: Answers to Seniors' Health Insurance Questions (on Medicare and Medicaid)   This site provides individual state phone numbers for the State Health Insurance Advisory Program (SHIP). SHIP, is a federally funded program found in all states under different names, helps elderly and disabled Medicare and Medicaid recipients understand their rights and options for healthcare. Services include assistance with bills, advice on buying supplement policies, explanation of rights, help with payment denials or appeals, and assistance in choosing a Medicare health plan.
http://www.insure.com/health/ship.html

End-of-Life Decisions

American Medical Association (AMA): Education for Physicians on End-of Life Care (EPEC)   Supported by a grant from the Robert Wood Johnson Foundation, EPEC is a program designed to educate physicians nationwide on "the essential clinical competencies in end-of-life care." Visitors will find an overview of the project's purpose, design, and scope; a call for EPEC training conference applications; previous conference details; a mailing list; and an annotated list of educational resource materials. EPEC resources such as *The Participant's Handbook,* a guide to end-of-life care, can be downloaded from the site. http://www.epec.net

Before I Die   The Web companion to a public television program exploring the medical, ethical, and social issues associated with end-of-life care in the United States is featured at this address. Personal stories, a bulletin board, a glossary of terms, contact details for important support sources and organiza-

tions, and suggestions on forming a discussion group are available at the site. A program description, viewer's guide, outreach efforts and materials, and credits for the program are also provided.
http://www.pbs.org/wnet/bid

Choice in Dying   Services offered by Choice in Dying include advance directives, counseling for patients and families, professional training, advocacy, and publications. Membership details, press releases, news, information on end-of-life issues, an online newsletter, state-specific advance directive documents, and a petition for end-of-life care are all found at this site. Visitors can also order publications and videos or access links to related sites.
http://www.echonyc.com/~choice

End of Life: Exploring Death in America   National Public Radio's "All Things Considered" presents transcripts of a recent series on death and dying and other resources at this informative site. Contact information and links to valuable organizations and other support sources; a bibliography of important publications; texts related to death, dying, and healing; and a forum for presenting personal stories are found at this address.
http://www.npr.org/programs/death

Last Acts   Designed to improve end-of-life care, Last Acts seeks to "bring end-of-life issues out in the open and to help individuals and organizations pursue the search for better ways to care for the dying." The site presents information on Last Acts activities, a newsletter, press releases, and discussion forums. Links are available to details of recent news headlines, sites offering additional information resources, grant-making organizations, and a directory of Robert Wood Johnson Foundation end-of-life grantees.
http://www.lastacts.org

Living Wills   A brief description of a living will is offered on this Web site, written by attorney Brian N. Durham. The purpose of the living will is described along with the importance of communicating last wishes to family members.   http://lawyers.about.com/careers/lawyers/library/weekly/aa102898.htm

Project on Death in America (PDIA): Transforming the Culture of Dying   The Project on Death in America supports initiatives in research, scholarship, the humanities, and the arts in transforming the American culture and experience of dying and bereavement. The PDIA also promotes innovations in care, public education, professional education, and public policy. Information is presented on the project's Faculty Scholars Program, as well as on various other funding initiatives, past and present, in such areas as nursing, social work, arts and humanities, public policy, legal issues, and community based issues. Other resources described at the site include Grantmakers Concerned with Care at the End of Life, media resources, and other publications offered by the PDIA.
http://www.soros.org/death

HOSPICE AND HOME CARE

American Academy of Hospice and Palliative Medicine (AAHPM)
This national nonprofit organization is composed of physicians "dedicated to the advancement of hospice/palliative medicines, its practice, research, and education." Academy details, contact information, news, press releases, position statements, events and meetings notices, employment listings, and links to related sites are found at this address. Publications, continuing medical education opportunities, and conference tapes are also available. http://www.aahpm.org

Hospice Association of America (HAA) Serving the needs of the most seriously ill patients with cancer and other diseases, the HAA offers a full menu of information about the field of hospice care, as well as a directory of home care and hospice state associations. Each localized association listing offers the name of the executive director, the address, telephone, fax, and e-mail contact. http://www.hospice-america.org

Hospice Foundation of America The Hospice Foundation of America offers a range of books and training services for hospice professionals and the general public. The Web site provides general information on hospices, and specific types of grief management. There is also a listing of other Web resources and useful literature for both the healthcare provider and the patient. An extensive A-to-Z topical section offers hundreds of relevant links. http://www.hospicefoundation.org

Hospice Net Hospice Net is dedicated to helping patients and families facing life-threatening illnesses. The site contains a listing of useful articles, FAQ sheets, caregiver information, and a listing of select links to other major Web resources. http://www.hospicenet.org

HospiceWeb This site contains general information, a listing of frequently asked questions, a discussion board, a hospice locator, and an extensive list of links to related sites. Links to other hospice organizations are categorized by state. http://www.hospiceweb.com/index.htm

National Association for Home Care (NAHC) NAHC is a trade association representing more than 6,000 home care agencies, hospices, and home care aide organizations. The site offers news and association announcements, a newsletter on pediatric home care, links to affiliates, international employment listings, legislative and regulatory information, statistics and technical papers, and directories of related state associations. Visitors can access a home care and hospice search tool for finding local service providers, and a consumer section offers information on choosing a home care provider, including descriptions of agencies providing home care; tips for finding information about agencies; and discussions of services, payment, patients' rights, accrediting agencies, and state resources. One section is restricted to members.
(some features fee-based) http://www.nahc.org

National Hospice and Palliative Care Organization (NHPCO) The NHPCO offers a comprehensive site providing information on all aspects of hospice care for the seriously and terminally ill, along with a state-by-state and city-by-city guide to hospice organizations in the United States. For each listing of a hospice facility, there is a telephone number and contact person.
http://www.nhpco.org

Medical Insurance and Managed Care

Agency for Healthcare Research and Quality (AHRQ): Checkup On Health Insurance Choices This discussion of health insurance choices informs consumers on topics including why individuals need insurance, sources of health insurance, group and individual insurance, making a decision of coverage, and managed care. Types of insurance described at the site include fee-for-service and "customary" fees, health maintenance organizations, preferred provider organizations, Medicaid, Medicare, disability insurance, hospital indemnity insurance, and long-term care insurance. The site also includes a checklist and worksheet to determine features important to an individual when choosing insurance. A glossary of terms is available for reference.
http://www.ahcpr.gov/consumer/insuranc.htm

American Association of Health Plans Located in Washington, D.C., the American Association of Health Plans represents more than 1,000 HMOs, PPOs, and other network-based plans. The site offers information on government and advocacy activities, public relations materials, reports and statistics, selected bibliographies listed by subject, information on services and products, conference details, and training program information. Consumer resources include information on choosing a health plan, descriptions of different types of health plans, women's health resources, and fact sheets about health plans. Users can search each specific area of the site for information by keyword.
http://www.aahp.org

drkoop.com: Insurance Center Part of a larger drkoop.com Web page, this site features an interactive Plan Profiler and Policy Chooser to help determine what type of plan is right for an individual consumer. An insurance library, glossary of insurance terms, and health insurance news updates are featured at the site.
http://www.drkoop.com/hcr/insurance

Employer Quality Partnership (EQP) Developed by Employer Quality Partnership, a volunteer coalition of employer organizations interested in promoting positive change in the healthcare marketplace and in educating employees regarding their employer-based healthcare plans, this site offers useful information on healthcare plans. There is a guide for employees on selecting and understanding healthcare plans, assistance for employers in evaluating health-

care plans, and also guides for employers on ways to improve the quality of their health plans.
http://www.eqp.org

Glossary of Managed Care and Organized Healthcare Systems Terms   Users will find an extensive list of managed care and organized healthcare terms and acronyms defined at this site.
http://www.uhc.com/resource/glossary.html

Healthcare Financing Administration   This federal site provides a wealth of information on Medicare and Medicaid for both patients and healthcare professionals. It covers the basic features of each program and discusses laws, regulations, and statistics about federal healthcare programs. Information is also provided at the state level (state Medicaid), providing a list of sites with important state information.
http://www.hcfa.gov

Joint Commission of Accreditation of Healthcare Organizations (JCAHO)   The Joint Commission of Accreditation of Healthcare Organizations evaluates and accredits nearly 18,000 healthcare organizations and programs. "Quality Check," a service offered by the commission, allows consumers to check ratings and evaluations of accredited organizations at the site. Information is available for the general public, employers, healthcare purchasers, and unions; the international community; and healthcare professionals and organizations. The site also contains information on filing complaints, career opportunities, news, and links to related sites.
http://www.jcaho.org

Managed Care Glossary   To be used for professional training purposes or as a general information source, this managed care glossary contains a continuously updated compilation of new terminology related to managed care with additional items in the field of information technology continuously being added. Physicians and other healthcare professionals may want to bookmark this site to ensure a more complete understanding of modern health maintenance and preferred provider organization structure and service delivery.
http://mentalhelp.net/articles/glossary.htm

Medical Insurance Resources   This site offers a large index of medical insurance resources on the Internet. Links are provided to major insurance companies and other related sites. Each link is accompanied by a brief explanation of what can be found at that particular site.
http://www.nerdworld.com/trees/nw1654.html

Medicare   The Health Care Financing Administration (HCFA) administers Medicare, the nation's largest health insurance program, which covers 39 million Americans. This site answers Medicare questions regarding eligibility, additional insurance, Medicare amounts, and enrollment. Consumer information includes answers to frequently asked questions on Medicare and help regarding

health plan options. Those interested in additional information can call 1-800-MEDICARE to receive help in organizing Medicare health options.
http://www.medicare.gov

National Committee for Quality Assurance (NCQA)   The National Committee for Quality Assurance is a private, nonprofit organization dedicated to assessing and reporting on the quality of managed healthcare plans. These activities are accomplished through accreditation and performance measurement of participating plans. Almost half the HMOs in the nation, covering three-quarters of all HMO enrollees, are involved in the NCQA accreditation process. A set of more than 50 standardized performance measures, called the Health Plan Employer Data and Information Set (HEDIS), is used to evaluate and compare health plans. The NCQA Web site allows the user to search the accreditation status list. The search results will include the accreditation status designation and a summary report of the strengths and weaknesses of the plan entered. NCQA accreditation results allow users to evaluate healthcare plans in such key areas as quality of care, member satisfaction, access, and service.
http://www.ncqa.org/Pages/Main/index.htm

U.S. News Online: America's Top HMOs   This site helps consumers to rate their managed care plan by ranking HMOs by state. Other useful tools include an HMO glossary, a medical dictionary, a best- hospitals finder, and a list of the 40 highest-rated HMOs in the United States. Fitness tips, articles related to HMOs, and an ask-the-doctor forum are all found at this site.
http://www.usnews.com/usnews/nycu/health/hetophmo.htm

13.5 ONLINE DRUG STORES

CVS Pharmacy   Consumers can order prescription and nonprescription drugs, along with other pharmacy items, on this Web page. The prescription section offers an extensive description of the purpose of the drug, side effects, precautions, drug interactions, and other prescribing information. Nonprescription drugs, vitamins, first aid, home care, and personal care items are also available. http://www.cvs.com

Drugstore.com   As one of the first online drugstores, drugstore.com has developed an extensive and informative site that provides prescription and non-prescription medicine, personal care products, vitamins, and other products. There are also articles on solutions to some health and beauty problems, an opportunity to ask a drugstore.com pharmacist questions, and opinions on products from customers.
http://www.drugstore.com

Eckerd.com   In addition to providing vitamins, beauty products, and health products, this online service offers a convenient store pickup feature, which allows visitors to place an order online and pick it up at their local store. A drug

information and pricing database, home delivery, and "Ask the Pharmacist" departments are available.
http://www.eckerd.come

Familymeds.com Familymeds is a prescription retailer with "brick and mortar" pharmacies as well as this online site. This online drug store can be used for both prescription and nonprescription needs. Nonprescription items are available in categories such as personal care, beauty care, healthcare, remedies, and nutrition. A personal health section features the latest news for topics such as asthma, diabetes, infant health, and women's health. A nutrition section offers fact sheets on vitamins, minerals, and herbal remedies, as well as on therapies such as acupuncture and yoga. For information and clinical recommendations on more than 200 common health concerns, the "Health Clinics" section provides fact sheets that cover causes, symptoms, natural remedies, and prescription remedies. Visitors have the option to view the entire site in Spanish.
http://www.familymeds.com/familymeds

HomePharmacy.com At Home Pharmacy visitors can perform a site-specific search for products or browse an A to Z listing of shopping categories. Popular products are displayed at the home page of this online drugstore, which provides a variety of healthcare products and several price specials.
http://www.homepharmacy.com

PRESCRIPTIONOnline.com After registering, visitors can shop for prescriptions on this Web page. When requesting a medication, a close-up photo of the medication appears along with drug information and price. Pharmacists are available through an online chat room or by e-mail, phone, or fax. The site contains a list of state licenses, as well as health plans accepted.
http://prescriptiononline.com/

Rx.com On this Web site, visitors can have their prescriptions filled or order nonprescription products. In addition, there is a variety of information posted for consumers such as Rx.magazine with full-text health articles. At the "Reference Desk" visitors will find the *Whole Health Guide,* which contains fact sheets on medical conditions, herbs, and supplements. Sections of the *Physicians Desk Reference Family Guide* are available in the health guides section with information on treating common disorders, a guide to lifelong health, and a guide to women's health. There are also drug fact sheets and an A-to-Z listing of conditions. http://www.rx.com/

Verified Internet Pharmacy Practice Sites (VIPPS) Program The Verified Internet Pharmacy Practice Sites Program of the National Association of Boards of Pharmacy (NABP) was developed in 1999 out of public concern for the safety of pharmacy practices on the Internet. This site contains a menu with links providing information on the criteria for VIPPS certification; a VIPPS list (which includes the pharmacy name and Web site address); VIPPS definitions; and links to Web sites of state boards of pharmacy, state medical boards, federal agencies, and professional organizations. http://www.nabp.net/vipps/intro.asp

VitaRx.com   Physicians can use the VitaRx.com site to order prescriptions or injectable drugs for their patients. Patients can refill their prescription online or place orders for over-the-counter medications. A disease support center provides patients with fact sheets on diseases such as Crohn's disease and rheumatoid arthritis, as well as directions on self-injection. There are also an "Ask a Pharmacist" and "Ask a Nurse" services where answers are posted online.
http://vitarx.com/

WebRx   This Web site offers customers a wide variety of products, including over-the-counter medicine, personal care items, vitamins, electronics, and prescription medicine. New patients must register by filling out an online form and provide a way to contact their doctors for prescription information. Prescriptions are processed by a registered pharmacist. News and information on more than 90 health topics are included at this resource.
http://www.webrx.com

13.6 PATIENT EDUCATION

GENERAL RESOURCES

Patient information regarding various medical conditions and health issues can be obtained at any of the general medical search engines that are included. Below are listings of health Web sites accessible through the well-known search engines, as well as other sites that cover wide-ranging topics of interest to patients.

American Academy of Family Physicians (AAFP): Health Information for the Whole Family   Directed toward consumers, this site provides a collection of fact sheets on a variety of conditions that can be searched by keyword, population group, or region of the body. The fact sheets can also be browsed alphabetically under the "Health Information Handouts" section. Advice on topics such as lowering cholesterol, preventing flus and colds, and pain relief for lower back pain can be found under the AAFP family health facts section. Self-care flowcharts for health concerns covering symptoms, diagnosis, self-care, and when to see a doctor are also provided. In addition, there are databases for conventional drug information, herbal and alternative drugs, and drug interactions that explain proper use, side effects, and reactions. A national directory of family doctors is found, and the site can be translated into Spanish.
http://familydoctor.org

Columbia University: College of Physicians and Surgeons Complete Home Medical Guide   Patients will find this site to be a comprehensive resource for healthcare information. Topics include receiving proper medical care, the correct use of medications, first aid and safety, preventative medicine, and good nutrition. Chapters containing more specific information on health con-

cerns for men, women, and children; disorders; infectious diseases; mental and emotional health; and substance abuse are also available.
http://cpmcnet.columbia.edu/texts/guide

DiscoveryHealth.com   From the producers of the Discovery Channel, this site offers consumer health resources for all groups. News items, feature articles and reports, a site search engine, links to health reference materials, chat forums, a forum for asking health questions, and descriptions of recent research advances are all found at this site. Visitors can learn interesting health facts and access information specific to men, women, senior citizens, children, mental health, and health in the workplace. Nutrition, fitness, and weight management tools are also available at this site.
http://www.discoveryhealth.com

Federal Health Agencies   Consumers will find a list of links to Federal health agencies on this Web site, part of a larger Patient Rights.com Web page. Each link is preceded by a short explanation of what the federal agency does. On the same page, there are also links to elected officials, state health organizations, state insurance commissions, and state medical boards. Visitors can also research medical conditions through a list of links on conditions.
http://www.patientrights.com/links/links4.htm

Healthanswers.com   This site provides consumers with informational resources on a wide range of health topics, including senior health, men's health, women's health, children's health, pregnancy, nutrition, cancer, and STDs. In addition, a medical encyclopedia, a drug database, and discussion forums can be found.
http://www.healthanswers.com

HealthTalk Interactive   Consumers will find articles, interviews, audio clips, and live interactive events with health experts, on a variety of health topics, on this site. Information on specific diseases can be accessed through the section titled, "Patient Education Networks." Diseases covered include asthma, breast cancer, diabetes, lymphoma, menopause, multiple sclerosis, and rheumatoid arthritis. http://www.healthtalk.com/

InteliHealth   This comprehensive site offers consumers tips on healthy living, information, and other resources on specific conditions; a site search engine for specific information; health news by topic; special reports; an online newsletter; pharmaceutical drug information; and an online store offering health items for the home. Conditions and health topics discussed at the site include allergy, arthritis, asthma, diabetes, mental health, pregnancy, nutrition, and weight management. Links are available to other sites offering consumer health resources. The site obtains its information from various sources, including the Harvard Medical School and the University of Pennsylvania School of Dental Medicine.
http://www.intelihealth.com

G-0505

MayoClinic.com   Visitors to this informative site will find answers to patient questions, news and articles on featured topics, registration details for e-mail alerts of site updates, and site search engines for health information and prescription drug information. Specific information centers are devoted to allergy and asthma, Alzheimer's disease, cancer, children's health, digestive health, heart health, general medicine, men's and women's health, and nutrition. A library of answers to health questions, a glossary of medical terms, and a forum for asking specific questions are also available at the site.
http://www.mayohealth.org/home

 G-0506

MDAdvice.com   Information on a broad array of health topics is featured on this Web page, targeted for consumers. The "Health Center" section offers a health library, with patient fact sheets covering symptoms, conditions, medical tests, and surgeries; a drug information database; an ask-the-expert forum; and in-depth articles under the "Informative Material" link. A section titled "Condition Centers" features a center on cancer and one on heart disease. Each center offers fact sheets, support groups, clinical trial information, and expert advice. There are also community message boards.
http://www.mdadvice.com

 G-0507

Med Help International   Visitors will find resources on a broad array of health topics on this site, especially for consumers. A comprehensive consumer health information library covers topics such as asthma, Hodgkin's disease, and diabetes; each topic contains related articles, a medical glossary, related questions and answers from their ask the expert forum, support groups, and clinical trials. The site also features ask the expert forums, a patient to patient network designed to serve as an online support group, and medical and health news.
http://www.medhelp.org

 G-0508

Medical Library   Of interest to consumers and professionals, the Medem site features a medical library, with information drawn from medical societies, such as the American Academy of Pediatrics and the American Medical Association. The library is separated into four categories: life stages, diseases and conditions, therapies and health strategies, and health and society. Information in the library is rated as introductory health information, general health information, advanced resources, and professional/research level. In addition to the library, under the "Products and Services" section, physicians can develop their own Web site with secure e-mail messaging to patients. There is also a section for a physician finder.
http://www.medem.com/MedLB/medlib_entry.cfm?
sid=103AF635-C640-11D4-8C0100508BF1C1F1&site_name=Medem

 G-0509

MedicineNet.com   An efficient and thorough source of information on hundreds of diseases and medical conditions, MedicineNet enables the user to click on subjects in an alphabetical list. The site's medical content is produced by board-certified physicians and allied health professionals. Topics include dis-

eases and treatments, procedures and tests, a pharmacy section, a medical dictionary, first aid information, and a list of poison control centers.
http://www.medicinenet.com

 MEDLINEplus A service of the National Library of Medicine, this consumer health site offers a wide variety of information categorized as health topics, drug information, dictionaries, directories, organizations, and publications. Under "Health Topics," there are hundreds of diseases and disorders, such as asthma, AIDS, epilepsy, and sickle cell anemia. Each condition contains links for more information such as overviews, symptoms, treatment, diagnostic tests, and research. The "Drug Information" section contains a guide to more than 9,000 prescription and over-the-counter medications. Also notable is a link to MEDLINE, the National Library of Medicine's bibliographic database of more than 11 million articles.
http://www.medlineplus.gov

 NetWellness NetWellness is a Web-based health information service with a large group of medical and health experts available to answer consumer questions online .Developed by the University of Cincinnati Medical Center, the Ohio State University, and Case Western Reserve University, nearly 200 health faculty answer questions on over 40 topics. Responses are usually provided within two to three days. Users are also encouraged to search archives of articles. (some features fee-based) http://www.netwellness.org

 New York Online Access to Health (NOAH) This site is offered as a public resource by many providers, including hospitals, institutes, foundations, research centers, and city and state agencies. Users can access information concerning a wide range of health topics, including diseases, mental health, and nutrition, with links provided to patient resources. A site-based search engine is available. A health information database containing abstracts and articles from selected health-related periodicals is only available to users accessing the site from specific institutions, including the New York Public Library branches.
http://www.noah-health.org/english/qksearch.html

 Quackwatch Quackwatch is a nonprofit corporation combating "health-related frauds, myths, fads, and fallacies." The group investigates questionable health claims, answers consumer inquiries, distributes publications, reports illegal marketing, generates consumer-protection lawsuits, works to improve the quality of health information on the Internet, and attacks misleading Internet advertising. Operation costs are generated solely from the sales of publications and individual donations. Sister sites, Chirobase and MLM Watch, offer a consumer's guide to chiropractors and a skeptical guide to multilevel marketing. Information for cancer patients includes alerts of questionable alternative health treatments, a discussion of how questionable practices may harm cancer patients, and other related discussions. Visitors to the site can purchase publications, read general information about questionable medical practices, and view details about specific questionable products and services. Links to government

agencies and other sites providing information about health fraud are available at this site, which can be translated into several foreign languages.
http://www.quackwatch.com

Virtual Hospital: Common Problems in Adults   The Virtual Hospital Web page offers consumers and professionals resources for information on common medical problems in adults. Provided by the University of Iowa, the site contains a table of links, with separate professional and patient sections. It covers more than 45 problems such as abdominal pain, arthritis, cancer, diabetes, pregnancy, and stroke. A link is provided to a similar site for children.
http://www.vh.org/CommonProblems/CommonProblems.html#Art

ADOLESCENT HEALTH

Adolescent Health Resources for Professionals   Provided by the Leadership Institute on Adolescent Health, this Web site offers a listing of more than 35 sites that provide adolescent health resources for professionals. The listing includes subject guides about adolescents, general subject guides, lists of resources from associations, adolescent health programs, and special topics such as accidents, drug abuse, and teen pregnancy. There are also professional organizations, philanthropic organizations, databases, and statistics, and pages from the federal government.
http://corc.oclc.org/WebZ/XPathfinderQuery?sessionid=0:term=196:xid=UMM

Centers for Disease Control and Prevention (CDC): Adolescent and School Health   Hosted by the Centers for Disease Control and Prevention, this site focuses on adolescent and school health. Healthcare professionals and consumers may find the resources on the site of interest. A report on adolescent health is featured that covers pregnancy, sexually transmitted diseases, and risk behaviors among adolescents. The report offers statistics, state profiles, and trend information. The site also has information on grant funding, along with publications, and data. School health initiatives are described, as well as ongoing research.
http://www.cdc.gov/nccdphp/dash/ahson/ahson.htm

Medscout: Adolescent Health   Dedicated to adolescent health, this site offers a comprehensive listing of Internet resources. There are more than 50 sites listed drawn from both domestic and international sources. Links are provided to many organizations dealing with adolescent health-related issues.
http://www.medscout.com/health/adolescent/

Society for Adolescent Medicine   Directed to professionals, the home page of the Society for Adolescent Medicine offers information on special interest groups for adolescent healthcare professionals, the SAM newsletter and a list of fellowships in adolescent medicine. Several position papers can be found in the "Activities" section. Of interest to consumers and professionals, there is a list of more than 50 related links covering eating disorders, gay and lesbian teens, adolescent health, sexuality, social development, substance abuse, and violence. http://www3.uchc.edu/~sam/samfinal/introduction-low.html

INFANT AND CHILDREN'S HEALTH

Centers for Disease Control and Prevention (CDC): Infants and Children Parents will find more than 65 fact sheets on infants and children's health on this Web page, part of a larger Centers for Disease Control and Prevention site. The fact sheets cover a variety of topics such as air bags, breastfeeding, child abuse, dog bites, fifth disease, immunizations, and swimming pool safety. Some Spanish-language articles are available.
http://www.cdc.gov/health/nfantsmenu.htm

KidsGrowth.com This site offers a wealth of resources on parenting and child development. A section on parenting offers hundreds of articles and answers from experts on a variety of topics, including discipline, parent skills, and school health. Articles and answers can also be found in a child development section, categorized by age group. A section on growth milestones offers parental guidance on development, with related articles arranged chronologically from the prenatal visit to the 10-year-old child. Also available are a free weekly e-mail newsletter, growth tables, an interactive car seat selector, and parent guides for vomiting, fever, coughing, and diarrhea.
http://www.kidsgrowth.com/index2.cfm

KidsHealth.org This site, created by the Nemours Foundation Center for Children's Health Media, provides expert health information about children from before birth through adolescence. Specific sections target children, teens, and parents, with age-appropriate information and language.
http://kidshealth.org

Medem Medical Library: Children's Health Provided by the American Academy of Pediatrics, information at this page includes coverage of more than 35 child-related health topics. The directory of subjects can be browsed by category and includes everything from asthma to youth violence. Medical news and a site-specific search engine are provided.
http://www.medem.com/MedLB/bufferpage_aap.cfm

Medscout: Children's Health A comprehensive listing of more than 100 links related to children's health are provided on this Web page, courtesy of Medscout. The sites are appropriate for both consumers and professionals and covers a broad range of topics relating to infants and children.
http://www.medscout.com/health/childrens/

Virtual Children's Hospital: Common Problems in Pediatrics Parents and professionals will find information on common health problems in children on this Web page, courtesy of the Virtual Children's Hospital. More than 45 health topics are covered such as asthma, behavior problems, diabetes, and sleep

problems. Resources for consumers and health providers are in different sections of the table of resources.
http://www.vh.org/VCH/CommonProblems/CommonProblems.html#An

MEN'S HEALTH

MEDLINEplus: Men's Health Topics   Information on a variety of men's health topics is provided on this Web page, maintained by the National Library of Medicine. Topics include circumcision, STDs, infertility, and prostate diseases. Each topic has links for additional information categorized as an overview, clinical trials, diagnosis/symptoms, prevention, specific aspects, and related organizations.
http://www.nlm.nih.gov/medlineplus/menshealth.html

Men's Health Network   Dedicated to education and advocacy on behalf of men's health, the Men's Health Network produces this Web page to provide information on their activities including education, advocacy, and health screening efforts. A library section contains links such as data and statistics on men's high-risk-job injuries, along with resources on prostate disease issues, stroke, diabetes, STDs, and fathers and parenting. The "Men's Links" section offers a long list of links covering health resources, workplace safety, domestic violence, and suicide, as well as journals and organizations.
http://www.menshealthnetwork.org/

New York Online Access to Health (NOAH): Men's Health   Directed at consumers, more than 35 links related to men's health are offered on this site, maintained by the New York Online Access to Health project (NOAH). The links cover basic information, such as anatomy and primary care for men; specific issues, such as fertility, impotence, prostate diseases, and testicular diseases; and information resources, including the Mayo Clinic.
http://www.noah-health.org/english/wellness/healthyliving/menshealth.html

MINORITY HEALTH

Department of Health and Human Services (HHS): Office of Minority Health   Located within the U.S. Department of Health and Human Services, the Office of Minority Health focuses on public health issues affecting minorities. Their Web page offers information on conferences, a list of online publications from federal and nonfederal sources, data and statistics, and related links. There is also a section on Federal clearinghouses that can be searched by topic; the appropriate clearinghouse and contact information is the result of the query. The "What's New" section of the site covers legislation and funding announcements. Visitors can also learn more about their initiatives, programs, and work on health disparities. A resource center offers publications,

funding information, and searchable databases of organizations, programs, and documents related to minority health.
http://www.omhrc.gov/

Health Information for Minority Women   The National Women's Health Information Center has provided this Web site dedicated to health information for minority women. In addition to an overview of minority health, there are sections of the site dedicated to health information specific to African Americans, Asian/Pacific Islanders, American Indian/Alaskan Natives, and Hispanic/Latinas. Each minority section contains fact sheets on a variety of health topics such as asthma, cancer, and diabetes. Each fact sheet also offers links to publications and related organizations. In addition, there is a link for a list of Federal minority offices. A fact sheet on leading causes of death among minority women, as well as a link to the Office on Women's Health site that describes their activities to promote minority health is provided.
http://www.4woman.org/minority/index.htm

HealthWeb-Minority Health   Examining minority health, this Web page offers a directory with hundreds of sites of interest to both professionals and the public. The sites are accessed by clicking on topics under the table of contents. Topics include general, education and training opportunities, African Americans, Asian Americans, Hispanic Americans, Native Americans, and research in minority health.
http://healthweb.org/browse.cfm?subjectid=53

SENIOR HEALTH

American Association of Retired Persons (AARP)   The feature finder at the site connects visitors to a variety of services of this organization, including guides to health and wellness, life transitions, and legislative issues of interest to older Americans. The Web edition of the *AARP Bulletin* offers stories for those entering their middle and later years, and a department on making educated healthcare choices is provided. An online discussion center, links to local AARP chapters, and the current online edition of *Modern Maturity* are, additionally, found. http://www.aarp.org/

Hardin Meta Directory: Geriatrics and Senior Health   The Hardin Meta Directory on this site features geriatrics and senior health. Categorized as large and medium lists, there are links to Web pages that contain lists of relevant Internet resources. The lists are drawn from both domestic and international sources and cover hundreds of sites. There are also links to additional directories of lists on Alzheimer's and Parkinson's.
http://www.lib.uiowa.edu/hardin/md/ger.html

National Institute on Aging (NIA)   The NIA, a division of the National Institutes of Health, leads the research effort to extend healthy lives and better understand the processes associated with aging. News and events about the divi-

sion, a publications and resource list, and details of their research programs can be located from the site's links. The Alzheimer's Disease Education and Referral (ADEAR), a service of the NIA, offers additional information on Alzheimer's disease and related conditions.
http://www.nih.gov/nia

WOMEN'S HEALTH

African American Women's Health   Visitors will find a variety of resources dedicated to the health of African American women. There is an A-to-Z listing of health topic such as alcohol addiction, diabetes, and fibroids; each topic has a fact sheet with references. There are also fact sheets categorized as nutrition and fitness, spiritual and mental health, and finances. In addition, there are a discussion forum and a business directory. Physicians can add their names to a physician locator service.
http://www.blackwomenshealth.com/

allHealth.com   Primarily directed toward female consumers, a variety of health resources are found at this iVillage Web page. The site offers "Health Tools," where visitors can take quizzes to test their knowledge of breast cancer or learn the difference between allergies and colds. In the same section are educational modules on managing conditions such as asthma, diabetes, and hypertension. Access to MEDLINE and related health databases is provided, as are articles, expert advice, and message boards on specific health concerns. Health topics can be browsed under an A-to-Z directory of conditions or researched in an illustrated medical encyclopedia.
http://www.allhealth.com

Department of Health and Human Services (HHS): National Women's Health Information Center   Focused on women's health, the National Women's Health Information Center offers resources for professionals and the public. The site can be searched by health topic or by keyword. Information on programs such as breastfeeding, violence against women, and healthy pregnancy is provided; each has consumer materials, publications, and a list of related links. A health professionals section offers links to medical journals, clinical trials, publications, and patient fact sheets. Also available are a media section with facts and statistics on women's health, a directory of residential and fellowship programs, and information on funding opportunities.
http://www.4woman.org/index.htm

Medscape: Women's Health   A variety of clinical information related to women's health is featured on this Web page, primarily for professionals. Resources on this site include the latest news, treatment updates, clinical management, and practice guidelines. There is also CME information with some online CME courses. A resource center provides condition-specific information. In addition, there are journals, related links, and an "Exam Room" with interactive case studies. Consumers can find disease information under a patient resources section. (free registration)

http://www.medscape.com/Home/Topics/WomensHealth/WomensHealth.html

University of Maryland: Women's Health Web Sites   Resources on women's health are featured on this site, maintained by the University of Maryland. The site contains a listing of links to more than 70 women's health Web pages. A short description of each site is provided.

http://research.umbc.edu/~korenman/wmst/links_hlth.html

Women's Health   A comprehensive consumer-oriented directory of links related to women's health is offered on this Web site. The site offers an A-to-Z listing of health topics, along with commonly referenced topics such as birth control, dieting, menopause, and STDs. Each section lists Internet resources with a description of site content. Also available are a physician locator, a section on surgical procedures, and a calculator/tools section with interactive quizzes on risk factors for disease.

http://womenshealth.about.com/health/womenshealth/library/blaward.htm

Women.com: Health   Primarily for consumers, the health and wellness section of the women.com site offers information on a variety of women's health topics. Visitors can access articles and fact sheets related to topics such as cold and flu, allergy, breast health, heart health, pregnancy, and sexual health. A "Health Resources" drop-down box offers an A-to-Z list of topics ranging from contraception to diabetes. A "tool kit" on the home page offers interactive tools such as a breast health risk assessment quiz, a calorie calculator, and a daily meal planner. An ask-the-expert section is available with a variety of health topics. Discussion forums are also provided.

http://www.women.com/health/

13.7 SUPPORT GROUPS

Genetic Alliance: Member Directory   The Genetic Alliance, formerly the Alliance of Genetic Support Groups, offers their membership directory of support groups on this site. The directory can be searched by genetic condition, organization name, or services offered. Alternatively, one can browse the entire directory. A resources section on the side of the site contains links to disease information and genetic issues.

http://www.geneticalliance.org/diseaseinfo/search.html

New York Online Access to Health (NOAH): Support Groups   This directory of Web sites and other resources includes links to other directories, general health sites, toll-free telephone numbers, face-to-face support groups, support organizations, newsgroups, mailing lists, chat forums, and other online support resources. Visitors can browse listings by type of resource or by specific medical conditions.

http://www.noah-health.org/english/support.html

Don't type in long URLs – add the site number to the eMedguides URL: www.eMedguides.com/**G-1234**.

Support-Group.com   Support-Group.com allows people with health, personal, and relationship issues to share their experiences through bulletin boards and online chats and also provides plenty of links to support-related information on the Internet. The A-to-Z listing offers hundreds of connections to disease-related support, bereavement assistance, marriage and family issue groups, and women's/men's issues, to name a few. The "Bulletin Board Tracker" lists the most recent messages and provides a complete cross-reference of topics. By visiting the Support-Group.com chat schedule page, dates, times, and group facilitators for upcoming chat events can be viewed. Users have the option of participating in real-time chat groups via Internet Relay Chat or JavaChat using a Java-capable Web browser. Complete instructions are available at the Web site.
http://www.support-group.com

University of Kansas Medical Center: Genetic and Rare Conditions
Organized by the Medical Genetics Department of the University of Kansas Medical Center, this site offers a comprehensive listing of links on genetics and rare conditions. The home page features an A-to-Z listing of genetic and rare conditions. Hyperlinks at the top of the site lead to hundreds of resources categorized as national and international organizations, specific conditions, genetic counselors, children and teens, and advocacy. Information on support groups can be found in the national and international organizations section.
http://www.kumc.edu/gec/support/groups.html

WEB SITE AND
TOPICAL INDEX

C

I

Journal of the International Neuropsychological
    Society, 47
Journal of Traumatic Stress, 47
Journal Watch Online, 372
Journals and Articles on the Internet
    Psychiatry, 25
Journals, Articles, and Latest Books, 25
Joy Ikelman's Information
    on Bipolar Disorder, 292
Jungian Psychology, 204

K

Kansas Commission on
    Disability Concerns, 170
Karger, 388
Karolinska Institutet
    Anatomy and Histology, 403
    Diseases, Disorders and Related Topics, 349
    Mental Disorders, 81
KidsGrowth.com, 454
KidsHealth.org, 454
KidSourceOnline
    Articulation Problems, 260
Kinsey Institute for Research in Sex, Gender, and
    Reproduction, 198
Kleptomania, 280
    Symptoms, 280
Kleptomaniacs and
    Shoplifters Anonymous, 280
Klinefelter's Syndrome, 319
Kluwer Academic Publishers, 388
Knowledge Exchange Network
    Advocacy/Consumers/Survivors, 152
    Alternative Treatment, 113
    Assistive Technology, 170
    Community Support, 162
    Community Support Programs, 163
    Depression, 296
    Disabilities, 170
    Eating Disorders News, 274
    HIV/AIDS Resources, 262
    Homelessness, 183
    Managed Care, 142
    Refugee Mental Health, 196
    Schizophrenia, 314
    Substance Abuse/Addiction, 330
Kyoto Encyclopedia of Genomes and Genetics
    (KEGG), 418

L

Laboratories at the National Institute of Mental
    Health (NIMH), Division of Intramural
    Research Programs, 224
Lancaster University Centre for Applied Statistics
    Statistics Glossary, 189
Last Acts, 443
Latest Research on Marital Adjustment and
    Satisfaction, 187
Law, 69
LD Online, 285
Learning Disabilities
    Association (LDA), 219, 285
Learning Disorders, 285
Legal and Criminological Psychology, 47
Leicester University Library
    Major Information Sources
        for Psychiatry, 86
LewyNet, 266
Light Therapy, 131
Light Therapy Center, 131
Limbic System
    The Center of Emotions, 100, 175
LINK
    Online Library
        Medicine, 382
Links to Funding Sources, 92
Links to Self-Injury Sites, 317
Lippincott Williams & Wilkins, 388
Listservs and Newsgroups, 23
Literature, Cognition, and the Brain, 105
Lithium and the Anticonvulsants in Bipolar
    Disorder, 133
Living Wills, 443
Living with Suicide, 340
Locating a Physician, 378
Long-Term Care, 69
Los Angeles Institute and Society for
    Psychoanalytic Studies, 227
Louis de la Parte Florida
    Mental Health Institute, 227
Louisiana State University
    Anticonvulsants, 133
Lucidity Institute, 174

M

MacArthur Research Network on Mental Health
    and the Law, 152
Malignant Self-Love

SERZONE®
Rx only

(nefazodone hydrochloride) Tablets

DESCRIPTION

SERZONE® (nefazodone hydrochloride) is an antidepressant for oral administration with a chemical structure unrelated to selective serotonin reuptake inhibitors, tricyclics, tetracyclics, or monoamine oxidase inhibitors (MAOI).

Nefazodone hydrochloride is a synthetically derived phenylpiperazine antidepressant. The chemical name for nefazodone hydrochloride is 2-[3-[4-(3-chlorophenyl)-1-piperazinyl]propyl]-5-ethyl-2,4-dihydro-4-(2-phenoxyethyl)-3H-1,2,4-triazol-3-on e monohydrochloride. The molecular formula is $C_{25}H_{32}ClN_5O_2 \bullet HCl$, which corresponds to a molecular weight of 506.5. The structural formula is:

Nefazodone hydrochloride is a nonhygroscopic, white crystalline solid. It is freely soluble in chloroform, soluble in propylene glycol, and slightly soluble in polyethylene glycol and water.

SERZONE is supplied as hexagonal tablets containing 50 mg, 100 mg, 150 mg, 200 mg, or 250 mg of nefazodone hydrochloride and the following inactive ingredients: microcrystalline cellulose, povidone, sodium starch glycolate, colloidal silicon dioxide, magnesium stearate, and iron oxides (red and/or yellow) as colorants.

CLINICAL PHARMACOLOGY

Pharmacodynamics

The mechanism of action of nefazodone, as with other antidepressants, is unknown.

Preclinical studies have shown that nefazodone inhibits neuronal uptake of serotonin and norepinephrine.

Nefazodone occupies central $5\text{-}HT_2$ receptors at nanomolar concentrations, and acts as an antagonist at this receptor. Nefazodone was shown to antagonize alpha$_1$-adrenergic receptors, a property which may be associated with postural hypotension. In vitro binding studies showed that nefazodone had no significant affinity for the following receptors: alpha$_2$ and beta adrenergic, $5\text{-}HT_{1A}$, cholinergic, dopaminergic, or benzodiazepine.

Pharmacokinetics

Nefazodone hydrochloride is rapidly and completely absorbed but is subject to extensive metabolism, so that its absolute bioavailability is low, about 20%, and variable. Peak plasma concentrations occur at about one hour and the half-life of nefazodone is 2–4 hours.

Both nefazodone and its pharmacologically similar metabolite, hydroxynefazodone, exhibit nonlinear kinetics for both dose and time, with AUC and C_{max} increasing more than proportionally with dose increases and more than expected upon multiple dosing over time, compared to single dosing. For example, in a multiple-dose study involving BID dosing with 50, 100, and 200 mg, the AUC for nefazodone and hydroxynefazodone increased by about 4-fold with an increase in dose from 200 to 400 mg per day; C_{max} increased by about 3-fold with the same dose increase. In a multiple-dose study involving BID dosing with 25, 50, 100, and 150 mg, the accumulation ratios for nefazodone and hydroxynefazodone AUC, after 5 days of BID dosing relative to the first dose, ranged from approximately 3 to 4 at the lower doses (50–100 mg/day) and from 5 to 7 at the higher doses (200–300 mg/day); there were also approximately 2- to 4-fold increases in C_{max} after 5 days of BID dosing relative to the first dose, suggesting extensive and greater than predicted accumulation of nefazodone and its hydroxy metabolite with multiple dosing. Steady-state plasma nefazodone and metabolite concentrations are attained within 4 to 5 days of initiation of BID dosing or upon dose increase or decrease.

Nefazodone is extensively metabolized after oral administration by n-dealkylation and aliphatic and aromatic hydroxylation, and less than 1% of administered nefazodone is excreted unchanged in urine. Attempts to characterize three metabolites identified in plasma, hydroxynefazodone (HO-NEF), meta-chlorophenylpiperazine (mCPP), and a triazole-dione metabolite, have been carried out. The AUC (expressed as a multiple of the AUC for nefazodone dosed at 100 mg BID) and elimination half-lives for these three metabolites were as follows:

AUC Multiples and $T_{1/2}$ for Three Metabolites of Nefazodone (100 mg BID)		
Metabolite	AUC Multiple	$T_{1/2}$
HO-NEF	0.4	1.5 – 4 h
mCPP	0.07	4 – 8 h
Triazole-dione	4.0	18 h

HO-NEF possesses a pharmacological profile qualitatively and quantitatively similar to that of nefazodone. mCPP has some similarities to nefazodone, but also has agonist activity at some serotonergic receptor subtypes. The pharmacological profile of the triazole-dione metabolite has not yet been well characterized. In addition to the above compounds, several other metabolites were present in plasma but have not been tested for pharmacological activity.

After oral administration of radiolabeled nefazodone, the mean half-life of total label ranged between 11 and 24 hours. Approximately 55% of the administered radioactivity was detected in urine and about 20–30% in feces.

Distribution—Nefazodone is widely distributed in body tissues, including the central nervous system (CNS). In humans the volume of distribution of nefazodone ranges from 0.22 to 0.87 L/kg.

Protein Binding—At concentrations of 25–2500 ng/mL nefazodone is extensively (>99%) bound to human plasma proteins in vitro. The administration of 200 mg BID of nefazodone for 1 week did not increase the fraction of unbound warfarin in subjects whose prothrombin times had been prolonged by warfarin therapy to 120-150% of the laboratory control (see PRECAUTIONS: Drug Interactions). While nefazodone did not alter the in vitro protein binding of chlorpromazine, desipramine, diazepam, diphenylhydantoin, lidocaine, prazosin, propranolol, or verapamil, it is unknown whether displacement of either nefazodone or these drugs occurs in vivo. There was a 5% decrease in the protein binding of haloperidol; this is probably of no clinical significance.

Effect of Food—Food delays the absorption of nefazodone and decreases the bioavailability of nefazodone by approximately 20%.

Renal Disease—In studies involving 29 renally impaired patients, renal impairment (creatinine clearances ranging from 7 to 60 mL/min/1.73m^2) had no effect on steady-state nefazodone plasma concentrations.

Liver Disease—In a multiple-dose study of patients with liver cirrhosis, the AUC values for nefazodone and HO-NEF at steady state were approximately 25% greater than those observed in normal volunteers.

Age/Gender Effects—After single doses of 300 mg to younger (18-45 years) and older patients (>65 years), C_{max} and AUC for nefazodone and hydroxynefazodone were up to twice as high in the older patients. With multiple doses, however, differences were much smaller, 10–20%. A similar result was seen for gender, with a higher C_{max} and AUC in women after single doses but no difference after multiple doses.

Treatment with SERZONE (nefazodone hydrochloride) should be initiated at half the usual dose in elderly patients, especially women (see DOSAGE AND ADMINISTRATION), but the therapeutic dose range is similar in younger and older patients.

Clinical Efficacy Trial Results

Studies in Outpatients with Depression

During its premarketing development, the efficacy of SERZONE was evaluated at doses within the therapeutic range in five well-controlled, short-term (6–8 weeks) clinical investigations. These trials enrolled outpatients meeting DSM-III or DSM-IIIR criteria for major depression. Among these trials, three demonstrated the effectiveness of SERZONE, and two provided additional support for that conclusion.

One trial was a 6-week dose-titration study comparing SERZONE in two dose ranges (up to 300 mg/day and up to 600 mg/day [mean modal dose for this group was about 400 mg/day], on a BID schedule) and placebo. The second trial was an 8-week dose-titration study comparing SERZONE (up to 600 mg/day; mean modal dose was 375 mg/day), imipramine (up to 300 mg/day), and placebo, all on a BID schedule. Both studies demonstrated SERZONE, at doses titrated between 300 mg to 600 mg/day (therapeutic dose range), to be superior to placebo on at least three of the following four measures: 17-Item Hamilton Depression Rating Scale or HDRS (total score), Hamilton Depressed Mood item, Clinical Global Impressions (CGI) Severity score, and CGI Improvement score. Significant differences were also found for certain factors of the HDRS (e.g., anxiety factor, sleep disturbance factor, and retardation factor). In the two supportive studies, SERZONE was titrated up to 500 or 600 mg/day (mean modal doses of 462 mg/day and 363 mg/day). In the fifth study, the differentiation in response rates between SERZONE and placebo was not statistically significant. Three additional trials were conducted using subtherapeutic doses of SERZONE.

Overall, approximately two thirds of patients in these trials were women, and an analysis of the effects of gender on outcome did not suggest any differential responsiveness on the basis of sex. There were too few elderly patients in these trials to reveal possible age-related differences in response.

Since its initial marketing as an antidepressant drug product, additional clinical investigations of SERZONE have been conducted. These studies explored SERZONE's use under conditions not evaluated fully at the time initial marketing approval was granted.

Studies in "Inpatients"

Two studies were conducted to evaluate SERZONE's effectiveness in hospitalized depressed patients. These were 6-week, dose-titration trials comparing SERZONE (up to 600 mg/day) and placebo, on a BID schedule. In one study, SERZONE was superior to placebo. In this study, the mean modal dose of SERZONE was 503 mg/day, and 85% of these inpatients were melancholic; at baseline, patients were distributed at the higher end of the 7-point CGI Severity scale, as follows: 4=moderately ill (17%); 5=markedly ill (48%); 6=severely ill (32%). In the other study, the differentiation in response rates between SERZONE and placebo was not statistically significant. This result may be explained by the "high" rate of spontaneous improvement among the patients randomized to placebo.

Studies of "Relapse Prevention in Patients Recently Recovered (Clinically) from Depression"

Two studies were conducted to assess SERZONE's capacity to maintain a clinical remission in acutely depressed patients who were judged to have responded adequately (HDRS total score ≤10) after a 16-week period of open treatment with SERZONE (titration up to 600 mg/day). In one study, SERZONE was superior to placebo. In this study, patients (n=131) were randomized to continuation on SERZONE or placebo for an additional 36 weeks (1 year total). This study demonstrated a significantly lower relapse rate (HDRS total score ≥18) for patients taking SERZONE compared to those on placebo. The second study was of appropriate design and power, but the sample of patients admitted for evaluation did not suffer relapses at a high enough incidence to provide a meaningful test of SERZONE's efficacy for this use.

Comparisons of Clinical Trial Results

Highly variable results have been seen in the clinical development of all antidepressant drugs. Furthermore, in those circumstances when the drugs have not been studied in the same controlled clinical trial(s), comparisons among the findings of studies evaluating the effectiveness of different antidepressant drug products are inherently unreliable. Because conditions of testing (e.g., patient samples, investigators, doses of the treatments administered and compared, outcome measures, etc.) vary among trials, it is virtually impossible to distinguish a difference in drug effect from a difference due to one or more of the confounding factors just enumerated.

INDICATIONS AND USAGE

SERZONE (nefazodone hydrochloride) is indicated for the treatment of depression.

The efficacy of SERZONE in the treatment of depression was established in 6–8 week controlled trials of outpatients and in a 6-week controlled trial of depressed inpatients whose diagnoses corresponded most closely to the DSM-III or DSM-IIIR category of major depressive disorder (see **CLINICAL PHARMACOLOGY**).

A major depressive episode implies a prominent and relatively persistent depressed or dysphoric mood that usually interferes with daily functioning (nearly every day for at least 2 weeks). It must include either depressed mood or loss of interest or pleasure and at least five of the following nine symptoms: depressed mood, loss of interest in usual activities, significant change in weight and/or appetite, insomnia or hypersomnia, psychomotor agitation or retardation, increased fatigue, feelings of guilt or worthlessness, slowed thinking or impaired concentration, a suicide attempt or suicidal ideation.

The efficacy of SERZONE in reducing relapse in patients with major depression who were judged to have had a satisfactory clinical response to 16 weeks of open-label SERZONE treatment for an acute depressive episode has been demonstrated in a randomized placebo-controlled trial (see **CLINICAL PHARMACOLOGY**). Although remitted patients were followed for as long as 36 weeks in the study cited (i.e., 52 weeks total), the physician who elects to use SERZONE for extended periods should periodically reevaluate the long-term usefulness of the drug for the individual patient.

CONTRAINDICATIONS

Coadministration of terfenadine, astemizole, cisapride, pimozide, or carbamazepine with SERZONE is contraindicated (see **WARNINGS** and **PRECAUTIONS**).

SERZONE is contraindicated in patients with known hypersensitivity to nefazodone or other phenylpiperazine antidepressants.

The coadministration of triazolam and nefazodone causes a significant increase in the plasma level of triazolam (see **WARNINGS** and **PRECAUTIONS**), and a 75% reduction in the initial triazolam dosage is recommended if the two drugs are to be given together. Because not all commercially available dosage forms of triazolam permit a sufficient dosage reduction, the coadministration of triazolam and SERZONE should be avoided for most patients, including the elderly.

WARNINGS

Potential for Interaction with Monoamine Oxidase Inhibitors

In patients receiving antidepressants with pharmacological properties similar to nefazodone in combination with a monoamine oxidase inhibitor (MAOI), there have been reports of serious, sometimes fatal, reactions. For a selective serotonin reuptake inhibitor (SSRI), these reactions have included hyperthermia, rigidity, myoclonus, autonomic instability with possible rapid fluctuations of vital signs, and mental status changes that include extreme agitation progressing to delirium and coma. These reactions have also been reported in patients who have recently discontinued that drug and have been started on an MAOI. Some cases presented with features resembling neuroleptic malig-

nant syndrome. Severe hyperthermia and seizures, sometimes fatal, have been reported in association with the combined use of tricyclic antidepressants and MAOIs. These reactions have also been reported in patients who have recently discontinued these drugs and have been started on an MAOI.

Although the effects of combined use of nefazodone and MAOI have not been evaluated in humans or animals, because nefazodone is an inhibitor of both serotonin and norepinephrine reuptake, it is recommended that nefazodone not be used in combination with an MAOI, or within 14 days of discontinuing treatment with an MAOI. At least 1 week should be allowed after stopping nefazodone before starting an MAOI.

Interaction with Triazolobenzodiazepines

Interaction studies of nefazodone with two triazolobenzodiazepines, i.e., triazolam and alprazolam, metabolized by cytochrome P450 3A4, have revealed substantial and clinically important increases in plasma concentrations of these compounds when administered concomitantly with nefazodone.

Triazolam

When a single oral 0.25-mg dose of triazolam was coadministered with nefazodone (200 mg BID) at steady state, triazolam half-life and AUC increased 4-fold and peak concentrations increased 1.7-fold. Nefazodone plasma concentrations were unaffected by triazolam. *Coadministration of nefazodone potentiated the effects of triazolam on psychomotor performance tests.* If triazolam is coadministered with SERZONE, a 75% reduction in the initial triazolam dosage is recommended. Because not all commercially available dosage forms of triazolam permit sufficient dosage reduction, coadministration of triazolam with SERZONE should be avoided for most patients, including the elderly. In the exceptional case where coadministration of triazolam with SERZONE may be considered appropriate, only the lowest possible dose of triazolam should be used (see **CONTRAINDICATIONS** and **PRECAUTIONS**).

Alprazolam

When alprazolam (1 mg BID) and nefazodone (200 mg BID) were coadministered, steady-state peak concentrations, AUC and half-life values for alprazolam increased by approximately 2-fold. Nefazodone plasma concentrations were unaffected by alprazolam. If alprazolam is coadministered with SERZONE, a 50% reduction in the initial alprazolam dosage is recommended. No dosage adjustment is required for SERZONE (nefazodone hydrochloride).

Potential Terfenadine, Astemizole, Cisapride, and Pimozide Interactions

Terfenadine, astemizole, cisapride, and pimozide are all metabolized by the cytochrome P450 3A4 (CYP3A4) isozyme, and it has been demonstrated that ketoconazole, erythromycin, and other inhibitors of CYP3A4 can block the metabolism of these drugs, which can result in increased plasma concentrations of parent drug. Increased plasma concentrations of terfenadine, astemizole, cisapride, and pimozide are associated with QT prolongation and with rare cases of serious cardiovascular adverse events, including death, due principally to ventricular tachycardia of the torsades de pointes type. Nefazodone has been shown *in vitro* to be an inhibitor of CYP3A4. Consequently, it is recommended that nefazodone not be used in combination with either terfenadine, astemizole, cisapride, or pimozide (see **CONTRAINDICATIONS** and **PRECAUTIONS**).

Interaction with Carbamazepine

The coadministration of carbamazepine 200 mg BID with nefazodone 200 mg BID, at steady state for both drugs, resulted in almost 95% reductions in AUCs for nefazodone and hydroxynefazodone, likely resulting in insufficient plasma nefazodone and hydroxynefazodone concentrations for achieving an antidepressant effect for SERZONE. Consequently, it is recommended that SERZONE not be used in combination with carbamazepine (see **CONTRAINDICATIONS** and **PRECAUTIONS**).

PRECAUTIONS

General

Postural Hypotension

A pooled analysis of the vital signs monitored during placebo-controlled premarketing studies revealed that 5.1% of nefazodone patients compared to 2.5% of placebo patients (p≤0.01) met criteria for a potentially important decrease in blood pressure at some time during treatment (systolic blood pressure ≤90 mmHg *and* a change from baseline of ≥20 mmHg). While there was no difference in the proportion of nefazodone and placebo patients having adverse events characterized as 'syncope' (nefazodone, 0.2%; placebo, 0.3%), the rates for adverse events characterized as 'postural hypotension' were as follows: nefazodone (2.8%), tricyclic antidepressants (10.9%), SSRI (1.1%), and placebo (0.8%). Thus, the prescriber should be aware that there is some risk of postural hypotension in association with nefazodone use. SERZONE should be used with caution in patients with known cardiovascular or cerebrovascular disease that could be exacerbated by hypotension (history of myocardial infarction, angina, or ischemic stroke) and conditions that would predispose patients to hypotension (dehydration, hypovolemia, and treatment with antihypertensive medication).

Activation of Mania/Hypomania
During premarketing testing, hypomania or mania occurred in 0.3% of nefazodone-treated unipolar patients, compared to 0.3% of tricyclic- and 0.4% of placebo-treated patients. In patients classified as bipolar the rate of manic episodes was 1.6% for nefazodone, 5.1% for the combined tricyclic-treated groups, and 0% for placebo-treated patients. Activation of mania/hypomania is a known risk in a small proportion of patients with major affective disorder treated with other marketed anti-depressants. As with all antidepressants, SERZONE should be used cautiously in patients with a history of mania.

Suicide
The possibility of a suicide attempt is inherent in depression and may persist until significant remission occurs. Close supervision of high-risk patients should accompany initial drug therapy. Prescriptions for SERZONE (nefazodone hydrochloride) should be written for the smallest quantity of tablets consistent with good patient management in order to reduce the risk of overdose.

Seizures
During premarketing testing, a recurrence of a petit mal seizure was observed in a patient receiving nefazodone who had a history of such seizures. In addition, one nonstudy participant reportedly experienced a convulsion (type not documented) following a multiple-drug overdose (see **OVERDOSAGE**). Rare occurrences of convulsions (including grand mal seizures) following nefazodone administration have been reported since market introduction. A causal relationship to nefazodone has not been established (see **ADVERSE REACTIONS**).

Priapism
While priapism did not occur during premarketing experience with nefazodone, rare reports of priapism have been received since market introduction. A causal relationship to nefazodone has not been established (see **ADVERSE REACTIONS**). If patients present with prolonged or inappropriate erections, they should discontinue therapy immediately and consult their physicians. If the condition persists for more than 24 hours, a urologist should be consulted to determine appropriate management.

Use in Patients with Concomitant Illness
SERZONE has not been evaluated or used to any appreciable extent in patients with a recent history of myocardial infarction or unstable heart disease. Patients with these diagnoses were systematically excluded from clinical studies during the product's premarketing testing. Evaluation of electrocardiograms of 1153 patients who received nefazodone in 6- to 8-week, double-blind, placebo-controlled trials did not indicate that nefazodone is associated with the development of clinically important ECG abnormalities. However, sinus bradycardia, defined as heart rate ≤50 bpm and a decrease of at least 15 bpm from baseline, was observed in 1.5% of nefazodone-treated patients compared to 0.4% of placebo-treated patients (p≤0.05). Because patients with a recent history of myocardial infarction or unstable heart disease were excluded from clinical trials, such patients should be treated with caution.

In patients with cirrhosis of the liver, the AUC values of nefazodone and HO-NEF were increased by approximately 25%.

Information for Patients
Physicians are advised to discuss the following issues with patients for whom they prescribe SERZONE:

Time to Response/Continuation
As with all antidepressants, several weeks on treatment may be required to obtain the full antidepressant effect. Once improvement is noted, it is important for patients to continue drug treatment as directed by their physician.

Interference With Cognitive and Motor Performance
Since any psychoactive drug may impair judgment, thinking, or motor skills, patients should be cautioned about operating hazardous machinery, including automobiles, until they are reasonably certain that SERZONE therapy does not adversely affect their ability to engage in such activities.

Pregnancy
Patients should be advised to notify their physician if they become pregnant or intend to become pregnant during therapy.

Nursing
Patients should be advised to notify their physician if they are breast-feeding an infant (see **PRECAUTIONS: Nursing Mothers**).

Concomitant Medication
Patients should be advised to inform their physicians if they are taking, or plan to take, any prescription or over-the-counter drugs, since there is a potential for interactions. Significant caution is indicated if SERZONE is to be used in combination with XANAX®[1], concomitant use with HALCION®[1] should be avoided for most patients including the elderly, and concomitant use with SELDANE®[2], HISMANAL®[3], PROPULSID®[3], ORAP®[4], or TEGRETOL®[5] is contraindicated (see **CONTRAINDICATIONS and WARNINGS**).

Alcohol
Patients should be advised to avoid alcohol while taking SERZONE.

Allergic Reactions
Patients should be advised to notify their physician if they develop a rash, hives, or a related allergic phenomenon.

Visual Disturbances
There have been reports of visual disturbances associated with the use of nefazodone, including blurred vision, scotoma, and visual trails. Patients should be advised to notify their physician if they develop visual disturbances. (See **ADVERSE REACTIONS**.)

Laboratory Tests
There are no specific laboratory tests recommended.

Drug Interactions
Drugs Highly Bound to Plasma Protein
Because nefazodone is highly bound to plasma protein (see **CLINICAL PHARMACOLOGY: Pharmacokinetics**), administration of SERZONE to a patient taking another drug that is highly protein bound may cause increased free concentrations of the other drug, potentially resulting in adverse events. Conversely, adverse effects could result from displacement of nefazodone by other highly bound drugs.

Warfarin—There were no effects on the prothrombin or bleeding times or upon the pharmacokinetics of R-warfarin when nefazodone (200 mg BID) was administered for 1 week to subjects who had been pretreated for 2 weeks with warfarin. Although the coadministration of nefazodone did decrease the subjects' exposure to S-warfarin by 12%, the lack of effects on the prothrombin and bleeding times indicates this modest change is not clinically significant. Although these results suggest no adjustments in warfarin dosage are required when nefazodone is administered to patients stabilized on warfarin, such patients should be monitored as required by standard medical practices.

CNS-Active Drugs
Monoamine Oxidase Inhibitors—See **WARNINGS**.

Haloperidol—When a single oral 5-mg dose of haloperidol was coadministered with nefazodone (200 mg BID) at steady state, haloperidol apparent clearance decreased by 35% with no significant increase in peak haloperidol plasma concentrations or time of peak. This change is of unknown clinical significance. Pharmacodynamic effects of haloperidol were generally not altered significantly. There were no changes in the pharmacokinetic parameters for nefazodone. Dosage adjustment of haloperidol may be necessary when coadministered with nefazodone.

Lorazepam—When lorazepam (2 mg BID) and nefazodone (200 mg BID) were coadministered to steady state, there was no change in any pharmacokinetic parameter for either drug compared to each drug administered alone. Therefore, dosage adjustment is not necessary for either drug when coadministered.

Triazolam/Alprazolam—See **CONTRAINDICATIONS and WARNINGS**.

Alcohol—Although nefazodone did not potentiate the cognitive and psychomotor effects of alcohol in experiments with normal subjects, the concomitant use of SERZONE (nefazodone hydrochloride) and alcohol in depressed patients is not advised.

Buspirone—In a study of steady-state pharmacokinetics in healthy volunteers, coadministration of buspirone (2.5 or 5 mg BID) with nefazodone (250 mg BID) resulted in marked increases in plasma buspirone concentrations (increases up to 20-fold in C_{max} and up to 50-fold in AUC) and statistically significant decreases (about 50%) in plasma concentrations of the buspirone metabolite 1-pyrimidinylpiperazine. With 5-mg BID doses of buspirone, slight increases in AUC were observed for nefazodone (23%) and its metabolites hydroxynefazodone (17%) and mCPP (9%). The side effect profile for subjects receiving buspirone 2.5 mg BID and nefazodone 250 mg BID was similar to that for subjects receiving either drug alone. Subjects receiving buspirone 5 mg BID and nefazodone 250 mg BID experienced side effects such as lightheadedness, asthenia, dizziness, and somnolence. If the two drugs are to be used in combination, a low dose of buspirone (e.g., 2.5 mg QD) is recommended. Subsequent dose adjustment of either drug should be based on clinical assessment.

Pimozide—See **CONTRAINDICATIONS, WARNINGS,** and **PRECAUTIONS:** *Pharmacokinetics of Nefazodone in 'Poor Metabolizers' and Potential Interaction with Drugs that Inhibit and/or Are Metabolized by Cytochrome P450 Isozymes.*

Fluoxetine—When fluoxetine (20 mg QD) and nefazodone (200 mg BID) were administered at steady state there were no changes in the pharmacokinetic parameters for fluoxetine or its metabolite, norfluoxetine. Similarly, there were no changes in the pharmacokinetic parameters of nefazodone or HO-NEF; however, the mean AUC levels of the nefazodone metabolites mCPP and triazole-dione increased by 3- to 6-fold and 1.3-fold, respectively. When a 200-mg dose of nefazodone was administered to subjects who had been receiving fluoxetine for 1 week, there was an increased incidence of transient adverse events such as headache, lightheadedness, nausea, or paresthesia, possibly due to the elevated mCPP levels. Patients who are switched from fluoxetine to nefazodone without an adequate washout period may experience similar transient adverse events. The possibility of this happening can be minimized by allowing a washout period before initiating nefazodone therapy and by reducing the initial dose of nefazodone. Because of the long half-life of fluoxetine and its metabolites, this washout period may range from one to several weeks depending on the dose of fluoxetine and other individual patient variables.

Phenytoin—Pretreatment for 7 days with 200 mg BID of nefazodone had no effect on the pharmacokinetics of a single 300-mg oral dose of phenytoin. However, due to the nonlinear pharmacokinetics of phenytoin, the failure to observe a significant effect on the single-dose pharmacokinetics of phenytoin does not preclude the possibility of a clinically significant interaction with nefazodone when phenytoin is dosed chronically. However, no change in the initial dosage of phenytoin is considered necessary and any subsequent adjustment of phenytoin dosage should be guided by usual clinical practices.

Desipramine—When nefazodone (150 mg BID) and desipramine (75 mg QD) were administered together there were no changes in the pharmacokinetics of desipramine or its metabolite, 2-hydroxy desipramine. There were also no changes in the pharmacokinetics of nefazodone or its triazole-dione metabolite, but the AUC and C_{max} of mCPP increased by 44% and 48%, respectively, while the AUC of HO-NEF decreased by 19%. No changes in doses of either nefazodone or desipramine are necessary when the two drugs are given concomitantly. Subsequent dose adjustments should be made on the basis of clinical response.

Lithium—In 13 healthy subjects the coadministration of nefazodone (200 mg BID) with lithium (500 mg BID) for 5 days (steady-state conditions) was found to be well tolerated. When the two drugs were coadministered, there were no changes in the steady-state pharmacokinetics of either lithium, nefazodone, or its metabolite HO-NEF; however, there were small decreases in the steady-state plasma concentrations of two nefazodone metabolites, mCPP and triazole-dione, which are considered not to be of clinical significance. Therefore, no dosage adjustment of either lithium or nefazodone is required when they are coadministered.

Carbamazepine—The coadministration of nefazodone (200 mg BID) for 5 days to 12 healthy subjects on carbamazepine who had achieved steady state (200 mg BID) was found to be well tolerated. Steady-state conditions for carbamazepine, nefazodone, and several of their metabolites were achieved by day 5 of coadministration. With coadministration of the two drugs there were significant increases in the steady-state C_{max} and AUC of carbamazepine (23% and 23%, respectively), while the steady-state C_{max} and the AUC of the carbamazepine metabolite, 10,11 epoxy-carbamazepine, decreased by 21% and 20%, respectively. The coadministration of the two drugs significantly reduced the steady-state C_{max} and AUC of nefazodone by 86% and 93%, respectively. Similar reductions in the C_{max} and AUC of HO-NEF were also observed (85% and 94%), while the reductions in C_{max} and AUC of mCPP and triazole-dione were more modest (13% and 44% for the former and 28% and 57% for the latter). Due to the potential for coadministration of carbamazepine to result in insufficient plasma nefazodone and hydroxynefazodone concentrations for achieving an antidepressant effect for SERZONE (nefazodone hydrochloride), it is recommended that SERZONE not be used in combination with carbamazepine (see CONTRAINDICATIONS and WARNINGS).

General Anesthetics—Little is known about the potential for interaction between nefazodone and general anesthetics; therefore, prior to elective surgery, SERZONE should be discontinued for as long as clinically feasible.

Other CNS-Active Drugs—The use of nefazodone in combination with other CNS-active drugs has not been systematically evaluated. Consequently, caution is advised if concomitant administration of SERZONE (nefazodone hydrochloride) and such drugs is required.

Cimetidine

When nefazodone (200 mg BID) and cimetidine (300 mg QID) were coadministered for one week, no change in the steady-state pharmacokinetics of either nefazodone or cimetidine was observed compared to each dosed alone. Therefore, dosage adjustment is not necessary for either drug when coadministered.

Theophylline

When nefazodone (200 mg BID) was given to patients being treated with theophylline (600-1200 mg/day) for chronic obstructive pulmonary disease, there was no change in the steady-state pharmacokinetics of either nefazodone or theophylline. FEV_1 measurements taken when theophylline and nefazodone were coadministered did not differ from baseline dosage (i.e., when theophylline was administered alone). Therefore, dosage adjustment is not necessary for either drug when coadministered.

Cardiovascular-Active Drugs

Digoxin—When nefazodone (200 mg BID) and digoxin (0.2 mg QD) were coadministered for 9 days to healthy male volunteers (n=18) who were phenotyped as CYP2D6 extensive metabolizers, C_{max}, C_{min}, and AUC of digoxin were increased by 29%, 27%, and 15%, respectively. Digoxin had no effects on the pharmacokinetics of nefazodone and its active metabolites. Because of the narrow therapeutic index of digoxin, caution should be exercised when nefazodone and digoxin are coadministered; plasma level monitoring for digoxin is recommended.

Propranolol—The coadministration of nefazodone (200 mg BID) and propranolol (40 mg BID) for 5.5 days to healthy male volunteers (n=18), including 3 poor and 15 extensive CYP2D6 metabolizers, resulted in 30% and 14% reductions in C_{max} and AUC of propranolol, respectively, and a 14% reduction in C_{max} for the metabolite, 4-hydroxypropranolol. The kinetics of nefazodone, hydroxynefazodone, and triazole-dione were not affected by coadministration of propranolol. However, C_{max}, C_{min}, and AUC of m-chlorophenylpiperazine were increased by 23%, 54%, and 28%, respectively. No change in initial dose of either drug is necessary and dose adjustments should be made on the basis of clinical response.

HMG-CoA Reductase Inhibitors—When single 40-mg doses of simvastatin or atorvastatin, both substrates of CYP3A4, were given to healthy adult volunteers who had received SERZONE (nefazodone hydrochloride) 200 mg BID for 6 days, approximately 20-fold increases in plasma concentrations of simvastatin and simvastatin acid and 3- to 4-fold increases in plasma concentrations of atorvastatin and atorvastatin lactone were seen. These effects appear to be due to the inhibition of CYP3A4 by SERZONE because, in the same study, SERZONE had no significant effect on the plasma concentrations of pravastatin, which is not metabolized by CYP3A4 to a clinically significant extent.

There have been rare reports of rhabdomyolysis involving patients receiving the combination of SERZONE and either simvastatin or lovastatin, also a substrate of CYP3A4 (see **ADVERSE REACTIONS: Postintroduction Clinical Experience**). Rhabdomyolysis has been observed in patients receiving HMG-CoA reductase inhibitors administered alone (at recommended dosages) and in particular, for certain drugs in this class, when given in combination with inhibitors of the CYP3A4 isozyme.

Caution should be used if SERZONE is administered in combination with HMG-CoA reductase inhibitors that are metabolized by CYP3A4, such as simvastatin, atorvastatin, and lovastatin, and dosage adjustments of these HMG-CoA reductase inhibitors are recommended. Since metabolic interactions are unlikely between SERZONE and HMG-CoA reductase inhibitors that undergo little or no metabolism by the CYP3A4 isozyme, such as pravastatin or fluvastatin, dosage adjustments should not be necessary.

Immunosuppressive Agents

There have been reports of increased blood concentrations of cyclosporine and tacrolimus into toxic ranges when patients received these drugs concomitantly with SERZONE. Both cyclosporine and tacrolimus are substrates of CYP3A4, and nefazodone is known to inhibit this enzyme. If either cyclosporine or tacrolimus is administered with SERZONE, blood concentrations of the immunosuppressive agent should be monitored and dosage adjusted accordingly.

Pharmacokinetics of Nefazodone in 'Poor Metabolizers' and Potential Interaction with Drugs that Inhibit and/or Are Metabolized by Cytochrome P450 Isozymes

CYP3A4 Isozyme—Nefazodone has been shown in vitro to be an inhibitor of CYP3A4. This is consistent with the interactions observed between nefazodone and triazolam, alprazolam, buspirone, atorvastatin, and simvastatin, drugs metabolized by this isozyme. Consequently, caution is indicated in the combined use of nefazodone with any drugs known to be metabolized by CYP3A4. In particular, the combined use of nefazodone with triazolam should be avoided for most patients, including the elderly. The combined use of nefazodone with terfenadine, astemizole, cisapride, or pimozide is contraindicated (see **CONTRAINDICATIONS** and **WARNINGS**).

CYP2D6 Isozyme—A subset (3% to 10%) of the population has reduced activity of the drug-metabolizing enzyme CYP2D6. Such individuals are referred to commonly as "poor metabolizers" of drugs such as debrisoquin, dextromethorphan, and the tricyclic antidepressants. The pharmacokinetics of nefazodone and its major metabolites are not altered in these "poor metabolizers." Plasma concentrations of one minor metabolite (mCPP) are increased in this population; the adjustment of SERZONE dosage is not required when administered to "poor metabolizers." Nefazodone and its metabolites have been shown in vitro to be extremely weak inhibitors of CYP2D6. Thus, it is not likely that nefazodone will decrease the metabolic clearance of drugs metabolized by this isozyme.

CYP1A2 Isozyme—Nefazodone and its metabolites have been shown in vitro not to inhibit CYP1A2. Thus, metabolic interactions between nefazodone and drugs metabolized by this isozyme are unlikely.

Electroconvulsive Therapy (ECT)

There are no clinical studies of the combined use of ECT and nefazodone.

Carcinogenesis, Mutagenesis, Impairment of Fertility

Carcinogenesis

There is no evidence of carcinogenicity with nefazodone. The dietary administration of nefazodone to rats and mice for 2 years at daily doses of up to 200 mg/kg and 800 mg/kg, respectively, which are approximately 3 and 6 times, respectively, the maximum human daily dose on a mg/m^2 basis, produced no increase in tumors.

Mutagenesis

Nefazodone has been shown to have no genotoxic effects based on the following assays: bacterial mutation assays, a DNA repair assay in cultured rat hepatocytes, a mammalian mutation assay in Chinese hamster ovary cells, an *in vivo* cytogenetics assay in rat bone marrow cells, and a rat dominant lethal study.

Impairment of Fertility

A fertility study in rats showed a slight decrease in fertility at 200 mg/kg/day (approximately three times the maximum human daily dose on a mg/m^2 basis) but not at 100 mg/kg/day (approximately 1.5 times the maximum human daily dose on a mg/m^2 basis).

Pregnancy

Teratogenic Effects—Pregnancy Category C

Reproduction studies have been performed in pregnant rabbits and rats at daily doses up to 200 and 300 mg/kg, respectively (approximately 6 and 5 times, respectively, the maximum human daily dose on a mg/m^2 basis). No malformations were observed in the offspring as a result of nefazodone treatment. However, increased early pup mortality was seen in rats at a dose approximately five times the maximum human dose, and decreased pup weights were seen at this and lower doses, when dosing began during pregnancy and continued until weaning. The cause of these deaths is not known. The no-effect dose for rat pup mortality was 1.3 times the human dose on a mg/m^2 basis. There are no adequate and well-controlled studies in pregnant women. Nefazodone should be used during pregnancy only if the potential benefit justifies the potential risk to the fetus.

Labor and Delivery

The effect of SERZONE (nefazodone hydrochloride) on labor and delivery in humans is unknown.

Nursing Mothers

It is not known whether SERZONE or its metabolites are excreted in human milk. Because many drugs are excreted in human milk, caution should be exercised when SERZONE is administered to a nursing woman.

Pediatric Use

Safety and effectiveness in individuals below 18 years of age have not been established.

Geriatric Use

Of the approximately 7000 patients in clinical studies who received SERZONE for the treatment of depression, 18% were 65 years and older, while 5% were 75 years and older. Based on monitoring of adverse events, vital signs, electrocardiograms, and results of laboratory tests, no overall differences in safety between elderly and younger patients were observed in clinical studies. Efficacy in the elderly has not been demonstrated in placebo-controlled trials. Other reported clinical experience has not identified differences in responses between elderly and younger patients, but greater sensitivity of some older individuals cannot be ruled out.

Due to the increased systemic exposure to nefazodone seen in single-dose studies in elderly patients (see **CLINICAL PHARMACOLOGY: Pharmacokinetics**), treatment should be initiated at half the usual dose, but titration upward should take place over the same range as in younger patients (see **DOSAGE AND ADMINISTRATION**). The usual precautions should be observed in elderly patients who have concomitant medical illnesses or who are receiving concomitant drugs.

ADVERSE REACTIONS

Associated with Discontinuation of Treatment

Approximately 16% of the 3496 patients who received SERZONE (nefazodone hydrochloride) in worldwide premarketing clinical trials discontinued treatment due to an adverse experience. The more common (≥1%) events in clinical trials associated with discontinuation and considered to be drug related (i.e., those events associated with dropout at a rate approximately twice or greater for SERZONE compared to placebo) included: nausea (3.5%), dizziness (1.9%), insomnia (1.5%), asthenia (1.3%), and agitation (1.2%).

Incidence in Controlled Trials

Commonly Observed Adverse Events in Controlled Clinical Trials

The most commonly observed adverse events associated with the use of SERZONE (incidence of 5% or greater) and not seen at an equivalent incidence among placebo-treated patients (i.e., significantly higher incidence for SERZONE compared to placebo, p≤0.05), derived from the table below, were: somnolence, dry mouth, nausea, dizziness, constipation, asthenia, lightheadedness, blurred vision, confusion, and abnormal vision.

Adverse Events Occurring at an Incidence of 1% or More Among SERZONE-Treated Patients

The table that follows enumerates adverse events that occurred at an incidence of 1% or more, and were more frequent than in the placebo group, among SERZONE-treated patients who participated in short-term (6- to 8-week) placebo-controlled trials in which patients were dosed with SERZONE (nefazodone hydrochloride) to ranges of 300 to 600 mg/day. This table shows the percentage of patients in each group who had at least one episode of an event at some time during their treatment. Reported adverse events were classified using standard COSTART-based Dictionary terminology.

The prescriber should be aware that these figures cannot be used to predict the incidence of side effects in the course of usual medical practice where patient characteristics and other factors differ from those which prevailed in the clinical trials. Similarly, the cited frequencies cannot be compared with figures obtained from other clinical investigations involving different treatments, uses, and investigators. The cited figures, however, do provide the prescribing physician with some basis for estimating the relative contribution of drug and nondrug factors to the side-effect incidence rate in the population studied.

Treatment-Emergent Adverse Experience Incidence in 6- to 8-Week Placebo-Controlled Clinical Trials[1], SERZONE 300 to 600 mg/day Dose Range

Body System	Preferred Term	SERZONE (n=393) Percent of Patients	Placebo (n=394) Percent of Patients
Body as a Whole	Headache	36	33
	Asthenia	11	5
	Infection	8	6
	Flu syndrome	3	2
	Chills	2	1
	Fever	2	1
	Neck rigidity	1	0
Cardiovascular	Postural hypotension	4	1
	Hypotension	2	1
Dermatological	Pruritus	2	1
	Rash	2	1
Gastrointestinal	Dry mouth	25	13
	Nausea	22	12
	Constipation	14	8
	Dyspepsia	9	7
	Diarrhea	8	7
	Increased appetite	5	3
	Nausea & vomiting	2	1
Metabolic	Peripheral edema	3	2
	Thirst	1	<1
Musculoskeletal	Arthralgia	1	<1
Nervous	Somnolence	25	14
	Dizziness	17	5
	Insomnia	11	9
	Lightheadedness	10	3
	Confusion	7	2
	Memory impairment	4	2
	Paresthesia	4	2
	Vasodilatation[2]	4	2
	Abnormal dreams	3	2
	Concentration decreased	3	1
	Ataxia	2	0
	Incoordination	2	1
	Psychomotor retardation	2	1
	Tremor	2	1
	Hypertonia	1	0
	Libido decreased	1	<1
Respiratory	Pharyngitis	6	5
	Cough increased	3	1
Special Senses	Blurred vision	9	3
	Abnormal vision[3]	7	1
	Tinnitus	2	1
	Taste perversion	2	1
	Visual field defect	2	0
Urogenital	Urinary frequency	2	1
	Urinary tract infection	2	1
	Urinary retention	2	0
	Vaginitis[4]	2	1
	Breast pain[4]	1	<1

[1] Events reported by at least 1% of patients treated with SERZONE (nefazodone hydrochloride) and more frequent than the placebo group are included; incidence is rounded to the nearest 1% (<1% indicates an incidence less than 0.5%). Events for which the SERZONE incidence was equal to or less than placebo are not listed in the table, but included the following: abdominal pain, pain, back pain, accidental injury, chest pain, neck pain, palpitation, migraine, sweating, flatulence, vomiting, anorexia, tooth disorder, weight gain, edema, myalgia, cramp, agitation, anxiety, depression, hypesthesia, CNS stimulation, dysphoria, emotional lability, sinusitis, rhinitis, dysmenorrhea[4], dysuria.

[2] Vasodilatation—flushing, feeling warm.

[3] Abnormal vision—scotoma, visual trails.

[4] Incidence adjusted for gender.

Dose Dependency of Adverse Events
The table that follows enumerates adverse events that were more frequent in the SERZONE (nefazodone hydrochloride) dose range of 300 to 600 mg/day than in the SERZONE dose range of up to 300 mg/day. This table shows only those adverse events for which there was a statistically significant difference (p≤0.05) in incidence between the SERZONE dose ranges as well as a difference between the high dose range and placebo.

Dose Dependency of Adverse Events in Placebo-Controlled Trials[1]

		Percent of Patients		
Body System	Preferred Term	SERZONE 300–600 mg/day (n = 209)	SERZONE ≤300 mg/day (n = 211)	Placebo (n = 212)
Gastrointestinal	Nausea	23	14	12
	Constipation	17	10	9
Nervous	Somnolence	28	16	13
	Dizziness	22	11	4
	Confusion	8	2	1
Special Senses	Abnormal vision	10	0	2
	Blurred vision	9	3	2
	Tinnitus	3	0	1

[1] Events for which there was a statistically significant difference (p≤0.05) between the nefazodone dose groups.

Visual Disturbances
In controlled clinical trials, blurred vision occurred in 9% of nefazodone-treated patients compared to 3% of placebo-treated patients. In these same trials abnormal vision, including scotomata and visual trails, occurred in 7% of nefazodone-treated patients compared to 1% of placebo-treated (see Treatment-Emergent Adverse Experience table, above). Dose-dependency was observed for these events in these trials, with none of the scotomata and visual trails at doses below 300 mg/day. However, scotomata and visual trails observed at doses below 300 mg/day have been reported in postmarketing experience with SERZONE. (See **PRECAUTIONS: Information for Patients**.)

Vital Sign Changes
(See **PRECAUTIONS**, *Postural Hypotension*.)

Weight Changes
In a pooled analysis of placebo-controlled premarketing studies, there were no differences between nefazodone and placebo groups in the proportions of patients meeting criteria for potentially important increases or decreases in body weight (a change of ≥7%).

Laboratory Changes
Of the serum chemistry, serum hematology, and urinalysis parameters monitored during placebo-controlled premarketing studies with nefazodone, a pooled analysis revealed a statistical trend between nefazodone and placebo for hematocrit, i.e., 2.8% of nefazodone patients met criteria for a potentially important decrease in hematocrit (≤37% male or ≤32% female) compared to 1.5% of placebo patients (0.05<p≤0.10). Decreases in hematocrit, presumably dilutional, have been reported with many other drugs that block alpha$_1$-adrenergic receptors. There was no apparent clinical significance of the observed changes in the few patients meeting these criteria.

ECG Changes
Of the ECG parameters monitored during placebo-controlled premarketing studies with nefazodone, a pooled analysis revealed a statistically significant difference between nefazodone and placebo for sinus bradycardia, i.e., 1.5% of nefazodone patients met criteria for a potentially important decrease in heart rate (≤50 bpm and a decrease of ≥15 bpm) compared to 0.4% of placebo patients (p<0.05). There was no obvious clinical significance of the observed changes in the few patients meeting these criteria.

Other Events Observed During the Premarketing Evaluation of SERZONE
During its premarketing assessment, multiple doses of SERZONE (nefazodone hydrochloride) were administered to 3496 patients in clinical studies, including more than 250 patients treated for at least one year. The conditions and duration of exposure to SERZONE varied greatly, and included (in overlapping categories) open and double-blind studies, uncontrolled and controlled studies, inpatient and outpatient studies, fixed-dose and titration studies. Untoward events associated with this exposure were recorded by clinical investigators using terminology of their own choosing. Consequently, it is not possible to provide a meaningful estimate of the proportion of individuals experiencing adverse events without first grouping similar types of untoward events into a smaller number of standardized event categories.

In the tabulations that follow, reported adverse events were classified using standard COSTART-based Dictionary terminology. The frequencies presented, therefore, represent the proportion of the 3496 patients exposed to multiple doses of SERZONE who experienced an event of the type cited on at least one occasion while receiving SERZONE. All reported events are included except those already listed in the Treatment-Emergent Adverse Experience Incidence table, those events listed in other safety-related sections of this insert, those adverse experiences subsumed under COSTART terms that are either overly general or excessively specific so as to be uninformative, those events for which a drug cause was very remote, and those events which were not serious and occurred in fewer than two patients.

It is important to emphasize that, although the events reported occurred during treatment with SERZONE (nefazodone hydrochloride), they were not necessarily caused by it.

Events are further categorized by body system and listed in order of decreasing frequency according to the following definitions: frequent adverse events are those occurring on one or more occasions in at least 1/100 patients (only those not already listed in the tabulated results from placebo-controlled trials appear in this listing); infrequent adverse events are those occurring in 1/100 to 1/1000 patients; rare events are those occurring in fewer than 1/1000 patients.

Body as a whole—Infrequent: allergic reaction, malaise, photosensitivity reaction, face edema, hangover effect, abdomen enlarged, hernia, pelvic pain, and halitosis. *Rare:* cellulitis.

Cardiovascular system—Infrequent: tachycardia, hypertension, syncope, ventricular extrasystoles, and angina pectoris. *Rare:* AV block, congestive heart failure, hemorrhage, pallor, and varicose vein.

Dermatological system—Infrequent: dry skin, acne, alopecia, urticaria, maculopapular rash, vesiculobullous rash, and eczema.

Gastrointestinal system—Frequent: gastroenteritis. Infrequent: eructation, periodontal abscess, abnormal liver function tests, gingivitis, colitis, gastritis, mouth ulceration, stomatitis, esophagitis, peptic ulcer, and rectal hemorrhage. *Rare:* glossitis, hepatitis, dysphagia, gastrointestinal hemorrhage, oral moniliasis, and ulcerative colitis.

Hemic and lymphatic system—Infrequent: ecchymosis, anemia, leukopenia, and lymphadenopathy.

Metabolic and nutritional system—Infrequent: weight loss, gout, dehydration, lactic dehydrogenase increased, SGOT increased, and SGPT increased. *Rare:* hypercholesteremia and hypoglycemia.

Musculoskeletal system—Infrequent: arthritis, tenosynovitis, muscle stiffness, and bursitis. *Rare:* tendinous contracture.

Nervous system—Infrequent: vertigo, twitching, depersonalization, hallucinations, suicide attempt, apathy, euphoria, hostility, suicidal thoughts, abnormal gait, thinking abnormal, attention decreased, derealization, neuralgia, paranoid reaction, dysarthria, increased libido, suicide, and myoclonus. *Rare:* hyperkinesia, increased salivation, cerebrovascular accident, hyperesthesia, hypotonia, ptosis, and neuroleptic malignant syndrome.

Respiratory system—Frequent: dyspnea and bronchitis. Infrequent: asthma, pneumonia, laryngitis, voice alteration, epistaxis, hiccup. *Rare:* hyperventilation and yawn.

Special senses—Frequent: eye pain. Infrequent: dry eye, ear pain, abnormality of accommodation, diplopia, conjunctivitis, mydriasis, keratoconjunctivitis, hyperacusis, and photophobia. *Rare:* deafness, glaucoma, night blindness, and taste loss.

Urogenital system—Frequent: impotence[a]. *Infrequent:* cystitis, urinary urgency, metrorrhagia[a], amenorrhea[a], polyuria, vaginal hemorrhage[a], breast enlargement[a], menorrhagia[a], urinary incontinence, abnormal ejaculation[a], hematuria, nocturia, and kidney calculus. *Rare:* uterine fibroids enlarged[a], uterine hemorrhage[a], anorgasmia, and oliguria.

[a]Adjusted for gender.

Postintroduction Clinical Experience
Postmarketing experience with SERZONE has shown an adverse experience profile similar to that seen during the premarketing evaluation of nefazodone. Voluntary reports of adverse events temporally associated with SERZONE have been received since market introduction that are not listed above and for which a causal relationship has not been established. These include:

Anaphylactic reactions; angioedema; convulsions (including grand mal seizures); galactorrhea; gynecomastia (male); hyponatremia; liver necrosis and liver failure, in some cases leading to liver transplantation and/or death; priapism (see **PRECAUTIONS**); prolactin increased; rhabdomyolysis involving patients receiving the combination of SERZONE and lovastatin or simvastatin (see **PRECAUTIONS**); serotonin syndrome; and Stevens-Johnson syndrome; and thrombocytopenia.

DRUG ABUSE AND DEPENDENCE
Controlled Substance Class
SERZONE is not a controlled substance.

Physical and Psychological Dependence
In animal studies, nefazodone did not act as a reinforcer for intravenous self-admin-

istration in monkeys trained to self-administer cocaine, suggesting no abuse liability. In a controlled study of abuse liability in human subjects, nefazodone showed no potential for abuse.

Nefazodone has not been systematically studied in humans for its potential for tolerance, physical dependence, or withdrawal. While the premarketing clinical experience with nefazodone did not reveal any tendency for a withdrawal syndrome or any drug-seeking behavior, it is not possible to predict on the basis of this limited experience the extent to which a CNS-active drug will be misused, diverted, and/or abused once marketed. Consequently, physicians should carefully evaluate patients for a history of drug abuse and follow such patients closely, observing them for signs of misuse or abuse of SERZONE (e.g., development of tolerance, dose escalation, drug-seeking behavior).

OVERDOSAGE
Human Experience
In premarketing clinical studies, there were seven reports of nefazodone overdose alone or in combination with other pharmacological agents. The amount of nefazodone ingested ranged from 1000 mg to 11,200 mg. Commonly reported symptoms from overdose of nefazodone included nausea, vomiting, and somnolence. One nonstudy participant took 2000–3000 mg of nefazodone with methocarbamol and alcohol; this person reportedly experienced a convulsion (type not documented). None of these patients died.

In postmarketing experience, overdose with SERZONE (nefazodone hydrochloride) alone and in combination with alcohol and/or other substances has been reported. Commonly reported symptoms were similar to those reported from overdose in premarketing experience. While there have been rare reports of fatalities in patients taking overdoses of nefazodone, predominantly in combination with alcohol and/or other substances, no causal relationship to nefazodone has been established.

Overdosage Management
Treatment should consist of those general measures employed in the management of overdosage with any antidepressant.

Ensure an adequate airway, oxygenation, and ventilation. Monitor cardiac rhythm and vital signs. General supportive and symptomatic measures are also recommended. Induction of emesis is not recommended. Gastric lavage with a large-bore orogastric tube with appropriate airway protection, if needed, may be indicated if performed soon after ingestion, or in symptomatic patients.

Activated charcoal should be administered. Due to the wide distribution of nefazodone in body tissues, forced diuresis, dialysis, hemoperfusion, and exchange transfusion are unlikely to be of benefit. No specific antidotes for nefazodone are known.

In managing overdosage, consider the possibility of multiple drug involvement. The physician should consider contacting a poison control center for additional information on the treatment of any overdose. Telephone numbers for certified poison control centers are listed in the *Physicians' Desk Reference* (PDR).

DOSAGE AND ADMINISTRATION
Initial Treatment
The recommended starting dose for SERZONE is 200 mg/day, administered in two divided doses (BID). In the controlled clinical trials establishing the antidepressant efficacy of SERZONE, the effective dose range was generally 300 to 600 mg/day. Consequently, most patients, depending on tolerability and the need for further clinical effect, should have their dose increased. Dose increases should occur in increments of 100 mg/day to 200 mg/day, again on a BID schedule, at intervals of no less than 1 week. As with all antidepressants, several weeks on treatment may be required to obtain a full antidepressant response.

Dosage for Elderly or Debilitated Patients
The recommended initial dose for elderly or debilitated patients is 100 mg/day, administered in two divided doses (BID). These patients often have reduced nefazodone clearance and/or increased sensitivity to the side effects of CNS-active drugs. It may also be appropriate to modify the rate of subsequent dose titration. As steady-state plasma levels do not change with age, the final target dose based on a careful assessment of the patient's clinical response may be similar in healthy younger and older patients.

Maintenance/Continuation/Extended Treatment
There is no body of evidence available from controlled trials to indicate how long the depressed patient should be treated with SERZONE. It is generally agreed, however, that pharmacological treatment for acute episodes of depression should continue for up to 6 months or longer. Whether the dose of antidepressant needed to induce remission is identical to the dose needed to maintain euthymia is unknown. Systematic evaluation of the efficacy of SERZONE has shown that efficacy is maintained for periods of up to 36 weeks following 16 weeks of open-label acute treatment (treated for 52 weeks total) at dosages that averaged 438 mg/day. For most patients, their maintenance dose was that associated with response during acute treatment. (See **CLINICAL PHARMACOLOGY**.) The safety of SERZONE in long-term use is supported by data from both double-blind and open-label trials involving more than 250 patients treated for at least one year.

Switching Patients to or from a Monoamine Oxidase Inhibitor
At least 14 days should elapse between discontinuation of an MAOI and initiation of therapy with SERZONE. In addition, at least 7 days should be allowed after stopping SERZONE before starting an MAOI.

HOW SUPPLIED
SERZONE® (nefazodone hydrochloride) tablets are hexagonal tablets imprinted with BMS and the strength (i.e., 100 mg) on one side and the identification code number on the other. The 100 mg and 150 mg tablets are bisect scored on both tablet faces. The 50 mg, 200 mg, and 250 mg tablets are unscored.

NDC CODE	DESCRIPTION
NDC 0087-0031-47	50 mg light pink tablet, bottle of 60
NDC 0087-0032-31	100 mg white tablet, bottle of 60
NDC 0087-0039-31	150 mg peach tablet, bottle of 60
NDC 0087-0033-31	200 mg light yellow tablet, bottle of 60
NDC 0087-0041-31	250 mg white tablet, bottle of 60

U.S. Patent Nos. 4,338,317 and 6,008,222

Store at room temperature, below 40° C (104° F) and dispense in a tight container.

REFERENCES
1. HALCION® and XANAX® are registered trademarks of the Upjohn Company.
2. SELDANE® is a registered trademark of Merrell Pharmaceuticals, Incorporated, a subsidiary of Hoechst Marion Roussel.
3. HISMANAL® and PROPULSID® are registered trademarks of Janssen Pharmaceutica, Incorporated.
4. ORAP® is a registered trademark of Gate Pharmaceuticals, a division of Teva Pharmaceuticals USA.
5. TEGRETOL® is a registered trademark of Novartis Corporation.

 **Bristol-Myers Squibb Company**
Princeton, NJ 08543 U.S.A.

Revised February 2001   0032DIM-17
D5-B001-03-01